THE ITALIAN DRAWINGS AT WINDSOR CASTLE

GENERAL EDITOR: A. F. BLUNT

THE ITALIAN DRAWINGS OF THE XV AND XVI CENTURIES

BY A. E. POPHAM AND JOHANNES WILDE

PHAIDON

RAPHAEL: STUDY FOR THE FIGURE OF POETRY (Cat. No. 792)

THE ITALIAN DRAWINGS OF THE XV AND XVI CENTURIES

IN THE COLLECTION OF

HIS MAJESTY THE KING

AT WINDSOR CASTLE

BY

A. E. POPHAM

AND

JOHANNES WILDE

LONDON

THE PHAIDON PRESS LTD

1949
MADE IN GREAT BRITAIN
TEXT PRINTED BY TONBRIDGE PRINTERS LTD · TONBRIDGE
PLATES PRINTED BY HENRY STONE & SON LTD · BANBURY
BOUND BY KEY & WHITING LTD · LONDON

THE ITALIAN DRAWINGS
OF THE XV AND XVI CENTURIES

IN THE COLLECTION OF

HIS MAJESTY THE KING
AT WINDSOR CASTLE

BY
A. E. POPHAM
AND
JOHANNES WILDE

LONDON
THE PHAIDON PRESS LTD

1949
MADE IN GREAT BRITAIN
TEXT PRINTED BY TONBRIDGE PRINTERS LTD · TONBRIDGE
PLATES PRINTED BY HENRY STONE & SON LTD · BANBURY
BOUND BY KEY & WHITING LTD · LONDON

PREFACE

THE present volume should chronologically have been the first in the series of Catalogues of Italian drawings at Windsor Castle to be published, but the research involved in its preparation has delayed its appearance.

The name of Dr. Johannes Wilde appears on the title-page as the author of a particular section of the catalogue, perhaps the most important section of all, that dealing with the drawings of Michelangelo and his school (including Sebastiano del Piombo and Daniele da Volterra, as well as the drawings by the Florentine sculptors, Baccio Bandinelli and Raffaello da Montelupo). Though I have had valuable help, advice and encouragement from Dr. Wilde, it is I who am responsible for the catalogue in general, and in speaking of my obligations, I speak in the first person singular. Dr. Wilde, however, wishes to be associated with me particularly in what immediately follows, and also wishes me to record his gratitude to Mr. Jacob Leveen, for his kindness in translating the catalogue of Michelangelo originally written in German.

I am in the first place very greatly indebted to His Majesty's Librarian, Sir Owen Morshead, without whose continuing sympathy and continuing help such a work could never have been begun or completed. It was on his initiative that the drawings were evacuated to the National Library of Wales at Aberystwyth during the war, where I and Dr. Wilde were able to study them at leisure in conjunction with those from the British Museum, which had also found a refuge there. This was an unprecedented opportunity which has, I believe, contributed to the knowledge of both these great collections.

I have received continual help from Miss Scott-Elliot, Sir Owen Morshead's assistant in the Royal Library, since her appointment to that post. She has been responsible for much laborious work in checking the proofs. I am also very much indebted to Professor Anthony Blunt, the general editor of the series of catalogues of Italian drawings, for much help, especially in regard to the history of the collections. My friend, Mr. K. T. Parker, Keeper of the Ashmolean Museum, has been invariably helpful and has materially assisted Dr. Wilde and myself with photographs and advice.

As will be apparent from the introduction, my debt to two persons, Dr. Friedrich Antal and Mr. Philip Pouncey, is also very great. To the former I am under a particular obligation, as it was under his auspices that I first began to learn something of mannerist Italian painting and drawing, on which his authority is recognized. If I have in more than one instance differed from him or rejected the suggestions he had made, the fact remains that he was the first scholar to throw some light on the vast anonymous mass of mannerist drawings at Windsor. My debt to Philip Pouncey is even greater. I have had the benefit of his help, advice and suggestions throughout the protracted course of this work, and his part is not confined to the attributions of the drawings, which bear his initials. Many which bear my own are the result of discoveries made by him, from which they logically depend.

Finally I have to thank my step-daughter Chloe Green for considerable help in the early stages of the work, and my daughter Anne Popham for the very arduous work of final revision.

I have made use of the suggestions written on the mounts by many eminent scholars. I hope I have made acknowledgment for these in each particular instance. The annotations themselves have, with the concurrence of the Royal Librarian, been erased. Their appearance was disturbing and their substance is now permanently recorded.

A. E. POPHAM

Most of the reproductions in this volume are from a new set of photographs taken by Alfred Carlebach, F.R.P.S.

CONTENTS

INTRODUCTION

I

THE ITALIAN DRAWINGS of the XV and XVI centuries at Windsor are widely known only as comprising certain series of supreme importance, first and foremost those by Leonardo da Vinci. These, which have been so admirably catalogued by Sir Kenneth Clark, are not included in the present volume. There remain the drawings by Michelangelo, those by Raphael, and a small number of individual drawings, especially of the XV century, which have been often reproduced and exhibited. Numerically, however, these form an insignificant fragment of the twelve hundred odd drawings catalogued below.

The list of artists classified in schools which follows the introduction will give the student a summary of what sort of drawings he will find catalogued below, and their numbers. The grouping of the plates in the same way will provide the general reader—I use 'general reader' in the absence of any other accepted term for the very large number of people who buy such books for their illustrations and do not study the text—with some more intelligible idea of the collection than the alphabetical arrangement followed for convenience in the catalogue would give. Nevertheless it may help the 'general reader' (as defined above) to give a brief account of the Italian drawings of the XV and XVI centuries.

He will not find a well-balanced chronological series illustrating the development of Italian art. Few collections of drawings do this. The preservation of drawings does not run parallel to that of paintings. Some artists were proud of their drawings and kept them carefully. Others threw them away when they had served their purpose, for it must be remembered that drawings for the most part were made to help an artist in the preparation of a work of art, and it was this last which was meant to survive. Some artists were much less dependent on drawings than others. They could paint on the canvas or the wall without much preparation. Altogether the incidence of survival in drawings is much more incalculable than it is in paintings.

Old connoisseurs were in fact conscious that the historical perspective in their collections was wrong. They sought to correct this in two ways. First by interpolating copies of paintings by the masters they thought should be represented, and, secondly, by arbitrarily assigning drawings to them. The first method was entirely laudable, even though it has led to confusion and abuse. The second was disastrous in its consequences.

To return to the composition of the collection at Windsor—in so far as it affects the present volume. Chronologically the series begins rather whimsically with the drawing of a camel by Pisanello, which must date from before 1450. There are a few admirable drawings of the highest quality by the Florentines of the XV century, Fra Filippo Lippi, Benozzo Gozzoli, Antonio Pollaiuolo, Domenico Ghirlandajo, Lorenzo di Credi; by the Umbrian Pietro Perugino and by Luca Signorelli of Cortona; and by the Venetians, Giovanni Bellini, Alvise Vivarini and Bartolommeo Montagna. The number of drawings of the XV century at Windsor (exclusive of the Leonardos) is, however, small. The emphasis is on the art of the High Renaissance and the phases which developed out of this. It opens with a particularly beautiful series of drawings by Fra Bartolommeo, one of the protagonists of the new movement in Florence, even though his art, as seen especially in the drawings here, preserves much of the flavour of the quattrocento. But it is with the drawings of Michelangelo that the real quality of the collection begins to appear. These include some of his most famous drawings, those elaborately finished compositions which he drew for his friend Tommaso Cavalieri, the 'Archers', the 'Bacchanal of Children' and the 'Phaethon', as well as many other studies for works of his maturity and old age. There are also at Windsor very numerous copies, brought together no doubt by their original collector with the object of illustrating the master's development as completely as possible and not purporting to be originals. Some of these have considerable interest as preserving lost drawings or compositions. Artists to a greater or lesser degree dependent on Michelangelo, Daniele da Volterra, Sebastiano del Piombo, Raffaello da Montelupo and Giulio Clovio, are also well represented in the collection.

Though the drawings of Raphael at Windsor are about equal in number to those of Michelangelo, they are not indispensable to an appreciation of him as a draughtsman in the same way as the Cavalieri drawings are in the case of Michelangelo. There are superb individual studies which, taken in conjunction with other drawings in the great English and European collections, fit into their place in his development. They do not in themselves form a particular phase not to be paralleled elsewhere. Copies after Raphael are even more numerous than those after Michelangelo; and Raphael's scholars, particularly Perino del Vaga, Polidoro da Caravaggio and Giulio Romano are well represented.

The drawings of the Roman and Florentine Mannerists of the middle and end of the XVI century, whose style is a complicated development out of that of Raphael and his followers combined with the later Michelangelo, are numerous and interesting to the student of this comparatively neglected field. Among the most brilliant were Francesco Salviati, and in the next generation Taddeo Zuccaro and the latter's brother Federico. All three can be studied to advantage in the Windsor collection. So can Federico Barocci, whose art represents a certain reaction against the extravagance of mannerism, and whose drawings show a particular sincerity. There are many other by no means negligible personalities among the Roman and Florentine Mannerists, but there would be no point in a detailed enumeration of them.

The figure of Correggio as a draughtsman has not yet been satisfactorily circumscribed, but there are at least two drawings at Windsor with good claims to be regarded as his. His brilliant follower Parmigianino is superbly represented, and so is the eclectic but interesting Lelio Orsi from the neighbouring Reggio, a compound of Correggio and Michelangelo with a curious Northern admixture, as well as the graceful Niccolò dell' Abbate of Modena. The mannerist painters of Bologna with Primaticcio and Pellegrino Tibaldi as the most interesting among them repay study. Indeed the Bolognese school of the XVI century, as might perhaps be inferred from the Bolognese provenance of a part of the collection, is consistently good.

One might expect Milan, Leonardo's second home, to be well represented at Windsor. There are in fact a few drawings by Cesare da Sesto and other Milanese followers of Leonardo, but they have been included in Sir Kenneth Clark's catalogue and will not be found recorded here a second time. There are also a few examples of the other draughtsmen of the beginning of the century, but the bulk of the Milanese drawings at Windsor is to be found in an album containing 121 drawings by Ambrogio Figino. Figino is known to have possessed a volume of Leonardo's drawings, but the presence side by side of the largest individual collection of both their drawings seem to be a pure coincidence. The Figino album was put together in the XVIII century by Consul Smith in Venice, while the Leonardo album came at a much earlier date from Spain to England and had belonged to Figino's contemporary, Leoni.

Towns near Milan with some claim to local schools, are Cremona and Brescia. There are a number of drawings by Bernardino Campi, who with his family dominated the art of the former for most of the century, and a few by Bernardino Gatti, perhaps the most interesting draughtsman of the school, whose studies have often passed for Correggio's.

In view of the considerable part which Consul Joseph Smith of Venice played in the formation of the collection, it might be expected that the great painters of Venice and Venetian territory in the XVI century would be represented with a distinction and abundance comparable to that of some of his own contemporaries. This is hardly the case: there are a few single outstanding drawings, one by Titian, one attributed to Giorgione, a few more by Pordenone, Domenico Campagnola and Tintoretto for example, but the only two Venetian artists to be really well represented are in fact Palma Giovane and Paolo Farinati. As we shall see, the drawings by the latter formed part of the old royal collection. There are also drawings by mannerist Venetian painters such as Battista Franco, Andrea Schiavone and Giuseppe Porta, but a large proportion of the Venetian drawings are copies.

II

Our knowledge of the formation of the collection is fragmentary, but it will be well to summarize what is known of it here.[1] There are three main sources recorded:

(i) The Old Royal Collection said to have been formed by Charles I or Charles II.

(ii) The collection or part of the collection of Dr. Richard Mead bought by Frederick, Prince of Wales, before 1751. A portion of this came from Cardinal Massimi's collection in Rome.

(iii) The collections acquired for George III, mainly through the agency of Richard Dalton (b. about 1715: d. 1791), his librarian. These comprised:

- (*a*) Collection or collections formed by the Albani family and purchased in 1762. A portion of these collections had belonged to the painter Carlo Maratta.
- (*b*) The collection formed by Consul Joseph Smith (d. 1770), which included three volumes from the Bonfiglioli collection.

Let us examine these three sources in greater detail.

(i) The only evidence about the contents of the old Royal Collection is the inventory drawn up at some date after 1735: 'A List of the Books of Drawings and Prints in the Buroe in His Majestys Great Closset at Kensington' (B.M. Add. 20,101, fol. 28). It seems better to reprint this inventory here in full.

No. 1. Drawings by Polidore, Julio Romano, Raphaell, Zuccaro, Daniell de Volterra, P. Ligorio, Jerom, Anniball Carraccio, Taddio, L. Cangiagio, J. Pantormo, Penis, Jognon di Vincenza, Barth. Passeroto, J. Salviati, P. Farrinato, B. Bandinelli,

No. 2. by Defferent hands,

No. 3x. by Hans Holben, those framed & hang at Richmond

No. 4. by Paolo Farinato,

No. 5x. Prints by Hollar, Deliverd to her Majty Augst 1735 & by her Lent to Lady Burlington Since put in Volumes & laid in ye Library at Kensington,

No. 6. Drawings by Leonardi de Vinci,

No. 7. by the Best hands,

No. 8. Prince Charle's Book with a few Drawings,

No. 9. Drawings by Julio Romano, M. Angello, Raphaell,

No. 10. by Polydor, P. Veronese, Guido Rene, Titian,

No. 11. by Defferent hands,

No. 12. Prints of the Revelations of St John by Albert Durer,

No. 13. Drawings by Leonardi di Vinci.

[1] The only recent account of the collection in general is that by the present writer in the Burlington Magazine, LXVI (1935), pp. 218 ff.

No. 14. A Book of Mathamaticall papers,
No. 15x. A Book with some Indian Pictures,
No. 16. A Cover with one Drawing by Cherubim Alberti,
No. 17. Drawings by Severall Hands,
No. 18. by Severell hands,
No. 19x. A Little Book of Heads Drawn on Vellum,
No. 20. Another of Defferent Figures,
No. 21x. Another by Parmesano,
No. 22. Another by the same hand,
No. 23. Another by the same hand,
Seven Drawings Rolled together, of the Cartoons after Raphael
A Drawing in a frame and Glass
x Five heads in Black frames unfinished by Cowper
A tin Box with A Drawing the Triumphs of Trajan
x These Mark'd with a Cross were deliver'd for her Maj[tys] use in y[e] year 1728.

Though not always specified as such, each of the 23 numbers in this list no doubt represents an album. Many of them, Nos. 3, 5, 6, 12, 13, 14, 15, can hardly have contained any of the drawings catalogued in the present volumes. Others, Nos. 2, 7, 11, 17, 18, 19, 20, are so cursorily described that identification is out of the question. But there are some numbers about which a guess may be made. In No. 1, for example, 'Jognon di Vincenza' can only apply to the drawing with the peculiar and no doubt correct attribution to 'Tonion di Vincenza' (No. 965), which is stamped with the small five-pointed star, attributed by Richardson to the younger Lanière. This mark and a method of pricing known to have been used by William Gibson[2] provide an indication that the drawing so marked was in England in the XVII century and did *not* form part of the collections acquired in Italy for George III. Working on this assumption it seems possible to identify, provisionally at least, some of the drawings mentioned in the inventory. (We must, however, remember that some of the drawings acquired by Frederick, Prince of Wales, from Dr. Richard Mead may have had an English provenance, though the only identifiable series is that of the Poussin drawings from the Massimi collection.)

The albums listed in the British Museum inventory were, with the exception of the Leonardo album and the four little Parmigianino volumes, broken up in the time of George III and their contents incorporated in new albums, which were made to contain the drawings recently acquired

---

[2] F. J. B. Watson, *On the Early History of Collecting in England*, Burlington Magazine, LXXXV (1944), p. 224 f. The association of the price marks with William Gibson (b. about 1645, d. 1703) is vouched for by the younger Richardson in a MS. note in the collected French edition of his father's works (Amsterdam, 1728), in the London Library, correcting the statement in the text that they had been put there by the Lanières. Richardson obtained this information from Gibson's widow, from whom he and his father bought a number of drawings, probably about 1733. Richardson's statement that Gibson had put them there 'for the use of his widow' seems to imply that he did so not long before his death in 1703. On the other hand, Richardson speaks of the price marks as accompanying the Lanière star, and though both the Lanière star and the price marks are found on drawings at Windsor, *in no case* are they found together.

The Rev. B. B. Woodward, in a review of Weigel's 'Catalogue of Fac-similes of Drawings' (Fine Arts Quarterly Review, I, N.S. (1866), p. 165 f.) goes at some length into the question of the stars and the price marks on the Windsor drawings. He dates the price marks 1600–1625 for reasons which are not apparent to me. He concludes, again on evidence which is not clearly stated, that drawings with the names of the supposed masters and the prices derive from the collection of Nicolas Lanière, and that those with the stars are from his brother's collection.

It may be noted that no drawing in the collection, with the exception of some of the Leonardos and possibly of three drawings by Parmigianino (Nos. 583, 586 and 587), was engraved by Hollar, Vorsterman or other engravers employed by the Earl of Arundel to reproduce drawings in his collection.

The total number of drawings which bear either the marks of known English collections, the price marks associated with William Gibson, or which are recorded in either of the MS. inventories made at the end of the XVIII century as having formed part of the collections discovered in the famous bureau at Kensington, only amounts to 79. In addition, there were the Parmigianino drawings which cannot all be individually identified, but the number of which was 68 according to the inventory. This only gives 147 with a certain or probable English provenance out of the 1207 numbers of the present catalogue.

in Italy. The present inventory numbers follow that of the new arrangement and provide no indication of the order in which they were previously mounted, nor do the bindings of these old albums survive, so that any identification is hypothetical.

There are, however, drawings by Polidoro (No. 740), Giulio Romano (Nos. 361 and 387), Raphael (No. 850), Taddeo Zuccaro (No. 1067), Tognon di Vicenza (No. 965), Passerotti (No. 663), and J. Salviati (if Giuseppe Porta is meant, No. 753; if Francesco Salviati, No. 904). There are no drawings in the collection now which can be attributed to Pontormo, and the identity of both 'Penis' and 'Jerom' is doubtful. The former may be intended for Perino del Vaga (No. 974 has the star), or possibly Luca Penni; the name 'Jerom' is found written on the back of two drawings, one by Alessandro Allori (No. 6018, which has the star) and another attributed to Primaticcio (No. 1104, which has no mark). But then it will be observed that there are other volumes in the inventory containing drawings by Polydor, P. Veronese, Guido Rene, Titian, or by the 'Best hands'!

Four drawings, all by Raphael or his school (Nos. 792, 808, 815 and 850), are specifically stated, in the MS. inventories made in the time of George III, to have come from the 'old buroe in Kensington' assumed to have formed part of the collection of Charles I.

This, in the absence of any further evidence, is as far as we can get in identifying the contents of the old Royal Collection.

(ii) The collection bought by Frederick, Prince of Wales (d. 1751), from Dr. Richard Mead. There is a great probability that the volume of Poussin drawings, including those made for the poet Marino, subsequently in the Massimi collection at Rome, belonged to Dr. Mead (see Catalogue of French Drawings, p. 32), but there seems to be no other evidence whatever about the contents of this part of the Royal Collection. It is possible, as I have already suggested, that the drawings with price marks, if these are in fact Gibson's, came from Dr. Mead, but this is merely a possibility.

(iii) Drawings purchased for George III in Italy.

(*a*) It is known that the architect James Adam purchased the whole of the collection of drawings belonging to Cardinal Alessandro Albani in 1762. This comprised the collection of drawings formed by the painter Carlo Maratta (1625–1713), from whose hand an extensive series of drawings is preserved at Windsor, and who had also acquired the vast collection of drawings by Domenichino still in the Royal Library.[3]

(*b*) The collections formed by Consul Joseph Smith (d. 1770) in Venice, bought for the Royal Library by Richard Dalton in 1773. This collection included the album of drawings by Ambrogio Figino (No. 326), an album with copies from Trajan's column attributed to Giulio Campi, which is to be included in a projected catalogue of drawings from the antique, the album of drawings by Canaletto (catalogued by K. T. Parker) and other XVIII century Venetian drawings, which do not concern us here. There is little if anything else that can be identified as coming from Consul Smith, with the exception of some of the drawings from the collection of the Bonfiglioli family in Bologna, a collection which had been purchased *en bloc* by Procurator Zaccaria Sagredo of Venice in 1727 or the beginning of 1728, and had been acquired from the latter by Smith.

In the George III 'Inventory A', Raffaello d'Urbino e Scuola, No. 10, it is stated that this drawing (No. 790) and Nos. 8 and 9 (Nos. 392 and 800) 'were in the Buonfigluiolo (sic) Collection in one

[3] The early drawing by Raphael (No. 788) was found among the series of Maratta drawings, and had presumably belonged to him. The same applies to the copies from the Loggie frescoes (Nos. 835–844). An inventory 'delle cose piu singolari del Signo Cavalier Carlo Maratti', made by Maratta himself in 1712, was published in L'Archiginnasio XXII (1927), p. 217 f., and XXIII (1928), p. 59 f. It included a few drawings, but all apparently were large framed drawings, and none can be identified with any now at Windsor. For Maratta's collection in general the reader may be referred to the introduction by Mr. Pope-Hennessy to his catalogue of the drawings by Domenichino at Windsor, p. 9 f.

of the three Volumes purchased in Mr. Smith's Collection at Venice'.[4] These albums were broken up in the time of George III (the next number in the same inventory, No. 11 (No. 815), is stated to have come from Kensington) and incorporated with the other collections, so that they cannot be identified by their order in these albums.

There are two other sources, however, which throw some light on the contents of the Bonfiglioli Collection. The one is the inventory of the goods of the late Silvestro Bonfiglioli drawn up in 1696,[5] the other the account of the collection made by the younger Richardson and published in 1722.[6] Both are confined to drawings framed and hanging on the walls. Richardson states specifically 'Signior Bonfiglioli has many more in Books, but he being out of Town, I lost the Sight of them'.

It is clear that some of the drawings listed in the inventory or mentioned by Richardson are not now at Windsor, and it is impossible, owing to the vagueness of the descriptions, to be certain about the majority. But a certain number can be identified with a great degree of probability, so that one cannot assume that the three albums acquired by Smith were from the 'many more in Books' which Richardson did not see. It is probable that either Sagredo or Smith remounted them. It does not seem possible to determine whether part of the Bonfiglioli collection had been alienated before Sagredo bought it, or at what stage some of it disappeared. In any case, it certainly did not enter the Royal Library in its entirety.

It is hardly necessary to mention the few drawings—they hardly amount to two dozen in all—which have been acquired for the Royal Library since the time of George III. The reader will easily be able to identify them in the index of collections.

III

Does the imperfect picture we have been able to draw of the formation of the collection help us to an estimate of its character? To a certain extent it does. We may expect the old albums from the royal collection to have represented the taste and connoisseurship of the great English collectors of the XVII century, with the Earl of Arundel at their head. His personality is strongly felt in the Royal Library in general, though less apparently in the section with which we are here concerned. Leonardo and Holbein were the two draughtsmen who perhaps most strongly appealed to him. The two matchless series of drawings by these artists at Windsor both passed through his hands. Next to Leonardo, the Italian artist who delighted him most was Parmigianino and, though the admirable and numerous drawings by Parmigianino at Windsor do not seem to have belonged to him, they, or some of them, may represent the parallel taste of his master, Charles I. Apart from the marks associated with the Lanières, the only other English collector's mark of the XVII century to be found is that of Sir Peter Lely. This appears on some of the drawings by Paolo Farinati, which must, therefore, have entered the Royal Library after Lely's death in 1680, when the mark is known to have been stamped on them. But it is not possible to determine whether the whole album of

[4] The statement is borne out by Consul Smith's will (printed in full by K. T. Parker, *Canaletto Drawings*, p. 59 f.). The passage having reference to the Bonfiglioli collection is as follows: 'The Drawings consist of numbers of Original Pieces by the greatest masters, particularly are among them the three large Volumes, formerly collected in the time of the Carracci, by the family of Bonfiglioli of Bologna, and upon the death of Sigr. Bartolommeo were purchased by the Noble Venetian Zaccaria Sagredo, and cost 3,000 sequins, as appears by a letter printed about that time wrote by Anton Maria Zanetti of Venice to his Friend the Cavalier Gaburri of Florence'. The letter referred to, dated 11th January, 1728, is printed in G. Bottari, *Lêttere Pittoriche*, ed. Ticozzi, Vol. II, Milan, 1822, p. 186.

[5] In the Archivo Notarile at Bologna. A photographic copy of it was made for the Royal Library in 1930, and a transcription and index prepared by Dr. Gertrud Bing. It had been summarised in an article in Rassegna d'Arte, XXI (1921), p. 208 f. The author of this article, Lodovico Frati, identified some of the drawings with drawings in the Albertina, but the drawings there which seem to correspond are in fact copies of drawings at Windsor.

[6] Jonathan Richardson, [Sen. and Jun.], *An Account of some of the Statues, Bas-reliefs, Drawings and Pictures in Italy, Etc.* London, 1722, pp. 30 ff.

Farinati drawings mentioned in the inventory of the contents of the famous bureau at Kensington came from Lely's collection. The drawings with the Lely mark may have been added later. Raphael and Giulio Romano, we know, were appreciated in England in the XVII century—Charles I's purchase of the Mantua collection must have stimulated interest especially in the latter—and some drawings by them at Windsor from the old royal collection witness to this appreciation. Less expected is the presence of twelve drawings attributed to Michelangelo with marks of English provenance in the XVII century, even if only three of these are actually by the master. The remainder of the drawings with an old English provenance are too miscellaneous in character to make it worth enumerating them in detail. There are some very good drawings, some indifferent and some positively bad, but we do not get the impression of any consistent taste at work in their selection. They may of course represent only a fragment of what the old Royal collection contained, and may have been more intelligible in their context.

If we feel that we have some vague understanding of the taste which was responsible for the collection of this nucleus of the drawings at Windsor, there is no such clue to an understanding of the vast mass of material imported from Italy in the reign of George III. We can form no idea of the mind or intention of the individual collectors who brought together the elements of this vast agglomeration. There is no principle of taste to be discerned such as that which governed the Richardsons in the formation of their collection, and which had so profound an influence on the contents and arrangement of the other great English collections of the beginning of the XVIII century, those still surviving at Chatsworth and in the library of Christ Church and that formerly at Wilton House. Misleading and misguided as the Richardson's connoisseurship often is, it does provide us with some sort of Ariadne's thread to guide us through the labyrinth. They annotated their drawings and conscientiously recorded what information was available to them, often with its source, on the backs of the mounts. At Windsor there is nothing of the sort to help us, except occasionally the bare name of the artist. An attribution written on the drawing in a rather untidy slanting hand in pencil may have been copied from an old attribution written on the mount of the drawing, but as practically everything was remounted in the time of George III, we cannot tell. Occasionally old attributions or even signatures on the backs of the drawings, which can sometimes be deciphered if held against a powerful light, were not recorded at all.

We have, as I have said, the inventory and Richardson's account of the Bonfiglioli collection, part of which entered the Royal Library, and we can form from these some general idea of its character. We expect in a Bolognese collection formed in the XVII century an emphasis on the Carracci and the Bolognese eclectics, and they are in fact superlatively represented at Windsor. But such easily movable objects as drawings do not necessarily remain in the places of their origin, and the strength of the Windsor Collection in the later Bolognese may be due to drawings from the Albani Collection or some other source. It seems to me more probable that the earlier Bolognese drawings at Windsor, those by artists with a less general appeal to collectors than the Carracci, may have come from the Bonfiglioli collection. They are in fact rather well represented. But this supposition is not very much help. We are never justified in assuming that an unnamed drawing is likely to be Bolognese, because we do not even know the proportion of drawings with a provenance from Bologna.

We are in fact left very much to our own resources, and it is perhaps worth stating what these resources are. From the point of view of the cataloguer, the ideal is for a drawing to be in definite relation with a painting of which the artist is recorded. Given a close correspondence with a picture or some part of a picture, it is generally not difficult to determine whether the drawing is a study for or a copy from that picture. If we are satisfied that it is a study for a picture by the artist, we are in possession of a standard of comparison and should be able to identify other drawings, when we see them, as his work. But it depends on the individuality of the artist, his possession of constant and pronounced mannerisms, whether this is easy or certain. And we must not be distracted by the different 'look' which a different technique or a different intention on the part of an artist may give a drawing. It is the individual touch of a definite personality which seems to me to count. In many cases we can feel practical certainty. It is often said or implied that an undefinable faculty called a 'sense of quality' is an overriding consideration in the attribution of a drawing. If the actual handling of one drawing is demonstrably the same as that of another, both must be by the same artist, however inferior the one is to the other. This sense of quality can only help us to realize that the one drawing is *not* by the same hand as the other, say a deceptive copy. It is in fact implicit in our ability to distinguish one hand from another, which is the important thing.

Very often we are confronted with a drawing by a hand we do not recognize. It may be that we ought to be able to do so, that the artist's 'handwriting' is concealed under a different technique or a difference in scale, or that we do not know a sufficient number of his drawings to be able to form a clear idea of his individuality. In very many cases, however, it is the work of a man whose drawings we do not and cannot know. In that case we have to make a guess at when it was drawn and in what locality. The second of these requirements connotes the theory that there is certain quality overriding the personality which marks the work of all artists living or working in a particular town or district. This is obviously true up to a point, especially in a stable community, where tradition is strong. It is truer or certainly more obvious in the case of paintings than in the case of drawings. But to work out the lowest common denominator of the styles of a number of artists working in the same district, and apply it to an individual drawing is generally a method fraught with uncertainty. I emphasize this point, because I am far from satisfied with the division into schools of the anonymous drawings catalogued below.

IV

The scope and method of the present catalogue need some explanation.

It includes all Italian drawings of the XV and XVI centuries with, as has been stated, the very important exception of those by Leonardo da Vinci, catalogued by Sir Kenneth Clark. That catalogue was arranged in the order of the inventory numbers, Nos. 12275–12727, Nos. 19000–19152, and Nos. 054, 056–058, 063–065, 068, 12793, 12809 (wrongly for 12908). Some of the intermediate and most of the final numbers are not, as was of course recognized by Sir Kenneth Clark, by Leonardo. He catalogued them because for the most part they came from the Leonardo volume and bore Leoni's numbers. Some are definitely by Cesare da Sesto. I have not included them here because I had nothing to add to Sir Kenneth Clark's descriptions and attributions, except in one instance where a drawing was wrongly numbered by him (12801 instead of 12808 = my number 32). Apart from these 600 odd drawings by Leonardo, there are only some 37 which can be assigned to the XV century.

To decide in which of two centuries a particular artist's work should be included is not always simple. The Carracci, for instance, a great part of whose activity fell in the XVI century, are not catalogued here. A compromise between style and chronology has relegated them to the *seicento*. I have, on the other hand, included some painters like Camillo Procaccini, Morazzone, Cerano, Salmeggia, Bernardo Castello, Cesi, Jacopo da Empoli, Passignano, Tempesta, G. B. Ricci, Cristofano Roncalli and the Cavaliere d'Arpino, whose lives extended far into the XVII century, on the ground that their style remained substantially that of the later mannerists.

There has been a certain amount of overlapping with the French School. Professor Blunt has included in his volume two copies after Primaticcio as being probably French, while the originals by Primaticcio and other copies from his works are catalogued below (Nos. 755–767). Some of these copies may, for all I know, also be French.

On the other hand, I have headed a section among the anonymous 'School of Fontainebleau', as the most convenient designation for drawings which I believe to be Italian, but to have been drawn in France under the influence of Rosso and Primaticcio.

No drawings remaining in the large series of albums of architectural or antiquarian drawings are included. There are many belonging to the XVI century which logically should have found a place here. But the task involved research which was beyond my scope. I have, however, with the permission of the Royal Librarian, had a small number of particularly significant and important drawings, which were not in fact architectural, extracted and placed with the series of mounted drawings. These will be found catalogued below.

The arrangement of the catalogue is the following:

There are two alphabetical series, one for the XV and one for the XVI century, with a small section of miniatures (all, except one by Giulio Clovio, of the XV century) intervening (Nos. 38–43). The anonymous drawings, arranged as far as possible in schools, follow, in the case of each century, the alphabetical series.

The alphabetical arrangement adopted in cataloguing a collection so miscellaneous in character is a temptation to the compiler to find names for as many drawings as possible, so that he can place them in their alphabetical sequence. I am not sure that I have in all cases resisted this temptation. A name for a drawing, even if it is not actually from the hand of the artist named, is not always misleading and may be preferable to the limbo of anonymity. I find that there are some 300 drawings which either had no names of artists attached to them or which were absurdly named, often in a shaky upright script of the XVIII century, which I have called the 'deceptive' hand, on the grounds of its general unreliability.[7] The greater number of these new attributions are due either to Dr. Friedrich Antal, to my colleague Philip Pouncey, or to myself. Drawings are marked accordingly with our respective initials, F.A., P.M.R.P., or A.E.P.

I have only thought it worth while to give references to the existence of photographs of drawings at Windsor in cases where they are not otherwise reproduced.

The catalogue is preceded by a list of books referred to in abbreviated form, though this does not include works dealing with particular artists, which will be found enumerated under their particular names.

A great part of the drawings catalogued dates from a period, the second half of the XVI century, which is as yet quite insufficiently studied and charted. Comparatively few photographs exist of paintings and frescoes by the later mannerists, and the illustrations in the seven parts of the ninth volume of Venturi's *Storia dell' Arte*, invaluable as they are, are on too small a scale to be of much use in stylistic comparison.[8]

Few of the drawings themselves have hitherto been reproduced or catalogued, with the exception of those by Fra Bartolommeo, Michelangelo and Raphael, a certain number of the Florentines (in Berenson's great corpus), and some of the (comparatively unimportant) Venetian drawings in

[7] Thirty-five to be precise. Of these 35 attributions at least 19 are certainly and demonstrably wrong. The writing is occasionally to be met with on drawings in other collections. A drawing in the British Museum for example attributed in this hand to Giuseppe Porta Salviati (Tietzes, No. 1382, who accept the attribution) is clearly by Andrea Schiavone.

[8] I am particularly grateful to Mr. Ellis Waterhouse for placing at my disposal his fine collection of photographs of mannerist painters.

Hadeln's volumes and in the recently published work by the Tietzes. The greater part is absolutely untouched.

This fact indeed has its advantages in that the cataloguer is free to devote himself to an unbiassed consideration of the drawings themselves, without having to read, digest, and, more often than not, discount the opinions of his predecessors. I would refer especially to the vast literature which has accumulated round Michelangelo and almost buried even that gigantic figure. It has been the task of my distinguished collaborator, Dr. Johannes Wilde, to hew his way through these formidable accretions and present to the reader what, I am confident he will agree, is an intelligible picture of Michelangelo as a draughtsman.

Though Raphael also has been the target for a great deal of misdirected criticism, the work of elucidating his progress as a draughtsman has fortunately already been accomplished with singular success by the late Dr. Oskar Fischel, whose monumental catalogue of the drawings I have done little but paraphrase in the case of those at Windsor with which he had dealt.[9] Where I have differed from Dr. Fischel, or added to him, I have done so with the greatest circumspection. Unfortunately Dr. Fischel's work has not been completed, and in dealing with the tantalizing problems of Raphael's later work and that of his pupils, I have had to rely on my own judgment. The problem is one which I do not pretend to have resolved. In parenthesis I should like to recall that much of Fischel's work was based on the vast collection of reproductions assembled at Windsor on the initiative of the Prince Consort. This Windsor Raphael Collection remains to this day a model of the method of approaching the study of an artist's work, and Dr. Fischel admitted his great indebtedness to it.

The only other series of drawings at Windsor to be adequately dealt with by previous writers is that by Fra Bartolommeo, whose drawings have been catalogued by Berenson and in greater detail by von Gabelentz. But the Frate's drawings present on the whole few problems, though I have ventured to add one of some importance to his *œuvre*.

Frequent references are made in the text of the catalogue to the old inventories. There are two of these, dating partly from the late XVIII and partly from the beginning of the XIX century, to which the appellations George III 'Inventory A' and George III 'Inventory B' have been given. The former, the only one actually referred to here, is a composite work, which appears to have been rebound in the time of the Rev. B. B. Woodward (Royal Librarian 1860–1869), perhaps about 1862. It is made up of sections of varying date as appears from the watermarks in the paper composing them. The earliest portion may date from soon after the acquisition of the bulk of the collection, say about 1765–70, when a complete inventory was probably made. Part of this seems to have been lost and was replaced by copies about 1816–17, and later additions were made to this by Glover, who was librarian from 1825 to 1860. 'Inventory B', which is uniform but incomplete, was probably a fair copy of the original inventory of 1765–70, parts of which are incorporated in 'Inventory A'. I am indebted to Professor Blunt for these particulars.

[9] Part VIII of Dr. Fischel's Corpus only became available to me after I had completed the present catalogue. I have added Dr. Fischel's numbers to the bibliographical references, but I have not modified the text of the notes to the drawings.

ARTISTS ACCORDING TO SCHOOLS

The arrangement within each school is roughly chronological. The first column gives the number of the drawings by, or attributed to, the artist; the second, that of drawings of his school; and the third, that of copies from his works. The numbers of unnamed drawings, of the XV and XVI centuries respectively, are given at the end of each school.

NORTHERN ITALY

VENICE

		Originals	*School*	*Copies*
BELLINI, Gentile	*c.* 1429–1507			1
BELLINI, Giovanni	*c.* 1431 (?)–1516	1		
VIVARINI, Alvise	working 1457–1503	1		
CARPACCIO, Vittore	working 1486–*c.* 1525			1
CIMA DA CONEGLIANO, Giovanni Battista	*c.* 1459–1517/18		1	
GIORGIONE	*c.* 1478–1510			1
LOTTO, Lorenzo	1480–1556			1
PORDENONE, Giovanni Antonio da	*c.* 1484–1539	3	4	5
TITIAN	1485/88–1576	1		2
PORTA, Giuseppe (Salviati)	*c.* 1510–*c.* 1575	2		
BASSANO, Jacopo	1510 (?)–1592	1	7	2
FRANCO, Battista	1510 (?)–1561	4		2
TINTORETTO, Jacopo	1518–1594	1	5	1
SCHIAVONE, Andrea Meldolla	1522–1563	6		
VERONESE, Paolo Caliari	1528–1588	1	15	14
MONTEMEZZANO, Francesco	*c.* 1540–after 1602	1		
VICENTINO, Andrea	*c.* 1542–*c.* 1617	2		
PALMA, Jacopo (Giovane)	1544–1628	22		
BASSANO, Francesco da Ponte	*c.* 1549–1592	1		
MAZZA, Damiano	working 1573			1
TOGNONE, Antonio Vicentino		1		
CAMPAGNA, Girolamo	1552–after 1623			1
MAGANZA, Alessandro	1556–after 1630	1		
TINTORETTO, Marietta	*c.* 1556–1590	2		
ANONYMOUS, XVI century		12		

PADUA

		Originals	*School*	*Copies*
MANTEGNA, Andrea	1431–1506		3	1
CAMPAGNOLA, Domenico	1500–after 1552	32		

VERONA

		Originals	*School*	*Copies*
PISANELLO, Antonio	before 1395–1455	1		
FARINATI, Paolo	*c.* 1524–1606 (?)	49		
ANGOLO DEL MORO, Marco	*c.* 1537–after 1586	1		
ANONYMOUS, XVI century		3		

VICENZA

		Originals	*School*	*Copies*
MONTAGNA, Bartolommeo	1450–*c.* 1523	2		

MILAN

		Originals	*School*	*Copies*
SOLARIO, Andrea	working 1493–1515	1		
FERRARI, Gaudenzio	*c.* 1480–1546	1		
GIAMPIETRINO	working 1500–1510	1		
LUINI, Aurelio	1530–1593	4		

	Dates	*Originals*	*School*	*Copies*
LOMAZZO, Gian Paolo	*c.* 1538–1600	2		
FIGINO, Ambrogio	1548–1608	121		
PROCACCINI, Camillo	*c.* 1551 (?)–1629	12		1
MORAZZONE, Pier Francesco	1571–1626	4		
CERANO, Giovanni Battista Cresti	1575/6–1632	2		
ANONYMOUS, XV century		1		
ANONYMOUS, XVI century		10		
CREMONA				
CAMPI, Giulio	*d.* 1572	1		
CAMPI, Antonio	d. after 1591	1		
GATTI, Bernardino (Il Sojaro)	*c.* 1495–1575	4		
CAMPI, Bernardino	1522–after 1584	10		
ANGUISSOLA, Sophonisba	1527–1625	1		
TROTTI, Giovanni Battista (Malosso)	1555–1619	5		
ANONYMOUS, XVI century		1		
BERGAMO				
CASTELLO, Giovanni Battista (Il Bergamario)	*c.* 1510 (?)–1569	2		
SALMEGGIA, Enea (Il Talpino)	1546/50–1626	1		
BRESCIA				
ROMANINO, Girolamo	1484/89–1566 (?)	2		
GAMBARA, Lattanzio	1530–1574	1		
BOLOGNA				
ASPERTINI, Amico	1474(5?)–1552	2		
BAGNACAVALLO, Bartolommeo Ramenghi	1484–1542	2		
FRANCIA, Giacomo	before 1487–1557	1		1
INNOCENZO da Imola	1494–1550	2		
PUPINI, Biagio	working 1511–*d.* after 1575	5		
GIROLAMO da Treviso	*c.* 1497–1544	2		
PRIMATICCIO, Francesco	1504–1570	6	1	6
FANTUZZI, Antonio	*c.* 1510–after 1550			1
TIBALDI, Pellegrino	1527–1596	7		2
PASSAROTTI, Bartolommeo	1529–1592	10	6	
NOSADELLA, Giovanni Antonio Bezzi	*d.* 1571	1		
SAMACCHINI, Orazio	1532–1577	5		
CESI, Bartolommeo	1556–1629	3		
FACCINI, Pietro	1562–1602	4		
ANONYMOUS, XIV century		1		
ANONYMOUS, XVI century		9		
FAENZA, FORLÌ				
MENZOCCHI, Francesco	1502–1574	1		
MARCHETTI, Marco (da Faenza)	*d.* 1588 (?)	2		
PAGANELLI, Niccolò	1538–1620	1		
AGRESTI, Livio (da Forlì)	working 1550–before 1585	2		
FERRARA				
COSTA, Lorenzo	1460–1535		1	
GAROFALO, Benvenuto Tisi	1481–1559	1		
CARPI, Girolamo da	1501–1556	7		

		Originals	School	Copies
MODENA				
ABBATE, Niccolò dell'	*c.* 1506–1571	7	1	3
SETTI, Ercole	working 1568–1589	1		
ANONYMOUS, XVI century		1		
REGGIO				
ORSI, Lelio	1511 (?)–1587	13		
PARMA				
CORREGGIO, Antonio Allegri	1489(?)–1534	5		11
ANSELMI, Michelangelo	1491–1555/6	2		
PARMIGIANINO, Francesco	1503–1540	41		53
MAZZOLA-BEDOLI, Girolamo	*c.* 1500–*c.* 1569	2		
ANONYMOUS, XVI century		9		
GENOA				
CAMBIASO, Luca	1527–1585	3		2
CASTELLO, Bernardo	1557–1629	4		
ANONYMOUS, XVI century		5		
NORTH ITALIAN *UNSPECIFIED*				
ANONYMOUS, XV century		8		
ANONYMOUS, XVI century		13		
CENTRAL ITALY *FLORENCE*				
LIPPI, Fra Filippo	*c.* 1406–1469	1		
GOZZOLI, Benozzo	1420–1497	2		
POLLAIUOLO, Antonio	1429–1498	1		
GHIRLANDAIO, Domenico	1449–1494	1		
LIPPI, Filippino	1457–1504	2		
CREDI, Lorenzo di	1457–1537	2		1
BARTOLOMMEO, Fra	1475–1517	13		
MICHELANGELO Buonarroti	1475–1564	17	10	65
GRANACCI, Francesco	1477–1543	1		
SOGLIANI, Giovanni Antonio	1492–1544	1		
BANDINELLI, Baccio	1493–1560	6	9	1
BACCHIACCA, Francesco (Ubertini)	1494–1557	1		
ROSSO Fiorentino	1495–1540	4		2
BRONZINO, Agnolo	1503–1572	2		
RAFFAELLO da Montelupo	1504/05–1566/67	2		
SALVIATI, Francesco	1510–1563	21		
VASARI, Giorgio	1511–1574	6		1
VINCI, Pierino da	1531–1554	1		1
ALLORI, Alessandro	1535–1607	4		
TITO, Santi di	1536–1603	1		
NALDINI, Battista	1537–1591	1		
LIGOZZI, Jacopo	1547–1626	2		
POCCETTI, Bernardino Barbatelli	1548–1612	4		
BOSCOLI, Andrea	*c.* 1550–*c.* 1606	3		
EMPOLI, Jacopo Chimenti da	1551–1640	3		
PASSIGNANO, Domenico Cresti	1558/60–1638	7		
CIGOLI, Lodovico Cardi	1559–1613	6		
TEMPESTA, Antonio	1555–1630	51		
BALDUCCI, Giovanni (Cosci)	*c.* 1560–1600/05	1		
ANONYMOUS, XV century		2		
ANONYMOUS, XVI century		16		

		Originals	School	Copies
SIENA				
PERUZZI, Baldassare	1481–1536	3		
BECCAFUMI, Domenico	*c.* 1486–1551	5		2
NERONI, Bartolommeo (Riccio)	*d.* 1571	1		
CASOLANI, Alessandro	1552–1606	2		
VANNI, Francesco	1563–1610	4		
SALIMBENI, Ventura	*c.* 1567–1613	3		
ANONYMOUS, XVI century		2		
UMBRIA				
SIGNORELLI, Luca	1441 (?)–1523	2		
PERUGINO, Pietro	1446–1523	2		3
CIRCIGNANO, Niccolò (Pomerancio)	1516 (?)–after 1596	2		
ANONYMOUS, XV century		1		
URBINO				
SANTI, Giovanni	1430/40–1494	1		
VITI, Timoteo	1467–1523	1		
GENGA, Girolamo	*c.* 1476–1551	1		
BAROCCI, Federico	1526–1612	20		
ROME				
RAPHAEL (Raffaello Santi)	1483–1520	18	11	45
MARCANTONIO Raimondi	*c.* 1480–1527/34			2
SEBASTIANO del Piombo	*c.* 1485–1547	2		1
GIOVANNI da Udine	*c.* 1487–1564	1		1
POLIDORO da Caravaggio	1496/1500–1543	9		43
CLOVIO, Giulio	1498–1578	6		
GIULIO Romano	1499–1546	9	8	27
PERINO del Vaga	1500/01–1547	12		11
BONFRATELLI, Apollonio de'	working 1523–1572	1		
DANIELE da Volterra	1509 (?)–1566	4		2
LIGORIO, Pirro	*c.* 1510–1583	8		
SICIOLANTE DA SERMONETA, Girolamo	1521–*c.* 1580	3		1
MUZIANO, Girolamo	1528–1592	3		
ZUCCARO, Taddeo	1529–1566	10		3
NOGARI, Paris	*c.* 1536–1601	1		2
CESURA DELL' AQUILA, Pompeo	*d.* 1571	1		
ZUCCARO, Federico	1542/43–1609	16	9	
SARZANA, Leonardo da	working 1551–1589			1
RICCI, Giovanni Battista (da Novara)	1545–1620	10		
OLIVIERI, Pier Paolo	1551–1599	1		
ALBERTI, Cherubino	1553–1615			1
RONCALLI, Cristoforo (Pomerancio)	1552–1626	1		
CESARI, Giuseppe (Cavaliere d'Arpino)	1568–1640	16		
ANONYMOUS, XVI century		31		
UNCERTAIN SCHOOL				
ANONYMOUS, XVI century		15		
SCHOOL OF FONTAINEBLEAU				
PENNI, Luca	*d.* 1556	2		
ANONYMOUS, XVI century		3		

PLATES

I. FILIPPO LIPPI: STUDIES OF DRAPERY (Cat. No. 14)

2. GOZZOLI: HEAD OF A YOUTH (Cat. No. 11 *recto*)

3. GOZZOLI: HEAD OF A YOUTH (Cat. No. 10 *recto*)

4. GOZZOLI: FOUR SAINTS (Cat. No. 11 *verso*)

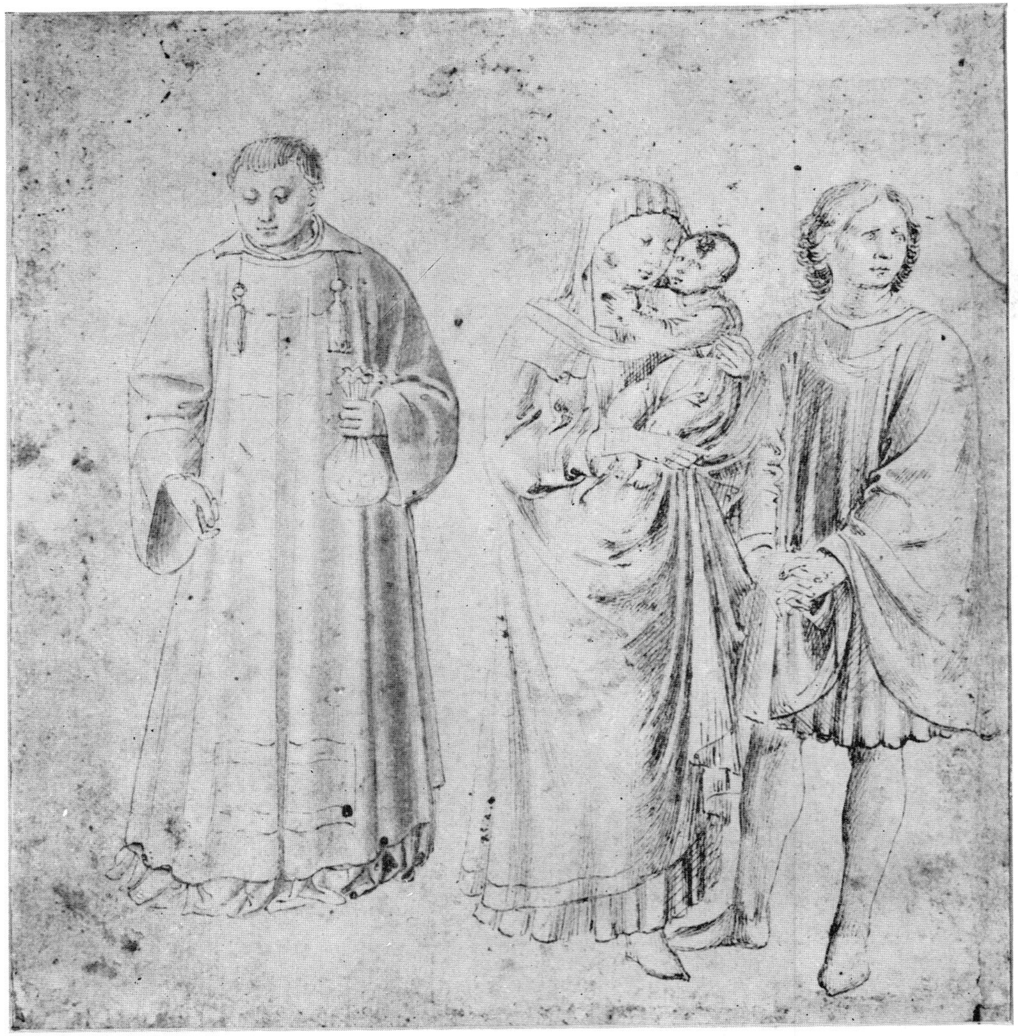

5. GOZZOLI: STUDIES OF ST. LAWRENCE DISTRIBUTING ALMS (Cat. No. 10 *verso*)

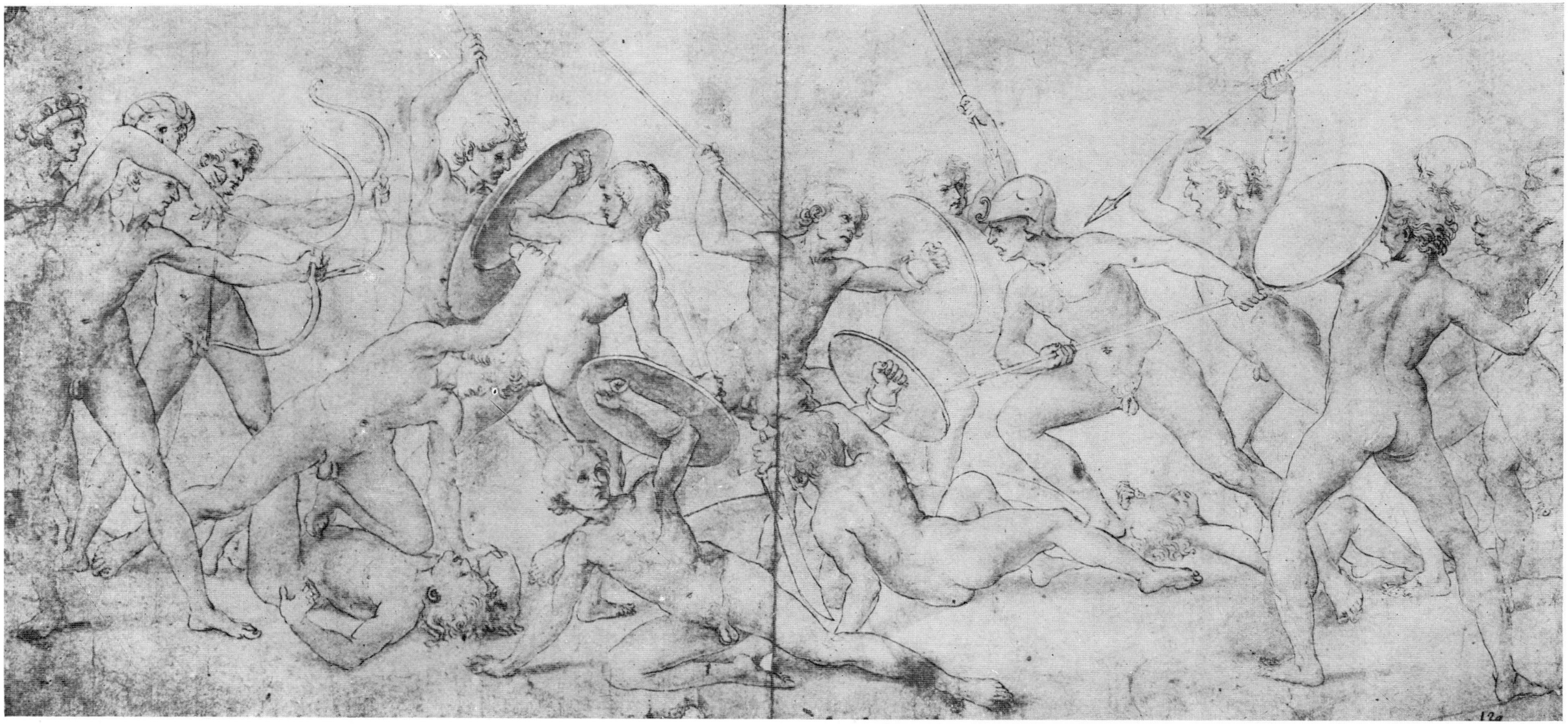

6. ANTONIO POLLAIUOLO: BATTLE OF NAKED MEN (Cat. No. 27)

7. FILIPPINO LIPPI: HEAD OF A MAN (Cat. No. 13 *recto*)

8. DOMENICO GHIRLANDAIO: HEAD OF AN OLD WOMAN (Cat. No. 9)

9. PERUGINO: HEAD OF THE VIRGIN (Cat. No. 22)

10. PERUGINO: STUDY OF ST. MICHAEL (Cat. No. 21)

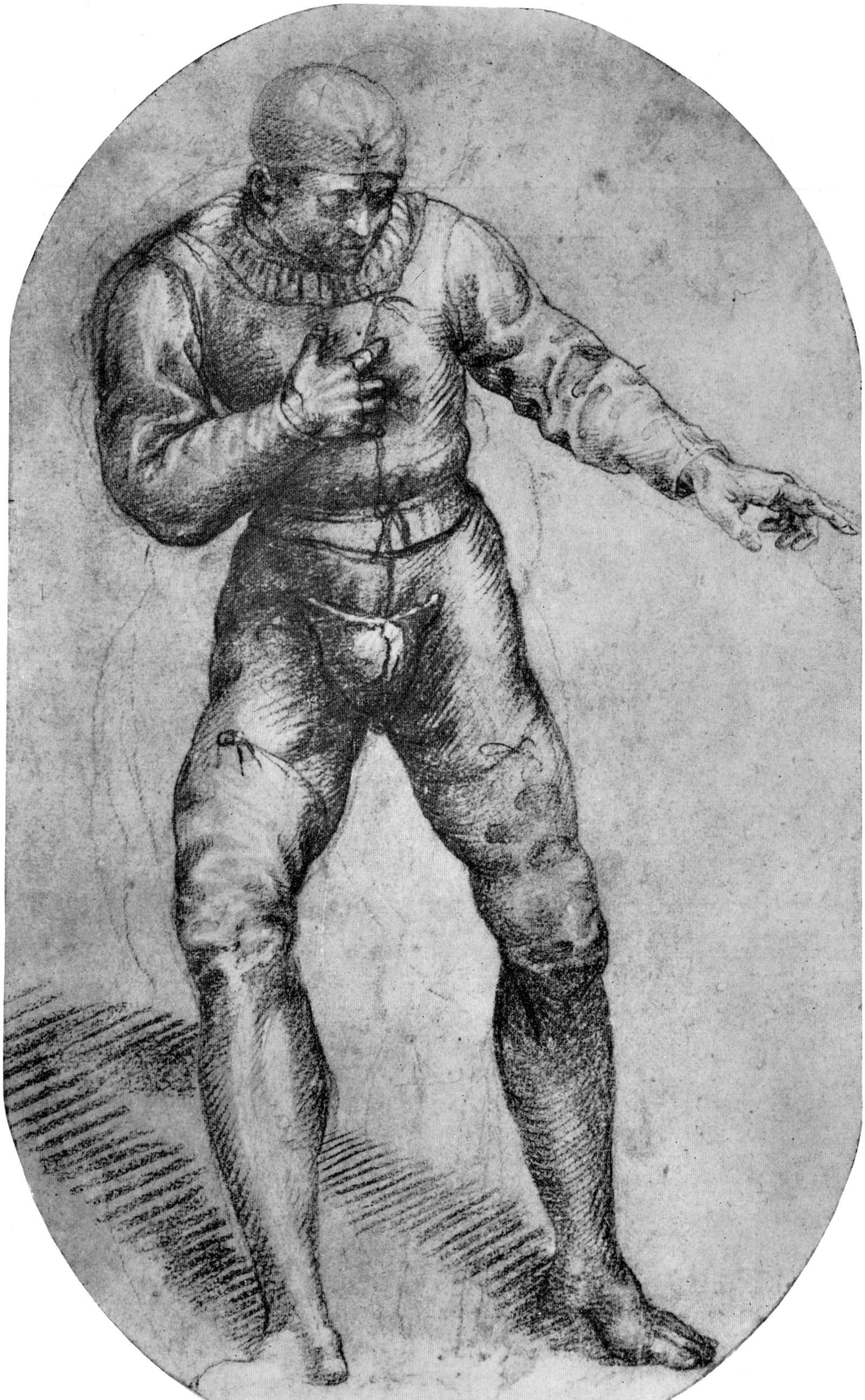

II. SIGNORELLI: MAN IN AN ATTITUDE OF TERROR (Cat. No. 30)

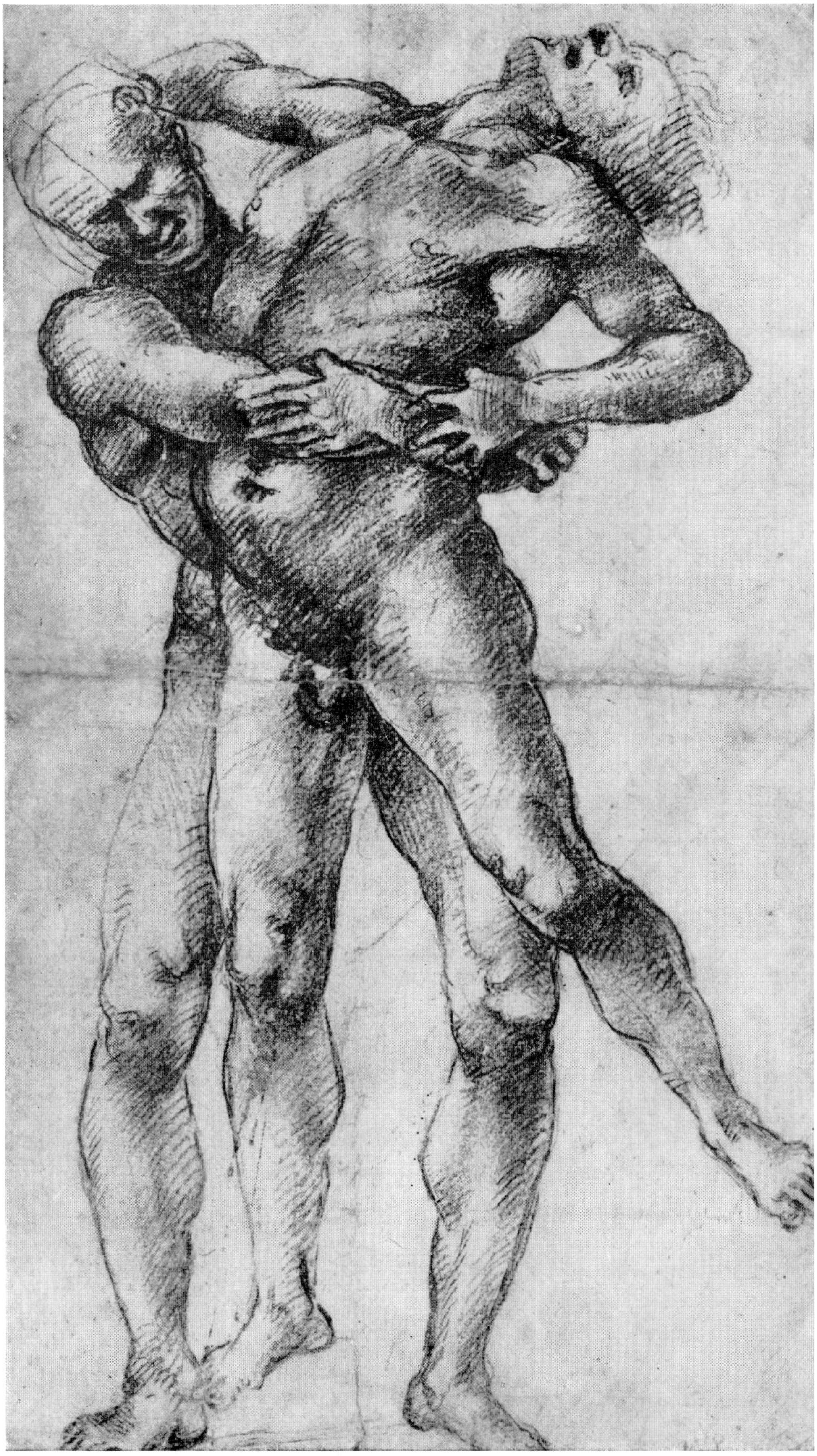

12. SIGNORELLI: HERCULES AND ANTAEUS (Cat. No. 29)

13. ANONYMOUS FLORENTINE: YOUTH DRAWING AND DOG (Cat. No. 33 *recto*)

14. FRA BARTOLOMMEO: STUDY FOR THE 'LAST JUDGMENT' (Cat. No. 108 *recto*)

15. FRA BARTOLOMMEO: VIRGIN AND CHILD (Cat. No. 113 *recto*)

16. FRA BARTOLOMMEO: THE TEMPTATION OF ST. ANTHONY (Cat. No. 115 *recto*)

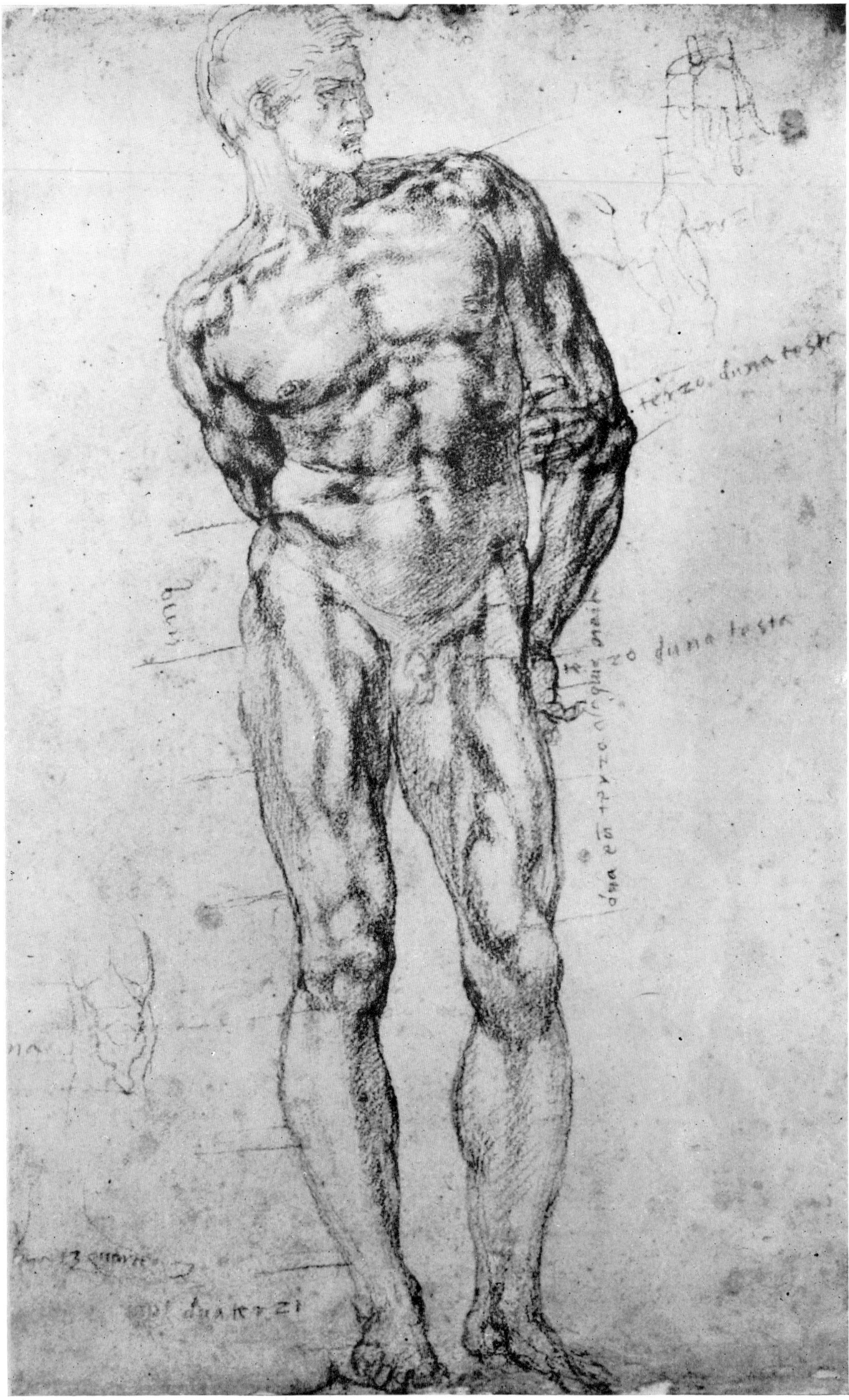

17. MICHELANGELO: MALE NUDE WITH PROPORTIONS (Cat. No. 421 *recto*)

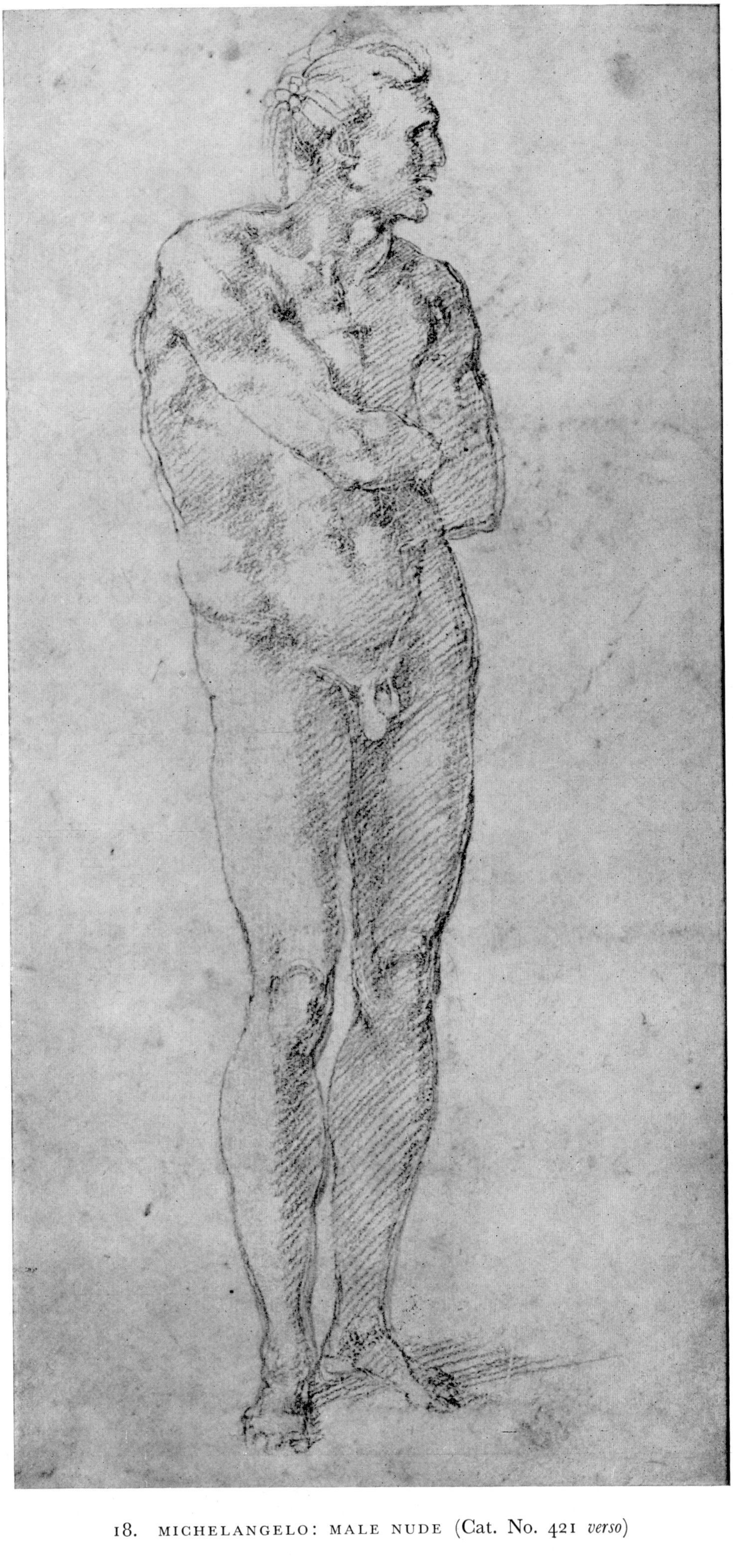

18. MICHELANGELO: MALE NUDE (Cat. No. 421 *verso*)

19. MICHELANGELO: THREE LABOURS OF HERCULES (Cat. No. 423)

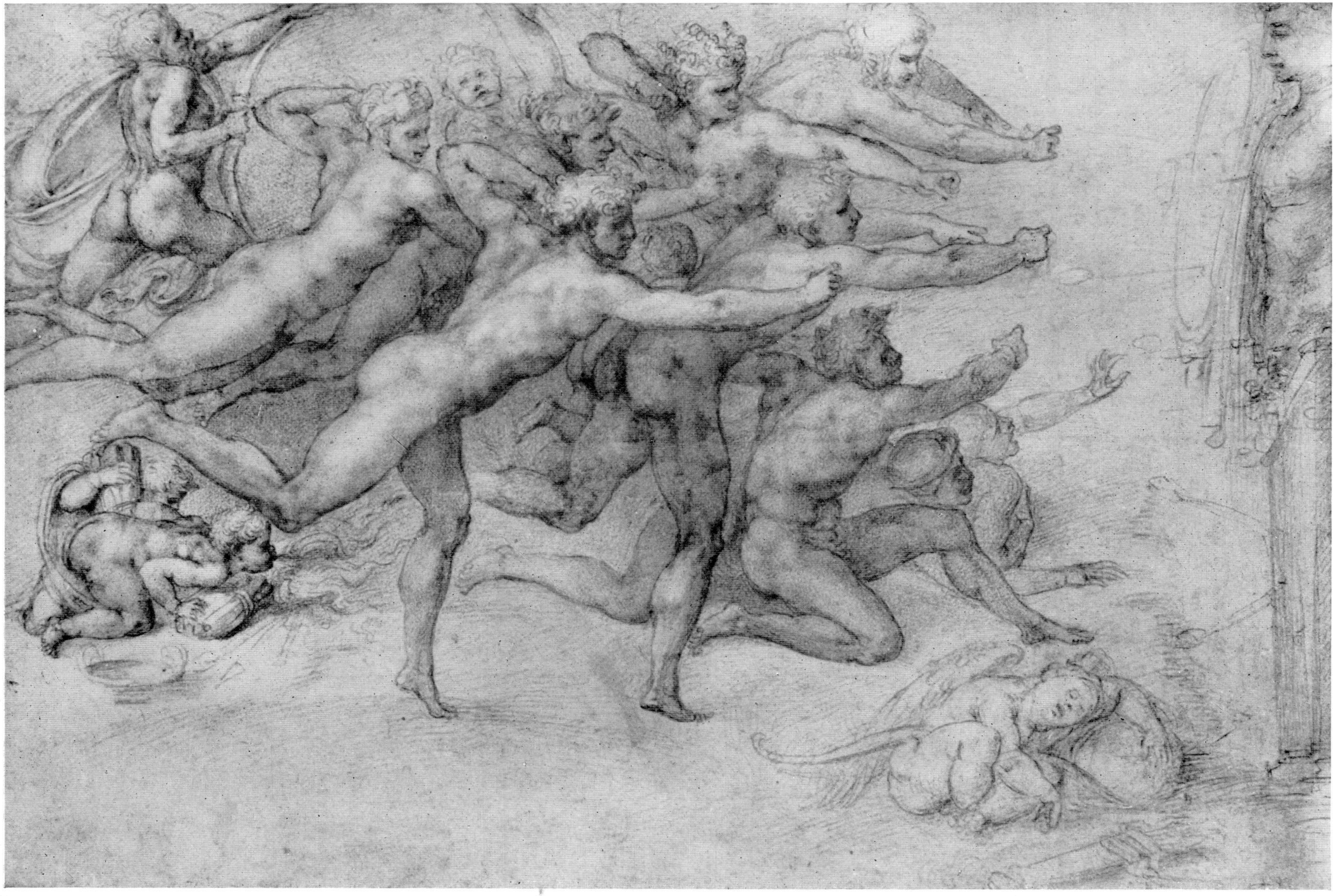

20. MICHELANGELO: ARCHERS SHOOTING AT A HERM (Cat. No. 424)

21. MICHELANGELO: TITYUS (Cat. No. 429)

22. MICHELANGELO: THE RESURRECTION (Cat. No. 427 *recto*)

23. MICHELANGELO: RECUMBENT MALE FIGURE AND MONK (Cat. No. 422 *recto*)

24. MICHELANGELO: HEAD OF A YOUNG WOMAN (Cat. No. 434 *recto*)

25. MICHELANGELO: THE RISEN CHRIST (Cat. No. 428)

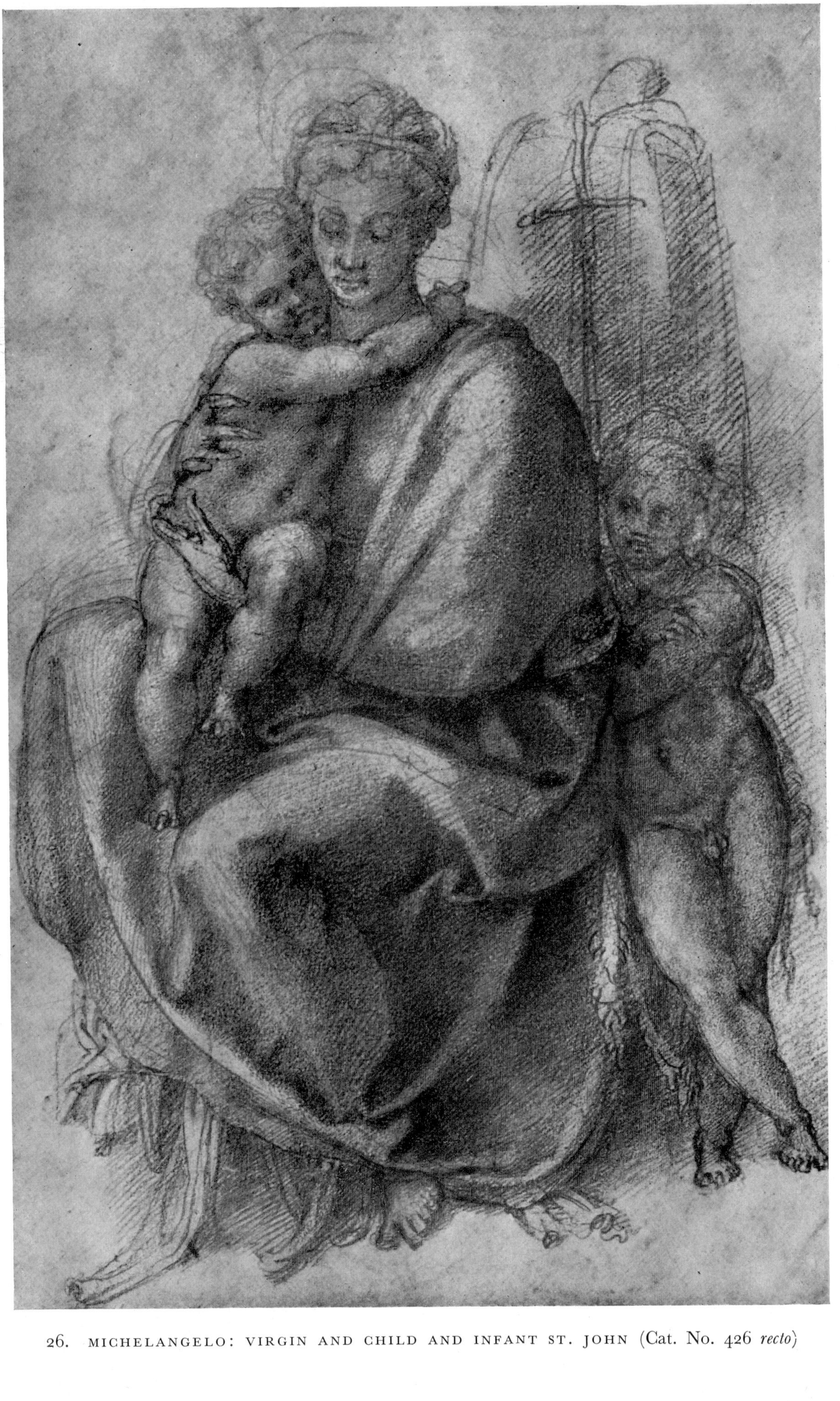

26. MICHELANGELO: VIRGIN AND CHILD AND INFANT ST. JOHN (Cat. No. 426 *recto*)

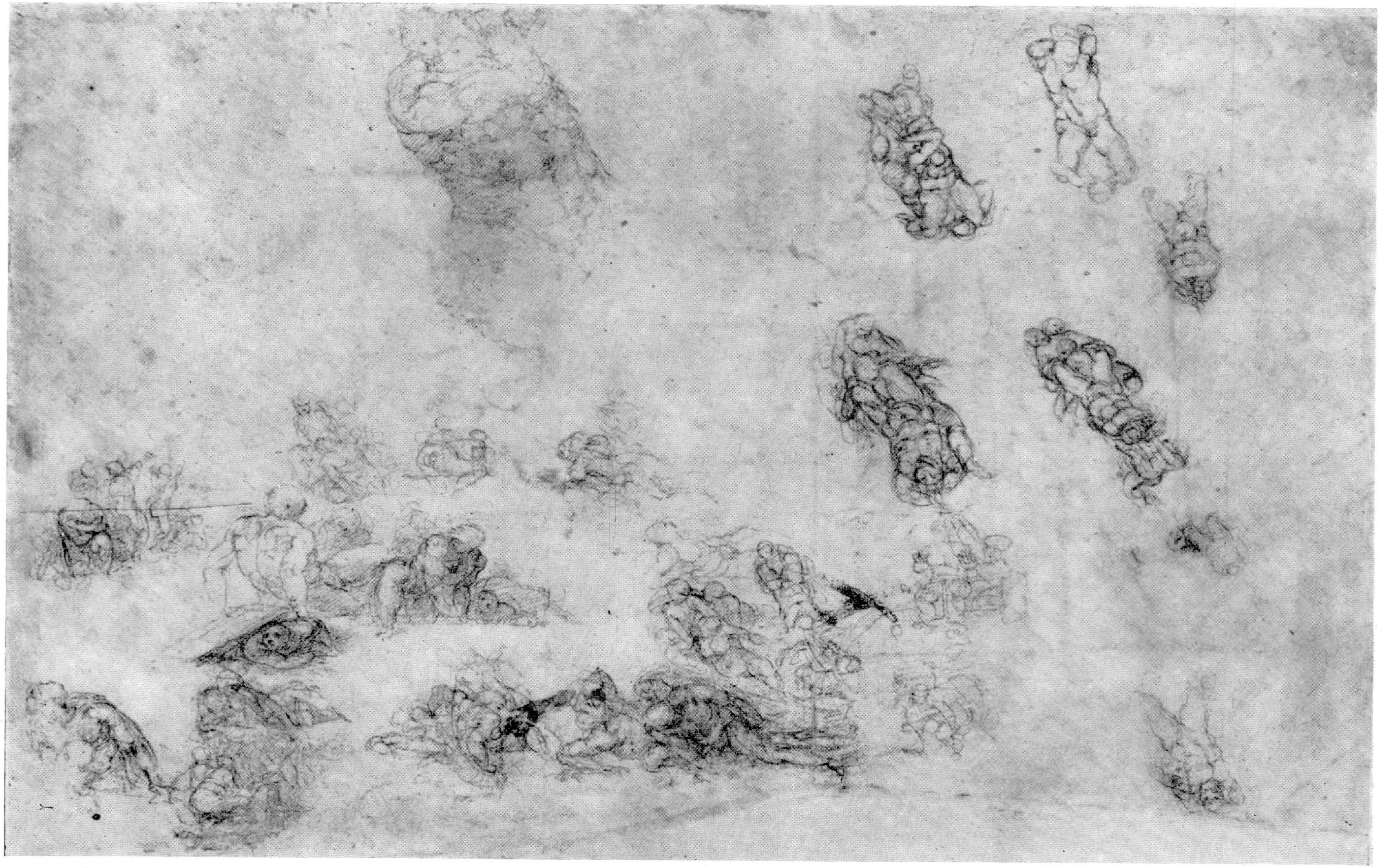

27. MICHELANGELO: STUDIES FOR THE 'LAST JUDGMENT' (Cat. No. 432 *recto*)

28. MICHELANGELO: BACCHANAL OF CHILDREN (Cat. No. 431)

29. MICHELANGELO: THE FALL OF PHAETHON (Cat. No. 430 *recto*)

30. MICHELANGELO: STUDIES FOR A PIETÀ (Cat. No. 433 *recto*)

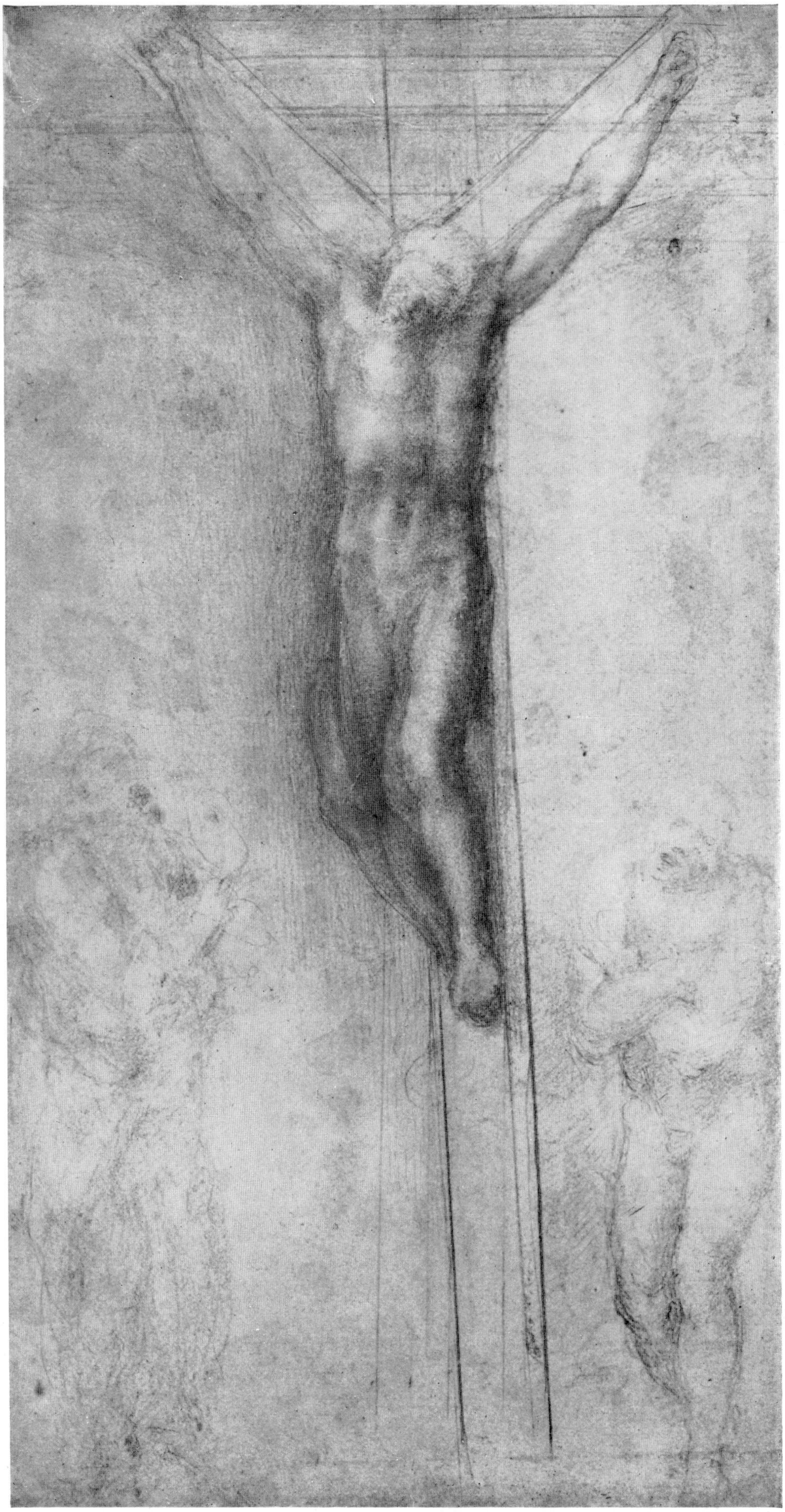

31. MICHELANGELO: CHRIST ON THE CROSS (Cat. No. 437 *recto*)

32. MICHELANGELO: CHRIST ON THE CROSS (Cat. No. 436)

33. SALVIATI: ALTARPIECE WITH THE VIRGIN AND CHILD AND SAINTS (Cat. No. 885)

34. BRONZINO: STUDY FOR 'CHRIST IN LIMBO' (Cat. No. 143)

35. SALVIATI: MAN AND DEAD YOUTH (Cat. No. 887)

36. ROSSO: STUDY FOR A 'MASSACRE OF THE INNOCENTS' (Cat. No. 875)

37. BECCAFUMI: DESIGNS FOR HOUSE-FAÇADES (Cat. No. 132)

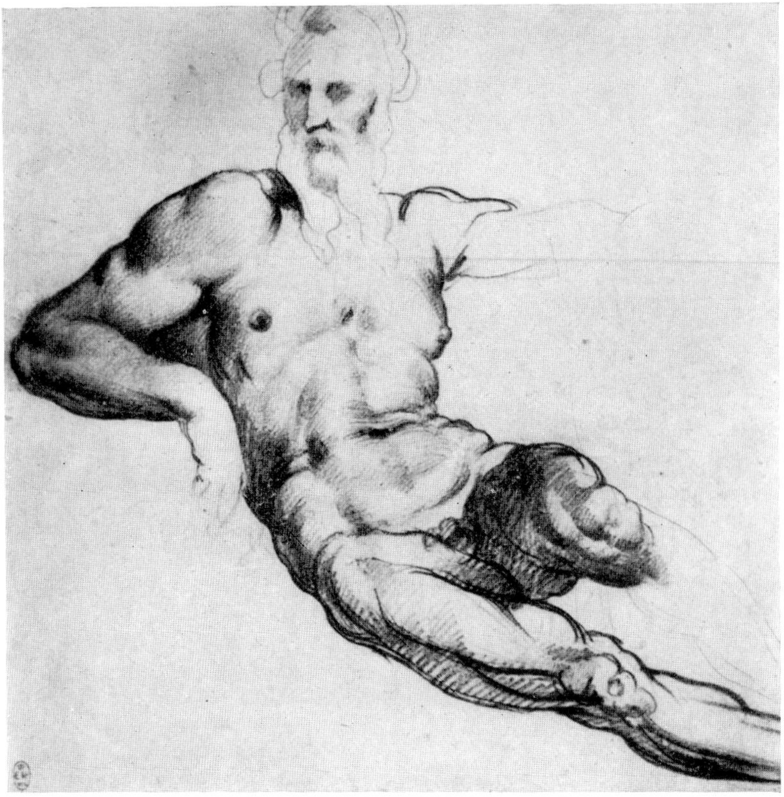

38. ANONYMOUS FLORENTINE: RIVER-GOD (Cat. No. 1090)

39. BANDINELLI: TWO SEATED NUDES (Cat. No. 73)

40. ALLORI: SOPRA-PORTE FOR POGGIO À CAJANO (Cat. No. 59)

41. CIGOLI: TWO SERVING-MEN
(Cat. No. 233)

42. CIGOLI: SERVING-WOMAN
(Cat. No. 234)

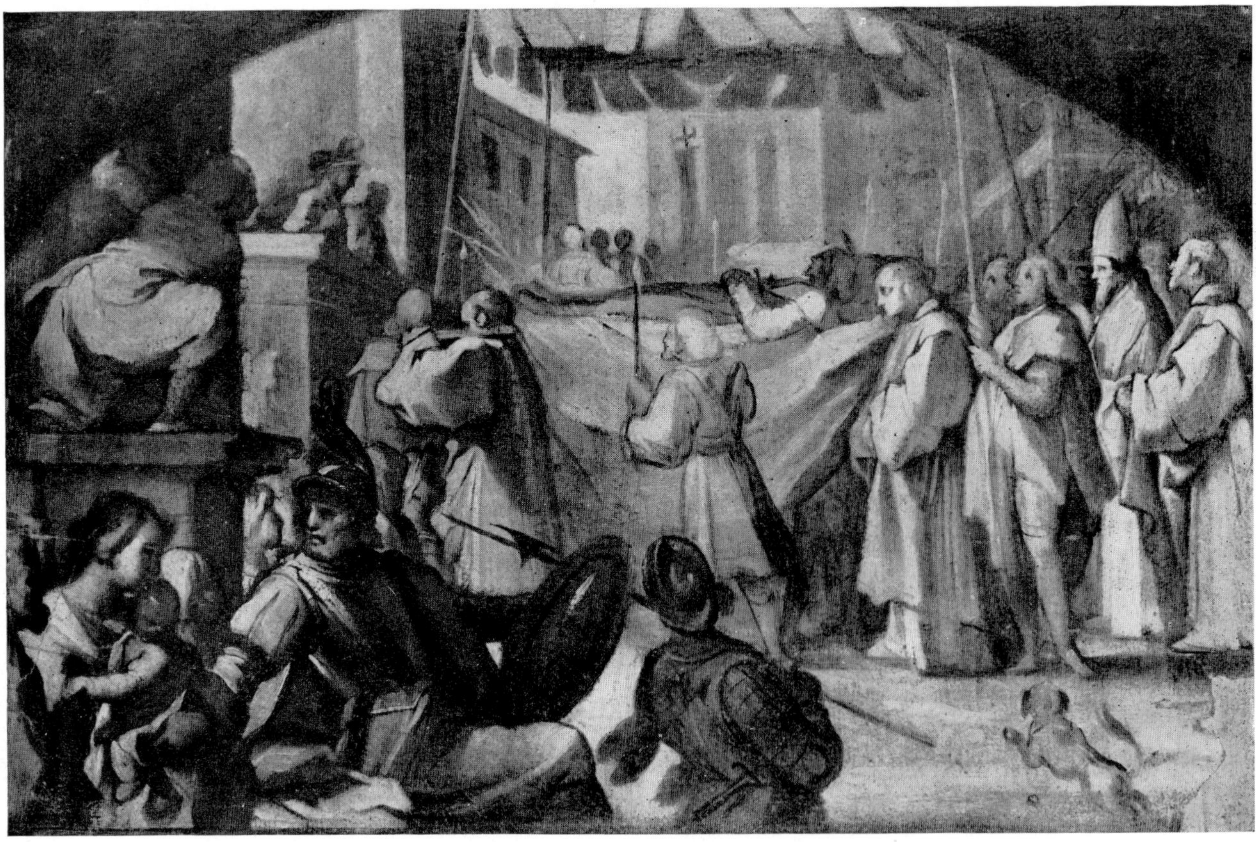

43. VANNI: FUNERAL OF A SAINT (Cat. No. 995)

44. CASOLANI: STUDIES IN A KITCHEN (Cat. No. 204)

45. SALIMBENI: MIRACLE OF ST. MICHAEL (Cat. No. 881)

46. RAPHAEL: STUDY OF HEADS FOR THE 'CORONATION OF THE VIRGIN' (Cat. No. 788)

47. RAPHAEL: HOLY FAMILY (Cat. No. 790)

48. RAPHAEL: STUDIES FOR THE 'PARNASSUS' (Cat. No. 796 *recto*)

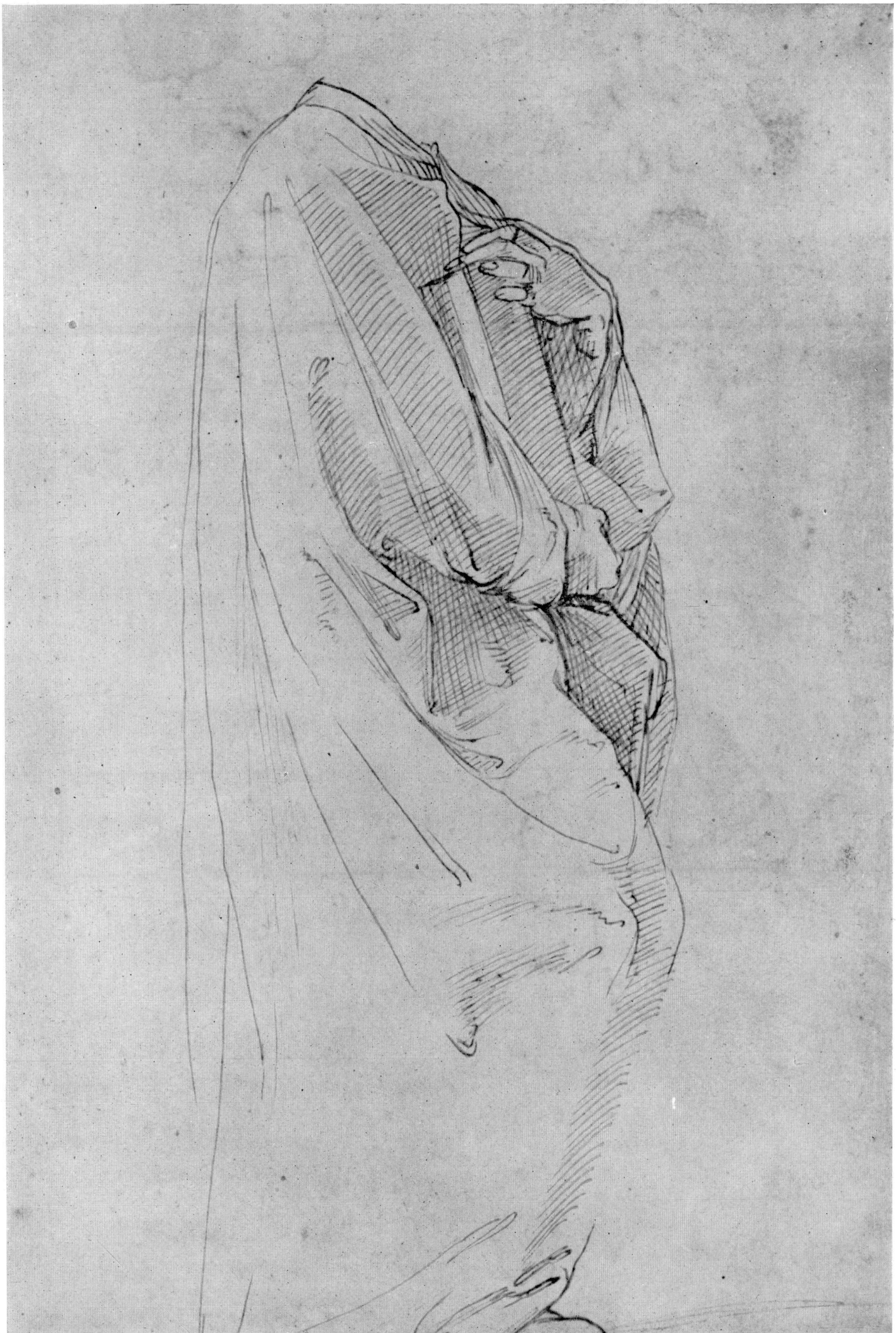

49. RAPHAEL: STUDY FOR DANTE IN THE 'PARNASSUS' (Cat. No. 796 *verso*)

50. RAPHAEL: LEDA AND THE SWAN (Cat. No. 789)

51. RAPHAEL: STUDY OF CATTLE (Cat. No. 799 *verso*)

52. RAPHAEL: THE DOCTRINE OF THE TWO SWORDS (Cat. No. 797 *recto*)

53. RAPHAEL: THE JUDGMENT OF ZALEUCUS (Cat. No. 797 *verso*)

54. RAPHAEL: STUDY FOR THE LEFT HALF OF THE 'DISPUTA' (Cat. No. 794)

55. RAPHAEL: THE MASSACRE OF THE INNOCENTS (Cat. No. 793 *recto*)

56. RAPHAEL: COMPOSITION STUDY FOR THE 'DISPUTÀ' (Cat. No. 795)

57. RAPHAEL: NUDE MAN FLEEING IN TERROR (Cat. No. 799 *recto*)

58. RAPHAEL: NUDE MEN CROUCHING ON THE GROUND (Cat. No. 798)

59. RAPHAEL: VIRGIN AND CHILD AND ST. ELIZABETH (Cat. No. 800)

60. RAPHAEL: LANDSCAPE WITH RUINS (Cat. No. 801)

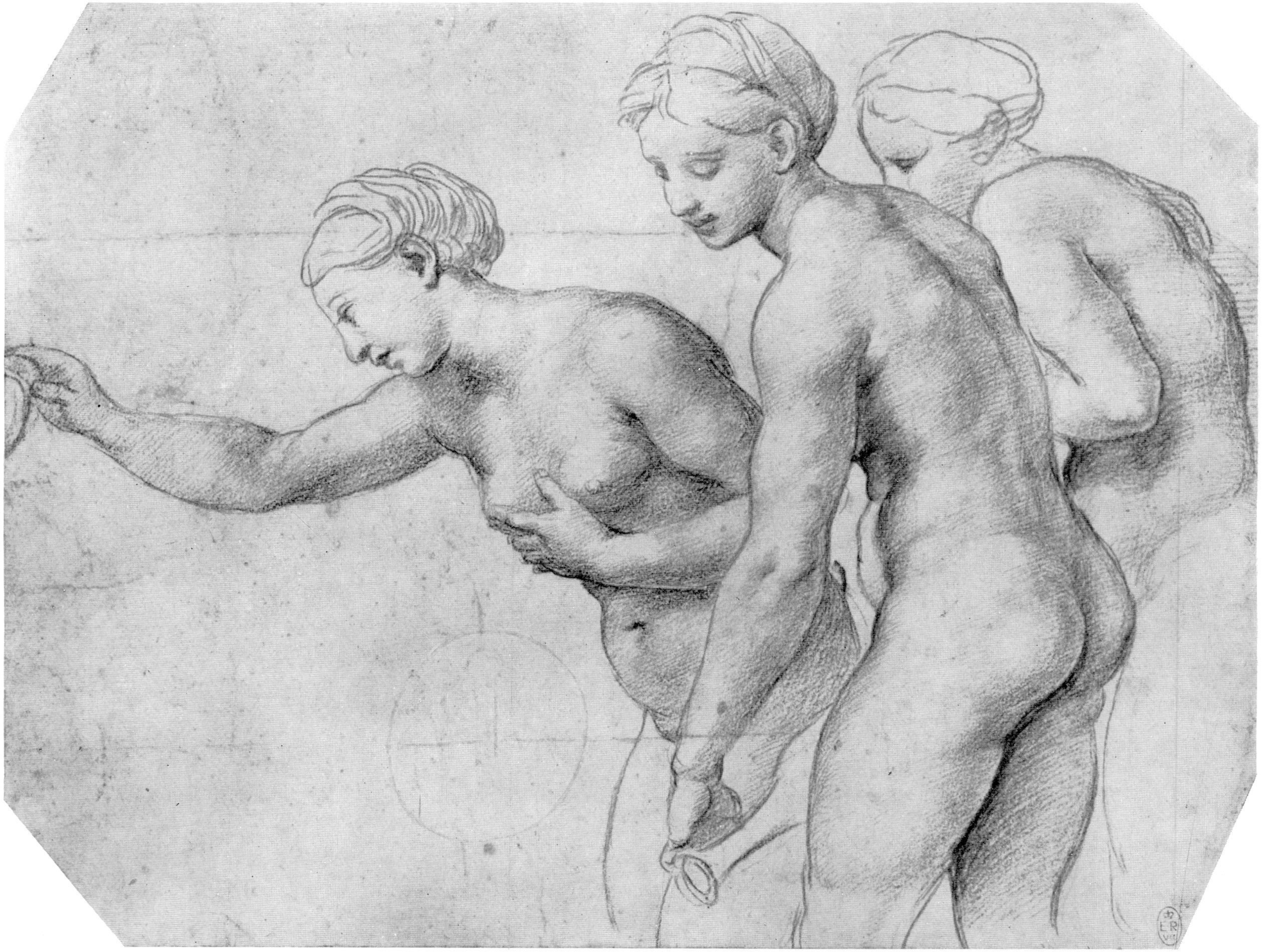

61. RAPHAEL: THE THREE GRACES (Cat. No. 804)

62. RAPHAEL: CHRIST GIVING THE KEYS TO ST. PETER (Cat. No. 802)

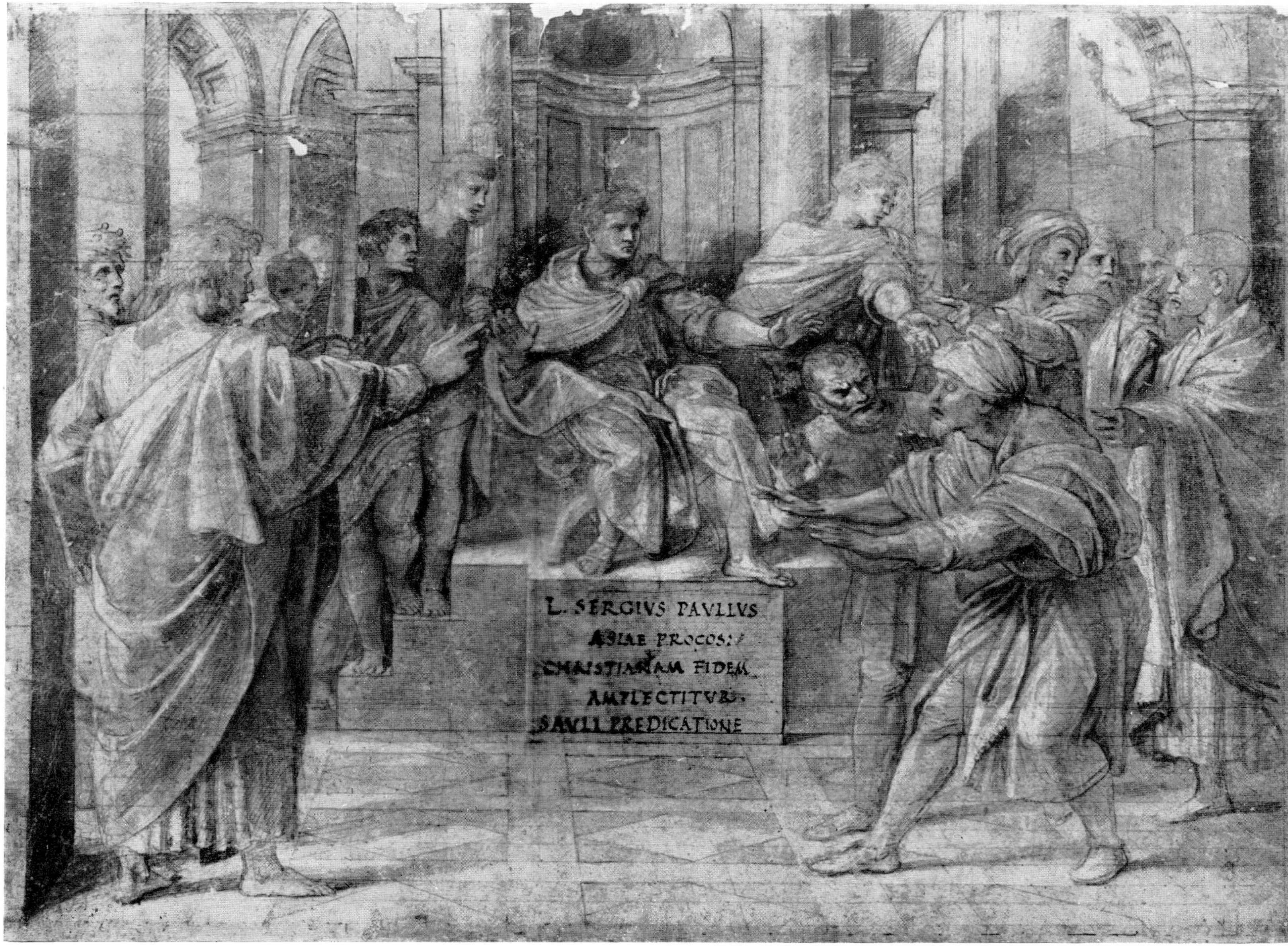

63. RAPHAEL: THE BLINDING OF ELYMAS (Cat. No. 803)

64. RAPHAEL: THE LAST SUPPER (Cat. No. 805)

65. ANONYMOUS ROMAN: DESIGN FOR A SCULPTURED ALTAR
(Cat. No. 1132)

66. PERUZZI: DESIGN FOR AN ORGAN-CASE (Cat. No. 683)

67. PERUZZI: JUPITER (Cat. No. 685)

68. ANONYMOUS ROMAN: WOMAN AND TWO PUTTI (Cat. No. 1134)

69. POLIDORO: SCENE OF WORSHIP (Cat. No. 693B)

70. POLIDORO: THE BETRAYAL (Cat. No. 692)

71. PERINO DEL VAGA: NEPTUNE CALMING THE TEMPEST
(Cat. No. 975)

72. PERINO DEL VAGA: SOLON GIVING LAWS TO THE ATHENIANS
(Cat. No. 976)

73. PERINO DEL VAGA: DESIGN FOR THE SALA DELLA GIUSTIZIA IN THE CASTLE OF ST. ANGELO
(Cat. No. 979)

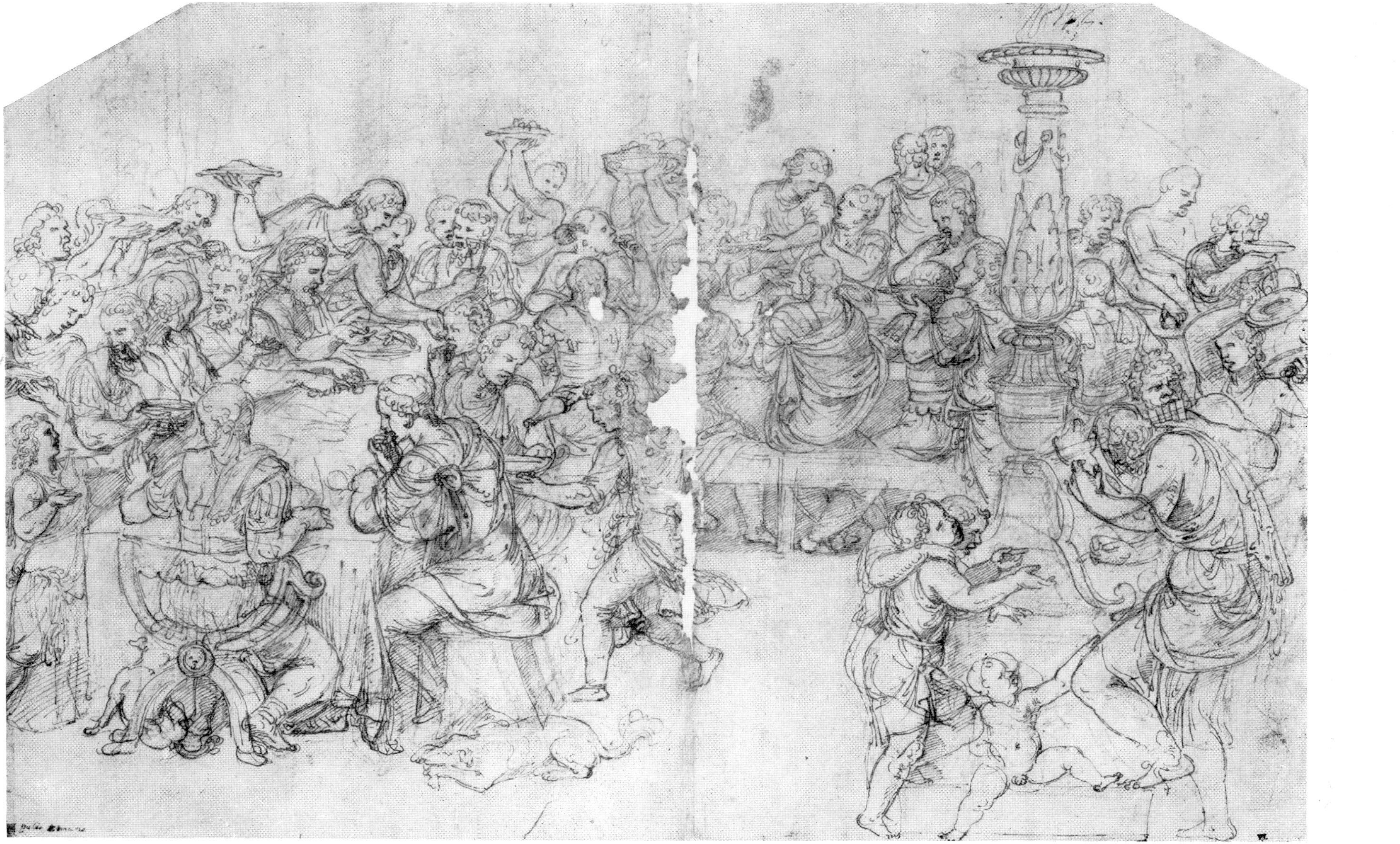

74. GIULIO ROMANO: SCIPIO FEASTING THE ROMAN TRIBUNES (Cat. No. 352)

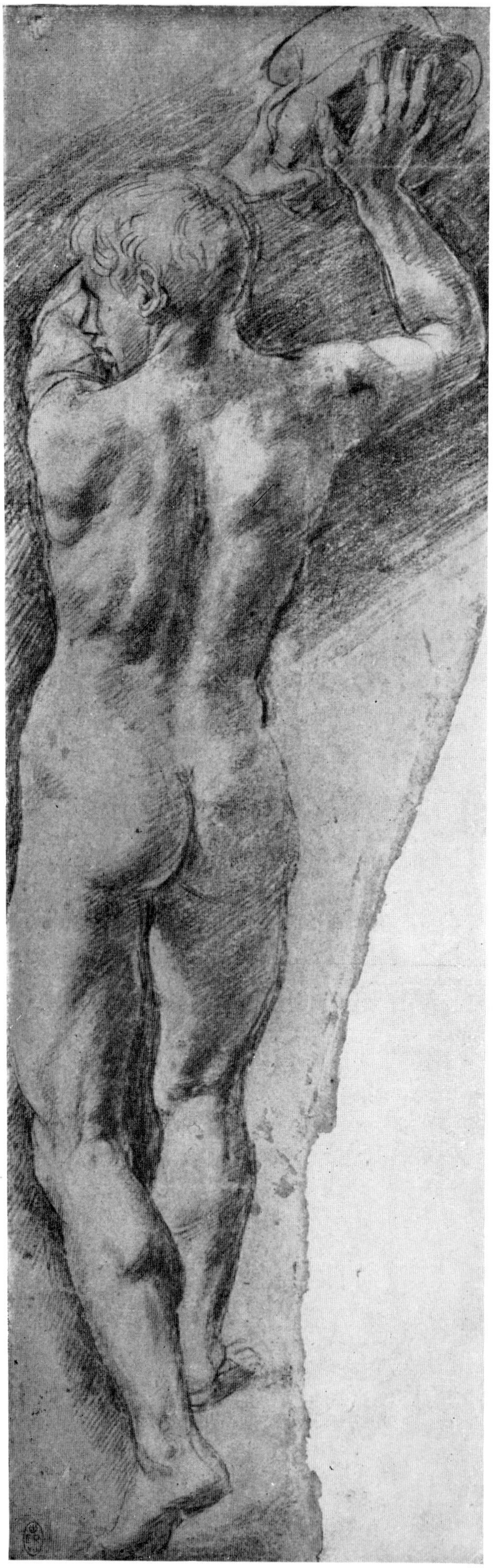

75. GIULIO ROMANO: NUDE MAN CASTING A STONE
(Cat. No. 348)

76. DANIELE DA VOLTERRA: SEATED APOSTLE (Cat. No. 262)

77. DANIELE DA VOLTERRA: DRAPED FEMALE FIGURE (Cat. No. 263)

78. CLOVIO: CHRIST HANDING THE KEYS TO ST. PETER (Cat. No. 244)

79. SEBASTIANO DEL PIOMBO: GOD THE FATHER (Cat. No. 924)

80. SEBASTIANO DEL PIOMBO: HOLY FAMILY (Cat. No. 923 *recto*)

81. MUZIANO: ST. JEROME (Cat. No. 518)

82. SICIOLANTE: VIRGIN AND CHILD (Cat. No. 927)

83. LIGORIO: ALLEGORICAL COMPOSITION (Cat. No. 399)

84. TADDEO ZUCCARO: THE BLINDING OF ELYMAS (Cat. No. 1067)

85. TADDEO ZUCCARO: OCCASION SEIZING FORTUNE BY THE FORELOCK (Cat. No. 1066)

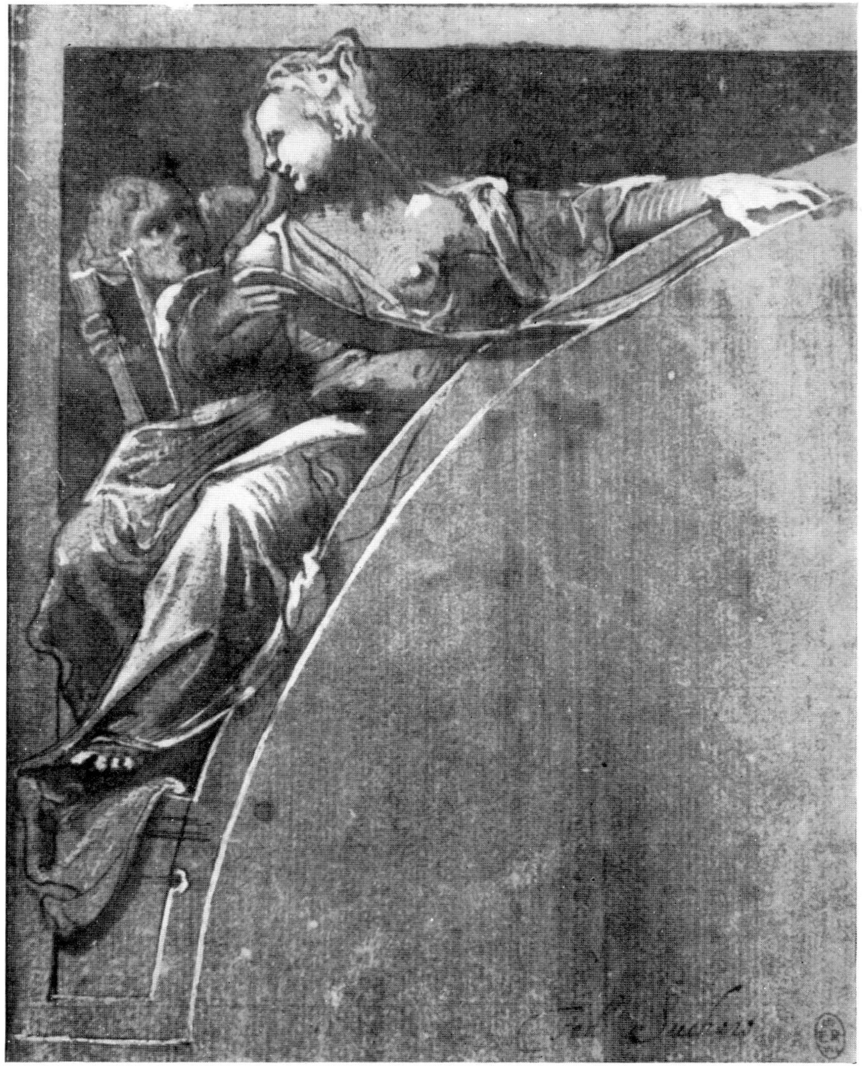

86. FEDERICO ZUCCARO: SIBYL AND CHILD (Cat. No. 1049)

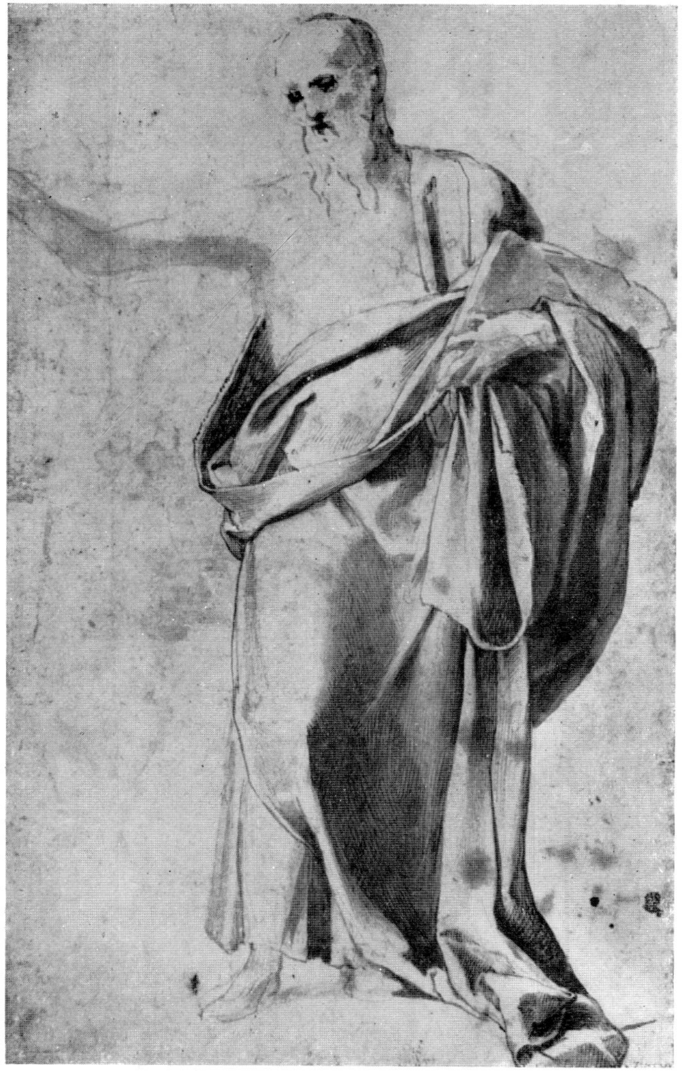

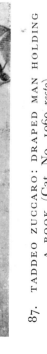

87. TADDEO ZUCCARO: DRAPED MAN HOLDING A BOOK (Cat. No. 1069 *recto*)

88. TADDEO ZUCCARO: PORTRAIT HEAD (Cat. No. 1073)

89. TADDEO ZUCCARO: SHEPHERDS FOR AN 'ADORATION' (Cat. No. 1071)

90. BAROCCI: THE CALLING OF ST. ANDREW (Cat. No. 107)

91. BAROCCI: HEAD OF A YOUNG WOMAN (Cat. No. 96)

92. BAROCCI: HEAD OF AN OLD MAN (Cat. No. 98)

93. BAROCCI: HEAD OF A MAN LOOKING DOWN
(Cat. No. 92)

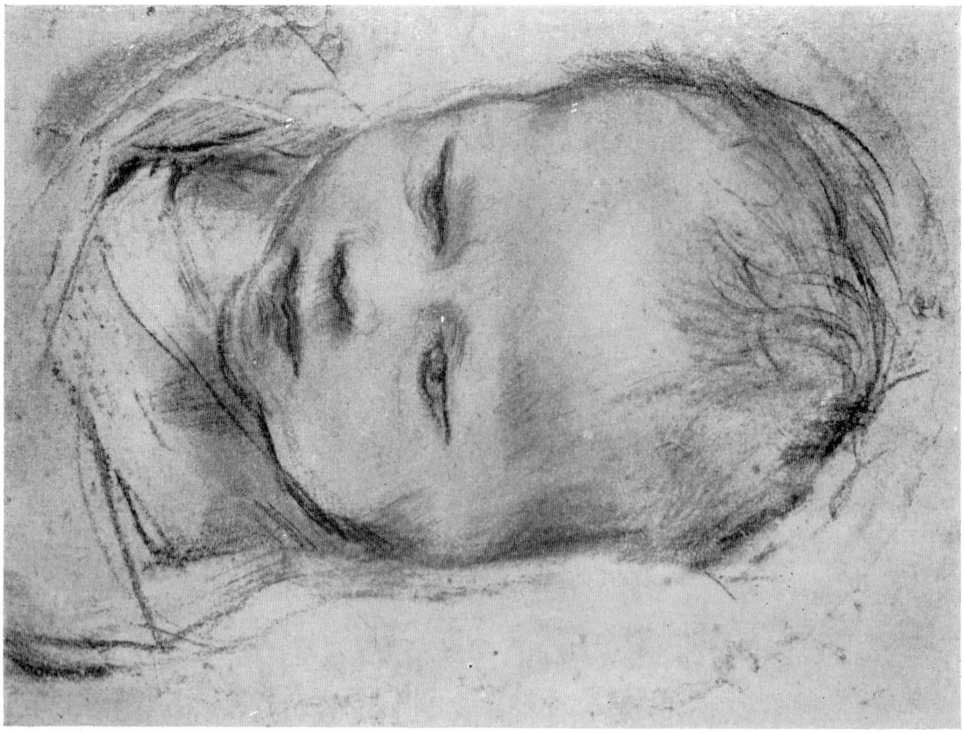

94. BAROCCI: HEAD OF A BABY (Cat. No. 89)

95. BAROCCI: SEATED YOUTH (Cat. No. 100)

96. CESARI: STUDIES OF FIGURES (Cat. No. 214)

97. SCHOOL OF COSTA: THE ADORATION OF THE SHEPHERDS (Cat. No. 5 *recto*)

98. PUPINI: THE ADORATION OF THE MAGI (Cat. No. 782)

99. GIROLAMO DA TREVISO: ENTHRONEMENT OF A BISHOP (Cat. No. 347)

100. GAROFALO: PROPHET IN A LUNETTE (Cat. No. 336)

101. GIROLAMO DA CARPI: SEATED APOSTLE OR PROPHET (Cat. No. 201)

102. GIROLAMO DA CARPI: THE ADORATION OF THE SHEPHERDS (Cat. No. 202)

103. ANONYMOUS, MODENA: LEGENDARY SCENE (Cat. No. 1122)

104. PRIMATICCIO: DISCORD AT THE WEDDING FEAST OF PELEUS AND THETIS
(Cat. No. 757)

105. PRIMATICCIO: TWO SEATED MEN (Cat. No. 759)

106. PRIMATICCIO: PUTTO RIDING ON A SEA-HORSE (Cat. No. 758)

107. NICCOLÒ DELL' ABBATE: ST. AUGUSTINE AND ST. GENEVIÈVE
(Cat. No. 49)

108. ANONYMOUS, BOLOGNA: WOMAN SEEN FROM THE BACK (Cat. No. 1080)

109. TIBALDI: A MIRACLE OF ST. MARK (?) (Cat. No. 947)

110. TIBALDI: ANGEL STRIKING WORSHIPPERS IN A TEMPLE (Cat. No. 949)

III. TIBALDI: DESIGN FOR A FRIEZE (Cat. No. 945)

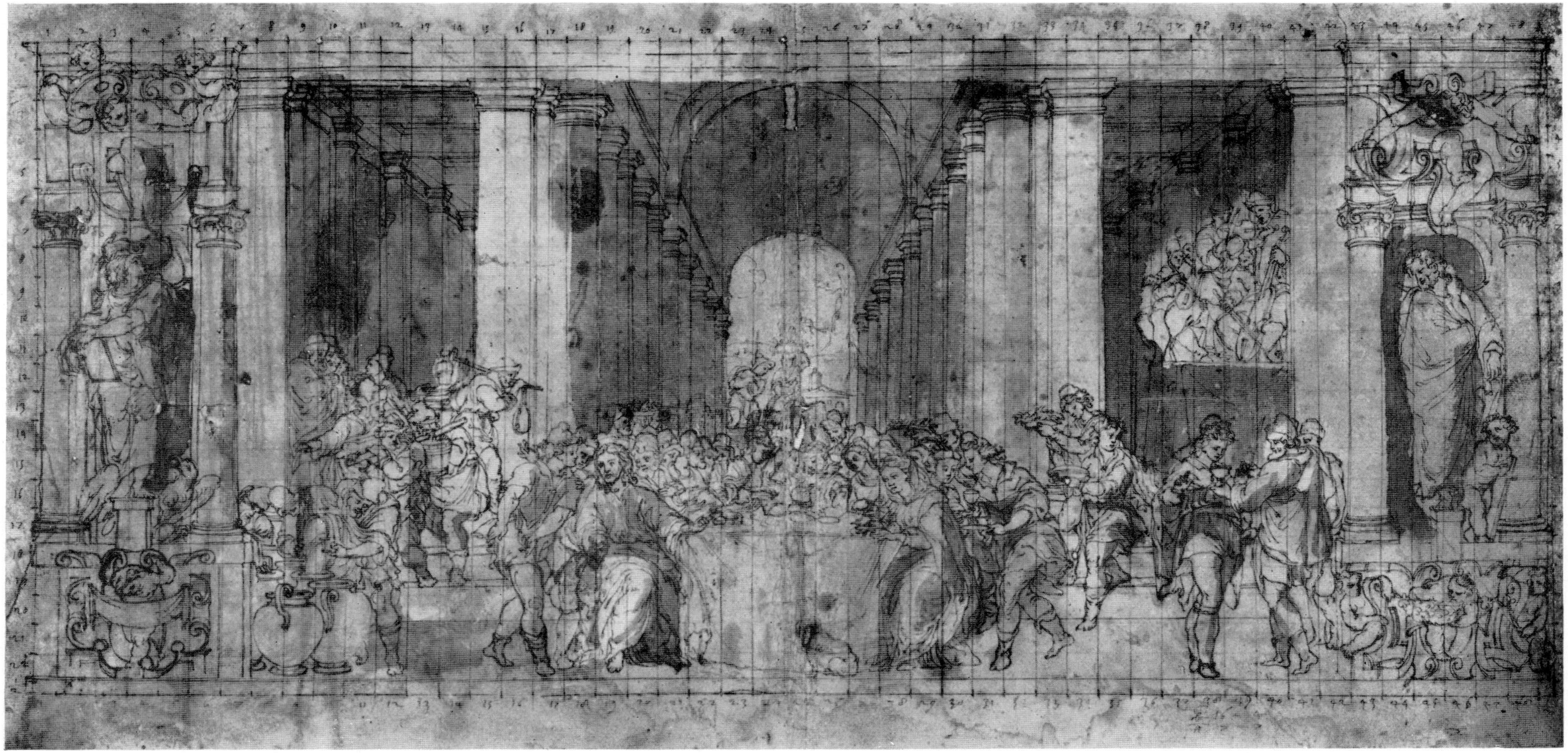

112. SETTI: THE MARRIAGE FEAST AT CANA (Cat. No. 926)

113. CESI: GOD THE FATHER AND ANGELS (Cat. No. 229)

114. NOSADELLA: THE VISITATION (Cat. No. 526)

115. BARTOLOMMEO PASSAROTTI: THE BURIAL OF THE VIRGIN (Cat. No. 658)

116. CORREGGIO: STUDY FOR 'ANTIOPE' (Cat. No. 246)

117. CORREGGIO: THE HOLY FAMILY (Cat. No. 248)

118. CORREGGIO: ADAM, ABRAHAM AND ISAAC (Cat. No. 247)

119. ANSELMI: STUDIES OF FORESHORTENED FIGURES (Cat. No. 64)

120. ANSELMI: SACRIFICE TO DIANA (Cat. No. 65)

121. PARMIGIANINO: THE ENTOMBMENT
(Cat. No. 573 *recto*)

122. PARMIGIANINO: DESIGN FOR A FRIEZE (Cat. No. 574)

123. PARMIGIANINO: SELF-PORTRAIT
(Cat. No. 566)

124. PARMIGIANINO: VIRGIN AND CHILD
(Cat. No. 581)

125. PARMIGIANINO: FOUR WOMEN'S HEADS (Cat. No. 601)

126. PARMIGIANINO: STUDIES FOR THE 'MADONNA DI S. MARGHERITA' (Cat. No. 582 *recto*)

127. PARMIGIANINO: THE ADORATION OF THE SHEPHERDS (Cat. No. 576)

128. PARMIGIANINO: DECORATION FOR THE STECCATA (Cat. No. 590)

129. PARMIGIANINO: DECORATION FOR THE STECCATA (Cat. No. 591)

130. PARMIGIANINO: DECORATION FOR THE STECCATA (Cat. No. 588)

131. PARMIGIANINO: DECORATION FOR THE STECCATA (Cat. No. 589)

132. PARMIGIANINO: THE CORONATION OF THE VIRGIN
(Cat. No. 597 *recto*)

133. PARMIGIANINO: VARIOUS STUDIES (Cat. No. 597 *verso*)

134. ORSI: CROSSBOWMAN (Cat. No. 529)

135. ORSI: PIETÀ (Cat. No. 528)

136. FERRARI: HEAD OF A WOMAN: (Cat. No. 325)

137. ANONYMOUS, CREMONA: HEAD OF A MAN (Cat. No. 1087)

138. SOLARIO: THE LAMENTATION (Cat. No. 932)

139. GATTI: THE REST ON THE FLIGHT INTO EGYPT
(Cat. No. 337)

140. BERNARDINO CAMPI: THE MARRIAGE OF ST. CECILIA AND ST. VALERIAN
(Cat. No. 185)

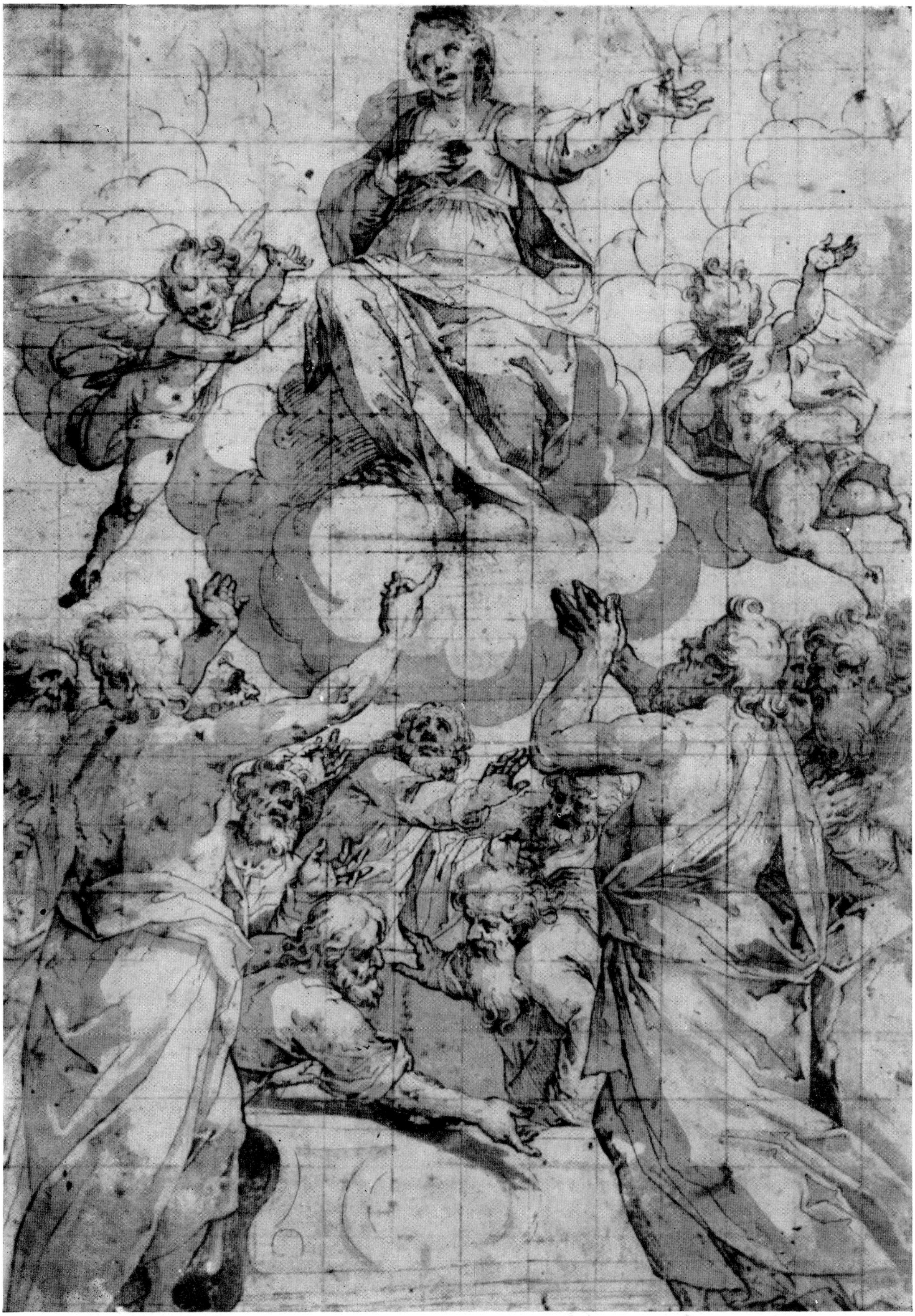

141. TROTTI: THE ASSUMPTION OF THE VIRGIN (Cat. No. 968)

142. FIGINO: THE CRUCIFIXION (Cat. No. 326/1)

143. FIGINO: THE ARCHANGEL MICHAEL AND REBEL ANGELS (Cat. No. 326/66)

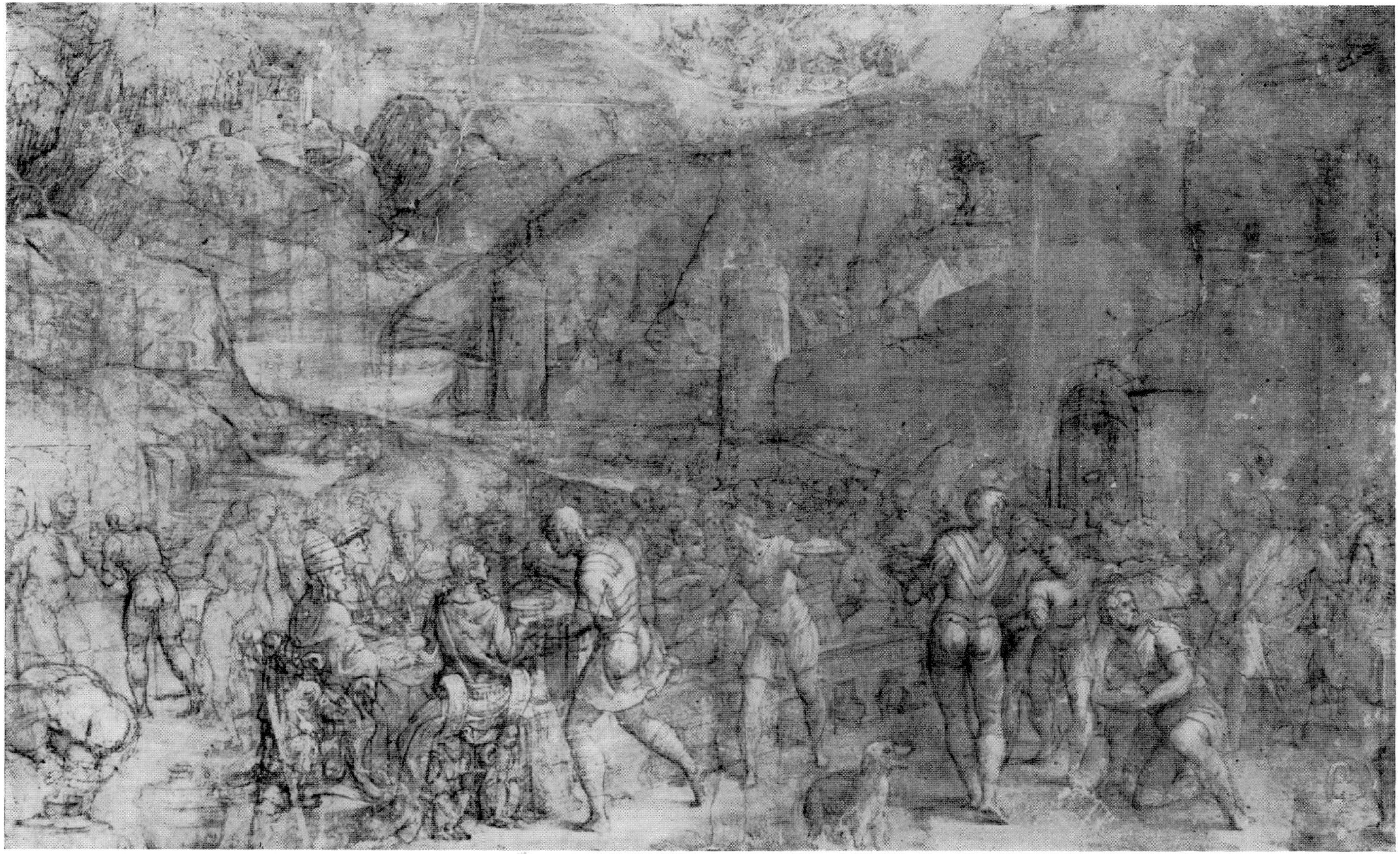

144. LOMAZZO: THE FEAST OF QUADRAGESIMA (Cat. No. 405)

145. FIGINO: SHEET OF STUDIES (Cat. No. 326/104 *recto*)

146. ANONYMOUS, MILAN: THE ASCENSION; DESIGN FOR ALTAR-PIECE
(Cat. No. 1114)

147. CERANO: BEGGAR ASKING ALMS (Cat. No. 211)

148. AURELIO LUINI: TWO SEATED PROPHETS (Cat. No. 408)

149. CAMILLO PROCACCINI: YOUTH ADMONISHED BY A SAGE (Cat. No. 778)

150. CAMILLO PROCACCINI: THE TRANSFIGURATION (Cat. No. 768)

151. BERNARDO CASTELLO: ASSAULT ON A CITY (Cat. No. 205)

152. ANONYMOUS, GENOA: MEN BUILDING SHIPS (Cat. No. 1107)

153. GIOVANNI BELLINI: HEAD OF ST. ANTHONY ABBOT (Cat. No. 2)

154. AFTER GENTILE BELLINI: THREE TURKS (Cat. No. 1)

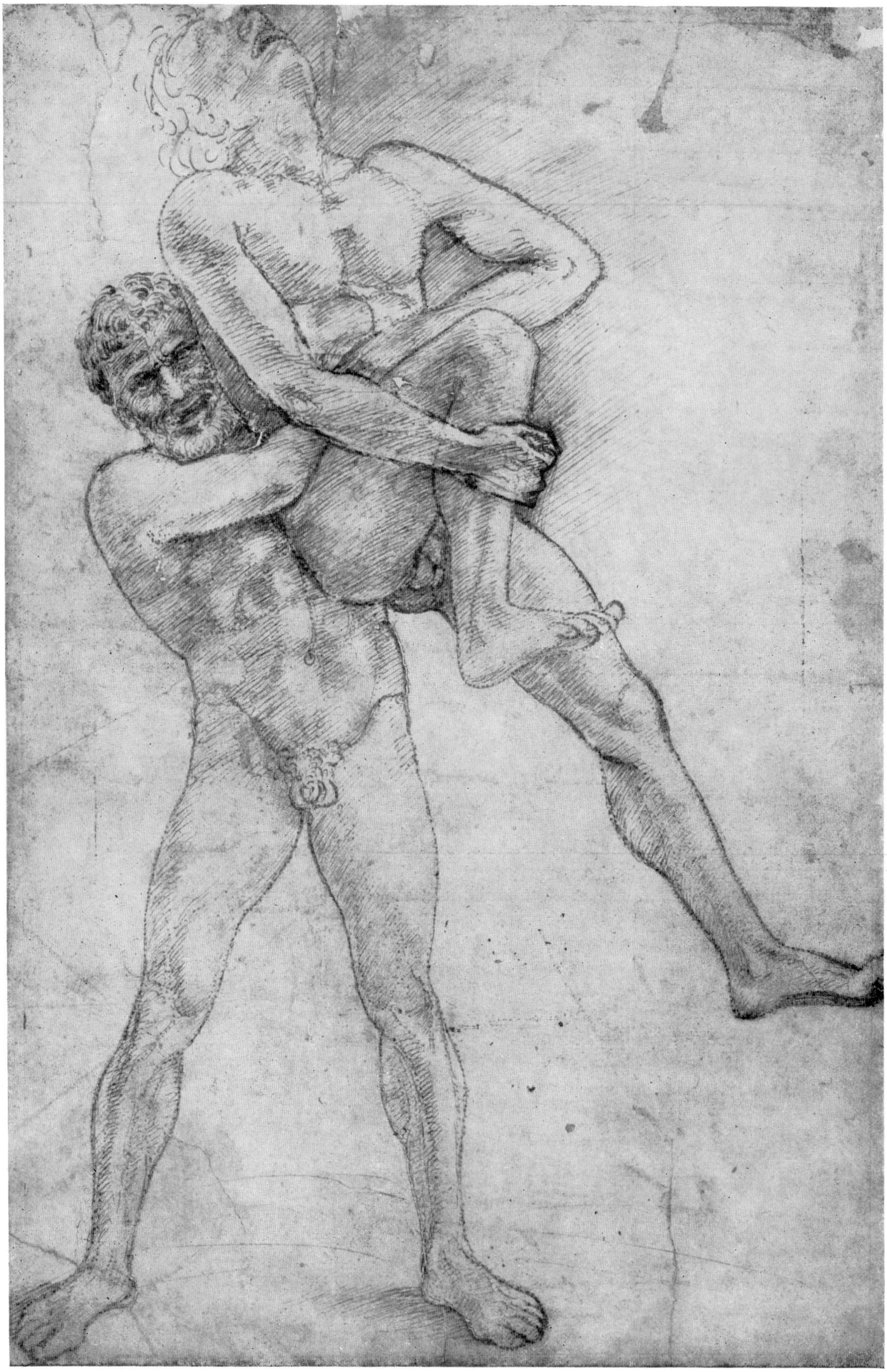

155. SCHOOL OF MANTEGNA: HERCULES AND ANTAEUS (Cat. No. 17)

156. SCHOOL OF MANTEGNA: SIX FIGURES (Cat. No. 18)

157. SCHOOL OF MANTEGNA: SOLDIER FOR A 'CHRIST RISING FROM THE TOMB' (Cat. No. 16 *recto*)

158. SCHOOL OF MANTEGNA: VARIOUS STUDIES (Cat. No. 16 *verso*)

159. SCHOOL OF CIMA: DESIGN FOR AN ALTAR-PIECE (Cat. No. 4)

160. ALVISE VIVARINI: DESIGN FOR AN ALTAR-PIECE (Cat. No. 31)

161. BARTOLOMMEO MONTAGNA: CHRIST ENTHRONED (Cat. No. 20)

162. AFTER GIORGIONE: THE ADORATION OF THE SHEPHERDS (Cat. No. 343)

163. PORDENONE: ST. AUGUSTINE (Cat. No. 741)

164. PORDENONE: PROPHETS AND SIBYL (Cat. No. 742)

165. ATTRIBUTED TO PORDENONE: THE STONING OF ST. STEPHEN (Cat. No. 751)

166. TITIAN: STUDY FOR 'ECCE HOMO'
(Cat. No. 961)

167. ROMANINO: MUSICIANS IN A BOAT (Cat. No. 873)

168. DOMENICO CAMPAGNOLA: ST. JOHN ON PATMOS (Cat. No. 161)

169. PORTA: VIRGIN AND CHILD, ST. GEORGE AND ANOTHER SAINT (Cat. No. 753)

170. SCHOOL OF TINTORETTO: TWO MEN (Cat. No. 953)

171. FRANCO: FIGURE FOR A 'FLAGELLATION' (Cat. No. 329)

172. TINTORETTO: FIGURE FOR A 'CRUCIFIXION' (Cat. No. 952)

173. JACOPO BASSANO: STUDY OF HEADS (Cat. No. 121)

174. FARINATI: THE EMPEROR VESPASIAN (Cat. No. 300 *recto*)

175. VERONESE: BEARDED PROPHET (Cat. No. 1006)

176. SCHOOL OF BASSANO: DOMESTIC INTERIOR (Cat. No. 125)

THE CATALOGUE

LIST OF BOOKS REFERRED TO IN ABBREVIATED FORM

ALBERTINA CAT. I. Alfred Stix and L. Fröhlich-Bum, *Beschreibender Katalog der Handzeichnungen in der . . . Albertina.* I. *Die Zeichnungen der Venezianischen Schule.* Vienna, 1926.

ALBERTINA CAT. III. Alfred Stix and L. Fröhlich-Bum, *Beschreibender Katalog der Handzeichnungen in der . . . Albertina.* III. *Die Zeichnungen der Toskanischen, Umbrischen und Römischen Schulen.* Vienna, 1932.

ALBERTINA CAT. VI. Alfred Stix and Anna von Spitzmüller, *Beschreibender Katalog der Handzeichnungen in der . . . Albertina.* VI. *Die Schulen von Ferrara, Bologna, Parma und Modena, der Lombardei, Genuas und Siziliens.* Vienna, 1941.

BALDINUCCI. Filippo Baldinucci, *Notizie de' professori del disegno.* 5 vols. Florence, 1845–47.

BARTSCH. Adam von Bartsch, *Le Peintre Graveur.* 21 vols. Vienna, 1803–1821.

B.B. Bernard Berenson. *The Drawings of the Florentine Painters.* 3 vols. Chicago, 1938.

CHAMBERLAINE. J. Chamberlaine, *Original Designs of the most celebrated Masters . . . in His Majesty's Collection.* London, 1812.

FENWICK CATALOGUE. A. E. Popham, *Catalogue of Drawings in the Collection formed by Sir Thomas Phillipps, Bart., F.R.S., now in the possession of . . . T. Fitzroy Phillipps Fenwick.* Privately printed, 1935.

FISCHEL, *Umbrer.* Oskar Fischel, *Die Zeichnungen der Umbrer.* Berlin, 1917.

HADELN, *Quattrocento.* Detlev Freiherr von Hadeln, *Venezianische Zeichnungen des Quattrocento.* Berlin, 1925.

HADELN, *Hochrenaissance.* Detlev Freiherr von Hadeln, *Venezianische Zeichnungen der Hochrenaissance.* Berlin, 1925.

HADELN, *Spätrenaissance.* Detlev Freiherr von Hadeln, *Venezianische Zeichnungen der Spätrenaissance.* Berlin, 1926.

HIND, B.M. CATALOGUE. A. M. Hind, *Catalogue of Early Italian Engravings in the British Museum.* London, 1910.

LUGT. Frits Lugt, *Les Marques de Collections de Dessins et d'Estampes.* Amsterdam, 1921.

POPHAM. A. E. Popham, *Italian Drawings Exhibited at the Royal Academy, Burlington House, London,* 1930. Oxford, 1931.

RICHARDSON, *An Account . . .* Jonathan Richardson, Sen. and Jun., *An Account of Some of the Statues, Bas-reliefs, Drawings and Pictures in Italy, etc., with Remarks.* London, 1722.

RIDOLFI. Carlo Ridolfi, *Le maraviglie dell' Arte.* Venice, 1648. Ed. D. Freiherr von Hadeln, Berlin, 1914 and 1924.

RULAND. C. Ruland, *The works of Raphael Santi as represented in the Royal Library at Windsor Castle.* Privately printed, 1876.

SCHÖNBRUNNER-MEDER. Joseph Schönbrunner and Joseph Meder, *Handzeichnungen alter Meister aus der Albertina und anderen Sammlungen.* Vienna, 1896–1908.

TAJA. Agostino Taja, *Descrizione del palazzo apostolico Vaticano.* Rome, 1750.

THIEME-BECKER. *Allgemeines Lexikon der bildenden Künstler von der Antike bis zur Gegenwart.* Begründet von Ulrich Thieme und Felix Becker. Leipzig, 1907 ff.

THURSTON THOMPSON, 1857. (Under heading 'Photo'.): *Drawings by Raffaelle, in the Royal Collection at Windsor Castle, Photographed by command of His Royal Highness Prince Albert, by C. Thurston Thompson,* 1857.

TIETZES. Hans Tietze and E. Tietze-Conrat, *The Drawings of the Venetian Painters in the 15th and 16th Centuries.* New York, 1944.

VAN MARLE. Raimond van Marle, *The Development of the Italian Schools of Painting.* The Hague, 1923–1937.

VASARI. Giorgio Vasari, *Le Vite de' più eccellenti pittori, scultori ed architettori.* Ed. G. Milanesi, Florence, 1878–1885.

VENTURI. Adolfo Venturi, *Storia dell' arte Italiana.* Milan, 1901–1936.

VOSS, *Spätrenaissance.* Hermann Voss, *Die Malerei der Spätrenaissance in Rom und Florenz.* 2 vols. Berlin, 1920.

WAAGEN. G. F. Waagen, *Treasures of Art in Great Britain.* 3 vols. and Suppl. London, 1854.

WEIGEL. Rudolph Weigel, *Die Werke der Maler in ihren Handzeichnungen.* Leipzig, 1865.

WICKHOFF. Franz Wickhoff, *Italienische Handzeichnungen der Albertina.* Jahrbuch der Sammlungen des allerhöchsten Kaiserhauses XII (1891) II Theil, CCV–CCCXIV and XII (1892) II Theil, CLXXV–CCLXXXIII.

XV CENTURY DRAWINGS

After GENTILE BELLINI (about 1429–1507)

1. THREE TURKS IN CONVERSATION (*Plate* 154) (062)

307 × 179 mm. Brush drawing in brown on light brown paper.

Lit.: Tietzes, No. 801 (pl. XIII, No. 2).

As noted by the Tietzes (*loc. cit.*) the group appears in the version of the *Reception of the Venetian Ambassadors at Cairo in 1512* belonging to Mme. Louis Stern in Paris. The Tietzes attribute the drawing to Mansueti but suggest that it may go back to Gentile Bellini. It appears to me to be in any case a copy, the original of which may well be Gentile Bellini's.

GIOVANNI BELLINI (About 1431(?)–1516)

2. HEAD OF AN OLD BEARDED MAN (*Plate* 153) (12800)

260 × 190 mm. Drawn with the point of the brush on blue paper ('carta azzura'), very much discoloured, heightened with white.

Lit.: K. T. Parker, Old Master Drawings III (1928), p. 19 and pl. 21; Van Marle, XVII, p. 344; Tietzes, No. 328; Exh. Venice, 1949, No. 137.

First claimed as Giovanni Bellini's by K. T. Parker on the strength of the close resemblance of the head in type to that of St. Anthony Abbot on one of the panels of the polyptych painted for the Church of the Carità at Venice (Venice Academy, No. 621A). The claim seems to me from the quality and character of the drawing to be fully justified. The actual handling is absolutely that of his early pictures, e.g. the National Gallery *Agony in the Garden*. The Tietzes deny any connection with the Carità pictures and regard the drawing as dating from the last years of the century.

After VITTORE CARPACCIO(?) (Working 1486 to about 1525)

3. THE PRESENTATION OF THE VIRGIN IN THE TEMPLE (*Figure* 1) (12810)

237 × 335 mm. Pen and brown ink and wash.
Coll.: N. Lanière (Lugt 2885).

Lit.: G. Ludwig and P. Molmenti, *Vittore Carpaccio.* Milan, 1906, p. 230; Hadeln, *Quattrocento* (p. 55, text to pl. 23); Van Marle, XVIII, p. 326, note; Tietzes, No. A641 (pl. CLXXXVIII, 1).

Regarded by Ludwig as the preliminary study for a composition of the same subject in the Uffizi (Hadeln 23), attributed by him and Hadeln to Carpaccio, rightly in my opinion, though the Tietzes reject it and call it school of Gentile Bellini. Their suggestion that the present drawing may be an alternative study by another artist for the same subject which was put out to competition by the Carità in 1504 also seems to me questionable. Though the drawing is not apparently an original, it has so many elements which are absolutely typical of Carpaccio that it must be a copy after him. He may well himself have provided alternative designs.

FIG. 1 Cat. No. 3

School of GIOVANNI BATTISTA CIMA DA CONEGLIANO (About 1459–1517/18)

4. ENTHRONED BISHOP BETWEEN A KING AND ANOTHER BISHOP (*Plate* 159) (12807)

377 × 245 mm. Drawn with the point of the brush on greenish paper, heightened with white.

Lit.: B. Berenson, *Study and Criticism of Italian Art*, London, 1901, p. 109; R. Burckhardt, *Cima da Conegliano*, Leipzig, 1905, p. 123; Hadeln, *Quattrocento*, p. 63 (pl. 79); Van Marle XVII, p. 461, note; Tietzes, No. 661.

Modello for an important altarpiece. Claimed by Berenson as an original by Cima, a claim contested by Burckhardt, Hadeln and the Tietzes.

School of LORENZO COSTA (1460–1535)

5. *Recto:* ADORATION OF THE SHEPHERDS (*Plate* 97) (12790)

266 × 191 mm. Pen and two shades of brown ink.

Verso: BAPTISM OF CHRIST

Black chalk.

Attributed by Berenson (in pencil on the mount) to Tamaroccio or Amico Aspertini. We know too little of the former to be able to attribute any drawing to him, and the touch is not quite that of the latter. It is quite certainly, however, of the school of Lorenzo Costa, and is best catalogued under his name.

LORENZO DI CREDI (1456 or 1459–1537)

6. THE ANNUNCIATION TAKING PLACE IN FRONT OF TWO ARCHES (*Figure* 2) (087)

179 × 143 mm. Very carefully drawn in fine pen and light brown ink with some additions in darker ink and some white (which has oxidised); the outlines pricked.

Lit.: B.B. 734.

Berenson regards the figures as Credi's, but not the architecture. This differentiation seems to me a little far-fetched.

7. HEAD OF A YOUTH TURNED SLIGHTLY TO THE L. (*Figure* 3) (12818)

160 × 124 mm. Metal-point on pale pink prepared surface, heightened with white.

Lit.: B.B. 734B (formerly 2756).

An excellent and characteristic drawing by Credi. I cannot find any picture for which it may have served as a study.

After LORENZO DI CREDI

8. HEAD OF AN OLD MAN WEARING A ROUND, FLAT CAP (12817)

195 × 171 mm. Metal-point on grey prepared surface, heightened with white.

Lit.: B.B. 733 (ill. Fig. 147); B. Degenhart, Münchner Jahrbuch IX (1932), p. 104.

This is clearly a rather mechanical copy from the admirable drawing by Credi in the Louvre (B.B. 713A; photo. Braun 86). Degenbert, *loc. cit.*, attributes the copy to the Master of the Göttingen Crucifixion (Gian. Jacopo di Castrocaro?). I am quite unable to follow Degenhart's elaborate division of the works of Credi's scholars in the article cited.

FIG. 2 Cat. No. 6

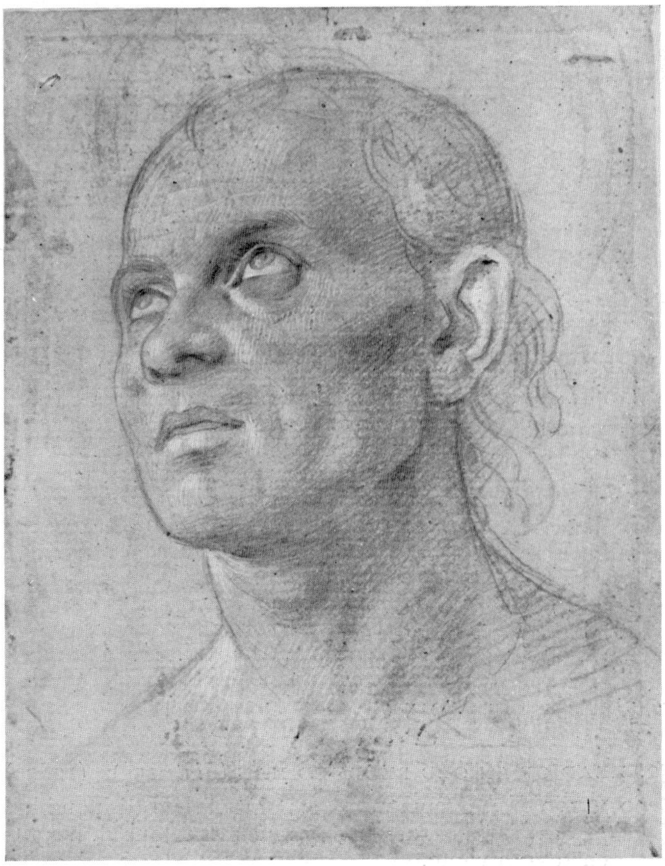

FIG. 3 Cat. No. 7

DOMENICO GHIRLANDAIO (About 1449–1494)

9. HEAD OF AN OLD WOMAN (*Plate* 8) (12804)

232 × 185 mm. Metal-point on prepared orange surface, heightened with white.

Lit.: B.B. 893 (Fig. 306); Popham 38 (pl. XXXIA).

Perhaps, as first suggested by Berenson, a study for the head of the woman last but one in the group to the L. in the fresco of the *Birth of the Virgin* in S. Maria Novella, Florence.

BENOZZO GOZZOLI (1420–1497)

10. *Recto:* HEAD OF ST. LAWRENCE(?) (*Plate* 3) (12812)

181 × 167 mm. Metal-point on prepared orange surface, heightened with white.

Verso: ST. LAWRENCE, WOMAN HOLDING CHILD AND YOUTH WITH CLASPED HANDS (*Plate* 5)

Pen and brown ink and wash on white paper.

Lit.: B.B. 163 (Figs. 19 and 20); R. Papini, L'Arte, XIII (1910), 290; F. Schotmüller, *Fra Angelico* (K. der K.). Leipzig (1924), *recto* ill. p. XXXII, *verso* ill. p. 223; Van Marle, X, 126 (*recto* ill. p. 127), XI, p. 125; Popham 22 (pl. XIX B).

Attributed by Berenson to Fra Angelico, by Papini to Benozzo. The *verso* is connected with the fresco of *St. Lawrence distributing alms* in the Chapel of St. Martin in the Vatican, now generally given to Benozzo. The head on the *recto*, which is almost exactly similar in handling to the *Head of a Youth*, described below and generally accepted as Benozzo's, does not differ in style or rise sufficiently in quality above this to warrant Berenson's attribution of it to Fra Angelico.

FIG. 4 Cat. No. 12

11. *Recto:* HEAD OF A CURLY-HAIRED YOUTH TURNED A LITTLE TO THE R. (*Plate* 2) (12811)

232 × 169 mm. Metal-point on brown prepared surface, heightened with white.

Verso: FOUR SEATED SAINTS (*Plate* 4)

Pen and ink and grey wash.

Lit.: B.B. 546 (Fig. 45); T. Borenius, Pantheon, 1930, p. 142; Popham 23 (pl. XIXA).

The four saints on the *verso* are by a different and feebler follower of Fra Angelico.

FILIPPINO LIPPI (1457/8–1504)

12. AN ANGEL RECEIVING THE CHILD FROM THE SEATED VIRGIN; AN ANGEL PLAYING THE LUTE (*Figure* 4) (12821)

145 × 187 mm. Pen and brown ink, heightened or corrected with white (much of which has oxidised) over a sketch drawn with the stylus.

Lit.: B.B. 1368 (Fig. 257); A. Scharf, *Filippino Lippi.* Vienna, 1935, p. 121, No. 189.

An admirable and characteristic late drawing by Filippino.

13. *Recto:* HEAD OF A MAN WITH LONG HAIR, TURNED TO THE L. (*Plate* 7) (12822)

Verso: STUDY OF PRAYING HANDS (*Figure* 5)

241 × 185 mm. Metal-point on a blue-grey prepared surface, heightened with blue.

Lit.: B.B. 1369; Scharf, op. cit., p. 130, No. 305 (*recto* Fig. 152).

An admirable original drawing of Filippino's later period.

FRA FILIPPO LIPPI (About 1406–1469)

14. TWO STUDIES OF DRAPERY (*Plate* 1) (12753)

200 × 200 mm. Metal-point and point of the brush on grey prepared surface, heightened with white.

Lit.: B.B. 1390A (Fig. 171); B. Berenson, O.M.D., VII (1932), p. 17, pl. 27; O. Fischel, Amtliche Berichte aus den Königlichen Kunstsammlungen (1911/12), p. 174.

The drapery on the L. corresponds with that of the woman leaning over the cot in the Berlin predella *The Infancy of St. Ambrose* (No. 95B); the drapery on the R. corresponds with that of the Baptist in the *Coronation of the Virgin* in the Uffizi (No. 8352), of which the Berlin panel formed the predella. The latter is in metal-point, the former is drawn with the brush. The character of the heightening in white is quite different and it is by another hand, though there appears to have been an outline sketch in metal-point underneath.

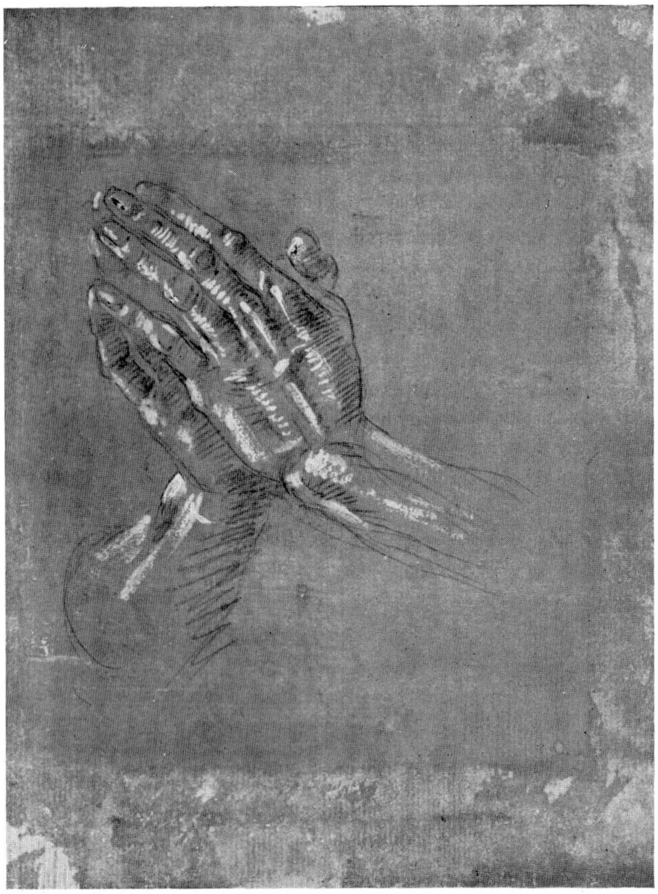

FIG. 5 Cat. No. 13 *v.*

After ANDREA MANTEGNA (1431–1506)

15. TWO SHEPHERDS FROM AN ADORATION (*Figure* 6) (12794)

301 × 219 mm. Drawn and shaded with the point of the brush in colour, the faces, hands, etc., in brown. A hole and some damage due to damp on the R. under the bridge.

Lit.: P. Kristeller, *Andrea Mantegna*, London, 1901, p. 459; C. Yriarte, *Mantegna*, Paris, 1901, p. 218 (ill. p. 217).

Copy of the R. hand portion of the *Adoration of the Shepherds* by Mantegna, now in the Metropolitan Museum, New York. The copy is of the XV century, by an artist of Mantegna's school. Adolfo Venturi has suggested on the mount that Bernardino Parentino was the copyist. It is certainly from this phase in Mantegna's art that Parentino derived his manner. A copy of the Madonna adoring the Infant Christ in the same picture is in the Uffizi (photo. Braun 788). It is by a different hand.

School of ANDREA MANTEGNA

16. *Recto:* A ROMAN SOLDIER SEATED ON HIS SHIELD WITH A RUNNING FIGURE BEHIND; CAPTIVES BEFORE A JUDGE AND OTHER FIGURES (*Plate* 157) (12795)

250 × 188 mm. The soldier is drawn with the brush in grey and heightened with white; the other studies are in light brown ink.

Verso: STUDY OF DRAPERY, ORNAMENTS, A MAN'S LEGS, etc. (*Plate* 158)

The drapery is in black chalk on paper washed with grey and heightened with white; the other studies are in light brown ink.

Lit.: P. Kristeller, *Andrea Mantegna*, London, 1901, p. 163 note.

The soldier must be copied from a lost picture of *Christ rising from the Tomb*, presumably by Mantegna, and of the same style and comparatively early date as the predella painting of the subject for the San Zeno altarpiece at Verona. A drawing of another soldier, formerly in the Wauters collection (F. Lees, *The Art of the Great Masters*, London, 1913, fig. 11), may be from the same hand. The pen and ink sketches on the *recto* seem to be by a later hand than the soldier. The drapery study, though also Mantegnesque, is in a different technique and apparently in a different style. It may be the work of a third hand.

The sheet looks as if it might have formed part of the same sketch-book as one in the Boymans Museum at Rotterdam (published by F. Schmidt Degener in the Burlington Mag., XVIII (1910/11), p. 255). The pen drawings on the *recto* of this certainly seem to be by the same hand as those on the *recto* of the Windsor sheet and the finished Mantegnesque drawings may well also be. The Boymans drawing (292 × 197 mm.) is slightly larger.

17. HERCULES AND ANTAEUS (*Plate* 155) (12802)

347 × 232 mm. Pen and light brown ink, reinforced in places (e.g. hand of Hercules and R. arm and hand of Antaeus), with darker ink; the outlines pricked; squared with the stylus.

Lit.: A. Stix, Belvedere IX (1930), p. 124; Popham 157 (pl. CXXXVI).

The drawing is based on an antique statue, much restored

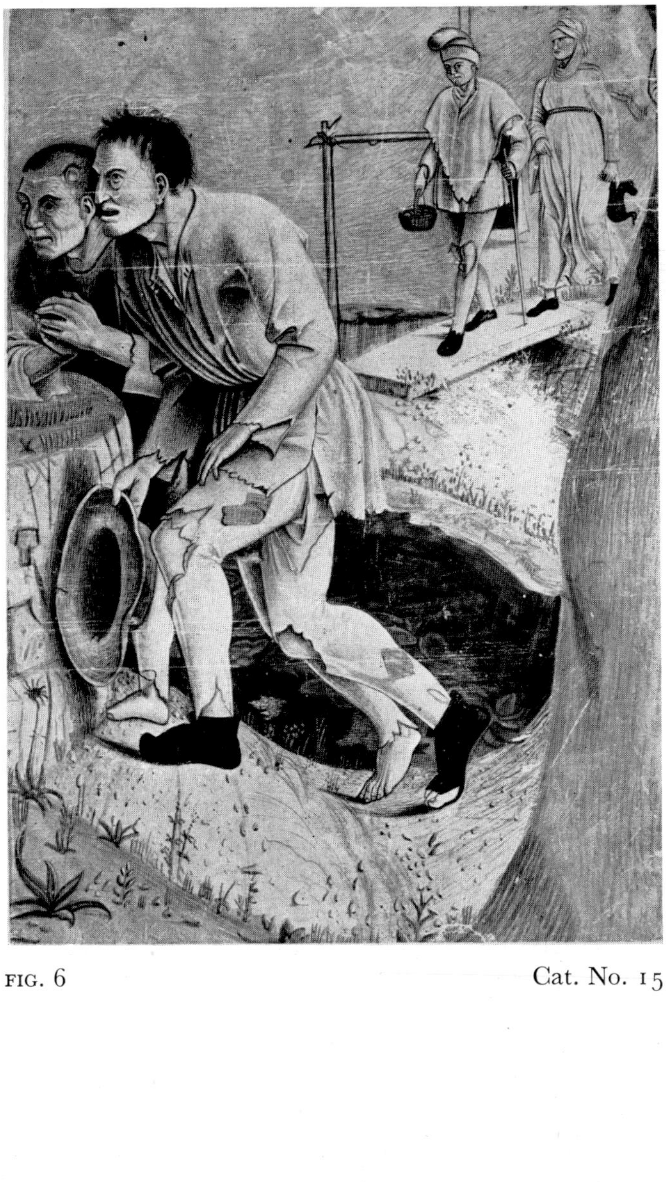

FIG. 6 Cat. No. 15

and now in the Pitti Gallery, Florence (S. Reinach, *Répertoire de la Statuaire Grecque et Romaine*, Paris, 1897, Vol. I, p. 472), but differs from it in Antaeus being on the R. instead of on the L., and in the position of his R. leg and both arms and head, all of which are, however, restorations. My attribution to Bramante proposed in the catalogue of the Italian drawings exhibited at Burlington House still seems to me possible, but we do not know enough of Bramante as a draughtsman for any certainty to be reached, and it is safer to leave the sheet under the school of Mantegna, to which, in the broadest sense, it certainly belongs. But it is not the work of a nonentity.

18. A MAN FACING TO THE FRONT HOLDING A CADUCEUS IN HIS R. AND A BOOK IN HIS L. HAND; FIVE FIGURES GROUPED BEHIND HIM (*Plate* 156) (12799)

211 × 152 mm. Pen and light brown ink with some wash on the figures behind.

Photo: Braun 143.

This is near in style to the drawing of a saint in the Venice Academy (repr. B. Berenson, *Study and Criticism of Italian Art*, III, p. 51) generally attributed to Giovanni Bellini, but the connection of the present drawing with him is even more dubious. It is obviously Mantegnesque in character.

BARTOLOMMEO MONTAGNA (About 1450–1523)

19. HEAD OF THE VIRGIN (*Figure* 7) (12824)

349 × 251 mm. Black chalk or charcoal on white paper.

Lit.: [G. Morelli], *Die Galerien zu München und Dresden*. Leipzig, 1891, p. 154; Rassegna d'Arte, V (1905), ill. p. 77; T. Borenius, *Painters of Vicenza*, London, 1909, p. 111.

Study for the head of the Virgin in the great altarpiece in the Brera at Milan (No. 165) signed and dated 1499. The drawing was first identified by Morelli (loc. cit.). Another version in the Library of Christ Church, Oxford (repr. S. Colvin, *Oxford Drawings*, Vol. II, pl. 131), is an almost exact repetition, and I do not feel able to determine which of the two is the better. Practically the only difference between them is that while the dress in the Windsor drawing is cut square, that in the Oxford drawing is round. In this respect the latter differs from the picture. The harder and more precise modelling of the Windsor head also seems more Montagnesque in character.

20. STUDY FOR A CHRIST ENTHRONED (*Plate* 161) (12823)

316 × 222 mm. Drawn with the brush and Indian ink on blue paper, heightened with white.

Lit.: G. Morelli, op. cit., p. 154; T. Borenius, op. cit., p. 112; K. T. Parker, *North Italian Drawings*, London, 1927, p. 33 (pl. 57).

Inscribed in an old hand on the *verso:* 'Gian: Bellino'. The convincing attribution to Montagna is due to Morelli.

PIETRO PERUGINO (About 1445–1523)

21. STUDY OF A MAN IN ARMOUR (*Plate* 10) (12801)

249 × 185 mm. Metal-point on blue prepared surface, heightened with white.

Lit.: Fischel, *Umbrer*, No. 54 (Fig. 126); Vasari Society, VII (1926), pl. 4; Popham 106 (pl. LXXXIX).

Study from Donatello's statue of St. George used by Perugino for the figure of St. Michael in the altarpiece in the National Gallery (No. 288) commissioned from the artist about 1496 for the Certosa, Pavia.

FIG. 7 Cat. No. 19

22. HEAD OF THE VIRGIN (*Plate* 9) (12744)

234 × 224 mm. Metal-point on pink prepared surface, heightened with white.

Lit.: Fischel, *Umbrer*, No. 44 (Fig. 113).

Study for the Virgin between St. John the Baptist and St. Sebastian from San Domenico, Fiesole, dating from 1493, and now in the Uffizi (W. Bombe, *Perugino* (K. der K.). Stuttgart, 1914, ill. p. 28).

After PIETRO PERUGINO

23. *Recto:* THREE SLEEPING APOSTLES, INCLUDING ST. PETER IN THE CENTRE (12792)
Verso: SLEEPING APOSTLE (ST. JOHN)

211 × 276 mm. Pen and light brown ink.

Lit.: Fischel, *Umbrer*, p. 41 (Figs. 43 and 44); Van Marle, XIV, p. 394.

Copies from a lost composition by Perugino of the *Agony in the Garden*. The original drawing of the sleeping St. John and of St. Peter, leaning his head on his right hand, is, or was, at Weimar (Fischel, loc. cit., p. 95, No. 22, Fig. 42). The figure of St. Peter (Fischel, loc. cit.) corresponds with the central sleeping figure in the landscape in the background of the *Last Supper* of Foligno (Perugino, K. der K., 96).

24. HEAD OF A YOUNG WOMAN IN A TURBAN-LIKE HEADDRESS (*Figure* 8) (12797)

191 × 135 mm. Metal-point on a brown ground, heightened with white.

FIG. 8 Cat. No. 24

Lit.: Fischel, *Umbrer*, No. 181.
Copy from a head in the style of Perugino's frescoes in the Sixtine Chapel. The head is very like that of the Madonna in the *Adoration of the Magi* from S. Girolamo at Spello (Fischel, loc. cit., Fig. 55). There is another copy of the same head in the so-called 'Raphael' sketch-book in the Venice Academy, fol. 20v. (Fischel, loc. cit., Fig. 197).

25. CHRIST HANDING THE KEYS TO ST. PETER WITH ST. JOHN ON THE R. (12816)

190 × 235 mm. Brush drawing over a sketch with the stylus, on greenish prepared surface, heightened with white. On *verso* 'Pietro Perugino' is written in an old hand. It is in fact the copy of three of the central figures in the fresco by Perugino in the Sistine Chapel (1480–82) by some moderately capable artist of the XV or early XVI century Umbrian School.

ANTONIO PISANO called PISANELLO (Before 1395–1455)

26. A DROMEDARY (*Figure* 10) (12815)

292 × 423 mm. Pen and faint brown ink.

Lit.: A. Venturi, L'Arte XXIV (1921), p. 96 (ill.).

Inscribed to the R. of the animal's hump in a hand of the XVI or XVII century 'manca u corda di gobba'; on the *verso* 'Leonardo da Vinci 1. 4' (William Gibson's method of pricing). First identified as Pisanello by Adolfo Venturi in the article cited above. There is an excellent copy of this drawing in the British Museum (1860–6–16–111). Pintoricchio must have possessed or borrowed one or other of these drawings, as he used it in the background of a fresco of the *Adoration of the Shepherds* at Spello.

ANTONIO POLLAIUOLO (1431/2–1498)

27. A BATTLE OF NAKED MEN ARMED WITH SHIELDS AND SPEARS AND BOWS AND ARROWS (*Plate* 6) (059)

205 × 435 mm. Pen and brown ink and brown wash.

Lit.: Van Marle, XI, p. 356.

Old number '129' in ink in bottom R. corner. The drawing shows a close analogy in subject and design with the two Pollaiuolo engravings of the *Battle of Naked Men* and the *Hercules and the Giants*. It is of high quality and drawn with extreme precision and neatness in the same manner as, for example, the *Adam* in the Uffizi (B.B. 1901). I see no reason for regarding it as a copy, though it has nowhere hitherto been admitted as an original.

Attributed to GIOVANNI SANTI (1430/40–1494)

28. A WOMAN STANDING IN FRONT OF SOME ROCKS (*Figure* 9) (12798)

248 × 180 mm. Brush drawing in brown on green surface, heightened with white.

Lit.: Fischel, *Umbrer*, No. 210; [G. Morelli], *Die Galerie zu Berlin*. Leipzig, 1893, p. 219 (ill.).

The old attribution was to Botticelli. Morelli first pointed out the connection between this drawing and a painting in the Corsini Gallery, Florence (Venturi, VII 2, Fig. 153), representing the Muse Clio, attributed to Giovanni Santi.

FIG. 9 Cat. No. 28

FIG. 10 Cat. No. 26

Santi also used the figure in the background of his painting of the *Visitation* in Sta. Maria Nuova, Fano (Venturi, VII 2, Fig. 151), so that the invention is certainly not his. Fischel suggests that the figure may go back to the circle of Fiorenzo di Lorenzo.

The present drawing is certainly not a copy from Santi's Muse Clio, and the wings attached to her head suggest that she is intended to represent a different personage, perhaps the Cimmerian sibyl (compare the engraving of that personage, A. M. Hind, *Early Italian Engraving*, London, 1938, pl. 247).

LUCA SIGNORELLI (1441 ?–1523)

29. HERCULES AND ANTAEUS (*Plate* 12) (12805)

283 × 163 mm. Grey chalk.

George III 'Inventory A', p. 51, Raffaello d'Urbino e Scuola, 37.

Lit.: J. D. Passavant, *Raphael d'Urbin*, Paris, 1860, Vol. II, p. 491, No. 435; Crowe & Cavalcaselle, *Life and Works of Raphael*, London, 1885, Vol. II, p. 238; B.B. 2509 J (Fig. 101); Gazette des Beaux-Arts, VII (1932), p. 177 (ill.).

Passavant (loc. cit.) accepted this drawing as Raphael's and regarded it as perhaps the original of Marcantonio's engraving (Bartsch XIV, p. 253, 346). He notes the obvious differences between engraving and drawing and suggests that Giulio Romano may have modified the sketch for the engraver. Crowe and Cavalcaselle (loc. cit.) recognised the drawing as Signorelli's and believed him to have drawn it in Rome in 1513, when he came to solicit the patronage of the newly-elected Pope, Leo X. 'The utmost that he was able to achieve was Marcantonio's acceptance of a drawing from which the splendid print of "Hercules and Antaeus" was adapted.' The connection, which does exist, is nevertheless not sufficiently close to justify such an inference and another engraving of the subject of the school of Mantegna, but perhaps deriving from Pollaiuolo (Bartsch XIII, p. 202, 1), is in fact nearer to the Windsor drawing. All are probably derived through Pollaiuolo from the antique. Berenson notes the Pollaiuolesque treatment and close analogies with Signorelli's Volterra altarpiece of 1491. He dates the drawing about 1490.

30. STUDY OF A MAN STARTING BACK IN TERROR (*Plate* 11) (070)

358 × 216 mm. (cut to an oval). Black chalk on cream-coloured paper, heightened with white.

George III 'Inventory A', p. 51, Raffaello d'Urbino e Scuola 38 (?).

Photo: Braun 250.

Whether Berenson intentionally excluded this superb drawing from his catalogue of Signorelli, I do not know, but it certainly is not there. I can see no other artist who could possibly have been responsible for it. It might well be a rejected study for one of the figures terrified at the signs of the end of the world at Orvieto (cf. L. Dussler, *Signorelli* (K. der K.). Berlin, 1926, ill. p. 97 left).

Attributed to ALVISE VIVARINI (After 1444–before 1505)

31. THE VIRGIN AND CHILD ENTHRONED IN A CHAPEL (*Plate* 160) (069)

347 × 249 mm. Pen and brown ink, the architecture ruled with the stylus.

A.E.P. This is the working drawing for the architecture of an important altarpiece which, to judge from the proportion of the figures to the architecture, would have measured about 12 ft. in height. The roughly sketched figures have at first sight something Emilian about them and had suggested Costa, but very summary figure drawings of this type are apt to be misleading. The architecture seems to me to point unequivocally to Venice or its territory, and Giovanni Bellini's S. Giobbe alterpiece as its ultimate source.

The closest parallel, however, is with Alvise Vivarini's great Berlin altarpiece with six saints (No. 38) and the smaller one with four saints in the same gallery (No. 1165). We have in both the Virgin seated at approximately the same height on the same sort of throne in front of a flat wall (not the more usual apse) across which the cornice is continued. We have the same sort of capital to the same square pilasters and cornices of similar section (their section is in fact identical with that in Alvise Vivarini's later altarpiece in Sta. Maria dei Frari, Venice (Van Marle XVIII, Fig. 99)). All this seems to point to Alvise Vivarini as the possible author of the drawing. I feel convinced that it is not a provincial work and the number of painters equal to undertaking an altarpiece of this calibre between about 1490 and 1500, which I suppose to be the date of the drawing, was limited.

FIG. 11 Cat. No. 33 *v.*

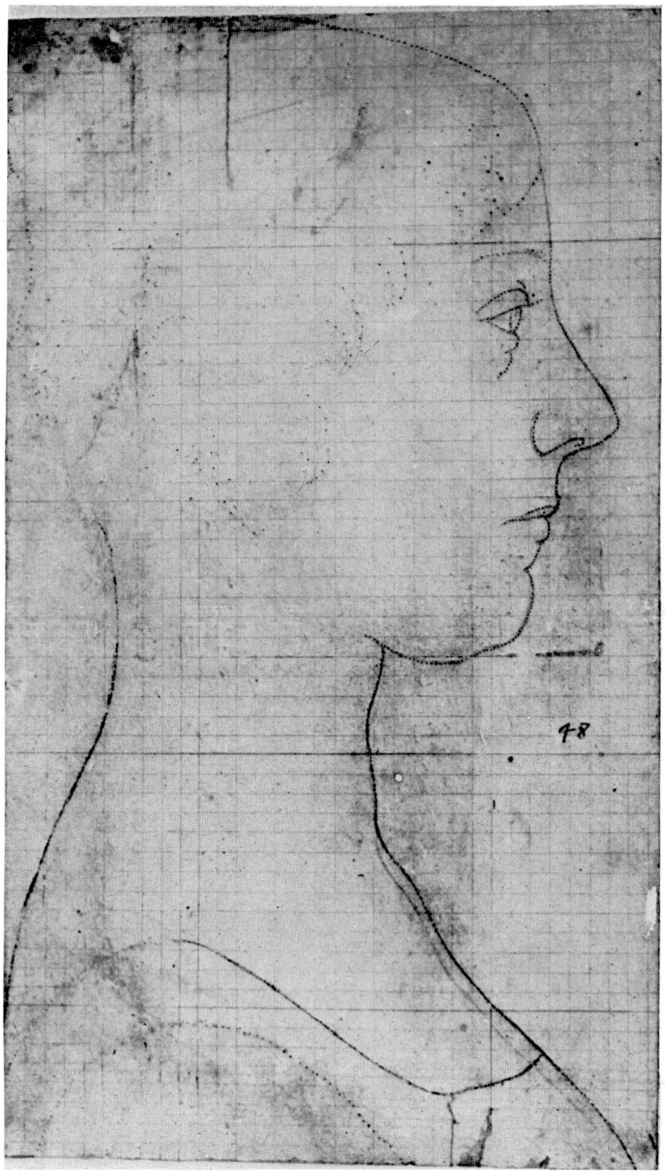

FIG. 12 Cat. No. 32

ANONYMOUS FLORENTINE

32. PROFILE OF A WOMAN TO THE R. (*Figure* 12) (12808)

364 × 209 mm. Outline drawing in black chalk or charcoal pricked; squared in fine pen and ink.

Lit.: W. Seidlitz, L'Arte XIV (1911), p. 278, No. 223.

Photo.: Braun 234.

The drawing was associated with the Leonardos and has the old number '48' in the hand with which they were marked, perhaps by Leoni. Adolfo Venturi (on the mount) has suggested an attribution to Antonio Pollaiuolo, which does not seem impossible, but it might equally well, I think, belong to the Verrocchio workshop. It is presumably no more than a tracing squared up for some purpose and is difficult to class. This drawing is described by Clark (p. 192 under the wrong number 12809, which he reproduces). No. 12809 is catalogued below as No. 342.

33. *Recto:* SEATED YOUTH DRAWING AND DOG, CURLED UP, ASLEEP (*Plate* 13) (12796)

Drawn with the brush and shaded, on blue paper, heightened with white.

Verso: STUDY OF AN OX. (*Figure* 11)

Black chalk, heightened with white.

Lit.: B.B. 862A.

Photo.: *recto*, Braun 145.

The traditional attribution was to Masaccio. Berenson in his second edition (it is not included in the first) gives it to David Ghirlandaio. The technique differs materially from that of the group of so-called David Ghirlandaio drawings which are all, as far as I know, drawn in metal-point on prepared coloured grounds. Nor in my opinion is the style the same. I cannot make any alternative suggestion, though I believe it to be Florentine.

ANONYMOUS NORTH ITALIAN

34. HEAD OF A MAN TURNED THREE-QUARTERS TO THE R. (*Figure* 13) (060)

210 × 188 mm. Broad pen and Indian ink.

The peculiar appearance of this drawing may be due, as Dr. Wilde has suggested to me, to its being a fragment of a design for glass. Its Mantegnesque character is obvious.

ANONYMOUS NORTH ITALIAN(?)

35. *Recto:* TWO MONKS SEATED AT A DESK, TWICE REPEATED; A MONK STANDING SEEN FROM BEHIND

Verso: A MONK OPENING A CUPBOARD, A MONK (ON A LARGER SCALE) AND A HALF-LENGTH FIGURE (12791)

150 × 190 mm. Pen and ink and brush on brown ground. Much faded.

Photo.: Thurston Thompson, 1857.

The old attribution is to Pesellino, with whose work it has no connection. It may possibly be Venetian in the neighbourhood of Carpaccio.

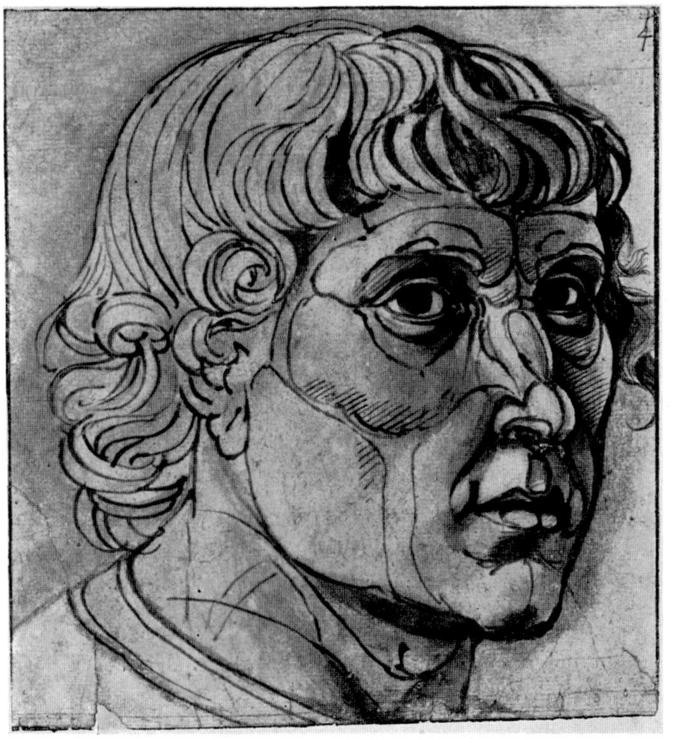

FIG. 13 Cat. No. 34

FIG. 14 Cat. No. 36

36. HEAD OF A YOUNG WOMAN (*Figure* 14) (12813)

250 × 157 mm. (partly silhouetted). Black chalk.

Attributed at one time to Francesco Bonsignori. The drawing appears to be the copy from a picture, but from what I am at a loss to say. The hairdressing and jewellery suggest Milan in the 90's. Perhaps it is a later attempt at historical reconstruction.

ANONYMOUS MARCHIGIAN

37. AN ELDERLY AND A YOUNG LADY KNEELING BEFORE A MIRACULOUS APPARITION OF ST. CAMILLA (*Figure* 15) (9063)

301 × 384 mm. In gouache, in colours on a prepared ground.

Coll.: Cassiano del Pozzo (detached from an album with drawings of antiquities in 1944).

Above the head of the younger lady is a large scroll with the following inscription:

O STVPENDO MIRACOLV C̅H̅ OꝒO IN MADONA/ IERADINA. DALLVMOTE Ꝓ SC̅TA M̂ IN CASCIANO/ IN VNASVA FIGLIOLA GENEVRA LA QVALE. L/ ATV̊O. IN. TERRA TRAMORTITA. E. TVCTA/ STORTA. Ᵽ. VNA CERTA. PAVRA. FACTO/LVVOTO. FO LIBERATA. DALLA. BEATA/CAMILA.

This rather ungrammatical inscription may be translated as follows: 'O amazin miracle wrought in Madonna

FIG. 15 Cat. No. 37

Ieradina (Geraldine ?) Dallumote of S. Maria in Casciano upon one of her daughters Genevra, who found her (la trovo?) on the ground faint and completely distorted by a certain fright on payment of a vow was set free by St. Camilla.'

There is an abbey of Casciano in the diocese of Imola. The palm branch in the hand of St. Camilla should indicate that she suffered martyrdom, which none of the Camillas are recorded to have done. She may be the St. Camilla who accompanied the corpse of St. Germain to Auxerre or, more probably, a Camilla Rovellone of the XIV or XV century, whose relics are in the church of San Domenico at San Severino in the Marches.

I can find no particulars of a family Dallumote.

The style of this rather peculiar work, obviously a votive painting made to record the miracle, points to a local painter in the Marches. Philip Pouncey has suggested Bernardo di Mariotto as the possible author. Bernardo worked at San Severino, and was particularly addicted to the elaborate rendering of brocades as found in this drawing (it should be noted that the upper part of Genevra was once covered in brocade, but this has flaked off or was never completed).

Perhaps Cassiano del Pozzo acquired the drawing in the belief that the Casciano mentioned in the inscription had something to do with his own name.

MINIATURES

38. THE FLAGELLATION OF OUR LORD, with the Virgin Mary introducing a company of seventeen hooded flagellants. (*Figure* 15A) (12814)

297 × 232 mm. Miniature on parchment.

According to a note on the mount by Sir Richard Holmes, this was bought in Florence in 1875 as by Altichiero. It appears to be Bolognese of the end of the XIV century.

39. INITIAL 'U' CONTAINING THE ANNUNCIATION: above, on a separate piece of parchment, two angels supporting the sacred monogram. (01414)

50 × 170 mm. and 163 × 165 mm. Miniature on parchment.

The style of this rather feeble work is certainly Milanese and very close to that of Antonio da Monza.

40–42. THREE INITIALS, CONTAINING HALF-LENGTH FIGURES OF SAINTS CUT FROM A CHOIR-BOOK

Miniatures on parchment.

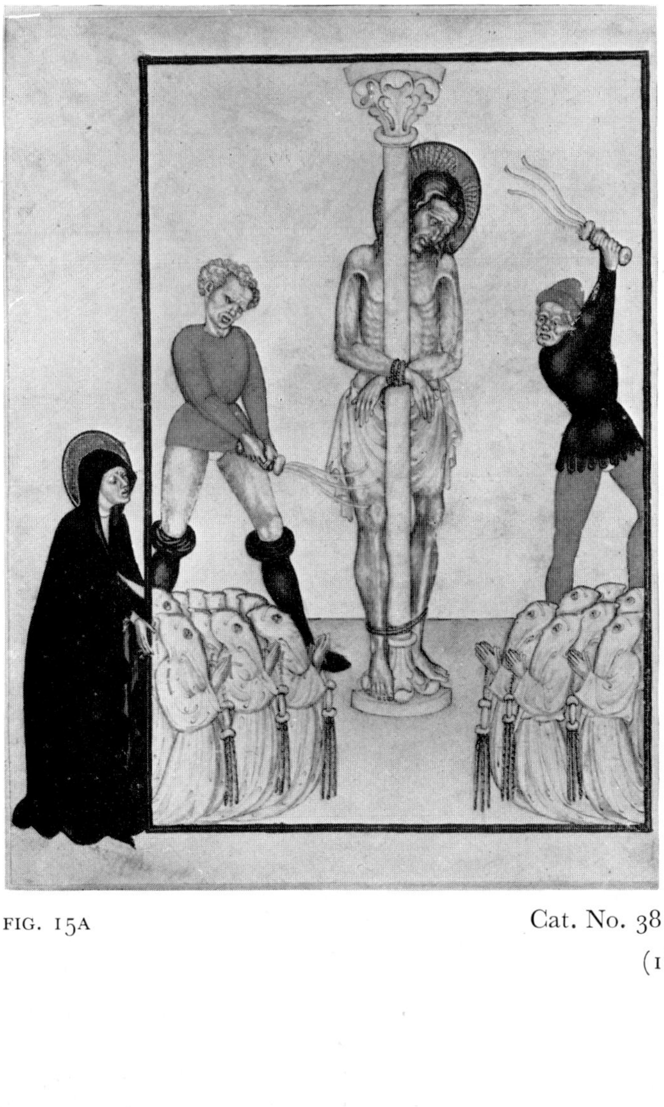

FIG. 15A Cat. No. 38

40. No. 01328A. Initial A containing the figure of a deacon holding an asperge.

110 × 110 mm.

41. No. 01328B. Initial H containing the figure of a prophet who holds a scroll with the inscription ECCE VIRGO CONCIPI . . . ET PAR . . .

112 × 108 mm.

42. No. 01328C. Initial P containing the figure of St. Andrew holding his cross.

120 × 132 mm.

On the back are fragments of text and musical notes. The work seems to be North Italian of the early XVI century.

GIULIO CLOVIO (1498–1578)

43. FRAGMENTS FROM ILLUMINATED CHOIR-BOOKS MADE UP TO FORM A PAGE. The principal part of the decoration consists of a large initial 'P'; the limb of this is a column decorated by three grotesque masks and supported on the backs of two kneeling men; in the loop of the 'P' is an interior with a cardinal seated behind a green-topped table; behind him stands a page, and on the opposite side of the table to the R. a white-robed ecclesiastic is seated; a soldier with a sword stands in front to the L. on the steps which give access to the room. The rest of the decoration consists of arabesques or scroll-work on a gold or pink ground with medallions of Roman busts and a full-length figure, in colours of St. Theodore, a knight in classical armour, with his foot on a dragon. In the bottom margin is an escutcheon, *Sable, three trefoils argent between a chevron, gules*, surmounted by the helmet of a knight and a bear, sable, chained, or. This appears to have been painted in later and may be English. (*Figure* 16; *detail*) (13035)

670 × 420 mm. Elaborately finished miniature paintings on parchment. Some text and musical notation on the *verso*.

Coll.: Consul Joseph Smith.

Signed on the block of stone on which the two figures supporting the upright of the 'P' kneel: *D IULIO CLOUIO F.* The miniature is described as follows in the MS.: 'Catalogue of Paintings of the Italian School . . .' from Consul Smith's collection acquired for George III (printed in the Burlington Magazine, XXIII (1913), p. 161, No. 345): 'Divers figures cut out of missals and elegantly pasted on cloth and ornamented with gold shading, and in the body of a great P is drawn Cardinal Grimani visiting Don Giulio in his chamber in the Convent H. 2.3W. 1. 4'. I am indebted to Dr. Otto Kurz for this identification and for the following suggestion about the provenance of the fragments. An anonymous Venetian artist of the XVIII century, who annotated a copy of the 1647 Bologna edition of Vasari's *Lives* (partly printed by A. Weixlgärtner in Die Graphischen Künste III (1938), pp. 125 ff.), writes as

FIG. 16 Cat. No. 43 (detail)

follows in reference to Vasari's statement 'Nel qual tempo (about 1530, Clovio) condusse un libro grande da Coro con minij sottili'. (Vasari, ed. Milanesi, VII, p. 559.): 'Il qual Libro è andato in pezzi, e disparse quà, e là le figure incuria degl' Abbati di quella Relligione in Candiana (a monastery near Padua mentioned by Vasari on the same page), e con mio sommo dolore ho ueduto in Casa di Signori dilettanti le migliori figure di detto Libro vendute per poco, da chì con egual conscienza che cognizione ha ardito(?) di separarle dall' opera, e uenderle priuando quella Canonica di un tanto tesoro.' The fact that an illuminated manuscript by Clovio (whether rightly identified by the commentator as the one mentioned by Vasari or not) was cut up and sold in North Italy at a time when Consul Smith was collecting and that fragments of such a manuscript found their way into his collection may be no more than a coincidence, but it seems worth recording.

The identification of the personages as Cardinal Grimani and Clovio himself proposed in the inventory lacks confirmation.

XVI CENTURY DRAWINGS

NICCOLÒ DELL' ABBATE (About 1506–1571)

44. FRIEZE OF FOUR MUSICIANS, A LADY PLAYING THE VIRGINALS AND THREE GENTLEMEN, ONE OF WHOM PLAYS THE HARP (0145)

207 × 392 mm. Drawn with the point of the brush in brown on light brown paper, with additions in black chalk, heightened with white.

Attributed in the 'deceptive' hand to 'Nicolo dell' Abate'. The drawing corresponds almost exactly with an elaborately finished drawing in the British Museum (Fenwick Collection Catalogue, pl. XX), which is *en suite* with another drawing also in the British Museum (Salting Bequest, 1910–2–12–1). Both these exactly reproduce painted friezes in the R. Galleria Estense, Modena, which formed part of the decorations of the 'Beccherie' at Modena (one ill. Venturi, IX 6, Fig. 338). There is documentary evidence (quoted by Venturi, IX 6, p. 580) that a certain Alberto Fontana was the author of the 'fregio sotto il cornicione' in the 'Beccherie', and that he completed it some time after September 18, 1537. But it is also known that Niccolò dell' Abbate assisted Fontana in these decorations, and it has always been assumed that they are, in fact, his work. No other work which can be assigned to Fontana is known, and there is no appreciable difference of style between the 'Beccherie' friezes and those in the castle at Scandiano (see below, No. 45, etc.). It seems more reasonable therefore to retain the drawing under the name of Abbate.

There is a further difficulty. Is the present drawing a copy from the Fenwick sheet or alternatively from the painting, or is it an original sketch? It is not so easy as it should be to decide this but, I think, on the whole we may regard it as a preliminary sketch and the Fenwick drawing as a copy. There seems to be no incompatibility of style between this sketch and that for the Scandiano painting next to be described.

45. AENEAS AND THE SIBYL AT THE GATES OF AVERNUS, WHICH ARE GUARDED BY CERBERUS (6318)

195 × 253 mm. Pen and brown ink and brown wash over black chalk on cream-coloured paper, heightened with white.

Lit.: F. Antal, Burlington Mag., LXXXI (1942), p. 226 (ill.).

Preliminary study for one of the series of paintings illustrating the Aeneid, which decorated a room in the Castle of Scandiano, but which are now in the Galleria Estense at Modena (Venturi, IX 6, Fig. 340, and Bollettino d'Arte, X (1930/31), p. 536). As pointed out by Antal (loc. cit.), the drawing illustrates the scene representing Æneas and the Sibyl at the gates of hell, a scene which, in the painting, appears on a small scale in the middle distance to the R. The drawing however in its general composition more closely resembles the main incident in the foreground on the L., where Æneas, accompanied by the Sibyl, is confronted by the Lernian Hydra and the Furies.

46. A MAN PLAYING ON THE FLUTE (*Figure* 17) (12995)

260 × 310 mm. (silhouetted). Pen and brown ink and brown wash on cream-coloured paper, heightened with white.

Cartoon (?) for the figure of the man playing the flute (Giulio Ascanio Boiardo ?) in the painting in the Galleria Estense at Modena (Venturi, IX 6, Fig. 345).

This drawing and the two fragments catalogued below are probably portions of the original cartoon for the octagon, which decorated the ceiling of the room in the Castle of Scandiano, on the walls of which the scenes from the Æneid already referred to under No. 45 were placed. The measurements correspond with those given by W. Bombe (Bollettino d'Arte X (1930/31), p. 542) for the painting. Bombe also discusses and identifies the members of the Boiardo family represented (loc. cit., p. 545).

FIG. 17 Cat. No. 46

47, 48. HEAD OF A MAN WITH A FEATHER IN HIS CAP AND PART OF A SLEEVE (12996 and 12997)

155 × 135 mm. and 105 × 103 mm. (each fragment silhouetted). Pen and brown ink and brown wash on cream-coloured paper, heightened with white.

Two further fragments of the cartoon (?) for the octagon in the Galleria Estense at Modena. The man with the feather in his cap is, according to Bombe, Matteo Maria Boiardo.

49. ST. AUGUSTINE WITH HEART AND CROZIER; ST. GENEVIÈVE HOLDING A TORCH, which an angel is preventing a devil, armed with bellows, from extinguishing. (*Plate* 107) (0146)

420 × 266 mm. Pen and brown ink and brown wash on light brown ground over black chalk, heightened with white.

'Nicolò Dell' Abate' in a hand apparently of the XVIII century is written on the drawing. On the *verso* also in ink, in a different hand, 'Nicolo del Abate' and the figures '6. 3.' (30 shillings in the system of pricing adopted by William Gibson). The style of the drawing leaves no doubt that it is an original design by the artist. It is surrounded by a decorated frame surmounted by an escutcheon bearing a heart with a coronet above and a winged recumbent angel as supporter. In the bottom R. corner in a circle is the monogram FAM or AFM. I have not been able to ascertain the significance of this monogram or whether the coat of arms has reference to a family or is connected with the heart carried as an emblem by St. Augustine. The drawing clearly belongs to the period of Abbate's activity in France.

After NICCOLÒ DELL' ABBATE

50. ALLEGORICAL FEMALE FIGURE OF PEACE (*Figure* 18) (4786)

357 × 28 mm. (L. hand bottom corner torn away). Black chalk and brown wash on blue paper, heightened with white.

A.E.P. The old attribution was to Paolo Farinati. It is the copy of a drawing in the Ecole des Beaux-Arts, Paris (Exhibition Catalogue of 1935, No. 100), there attributed to Polidoro da Caravaggio. Still another version (unattributed), as good as that in Paris, is in the collection of Mr. L. Lyons, Glasgow. The general style of all these points clearly to Niccolò dell' Abbate: the present version seems to be the weakest, but which of the other two is Abbate's original I cannot determine.

FIG. 18 Cat. No. 50

51. APOLLO SEATED, PLAYING A VIOLONCELLO, SURROUNDED BY THE NINE MUSES, ALL PLAYING VARIOUS INSTRUMENTS (0737)

264 × 270 mm. Pen and light brown ink and wash, heightened with white.

Inscribed in ink in an old hand in the bottom R. hand corner, 'Nicolas labadi'. The drawing is a copy of the sheet in the Albertina (Wickhoff, Scuola Bolognese 9; Photo. Braun 431: attributed to Primaticcio). There are (according to L. Dimier, *Le Primatice*, 1900, p. 417) three versions of the same composition. One of these is in the Louvre (No. 4855), a second in the Ecole des Beaux-Arts, Paris, and another was recently in the hands of F. A. Drey in London. It was also engraved by Etienne Delaune as Niccolò dell' Abbate. The style of the original is certainly Abbate's rather than Primaticcio's. On the *verso* is an elaborate 'paraphe', no doubt the mark of a previous owner.

52. THE SIBYL POINTING OUT TO AUGUSTUS THE VISION OF THE VIRGIN AND CHILD (*Figure* 19) (0144)

428 × 294 mm. Pen and ink and light brown wash. W.M., crossed arrows.

Inscribed in ink in the R. hand bottom corner, 'Nic. del Abbate'. The drawing is an exact copy of a much larger one at Chatsworth (No. 345, measuring 526 × 383 mm.) designed to fill the wall space under a pointed Gothic arch. The artist certainly knew Parmigianino's chiaroscuro of the subject as the columns on the R., supporting nothing, appear in the same position. It is the work of an artist of some distinction and, to judge from the existence of the present copy, and of a painting of the same subject now in the Louvre by Antoine Caron (which is partly based on it), a well-known work. I cannot entirely reconcile the style of the drawing with that of Niccolò dell' Abbate as I know it; but it is a different type of drawing from those already described, and the old attribution may be correct. The composition is not unlike his.

Attributed to NICCOLÒ DELL' ABBATE

53. A BEARDED MAN, CARRYING A RAM OVER HIS SHOULDER AND ANOTHER UNDER HIS ARM, WALKS TOWARDS A BOAT (5477)

394 × 524 mm. (top corners cut). Black chalk and brown wash, the outlines indented.

A.E.P. This is probably the fragment of a tapestry cartoon. It may be compared with one in the British Museum (Sloane 5214–298), anciently attributed to Niccolò dell' Abbate, which is for part of an existing tapestry (Teinture de Cibèle). The present drawing is, however, much less finished.

School of NICCOLÒ DELL' ABBATE

54. THE MUSE ERATO HOLDING A VIOLIN; CUPID WITH A LIGHTED TORCH TO THE L. (0143)

220 × 164 mm. Pen and brown ink and brown wash. Much wormed round the edges.

Inscribed by the artist ERATO. It was attributed to Niccolò dell' Abbate. It is certainly not from his hand, though it reflects his style.

LIVIO AGRESTI DA FORLÌ (Working from 1550; d. before 1585)

55. THREE SCENES FROM THE LIFE OF JOSEPH: he tells his dreams to his brothers; he is sold to the Ishmaelites; he relates his dream to the butler and baker in prison. (0342)

257 × 190 mm. Pen and brown ink.

Lit.: J. D. Passavant, *Raphael d'Urbin*, Paris, 1860, Vol. II, p. 494 R.; Ruland, p. 18, XI.

Photo.: Thurston Thompson, 1857.

A.E.P. The separate scenes in the life of Joseph were inscribed respectively by the artist—'prima', 'secondo', 'terza'. He also wrote the following: 'Adj II de Aprile del 1579 Ebbj dal factor de M Paulo Mactej –V–'. On the *verso* in the same hand is a statement of payment received in money and cloth, of which it is only necessary to transcribe the heading 'Danari et robbe havute dal fōdaco de M(aestro) Valerio cremado abōcato p(er) la opera dela Pictura facta in casa de S. Sig[re] di me M(aestr)o livi. . . .'

I think there can be little doubt that 'Maestro Livi . . .' is to be identified with Livio Agresti, from whose hand there is in the British Museum a drawing of the *Last Supper* (Cracherode, Ff. 1–31) very similar in style, on which there is an autograph inscription beginning 'Io M(aestr)o Livio . . .' The handwriting, though not absolutely identical, is so near as to suggest the same writer at a different period.

The drawing, in spite of the date, was for some reason associated with the Raphaels at Windsor. Ruland regarded it as Dutch, and the composition of Joseph in prison is indeed based on Lucas van Leyden's engraving of the subject.

Attributed to LIVIO AGRESTI

56. THE PILGRIMS TO EMMAUS (5144)

405 × 280 mm. (torn on the L.). Black chalk, squared with the stylus.

A.E.P. The drawing is the work of some provincial mannerist of about 1560–70, who may, I believe, be identified from the style as Livio Agresti.

After CHERUBINO ALBERTI (1553–1615)

57. *Recto:* JUSTICE AND CHARITY

Verso: PORTRAIT OF A POPE IN A DECORATIVE FRAME; TWO STUDIES OF A ST. SEBASTIAN (0107)

198 × 198 mm. Pen and brown ink.

A.E.P. At the top of the *recto* is an inscription in Italian of five lines (cut into on the R.), having reference to the qualities which a prince should or should not possess; at the bottom, one of three lines, also in Italian, referring to Lucullus bringing treasures before the Senate; still lower down and difficult to decipher are three lines in French, which appear to be a paraphrase of the Italian above.

The figures on the *recto* correspond (in the same direction) with those to L. and R. of the engraved portrait of Urban VII by Cherubino Alberti (Bartsch XVII, p. 96, 127). The engraving was, however, later altered to represent Gregory XIV, and the portrait on the *verso* is from this state of the print. The drawing must therefore date from after 1590. I do not know the original from which, presumably, the larger figure of St. Sebastian is copied.

ALESSANDRO ALLORI (1535–1607)

58. DESIGN FOR THE DECORATION OF A LUNETTE, PIERCED BY A CIRCULAR WINDOW (*Figure* 20) (0139)

184 × 364 mm. (the top is curved). Pen and brown ink and brown wash over black chalk, heightened with white and squared in black chalk.

A.E.P. Inserted in the blank space left by the circular opening is a coat of arms, said to be that of Pio of Savoy, with *putti* supporting a coronet and, in a smaller circular space below, the head of a bearded man wearing a turban. Both these drawings are on separate pieces of paper and have nothing to do with the original design, the coat of arms being apparently of the XVII century.

The design is for the lunette of the hall of the Medici villa at Poggio à Cajano (Pietro Toesca, *Affreschi decorativi*, Milan, 1917, pl. 158). According to his book of 'Ricordi', Allori was working at Poggio à Cajano in the summer months of 1579.

FIG. 19 Cat. No. 52

FIG. 20 Cat. No. 58

The drawing corresponds substantially with the fresco as carried out, indeed the R. hand side almost exactly. The L. hand half shows various differences. In the fresco Hercules is seated and the nude figure lying before him does not appear. The uppermost of the two allegorical females is turned to the front. See also No. 59 below.

59. DESIGN FOR THE DECORATION OF A SOPRA-PORTE, WITH THREE ALLEGORICAL FIGURES (*Plate* 40) (6018)

440 × 360 mm. Pen and brown ink and brown wash on light brown ground, heightened with white.

Coll.: N. Lanière (Lugt 2885).

Inscribed on the *verso* (visible through the backing): 'Alessandro Allori', in a hand which appears to be contemporary, and also, 'Jerom'. It is the design for a painted *sopra-porte* in the great hall of the Medici villa at Poggio à Cajano, on which Allori was working in the summer months of 1579 (see the preceding drawing). The *sopra-porte* can be seen in a photograph of the interior of the great hall reproduced in H. D. Eberlein, *Villas of Florence and Tuscany*, Philadelphia, 1922, pl. 125.

Attributed to ALLESSANDRO ALLORI

60. A MUSE DIRECTING A POET TO THE FOUNTAIN OF HELICON, while a second Muse crowns him with laurel; in the foreground on the L. is a river-god with an urn and a lion. (5143)

195 × 210 mm. Pen and brown ink and brown wash over black chalk on a light brown ground, heightened with white; squared in black chalk.

A.E.P. The style of the drawing, which was attributed to Federico Zuccaro, seems to me to point clearly to Allori. I do not know the occasion or the exact significance of the subject. It can hardly have been designed for the decoration of one of the arches for the marriage of Duke Cosimo de' Medici with Joanna of Austria in 1565 (see Bottari, *Lettere Pittoriche*, I, 1757, p. 106, and Vasari, VIII, p. 524), though Allori was in fact engaged on paintings for the arch on which Poetry was represented, as the description does not fit. It may have been for some similar decoration.

61. HEAD OF A CHILD, TURNED THREE-QUARTERS TO THE R. (5220)

288 × 214 mm. (bottom R. hand corner cut). Black and red chalk.

A.E.P. Old attribution in the bottom R. hand corner to 'Federico B . . .', which has been interpreted as Federico Barocci or Federico Bianchi. The Bronzino type of head as well as the handling of the chalk point definitely to Allori.

MARCO ANGOLO DEL MORO (About 1537–after 1586)

62. THE MARTYRDOM OF S. BIAGIO (5076)

274 × 213 mm. Pen and brown ink and pink wash over black chalk.

Inscribed in ink at the bottom to the L., 'marco del moro Verone^se^'. The style of the drawing leaves no doubt about the correctness of the attribution to this very individual draughtsman.

This drawing is not catalogued by Hadeln or by the Tietzes.

Attributed to SOPHONISBA ANGUISSOLA (1527–1625)

63. BUST OF A LADY TURNED THREE-QUARTERS TO THE R. (0603)

105 × 76 mm. Red and black chalk.

P.M.R.P. Attributed by Venturi on the mount to Barocci, by an unknown German hand to Zuccaro. It can hardly be by one or the other. The style suggests Sophonisba or one of her sisters.

Attributed to MICHELANGELO ANSELMI (1491–1554)

64. TWO MEN SEATED TO THE L., SEEN FROM BELOW, AND STUDY OF CROSSED LEGS (*Plate* 119) (0234)

211 × 283 mm. Red chalk, heavily heightened with white.

Coll.: N. Lanière (Lugt 2885).

Inscribed in ink in an old hand at the top to the R., 'di M. Agnol da Siena'. The whole question of drawings by Anselmi is obscure, but the style of this drawing is by no means incompatible with that of sheets which have been credibly attributed to him, notably the 'putti reggifestoni' in the Uffizi (No. 897F. ill. *Correggio Exhibition Catalogue*, Parma, 1935, p. 170).

One is, it is true, reminded to a certain extent of Primaticcio by the style of the drawing, but it can hardly be his, and the old attribution is certainly worth putting on record.

65. A SACRIFICE TO DIANA (*Plate* 120) (5100)

252 × 281 mm. Pen and brown ink and brown and reddish wash.

A.E.P. This interesting Parmigianinesque drawing seems to be by the same hand as one of *Venus and Cupid* in the Uffizi (No. 6265: ill. *Correggio Exhibition Catalogue.* Parma, 1935, p. 151) attributed to Parmigianino. Both seem to me impossible for Parmigianino and to resemble the drawing in the Uffizi, which has the best claim to be regarded as Anselmi's (see No. 64).

AMICO ASPERTINI (1474(5?)–1552)

66. *Recto:* THE ASSUMPTION OF THE VIRGIN

267 × 194 mm. Pen and brown ink and brown wash.

Verso: A DRAPED FIGURE SEEN FROM THE BACK

Brush drawing. (0102)

F.A. Design for an altarpiece or fresco with arched top. I can find no reference to any painting of the subject by Aspertini, but the style leaves no doubt that the drawing is by him.

Attributed to AMICO ASPERTINI

67. STUDIES OF FLYING AND KNEELING ANGELS AND OF GOD THE FATHER BLESSING (0320)

248 × 202 mm. Pen and light brown ink on brownish-toned paper.

A.E.P. The two groups of angels flying to the L. and to the R. correspond, with some variations, to those at the top of Raphael's *Disputà*. Neither of the two groups (of two kneeling angels each) nor the God the Father occur, or seem at any stage to have occurred, in the *Disputà*. The style of the drawing is Bolognese or Ferrarese. I have thought of Garofalo as possibly the draughtsman, but I think the style comes nearer to that of Aspertini.

Attributed to FRANCESCO (UBERTINI) BACCHIACCA (1494–1557)

68. BUST OF A BEARDED WARRIOR, WEARING A FANTASTIC CLASSICAL HELMET (*Figure* 21) (0463)

263 × 200 mm. Red chalk.

P.M.R.P. An attribution to Tempesta suggested on the mount is certainly wide of the mark. The head is probably Florentine about 1540–50, and the manner of drawing coming out of the school of Andrea del Sarto, as well as the *genre* makes the attribution to Bacchiacca very probable.

FIG. 21 Cat. No. 68

Attributed to BARTOLOMMEO (RAMENGHI) BAGNACAVALLO (1484–1542)

69. THE ANNUNCIATION, WITH GOD THE FATHER AND TWO PUTTI ABOVE (*Figure* 22) (5324)

380 × 259 mm. Black chalk, squared in the same medium.

P.M.R.P. Inscribed in ink in an old hand in the bottom L.

FIG. 22 Cat. No. 69

corner, 'Gian Giuseppe del Sole', an obviously absurd attribution, as the drawing dates from the first half of the XVI century and is by a Bolognese follower of Raphael. The suggestion that the draughtsman is Bagnacavallo, with whose type of face that of the Virgin perfectly agrees, is attractive, but in the absence of any well-authenticated drawing by this artist with which a comparison can be made, the attribution of this and the drawing next to be described must remain hypothetical.

70. THE VIRGIN AND CHILD ON CLOUDS (6007)

158 × 167 mm. Pen and brown ink and brown wash, the clouds in black chalk; squared in pen and ink.

P.M.R.P. The way the Virgin is holding the Child and His almost violent action, seem to be based on Raphael's *Madonna di Foligno*, and at once suggests one of his Bolognese imitators. The type of the Virgin is similar to that in the drawing previously described.

Attributed to GIOVANNI BALDUCCI (COSCI) (About 1560–1600/05)

71. THE SUPPER AT EMMAUS (5136)

197 × 153 mm. Pen and brown ink and brown wash over red chalk.

F.A. The sketch is too slight to allow of any certainty, but the style seems to accord very well with that of a drawing in the British Museum with an old attribution to Balducci (Fawkener 5212–27).

BACCIO BANDINELLI (1493–1560)

72. MALE MODEL POSED FOR A STATUE (*Figure* 23) (0454)
383 × 244 mm. Black chalk.
The figure is represented whole length dressed in a clinging garment; the R. leg is raised on a block, the R. arm hangs down, the L. hand holds some object, the head is turned to the R. The pose is reminiscent of that of Michelangelo's unfinished statue of St Matthew. It does not occur in Bandinelli's known works. About 1520–25.

73. TWO SEATED MALE NUDES (*Plate* 39) (0375)
265 × 332 mm. Pen and brown ink.
Very similar in style to the drawing in the Uffizi for the *Hercules and Cacus* group of 1525 (Venturi, X 2, Fig. 171).

74. *Recto:* TWO MALE NUDES
Verso: BUST OF A BEARDED MAN TURNED THREE-QUARTERS TO THE L. (0394)
400 × 265 mm. Pen and brown ink.
The L. hand figure on the *recto*, the younger, leans on a club; the R. hand figure stands facing to the front. On the lower half a head had previously been lightly sketched in red chalk probably by a *garzone*. Above are parts of an inscription in Bandinelli's hand partly cut away 'nena lionarda dona . . . /figliuola di lorenzo . . .'
The studies on *recto* and *verso* are excellent examples of Bandinelli's mature style.

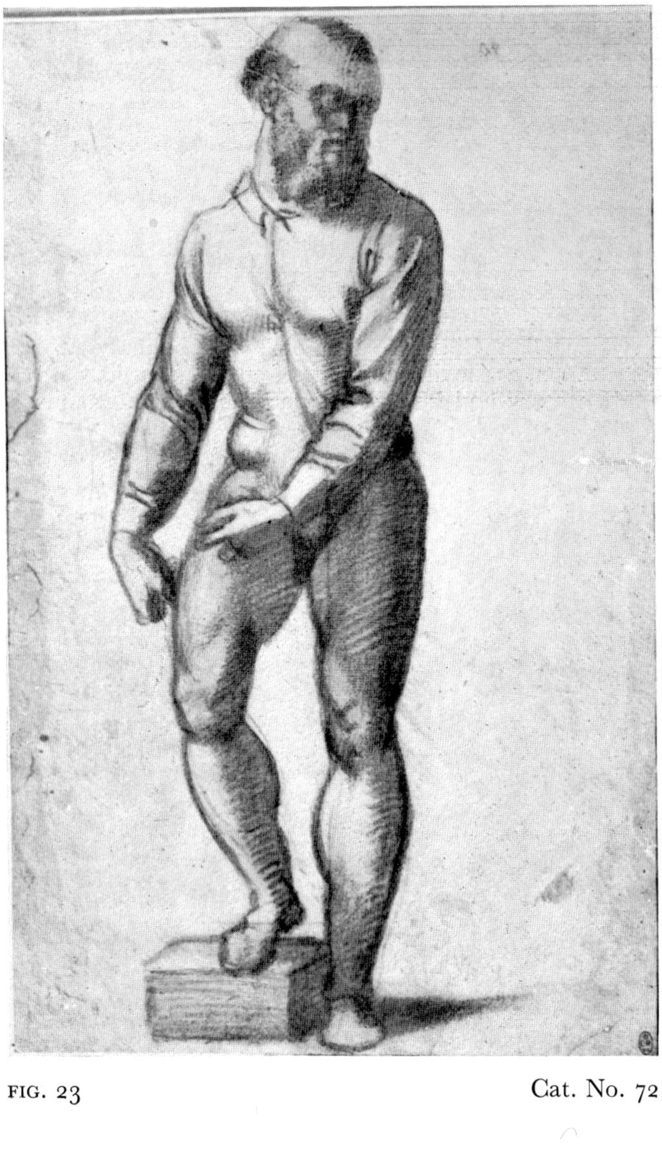
FIG. 23 Cat. No. 72

FIG. 24 Cat. No. 75

75. THREE MALE NUDES STANDING (*Figure* 24) (0376)
272 × 200 mm. Pen and brown ink. A number of holes, which the ink has bitten, have been made up.
The L. hand figure is turned three-quarters to the R.; the central one is in profile to the R., while the third faces to the front and kneels with his L. knee on a block of stone.
Possibly a study for *The three sons of Noah*. About 1525–30.

76. THE THREE AGES OF MAN (0396)
172 × 213 mm. (cut into on all sides and made up at the bottom). Pen and brown ink.
Represented by heads: on the L. that of a youth in profile to the L.; in the middle that of a middle-aged man turned three-quarters to the R.; on the R. that of a bald-headed old man facing to the front.

77. THREE SAGES, WRAPPED IN VOLUMINOUS MANTLES, two of them with large books, the figure on the R. unfinished. (0387)
184 × 249 mm. Pen and dark brown ink.
An example of Bandinelli's later style of drawing.

School of BACCIO BANDINELLI

78. THE ADORATION OF THE SHEPHERDS: the Virgin with the Child lying down is on the L.; Joseph sits on a saddle on the R; and behind him are five shepherd-boys. (0392)

253 × 395 mm. Pen and brown ink.

There is another version in the Uffizi (photo. Gernsheim 2433) differing only in minute details. Both are perhaps repetitions by the same pupil of an original by Bandinelli.

79. STANDING FIGURE OF HERCULES TURNED THREE-QUARTERS TO THE L. (0378)

385 × 219 mm. Pen and brown ink. Some holes made up. There is an exact repetition in the Albertina (photo. Braun 7). Both are probably copies by the same pupil from an original by Bandinelli.

80. YOUTH IN A VOLUMINOUS MANTLE SEATED ON A FOLDING STOOL, the body three-quarters to the R., the head to the front. (0389)

274 × 183 mm. (silhouetted and then made up to a rectangle). Pen and brown ink.

Perhaps only a copy by a pupil.

81. BEARDED HEAD TURNED THREE-QUARTERS TO THE R. (0416)

272 × 192 mm. (the l. hand top corner cut). Pen and brown ink.

George III 'Inventory A', p. 43, Michelangelo, I, 1.

Lit.: Chamberlaine, pl. LVI.

Inscribed at the bottom to the L. in a hand of the late XVI century 'michelagnolo'. The drawing was regarded as a portrait of Michelangelo. The head is in fact a variant of that in Bandinelli's *modello* for a statue of Andrea Doria in the British Museum (1895–9–15–553; about 1522/3). It occurs again in a drawing in the collection of Dr. F. Sprinzels (Apropos, 1946, Fig. 7), representing the three ages of man. Perhaps there existed a study by Bandinelli for the head of the Doria statue of this sort and No. 81 is a pupil's copy of it.

82. NUDE YOUTH CARRYING ANOTHER (0393)

268 × 185 mm. Pen and brown ink.

Pupil's copy.

83. JOHN THE BAPTIST AS FORERUNNER OF THE SAVIOUR (0399)

360 × 257 mm. Pen and dark brown ink over a preliminary sketch (or tracing) in black chalk.

On the L. Christ stands leaning on the globe, pointing to John the Baptist with His R. hand; on the R. is the Baptist, seated, holding a bowl in his R. hand and pointing to the Saviour with his L. hand. Copy of a late drawing by Bandinelli.

84. TWO MALE 'ÉCORCHÉS' IN PROFILE, WALKING TO THE R. (0395)

435 × 273 mm. Pen and dark brown ink.

Copy. There is an album in the British Museum with similar studies by Bandinelli.

85. *Recto:* EXTENDED RIGHT ARM AND A SECOND ARM HOLDING THE EDGE OF A CURTAIN

Verso: THE UPPER PART OF THE BODY OF A NUDE YOUTH IN PROFILE TO THE L. (The extended R. arm on the *recto* belongs to this figure). (0372)

310 × 212 mm. Red chalk. W.M., an object in a circle.

Inscribed 'Tadeo Zucco' in lower R. hand corner. Later school copies of studies by Bandinelli apparently made for the relief of the *Birth of the Virgin* at Loreto (begun in 1518). Compare Bandinelli's drawings in the British Museum, 1885–5–9–35 and 1925–2–14–1.

86. MALE NUDE IN VIOLENT MOTION TOWARDS THE R., THE R. ARM EXTENDED, THE L. HOLDING A CLOAK (0452)

398 × 250 mm. (partly made up on the R.). Black chalk. The movement of the figure is a variant of that of the Dioscuri on Monte Cavallo and the soldier with the lance in Michelangelo's cartoon of the *Bathers* dependent on them. By an imitator of Bandinelli's later style.

87. STUDIES OF A NUDE WARRIOR SEEN FROM THE BACK, OF ARMS, A HORSE'S HEAD, ETC. (5989)

162 × 189 mm. (the corners cut). Red chalk.

Formerly attributed to Primaticcio. The largest study, that of an arm which a woman seizes with her teeth, is copied from Marcantonio's engraving after Bandinelli of the *Massacre of the Innocents* (Bartsch, XIV, p. 24, 21). No doubt the other studies on the sheet are also copies. Late XVI or XVII century.

FEDERICO BAROCCI (1526–1612)

It is not possible to assign dates to drawings by Barocci of the type of those at Windsor, most of them studies of single heads, when they cannot be definitely connected with existing works by the artist. Though this is the case with a number of them, I have thought it simpler to arrange them all in the order of the inventory numbers. Many of them also have been considerably re-worked and their authenticity is doubtful, but it is safer to include these rather than to place them in the limbo of anonymous drawings, the only alternative. The series seems on the whole to be good, and there is a probability that they all came from the same source, the vast collection of studies which Barocci left in his studio at his death in 1612.

There are occasional references to the useful work by Filippo di Pietro, *Disegni . . . di Federico Barocci negli Uffizi.* Florence, 1913, quoted as 'di Pietro'.

88. HEAD OF A CHILD LOOKING DOWN TO THE L. (5222)

188 × 137 mm. (corners made up). Oil colour, perhaps over an original drawing in pastels; the outlines indented. Probably a study for the cherub in the top R. hand corner of the *Madonna del Popolo* in the Uffizi (Venturi, IX 7, Fig. 495; a better reproduction in di Pietro, Fig. 53). The picture was finished in 1569.

89. HEAD OF A BABY LYING DOWN (*Plate* 94) (5223)

160 × 221 mm. (the drawing had been cut to an oval and then inlaid into a rectangular piece of paper). Pastels on blue paper.

Lit.: Catalogue of the Exhibition of XVII cent. Art in Europe, London, 1938, No. 359 (ill. p. 99).

Study for the head of the Infant in the *Nativity* now in the Prado, Madrid, presented by the Duke of Urbino to Maria Cristina of Spain in 1597 (Venturi, IX 7, Fig. 525).

90 HEAD OF A YOUTH INCLINED AND TURNED THREE-QUARTERS TO THE L. (5224)

213 × 178 mm. Black chalk and pastel on blue paper, partly silhouetted.

The head might be a study for that of the youth punting the boat ashore in the *Calling of S. Andrew* at Brussels (Venturi, IX 7, Fig. 498), but his face in the picture is half covered by the pole and it is difficult to be certain. There is no doubt about the drawing being by Barocci.

91. HEAD OF A BOY TURNED THREE-QUARTERS TO THE R. (5225)

Pastels on blue paper, cut and made up.

222 × 173 mm.

This fragmentary head seems first to have been drawn as a profile and then extended to the R., with unsatisfactory results. It seems nevertheless to be by Barocci.

92. HEAD OF A YOUNGISH, BEARDED MAN, LOOKING, DOWN TO THE L. (*Plate* 93) (5226)

309 × 244 mm. Coloured chalks on greenish paper.

Possibly a study for the head of the man distributing alms, who appears on the R. in the *bozzetto* for the *Madonna del Popolo*, at Chatsworth (di Pietro, Fig. 45). This figure does not appear at all in the painting.

93. PORTRAIT DRAWING OF A BEARDED MAN WITH CLOSED EYES (5228)

190 × 259 mm. (corners made up). Black, red, and white chalk on blue paper, heightened with white.

The features are like those of the Duke Federico della Rovere, who, however, died after Barocci. It is possibly the portrait of the duke's brother, Cardinal Giuliano della Rovere, who died in 1578.

94. STUDY OF A WOMAN'S HEAD TURNED THREE-QUARTERS TO THE R., LOOKING DOWN (5229)

256 × 198 mm. (corners made up). Black, red, white and brown chalk on blue paper.

Study for the head of the Virgin in the *Madonna del Gatto*, of which the best version appears to be that in the National Gallery (Venturi, IX 7, Fig. 493). The head is, however, singularly like that of the Virgin in the version of the *Nativity* in the Mengarini Collection, Rome (Venturi, IX 7, Fig. 524), though reversed. There is a suggestion in the drawing of artificial lighting, which occurs here and not in the *Madonna del Gatto*.

95. HEAD OF A WOMAN LOOKING DOWN TO THE R. AND SLIGHT SKETCH OF THE SAME HEAD (5230)

222 × 185 mm. (corners made up). Black chalk and pastel on discoloured blue paper.

Coll.: N. Lanière (Lugt 2885).

'Federico Barocho' is written in ink in an old hand in the bottom R. hand corner. Study for the head of the *Madonna del Gatto*, of which the best version appears to be that in the National Gallery (Venturi, IX 7, Fig. 493).

96. HEAD OF A YOUNG WOMAN, TURNED THREE-QUARTERS TO THE R., HER EYES DIRECTED DOWNWARDS (*Plate* 91) (5231)

299 × 230 mm. (corners made up). Black, red and white chalk on blue paper.

Study for the head of the woman on the L., who points out to her two children the heavenly vision, in the *Madonna del Popolo* in the Uffizi (Venturi, IX 7, Fig. 495).

FIG. 25 Cat. No. 97

97. HEAD OF A VENERABLE, BEARDED MAN, LOOKING UP TO THE R. (*Figure* 25) (5232)

348 × 254 mm. Coloured chalks on blue paper.

I cannot find that this fine head is connected with any existing work by Barocci. It would appear to be for an apostle in an Assumption, but there is no such head in the Dresden picture, the only one of this subject painted by Barocci. The head is singularly like that of a St. Jerome by Niccolo Renieri in the Kaiser Friedrich Museum at Berlin (H. Voss, *Die Malerei des Barock in Rom*, Berlin, n.d., pl. 145), but this may be the result of chance or conscious imitation. I think there is little doubt that the present drawing is by Barocci.

98. HEAD OF AN OLD MAN TURNED THREE-QUARTERS TO THE L., INCLINED AND LOOKING DOWN (*Plate* 92) (5233)

378 × 260 mm. Coloured chalks on blue paper.

Study for the head of Anchises in the painting of *Aeneas rescuing Anchises*, in the Borghese Gallery, Rome (Venturi, IX 7, Fig. 511). This, Barocci's only non-religious painting, was made for the Emperor Rudolph in 1587–88.

99. HEAD OF A BEARDED MAN, WEARING A RUFF (5234)

366 × 255 mm. Coloured chalks, considerably damaged. The head has been silhouetted and inlaid and part of the body added in black chalk. Patches and wormholes all over the face have been repaired and made up.

Attribution in pencil on the drawing to 'Baroccio'. I have considerable doubt about the correctness of this, but the appearance of the drawing has been greatly altered, and it may perhaps once have been by Barocci. From the care with which it has been repaired it is obvious that it was considered of value.

100. HALF-LENGTH STUDY OF A SEATED YOUTH, HOLDING A STAFF IN HIS R. HAND AND AN OPEN BOOK ON HIS KNEE IN HIS L. (*Plate* 95) (5235)

190 × 213 mm. Black chalk on blue paper, with some touches of red and white chalk.

If the old attribution to Barocci is right, as I think it is, this might be a study for one of the allegorical figures in the angles of the vaulting of the Casino of Pius IV in the Vatican Gardens, though it does not correspond closely with any of these. The drawing, if Barocci's, is in any case early.

101. MOSES AND THE SERPENT (5238)

380 × 241 mm. Black chalk on blue paper, heightened with white.

Study from, or less probably for, the fresco of *Moses*, completed in 1560, in the large hall of the Belvedere in the Vatican (as noted on the mount). Another drawing, a finished composition sketch for the whole subject (but reversed) is in the Uffizi (H. Voss, *Malerei der Spätrenaissance im Rom und Florenz*, Berlin, 1920, Fig. 187). There are considerable differences between the figure of Moses here and in the Uffizi drawing.

102. THE VISITATION (5241)

396 × 283 mm. Pen and brown ink and brown wash over black chalk on blue paper, heightened with white.

This is no more than a careful copy from the painting in Sta. Maria in Vallicella, Rome (Venturi, IX 7, Fig. 499).

103. HEAD OF AN OLD BEARDED MAN, TURNED THREE-QUARTERS TO THE L., LOOKING DOWN (5357)

379 × 261 mm. Coloured chalks on blue paper

This may once have been by Barocci, but it appears to have been very much touched up, perhaps in the XVIII century.

104. HEAD OF WOMAN LOOKING UP TO THE R. AND TWO SLIGHT SKETCHES OF HEADS ALSO LOOKING UP (5358)

247 × 218 mm. Coloured chalks.

Though the style and the white paper are somewhat unusual for Barocci, I see no reason for doubting the old attribution. The head corresponds almost exactly with one on the extreme L. in the *Madonna del Popolo* in the Uffizi (Venturi, IX 7, Fig. 495), just above the portrait of the kneeling lady in profile.

105. HEAD OF A CHERUB TURNED THREE-QUARTERS TO THE R., LOOKING UP (5359)

278 × 270 mm. Coloured chalks.

The drawing is not a particularly characteristic one for Barocci, to whom it appears to have been anciently attributed, but its quality is good and it may be by him. If so, it is perhaps a study for the cherub above the head of the kneeling Virgin in the *Perdono* in S. Francesco, Urbino (di Pietro, Fig. 44).

106. HEAD OF A WOMAN LOOKING UP IN PROFILE TO THE L. (5425)

272 × 245 mm. Coloured chalks.

Unnamed. The head is very Correggiesque and is almost identical with that of the Cupid in the *Danae*, though reversed. The technique, however, is that generally associated with Barocci, and it is perhaps a study for that artist's early painting of St. Cecilia and other saints in the Duomo at Urbino (Venturi, IX 7, Fig. 486: the saint on the R.).

107. THE CALLING OF ST. ANDREW (*Plate* 90) (6830)

470 × 347 mm. Pen and brown ink and brown wash, heightened with white.

The drawing is apparently the *bozzetto* for the painting dated 1580, commissioned by the Duchess of Urbino for the Guild of Fishermen at Pesaro. The painting, now lost, was subsequently given to Philip II of Spain by the Duke of Urbino. Meanwhile Barocci was asked to paint a replica for the Guild at Pesaro, which he completed in 1583. This is the painting now in the Royal Museum at Brussels (di Pietro, Fig. 56: engraved by G. Sadeler in 1594). The landscape background is very different from that in the Brussels painting, which seems to imply that the drawing is for the earlier painting.

A copy from Correggio (No. 251) is attributed with some plausibility to Barocci.

FRA BARTOLOMMEO (BACCIO DELLA PORTA) (1475–1517)

References are given to the following works on Fra Bartolommeo:

Fritz Knapp, *Fra Bartolommeo della Porta und die Schule von S. Marco*. Halle, 1903 (quoted as Knapp).

Hans von der Gabelentz, *Fra Bartolommeo und die Florentiner Renaissance*. 2 vols. Leipzig, 1922 (quoted as Gabelentz).

B. Berenson, *Drawings of the Florentine Painters* (see general bibliography).

The drawings are arranged in a rough chronological order, following on the whole the dating given to them by von Gabelentz.

108. *Recto:* STUDY OF A MAN SEATED, TURNED TO THE L.; HE WEARS A TURBAN AND AMPLE DRAPERY (*Plate* 14)

260 × 178 mm. (top corners cut). Metal-point on blue prepared surface, heightened with white.

Verso: STUDY OF THE DRAPERY OVER THE LEGS OF A FIGURE SEATED TO THE R.; A SEATED MAN; A PROFILE (*Figure* 26)

Metal-point on pale pink prepared surface, the profile in black chalk. Splodges of blue and red. (12825)

A.E.P. A label attached to the *verso* has inscribed on it in William Gibson's (?) hand, '6.3 [= 30 shillings] Leonardo da Vinci'. The drawing has not apparently been published or referred to. It is of a type not hitherto connected with Fra Bartolommeo, but the cast of drapery is characteristic of his early style. There is further a close resemblance between the figure on the *recto* and the seated apostle on the extreme R. in the fresco of the *Last Judgment*, commissioned of Fra Bartolommeo by Gerozzo Dini for Sta. Maria Nuova in 1498 (ill. by Knapp from the engraving, p. 20), while the drapery study on the *verso* corresponds very closely with that of the apostle on the extreme L. in the same fresco. The fact that the man in the drawing wears a turban is curious, and

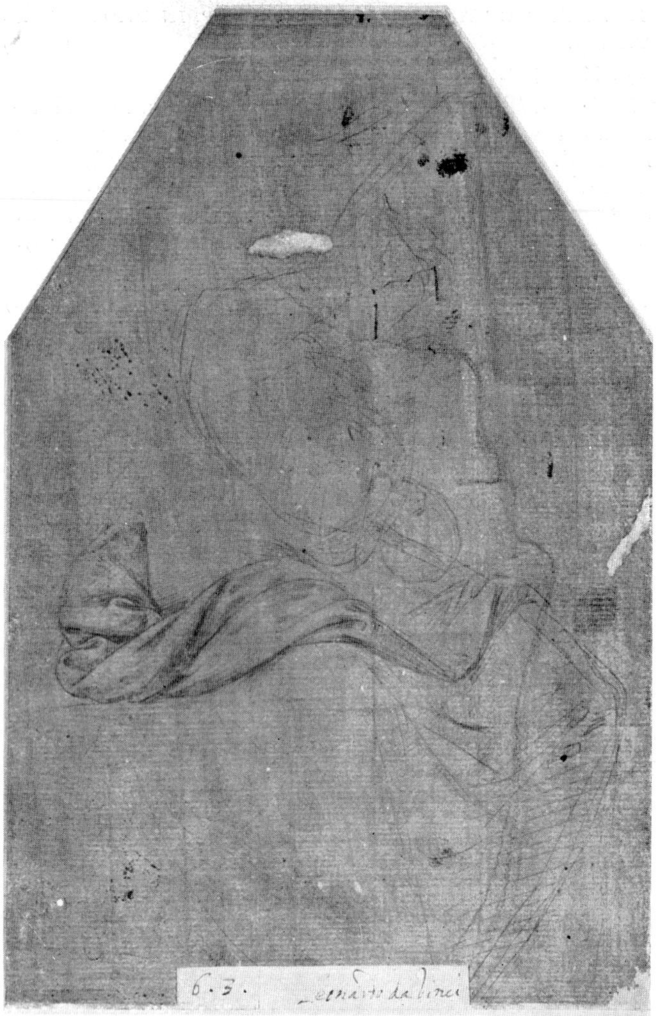

FIG. 26 Cat. No. 108 *v.*

seems to exclude its being a direct study for the apostle in the fresco.

Another possibility which I have considered is that the drawing is by Albertinelli, who is recorded to have completed the *Last Judgment* after Fra Bartolommeo's retirement from the world in 1500. But, according to Vasari, the Frate had already by 1500 finished the upper half of the fresco, and it is most improbable that Albertinelli (though he had entered into partnership with Fra Bartolommeo as early as 1494) should have been concerned with preliminary drawings (as this must be) for that portion. A drawing of a kneeling angel (for the *Annunciation* in the Cathedral at Volterra: B.B. 7, Fig. 459) very similar in style to the present drawing, is in fact attributed to Albertinelli, as are also two studies of angels in the *Last Judgment* (B.B. 14; Knapp, Fig. 8), but I fail to see the reason for these attributions, and I think they should in fact all be given to Fra Bartolommeo. They are indistinguishable in style from the *St. Michael* in the Ashmolean Museum (published by Fischel in O.M.D., IV (1929–30), pl. 38, as a study by Fra Bartolommeo for the *Last Judgment*, and accepted as such by Berenson).

The sketch for a seated man (on the *verso*, the other way up to the drapery study) may be for one of the other apostles on the R. of the *Last Judgment*, but it is too slight for any definite conclusion to be arrived at. The profile in black chalk is a childish scribble by another hand.

109. STUDY OF FIVE FIGURES, THREE MEN AND TWO WOMEN (12789)

152 × 216 mm. Pen and light brown ink on paper slightly tinted with red chalk, heightened with white and partially washed with brown.

Lit.: B.B. 527; Knapp, p. 315, No. 9, Fig. 6; Gabelentz 880.

Regarded by Knapp and by Gabelentz as a study for the *Last Judgment*. Berenson does not commit himself. The drawing is certainly early, before 1500, and there is a general resemblance to the figures standing below in the fresco. The resemblance is not however sufficiently close for one to be able to say that it is definitely a study for it.

110. THE VIRGIN AND CHILD (*Figure* 27) (12781)

165 × 113 mm. Pen and brown ink with some touches of white, which has oxidised.

Lit.: B.B. 525; Gabelentz 872.

Dated by Gabelentz about 1500. Very similar to No. 111.

111. *Recto:* THE VIRGIN AND CHILD (*Figure* 28)

Verso: SMALL SKETCH OF A CHILD LIFTING A TRAP-DOOR (?) (12788)

163 × 113 mm. Pen and different shades of brown ink.

Lit.: B.B. 526; Gabelentz 879.

Dated by Gabelentz about 1500. Very similar in style to No. 110.

112. *Recto:* THE VIRGIN SEATED WITH THE CHILD ON HER LAP, TO WHOM ST. JOSEPH, ON THE R., PRESENTS THE INFANT ST. JOHN (*Figure* 29) (12786)

221 × 157 mm. Pen and ink and wash on paper tinted with red chalk, the outlines of the Child Christ pricked through.

Verso: AN ELDERLY SAINT WITH ST. JOHN THE BAPTIST (*Figure* 30)

Pen and ink and wash with some white.

Lit.: B.B. 523; Knapp, p. 315, No. 5 (*recto* only mentioned); Gabelentz 877.

Photo.: Braun 094 (*recto* only).

Dated by Gabelentz about 1500–05. He connects it with other drawings, in which the infant St. John is introduced by an angel (British Museum, Pp. 1–51, Gabelentz 275; Pp. 1–52, Gabelentz 274; Louvre, Gabelentz 390, B.B., Fig. 435; Munich, Gabelentz 320, ill. Schmidt, *Munich Drawings*, 34a; and Uffizi, Santarelli 242, Gabelentz 43, pl. 27). The connection between all these drawings is not, however, very close and Gabelentz assigns various dates to them. The saints on the *verso* are for an important *Sacra Conversazione*, of the type for which Windsor, No. 117 *recto*, is the sketch.

113. *Recto:* SKETCH FOR A TONDO: THE VIRGIN STANDS, HOLDING THE INFANT CHRIST; the infant St. John with two angels is on the L. and three kneeling angels are on the R. (*Plate* 15) (12782)

224 × 163 mm. Pen and ink on paper rubbed with red chalk, with touches of white.

Verso: TO THE VIRGIN SEATED WITH THE CHILD ON HER LAP AN ANGEL, KNEELING ON THE R., PRESENTS A BOOK (?); a second angel kneels on the L., and there is a study of an infant (at right angles) on the R. (*Figure* 31)

Pen and ink.

FIG. 27 Cat. No. 110

FIG. 28 Cat. No. 111 *r.*

Lit.: B.B. 520; Knapp, pp. 314, 315, Nos. 1 and 4 (*verso*, Fig. 20); Gabelentz 73.

As pointed out by Gabelentz, this seems to be the design for the same projected picture (not known to exist) as No. 114, next to be described; as two drawings in the Uffizi (Gabelentz 151 *recto* and *verso:* photo. Gernsheim 1448, 1449, and Gabelentz 153 *recto:* photo. Gernsheim 1451); a *Virgin and Child with an angel and an Infant St. John* on a sheet with *Christ carrying the Cross*, also in the Uffizi (Gabelentz 174, *recto*, pl. 11), and as a *Virgin and Child with an Infant St. John* formerly in the Oppenheimer collection (Gabelentz 307). Gabelentz dates this sheet about 1505.

There is also some relation to a composition represented by a drawing in the British Museum (1875–6–12–1: Gabelentz 276) in which the Virgin is seated. There is a painted tondo by Albertinelli in the Kress collection (No. 148) based on this or similar drawings by Fra Bartolommeo.

114. SKETCH FOR A TONDO: THE VIRGIN STANDING HOLDING THE INFANT CHRIST; the infant St. John with two angels on the L. and a kneeling monk with two angels on the R. (*Figure* 32) (12783)

220 × 165 mm. Pen and brown ink on paper rubbed with red chalk, with some white.

Lit.: B.B. 519; Knapp, p. 314, No. 3; Gabelentz 874.

Photo.: Braun 092.

Design for the same *tondo* as No. 113 already discussed.

115. *Recto:* THE TEMPTATION OF ST. ANTHONY (*Plate* 16)

233 × 166 mm. Pen and brown ink and wash on yellow-tinted paper heightened with white.

Verso: A WOMAN CARRYING A CHILD ON HER SHOULDER IN FLIGHT TO THE R.; a Roman horseman galloping in the same direction. (*Figure* 33) (12784)

Pen and two shades of brown ink. W.M., a six-pointed star in a circle.

Lit.: B.B. 522; Knapp, p. 315, Nos. 6 and 7, Fig. 65; Gabelentz 875.

Photo.: Braun 095, 096.

Inscribed in ink in an old hand on *recto*, 'N. dell Frate'. The horseman on the *verso* (formerly *recto*), which was first drawn on the sheet, if by Fra Bartolommeo, was drawn by him at a very early period, when his style had not developed. It is in any case copied from a drawing of a relief in the Codex Escurialensis, fol. 59 *verso* (see Hermann Egger, *Codex Escurialensis*. Vienna, 1906). That it is copied from the codex and not from the relief (now in Mantua) is clear from the fact that the arbitrary restorations introduced by the draughtsman of the codex into his representation of the relief are exactly followed here. There is, however, another drawing in the Dal Pozzo album in the Department of Greek and Roman Antiquities in the British Museum (I, fol. 118) which exactly corresponds with the drawing in the Codex Escurialensis, and consequently, I presume with

FIG. 29 Cat. No. 112 *r.*

FIG. 30 Cat. No. 112 *v.*

FIG. 31 Cat. No. 113 *v.*

the present drawing, and it was in fact attributed to Fra Bartolommeo. The fleeing woman on the other hand is a most characteristic and charming drawing by Fra Bartolommeo. So likewise is the *Temptation of St. Anthony* on the *recto*. There is another drawing of this subject at Dresden (Gabelentz 34, repr. Dresden Drawings VI, 7) obviously done at about the same time and, according to Gabelentz, two drawings in the Weimar albums (now in the Koenigs collection, Boymans Museum, Rotterdam). Gabelentz dates the drawings 1505–1508.

116. AN ANGEL IN FLIGHT TOWARDS THE R. (12785)

120 × 150 mm. Pen and brown ink, heightened with white.

Lit.: B.B. 521; Gabelentz 876.

Dated by Gabelentz after 1508. The drapery of the lower part of the body with its extraordinary swirls is almost identical with that of the angel playing the fiddle in the *Assumption of the Virgin* at Berlin of about 1507–08, for which it may well be a study. There is an inscription (of the XVI or XVII century (?)) on the *verso* which I cannot decipher.

117. *Recto:* THE VIRGIN AND CHILD ENTHRONED WITH SAINTS AND ANGELS (*Figure* 33A)

Verso: SEATED VIRGIN AND CHILD AND SKETCH OF ORNAMENT (*Figure* 34) (12787)

200 × 157 mm. Pen and brown ink on paper rubbed with red chalk; the outlines of the Child on the *recto* are pricked through.

Lit.: B.B. 524; Knapp, p. 314, No. 2, Fig. 120; Gabelentz 878.

Photo.: Braun 091 (*recto* only).

FIG. 32 Cat. No. 114

FIG. 33 Cat. No. 115 *v.*

FIG. 33A Cat. No. 117 *r.*

Dated by Gabelentz about 1508 during Fra Bartolommeo's visit to Venice. The composition shows the influence of Giovanni Bellini's altarpieces, like that for S. Giobbe.

118. *Recto:* ANTIQUE STANDING FIGURE OF A DRAPED WOMAN WITH A TORCH IN HER R. HAND (*Figure* 35)

Verso: A WOMAN WITH HER R. ARM RAISED ABOVE HER HEAD (*Figure* 36) (12780)

223 × 104 mm. Pen and brown ink.

Lit.: B.B. 528A; Knapp, p. 315, No. 8; Gabelentz 871.

Photo.: Braun 097 (*recto* only).

The figure on the *recto* is dismissed by Knapp and Gabelentz as not being by Fra Bartolommeo. It is in fact like the horseman on No. 115 *verso*, a copy from a drawing in the Codex Escurialensis, fol. 54 *verso* (see Hermann Egger, *Codex Escurialensis*, Vienna, 1906). It is almost certainly a very early drawing by Fra Bartolommeo himself. That it is copied from the Codex Escurialensis, the source of the codex or some close copy from it, is again evident from the arbitrary restorations of the head and R. arm with the torch, which are practically identical in both drawings.

The drawing on the *verso*, which is apparently also condemned by Gabelentz with even less excuse, is of much later date. The handling is precisely that of the study in the Uffizi (Gabelentz 138, pl. 57) for the *Madonna della Misericordia* at Lucca dating from 1515. I take it it must be the study for a composition of *Judith and her attendant with the head of Holofernes* (the indistinct object projecting from the L.). It is obviously the same figure as that on No. 119 *verso*, and the R. arm was originally drawn in the same position as there. It seems to be for the figure, interpreted by Gabelentz as Justice, in a drawing in one of the Weimar-Koenigs albums (Gabelentz 589: photo. Braun 33), though the drapery and the position of the head are different. Gabelentz dates this 1514–16, and truly remarks that the position recalls that of the Madonna in the picture at Lucca to which I have already alluded.

119. *Recto:* A WOMAN IN ANTIQUE DRAPERY HOLDING UP HER R. HAND; A SEATED VIRGIN AND CHILD

200 × 323 mm. (top R. hand corner cut). Pen and brown ink (the standing woman); red chalk (the Virgin and Child).

Verso: COPY FROM TRAJAN'S COLUMN: DACIANS CROSSING THE DANUBE (12779)

Pen and light brown ink and wash over black chalk.

W.M., an eagle displayed.

Lit.: B.B. 528; Gabelentz 870.

The drawing on the *verso* (formerly the *recto*), copied from Trajan's column, seems to have no connection with Fra Bartolommeo or his school, though curiously it also corresponds closely with a page of the Codex Escurialensis (fol. 60 *verso*), from which it also, like Nos. 115 *verso*, and 118, appears to be copied. Its style rather suggests the school of Raphael, but it is not easy to be definite about a copy of this character. The standing woman on the *recto* (tentatively attributed by Gabelentz to Sogliani) seems to me to be by Fra Bartolommeo himself, and to be a study for the Judith already discussed under No. 118 *verso*.

The Virgin and Child in red chalk (accepted by Gabelentz as Fra Bartolommeo's) may perhaps be connected with the unfinished altarpiece in San Marco of the *Virgin and Child with St. Anne*, commissioned in 1510. The position of the Virgin's legs is the same, though there is little resemblance otherwise.

Attributed to FRA BARTOLOMMEO

120. TWO ACANTHUS VOLUTES (5583)

201 × 75 mm. Pen and brown ink.

A.E.P. Apparently at one time with the series of drawings by Bernini. The pen-work is that of the very early XVI century, and suggests a connection with Fra Bartolommeo. The type of volute occurs in a similar but more evolved form on the pilasters of the *Loggie*.

JACOPO BASSANO (1510?–1592)

121. TWO STUDIES OF THE HEAD OF A BEARDED MAN (*Plate* 173) (0835)

415 × 266 mm. Black chalk or charcoal on green (discoloured) paper, heightened with white. A large oil stain on the R.

This fine sheet of studies is obviously Bassanesque, and I think it can be attributed with some confidence to Jacopo the elder. I have not been able to connect it with any existing picture.

After JACOPO BASSANO

122. THE MARTYRDOM OF ST. SEBASTIAN (6673)

346 × 505 mm. Black chalk with light brown wash on blue paper.

FIG. 34 Cat. No. 117 *v.*

FIG. 35 Cat. No. 118 *r.*

FIG. 36 Cat. No. 118 *v.*

Dated 1574 on the pillar in the centre. A picture corresponding with this drawing was in the collection of Archduke Leopold Wilhelm (No. 329 in the inventory of 1659). There is an engraving of it in reverse by Ossenbeck in Teniers' *Theatrum Pictorium* (No. 143 of the later editions). The picture is described in Christian van Mechel's Catalogue of the Vienna Gallery of 1783 (p. 75, No. 30: canvas, 2 ft. × 2 ft. 5 in., signed IAC: BASSANENSIS f:). The picture has since disappeared. I owe the above particulars to Johannes Wilde.

FRANCESCO BASSANO (About 1549–1592)

123. STUDY FOR THE FIGURE OF CHRIST IN A BAPTISM (6671)

250 × 172 mm. Black chalk on blue paper, heightened with white.

Lit.: Hadeln, *Spätrenaissance*, p. 15 (pl. 85); Tietzes, No. 105. Inscribed in ink in an old hand in bottom L. hand corner, 'Bassano'. Hadeln's attribution to Francesco Bassano seems acceptable.

School of THE BASSANI

124. DOMESTIC INTERIOR: on the R., a woman seated at a loom; in the centre, another making lace; and on the L., a third with a distaff; above is a vision of a kneeling man, on whom rays of light descend. (4778)

478 × 398 mm. (on four pieces of paper stuck together). Drawn with the point of the brush in blue on cream-coloured paper, heightened with white.

125. DOMESTIC INTERIOR: a man kneels before the hearth in the foreground while, further back, a woman with a torch and a basin speaks to a man emerging from behind a curtain. (*Plate* 176) (4779)

438 × 335 mm. (on two pieces of paper stuck together). Drawn with the point of the brush in blue on cream-coloured paper, heightened with white.

126. CHRIST MOCKED (4780)

312 × 425 mm. (on four pieces of paper stuck together). Drawn with the point of the brush in blue on cream-coloured paper, heightened with white.

Nothing could be more obviously Bassanesque than these three compositions, drawn in the same technique by the same hand and at the same period, but it is not so easy to say to which member of the family or school they should be assigned or for what purpose they were drawn. They seem nearest in style to drawings given by Hadeln to Francesco (*Spätrenaissance*, pls. 86, 87), but it would be rash to assign them definitely to him. The subject of No. 126 is perfectly clear, but those of Nos. 124 and 125 are difficult to interpret. They are in all probability also intended to represent New Testament subjects. Perhaps No. 124 is the *Three Maries at work*, but I cannot explain the vision in the background. The woman with the lace cushion appears in almost exactly the same position in a picture in the Doria Gallery assigned by Wart Arslan to Jacopo and Francesco (Bolletino d'Arte III (1937–38), p. 465).

I do not know whether the three drawings are to be regarded as *modelli* for paintings or as substitutes for paintings. I cannot point to any Bassano drawings in exactly this technique.

127. THE GATHERING OF MANNA IN THE DESERT: on the R. two elderly bearded men converse while, in the centre, a group of kneeling women with baskets gather the manna; to the L. sits a young man leaning on his elbow; in the background are tents and groups of figures and animals. (4781 and 4782)

354 × 357 mm. and 350 × 350 mm. (two halves of the same drawing). Drawn with the point of the brush over black chalk and washed with brown.

An obviously Bassanesque composition.

128. HEAD OF A WOMAN TURNED THREE-QUARTERS TO THE R. (5410)

204 × 149 mm. Black chalk on blue paper, with touches of red and white chalk.

I do not know to whom the attribution to Bassano is due. It would be rash to assign it to any particular member of the family. It might be for the head of a Madonna in the *Nativity*.

129. HEAD OF AN ELDERLY WOMAN, LOOKING BACK OVER HER L. SHOULDER (5390)

278 × 201 mm. Black chalk on blue paper, heightened with white.

The drawing appears to belong to the Bassano school.

130. THE GOOD SAMARITAN (6672)

347 × 440 mm. Drawn with the point of the brush in blue on blue paper, heightened with white (oxidised).

Inscribed at the bottom in ink in an old hand, 'del basan vechio'. I cannot find any corresponding composition by the Bassani, though it is certainly in their manner. The actual handling comes very close to that of Frans Floris, who had certainly studied the works of the Bassani.

After BASSANO

131. PASTORAL SCENE: a herd asleep on the L.; a horse, a donkey with packs, a cow, goats, etc., towards the R. (4783)

252 × 382 mm. Brush drawing in brown over black chalk on blue paper, heightened with white.

A copy, perhaps of the XVIII century, of a composition which is obviously from the Bassano workshop, but which I cannot find elsewhere reproduced.

DOMENICO BECCAFUMI (About 1486–1551)

132. DESIGNS FOR FRESCOED FAÇADES OF HOUSES (*Plate* 37) (5493)

(*a*) 189 × 198 mm., (*b*) 139 × 198 mm. (two separate drawings mounted together). Pen and brown ink and wash and some water-colour and white.

Lit.: E. Panofsky, Städel-Jahrbuch VI (1930), pp. 68–72, pl. XV.

At first pointed out by Panofsky (loc. cit.), the two halves of the drawing are quite unconnected. The upper one represents the design for a shop-front, as the counter in the central opening shows. The subject of the paintings is obscure. Panofsky suggests that the scene at the top on the L. is the *Presentation of Christ*, but that on the R. can hardly be an illustration of sacred history, and it seems unlikely that one would be profane and the other sacred. The two figures in niches appear to be saints, and Panofsky suggests that the scene on the front of the counter is the *Drunkenness of Noah* and the shop a wineshop. The subject might equally well be the *Good Samaritan.* The two scenes on the lower façade appear to be drawn from Roman history. A drawing in the British Museum (1948–3–1–1) by Beccafumi shows an alternative design for the lower of the two façades.

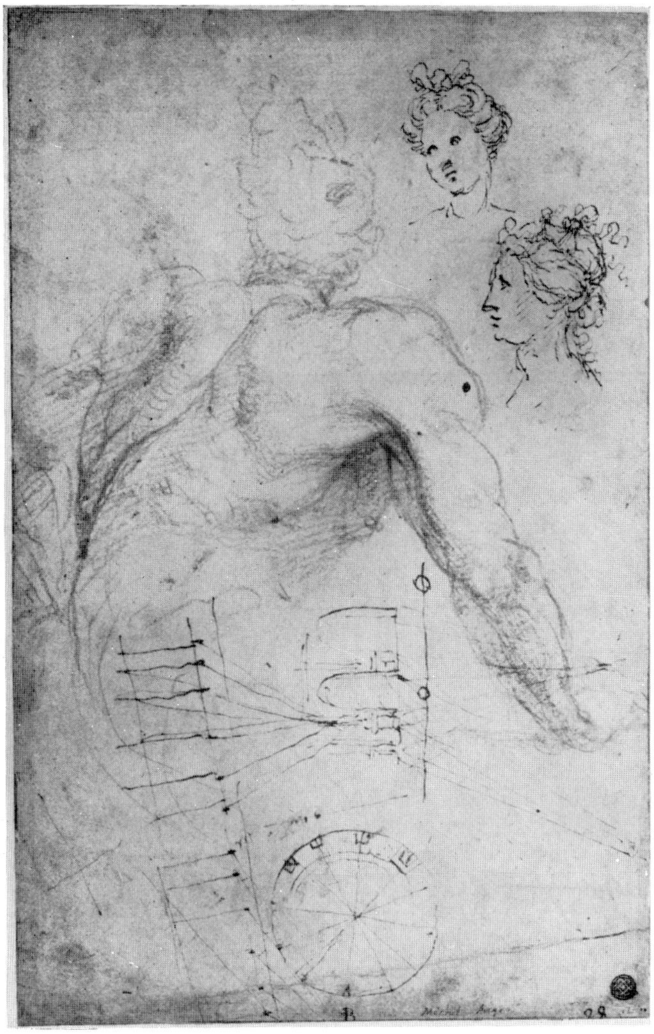

FIG. 37 Cat. No. 133 *r*.

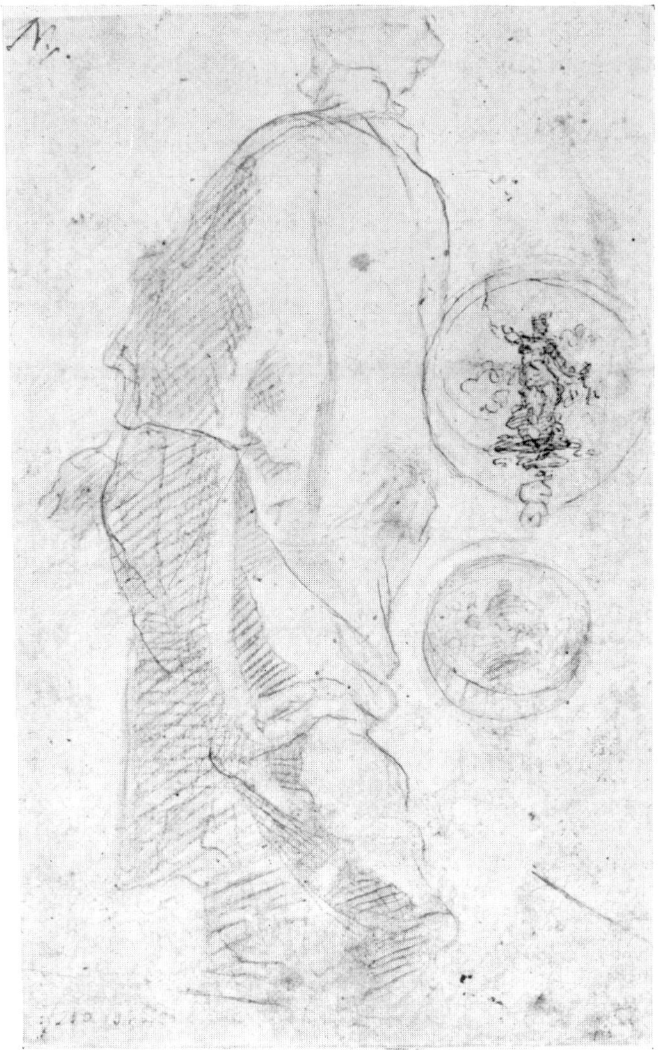

FIG. 38 Cat. No. 133 *v*.

133. *Recto:* SHEET OF A SKETCH-BOOK WITH A NUDE MAN seen from the back leaning on his R. arm, women's heads, etc. (*Figure* 37)

Verso: DRAPED FIGURE TURNED TO THE L.; TWO STUDIES FOR A CUPOLA (*Figure* 38) (0434)

211 × 133 mm. Red chalk and pen and ink.

Coll.: J. D. Lempereur (Lugt 1740).

A.E.P. Inscribed in ink at the bottom, 'Michel Ange', and with the number '28'. The half-length figure of a nude man seen from the back on the *recto* is the study for a figure in the subject of *Moses breaking the Tables of the Law* on the pavement in the Duomo at Siena. The figure appears in the reversed engraving of the subject by Lelio Cosatti to the L. of Moses. His L. hand (corresponding to the R. hand in the drawing) rests on a flute on the ground, and his legs are twisted round in an extraordinary position. The cloaked figure on the *verso* is apparently for the figure just above and to the L. of the Golden Calf in the same subject. The lower of the two circular sketches on the *verso* would seem to be for the *Allegory of Justice* on the ceiling of the Sala del Concistorio in the Palazzo Pubblico, Siena (Venturi, IX 5, Fig. 260). Of these works the frescoes in the Sala del Concistorio were allocated to Beccafumi on April 5, 1529, but were not completed until August 2, 1535, while the design for the subject on the pavement was paid for on August 30, 1531. We thus have a probable date for the drawing of between 1529 and 1531.

134. FIVE STUDIES OF ARMS AND ONE SEPARATE STUDY OF A HAND (0290)

150 × 210 mm. Red chalk heightened with white, with one in pen and ink.

Coll.: N. Lanière (Lugt 2885).

Inscribed to the right (in the artist's hand (?)), 'fuma'; below, to the L. in a XVII century (?) hand, 'Domenicho Beccha Fumo'. A very characteristic original drawing. There are very similar studies of arms in the *taccuino* (fol. 29 *recto*) belonging to Coghlan Briscoe, published in Rivista d'Arte XVII (1935), p. 179.

135. THE APPEARANCE OF THE ARCHANGEL MICHAEL ON THE CASTLE OF ST. ANGELO TO POPE GREGORY THE GREAT (5029)

215 × 342 mm. Pen and brown ink and brown wash.

The drawing is a rather puzzling repetition of one in the Uffizi (Santarelli, No. 1240; ill. Bolletino d'Arte III (1933–4), p. 368). It seems possible that both drawings, in spite of their very close resemblance to each other, are originals by Beccafumi. C. Brandi, in his publication of the Uffizi drawing, suggests that it is the design for one of the lost predellas of the painting of *St. Michael subduing the Rebel Angels* in the Church of the Carmine at Siena (Venturi, IX 5, Fig. 271), which was probably painted some time after 1538.

136. DECORATION OF THE ANGLE OF A VAULT IN THE FORM OF A TRIANGLE, the point upwards, containing a circle: in the circle are figures floating on rafts (the Flood ?); in the angles, figures; that on the R. unfinished. (0280)

299 × 407 mm. Black chalk.

W. M. an escutcheon charged with a ladder, surmounted by a star.

Inscribed in lower margin 'Macharino' in pencil. Corresponds with part of the decoration of the vaulting of the Palazzo Bindi-Sergardi at Siena (Venturi, IX 5, Fig. 256, bottom to the L.) In spite of the almost exact correspondence with the fresco the drawing is carried out in Beccafumi's very individual manner and seems to be an original.

After DOMENICO BECCAFUMI

137. THE ROMAN TRIBUNE OF THE PEOPLE PUBLIUS MUCIUS ORDERING NINE OF HIS COLLEAGUES TO BE BURNT ALIVE (01224)

305 × 477 mm. Finished drawing in pen and brown ink and brown wash on light brown paper, heightened with white.

Inscribed in the 'deceptive' hand, 'Giulio Campi'. The drawing in fact corresponds exactly with one of the compositions painted by Beccafumi between 1529 and 1535 on the vaulting of the Sala del Concistorio in the Palazzo Pubblico at Siena. A portion of it (the woman with the child on the extreme R.) can be distinguished in the illustration given by Venturi (IX 5, Fig. 263). It appears to be a good contemporary copy from the fresco or from a cartoon rather than an original *bozzetto*.

138. ST. PHILIP STANDING HOLDING A CROSS IN HIS L. HAND (0402)

423 × 260 mm. Pen and brown ink and brown wash.

Corresponds closely with the chiaroscuro woodcut by or after Domenico Beccafumi (Bartsch, XII, p. 71, 13), from which it is copied.

APOLLONIO DE' BONFRATELLI

(Working 1523–1572)

139. THE VIRGIN FAINTING AT THE FOOT OF THE CROSS; A MAN BRINGING A LADDER ON THE R. (6035)

290 × 195 mm. Pen and brown ink and brown wash, with some white.

Sir Richard Holmes had noted on the mount the fact that a miniature by Bonfratelli from this design existed among the fragments purchased for the British Museum at the S. Rogers sale on May 6 (eighth day), 1856. The fragments are now Add. 21, 412, and the miniature in question, Fol.42. H. Bodmer had suggested Prospero Fontana as the draughtsman, but there seems no reason for supposing that it is not Bonfratelli's own design for his miniature. It is quite sufficiently feeble for this accomplished, but lifeless, pupil of Clovio.

FIG. 39 Cat. No. 141

ANDREA BOSCOLI (About 1550–about 1606)

140. THE CIRCUMCISION (0104)

253 × 164 mm. Pen and brown ink and wash on blue paper, heightened with white.

Attribution to Andrea Boscoli in pencil on the mount. The drawing corresponds with the painting of the subject in the Duomo at Fermo (Venturi, IX 7, Fig. 419). It is very close to the painting, but there are differences (e.g. in the position of the dog). The style of the drawing seems to be Boscoli's, though not so emphatic as his sometimes is, and I think it is more probably an original than a copy.

Attributed to ANDREA BOSCOLI

141. THE PRESENTATION OF THE VIRGIN (*Figure* 39) (5196)

195 × 225 mm. Pen and brown ink and brown wash.

P.M.R.P. Inscribed in ink in the 'deceptive' hand 'Cavalier Pasignano', the style is, however, clearly that of Boscoli.

142. THE SUPPER AT EMMAUS (*Figure* 40) (3817)

220 × 305 mm. Red chalk.

FIG. 40 Cat. No. 142

A.E.P. Inscribed in ink at the bottom, 'Taliarino', which is probably the transcription of a name on the *verso* visible through the backing which seems to read 'Del Talarino' or 'balarino' or 'balarmo', but I can find no artist with any name approaching this. The style seems to be that of Boscoli, to whom I would attribute it.

For a copy after Raphael, perhaps by Boscoli, see No. 834.

AGNOLO BRONZINO (1503–1572)

143. STUDY OF A NUDE MAN CRAWLING ON ALL FOURS TO THE R., HIS L. HAND EXTENDED (*Plate* 34) (0447)

233 × 389 mm. Grey chalk.

A.E.P. Inscribed in ink in an old hand in top L. hand corner, 'Daniel da Volterra'. It is in fact the study for a man who crawls forward under the legs of Our Saviour in the painting by Bronzino of *Christ in Limbo* in the Museo di Santa Croce, Florence (Venturi, IX 6, Fig. 43), dated 1552.

Attributed to AGNOLO BRONZINO

144. THE ANNUNCIATION (5127)

263 × 181 mm. Pen and grey ink and grey wash, heightened with white, squared in black chalk. On separate pieces of paper, attached at one side, are alternative positions for the legs and for the right arm of the angel.

Inscribed in ink in the bottom left corner, 'Bronzino' (by which Bronzino rather than Allori, who was often so called after his master, is intended); in top right corner, '45'. The style of the drawing does not seem to me conclusively in favour of the old attribution.

LUCA CAMBIASO (1527–1585)

145. THE ERECTION OF THE THREE CROSSES: Christ is seated on one to the R.; the two thieves are brought under escort from the same side; men are at work on the crosses. (6845)

417 × 570 mm. Pen and light brown ink and wash.

There is an old inscription, apparently the name Cambiaso or Cangiaso, just visible through the backing. This drawing and its companion, No. 146, seem to be original drawings by Cambiaso.

146. CHRIST NAILED TO THE CROSS; one cross, with the thief upon it, is already erected on the L., the second thief is being bound to his on the R. (6844)

420 × 565 mm. Pen and light brown ink and wash.

147. A PRINCE, ON HORSEBACK, WITH A MOUNTED RETINUE, IS MET BY A YOUTH holding a sword and some object covered by a cloth. (0133)

205 × 253 mm. Pen and brown ink and brown wash.

A.E.P. Attributed to Bernardo Castello. The style appears indistinguishable from that of drawings always associated with Cambiaso, and different from that of a drawing which, there is good evidence for thinking, is Castello's (see below, No. 205). It is in any case a spirited original drawing.

After LUCA CAMBIASO

148. THE REST ON THE FLIGHT INTO EGYPT; the Virgin, holding the Child, is seated under an awning attached to a tree; St. Joseph and the Infant St. John approach from behind the tree on the L. (5978)

249 × 175 mm. Pen and brown ink and brown wash over lead pencil on light brown paper.

Attribution 'Cangiasi' in pencil on the mount. The best Cambiaso drawings known to me seem to be drawn free-hand in pen and ink with no under-drawing as here. Lead pencil, though not impossible, is certainly unusual, at that time. The drawing may therefore well be a copy, though its quality is good.

149. ST. CHRISTOPHER STEPPING OFF THE BANK INTO THE WATER WITH THE CHILD ON HIS SHOULDER (5210)

364 × 278 mm. Pen and brown ink over lead pencil.

The exaggeration of the mannerism and the under-drawing in pencil point to this being a copy.

See also Anon. Genoese school, No. 1110.

After GIROLAMO CAMPAGNA (1552—after 1623)

150. A GLOBE, ON WHICH STANDS GOD THE FATHER, SUPPORTED BY FOUR EVANGELISTS (0110)

282 × 189 mm. Red chalk.

As noted (by Ulrich Middeldorf?) on the mount, the drawing is sketched from the monument by Girolamo Campagna in S. Giorgio Maggiore, Venice (Venturi, X 3, Fig. 174). It might well be of the late XVI or early XVII century.

DOMENICO CAMPAGNOLA (1500–after 1552)

The problem of drawings attributed to Campagnola has never been systematically tackled, and I can say little or nothing about the series at Windsor. I have not attempted to arrange these chronologically, and have listed them in the order of their inventory numbers. In their recent book the Tietzes only include two of the drawings at Windsor attributed to Domenico Campagnola; another twenty-seven (Nos. 151–155 and 161–182) seem to me to have at least an equal claim to be regarded as authentic.

151. A NUDE WOMAN LYING IN THE OPEN AIR WITH FOUR PUTTI UNDER A TREE IN THE BACKGROUND (6657)

167 × 389 mm. Pen and brown ink on parchment.

The attribution to Domenico Campagnola, that of Sir J. C. Robinson, seems to me to be perfectly correct. I do not remember having seen a drawing by Campagnola on parchment before, but there is no reason why he should not have used it. The style of the drawing of the *putti* under the tree seems to me particularly characteristic of Domenico in his early period about 1520.

152. LANDSCAPE WITH HOUSES AMONG ROMAN RUINS ON THE R. (4768)

113 × 212 mm. (top corners cut). Pen and brown ink.

153. LANDSCAPE IN A FLAT OVAL, A TREE ON THE R. (4769)

103 × 129 mm. Pen and brown ink.

154. LANDSCAPE WITH A CASTLE ON AN EMINENCE IN THE CENTRE, WITH THE SPIRE AND TOWERS OF A TOWN ON EITHER SIDE (4770)

97 × 148 mm. Pen and brown ink.

A certain reminiscence of the landscape with a castle in the British Museum (Malcolm 1895–9–15–832: Hadeln 43) was perhaps the reason which induced Adolfo Venturi to suggest that Titian was the author of this rather scratchy sketch.

155. LANDSCAPE IN A FLAT OVAL: A STREAM RUSHING OVER A WEIR (4771)
248 × 370 mm. (oval). Pen and brown ink; several holes repaired.
A good drawing of its type. If by Domenico Campagnola, certainly late.

156. LANDSCAPE WITH A TREE IN THE CENTRE AND A MAN AND WOMAN LEADING A DONKEY ON THE R. (4772)
113 × 180 mm. (top corners cut and made up). Pen and brown ink.
A rather feeble little drawing, possibly a copy.

157. LANDSCAPE: A CASTLE ON A RIVER BACKED BY MOUNTAINS; THE SUN SETTING ON THE R. (4773)
161 × 255 mm. Pen and brown ink.
Lit.: Tietzes, No. 571.
The Tietzes regard the drawing as late, and it is very loose in handling, but it has the foreground which is so characteristic of early drawings.

158. ST. JEROME IN PENITENCE IN THE WILDERNESS: he is seated on the R. on a block of stone in front of a tree-crowned bluff, through an arch in which the path runs. (4774)
278 × 440 mm. Pen and light brown ink.
Lit.: Tietzes, No. 572.
Described by the Tietzes as 'late shop': late, yes; shop, not necessarily.

159. LANDSCAPE WITH BUILDINGS IN THE DISTANCE AND A MAN SEATED IN THE CENTRE, PLAYING A VIOL-DA-GAMBA (5722)
180 × 277 mm. Pen and dark brown ink.
This may well be a Bolognese copy.

160. A PILE OF DOMESTIC BUILDINGS BUILT ON OR ACROSS A STREAM; TREES ON THE R. (5726)
176 × 218 mm. Pen and pale brown ink.
Some sketches on the *verso* are partly visible from in front. This rather finicky little drawing appears to be either a copy or a work of the shop.

161–182. Album covered in marbled paper and backed with leather, measuring 612 × 475 mm., lettered on back THE/REVELATIO/BY/THEO: BER: AMST:, and decorated with the crown and monogram of George III.
The album now contains twenty-two drawings illustrating the Apocalypse. The twenty-third drawing, No. 7786, which was in fact the work of the Dirk Barents, to whom the lettering on the back refers, has now been removed. It was catalogued by Puyvelde as No. 3 of the Flemish drawings.
The subjects are not mounted in the album in the order of their occurrence in Revelations, nor do they provide a complete or consistent illustration of them (if that is possible). On the other hand, four drawings cannot be definitely or certainly related to passages in Revelations.
The iconography of the series is curious. It bears no relation to Albrecht Dürer's woodcut *Apocalypse*, which, even in Italy, had an almost universal vogue. The naiveté of the presentation suggests some earlier mediæval prototype.
It is difficult to avoid the conclusion that the drawings are by Domenico Campagnola himself. Weak as they are, the handling seems indisputably his. Their feebleness can be accounted for in part at least by the unfamiliarity of the subject, which lay far beyond the range of Domenico Campagnola's limited talents.
All the drawings are executed in pen and brown ink, over black chalk, which is only however visible in occasional passages.

161. ST. JOHN ON THE ISLAND OF PATMOS SEES THE SEVEN CANDELABRA AND THE FIGURE HOLDING THE SEVEN STARS; the seven churches symbolized by the seven candelabra are also represented. (*Plate* 168) (7764)
Revelations i. 12–20.
310 × 258 mm. The churches all bear a striking resemblance to the Campo Santo at Padua.

162. THE ANGEL CLOTHED WITH A CLOUD, WITH A RAINBOW ON HIS HEAD, HIS R. FOOT IN THE SEA AND HIS L. ON THE EARTH, GIVES ST. JOHN THE LITTLE BOOK TO EAT (7765)
Rev. x.
398 × 260 mm.

163. ONE LIKE UNTO THE SON OF MAN SEATED ON A CLOUD, having on His head a golden crown and in His hand a sharp sickle; the angel comes out of the temple and cries to Him with a loud voice. (7766)
Rev. xiv. 14, 15.
347 × 258 mm.

164. AN ANGEL WITH A CENSER STANDING BEHIND AN ALTAR with six angels on the L. and a group of saints or patriarchs on the R. (7767)
Rev. viii 4, 5 (?)
385 × 253 mm.

165. SEVEN ANGELS, OF WHOM THE FOREMOST HOLDS A CROSS, ON CLOUDS, SWEEPING TO THE R. (7768)
276 × 232 mm.

166. A CHERUB AMONG CLOUDS, HOLDING IN HIS R. HAND FOUR, IN HIS L. HAND THREE, VIALS (7769)
342 × 234 mm.

167. AN ANGEL IN A MANDORLA HOLDING UP HIS R. HAND IN BENEDICTION AND HOLDING AN ORB IN HIS L. HAND (7770)
232 × 197 mm.

168. AN ANGEL HOLDING A SCEPTRE SOARS ALOFT; on the ground lies a woman, who seems to be on fire; to the L. stand three kings and three elders, and a fourth king kneels; on the R. are two men and a woman. (*Figure* 41) (7771)
314 × 255 mm. This obviously apocalyptic scene does not, as far as I can see, illustrate any passage in Revelations.

169. THREE ANGELS FLYING TO THE R., ONE ABOVE THE OTHER: the uppermost holds a book, the other two hold the ends of the stoles, which they wear, in front of them. (7772)
365 × 219 mm.

170. THE SIXTH ANGEL POURS OUT HIS VIAL UPON THE GREAT RIVER EUPHRATES (7773)
Rev. xvi. 12.
383 × 231 mm.

FIG. 41 Cat. No. 168

171. THE FIFTH ANGEL POURING OUT HIS VIAL UPON THE SEAT OF THE BEAST (7774)

Rev. xvi. 10.

380 × 222 mm.

172. THE ANGEL WITH THE KEY OF THE BOTTOMLESS PIT BINDS THE OLD SERPENT WITH A GREAT CHAIN (7775)

Rev. xx. 1, 2.

290 × 235 mm.

173. HE THAT IS CALLED FAITHFUL AND TRUE, CROWNED WITH THREE CROWNS, RIDES TO THE R. on His white horse, followed by the armies that were in Heaven. (7776)

Rev. ix. 11–14.

290 × 235 mm.

174. THE BEAST WITH TWO HORNS LIKE A LAMB: he stands on his hind legs vomiting fire; in the foreground to the R. are five worshippers, three of whom wear turbans. (7777)

Rev. xiii. 11.

354 × 251 mm.

175. THE FOUR ANGELS AT THE FOUR CORNERS OF THE WORLD HOLDING THE FOUR WINDS; the other angel, having the seal of the Living God, soaring above them. (7778)

Rev. vii. 1, 2.

415 × 260 mm.

176. THE MIGHTY ANGEL CASTING THE STONE LIKE A GREAT MILLSTONE INTO THE SEA: the seven-headed beast is lying on its back in the foreground, and the beast with two horns like a lamb is charging, apparently at the millstone. (7779)

Rev. xviii. 21.

371 × 235 mm.

177. THE WHORE OF BABYLON MOUNTED ON THE MONSTER WITH SEVEN HEADS AND TEN HORNS

Rev. xvii. 3, 4. (7780)

345 × 248 mm.

178. THE BEAST WITH SEVEN HEADS AND TEN CROWNS. He is represented without horns and mitres take the place of crowns; one of the heads with two mitres attached falls down 'as it were wounded unto death'. (7781)

Rev. xiii. 1–3.

330 × 264 mm.

179. THE WOMAN CLOTHED WITH THE SUN AND WITH THE MOON UNDER HER FEET is attacked by the beast having seven heads and ten horns with crowns upon them. (7782)

Rev. xii. 1–4.

370 × 273 mm.

180. THE ANGEL SOUNDS THE SECOND TRUMPET and a third part of the ships in the sea are destroyed. (7783)

Rev. viii. 8.

383 × 273 mm.

181. THE ANGEL SHOWING ST. JOHN THE VISION OF THE THRONE OF THE LORD: He is represented in a mandorla with the lamb having seven horns and seven eyes on His lap; the symbols of the four evangelists are within the mandorla and outside are angels and elders with musical instruments. (7784)

Rev. iv. and v.

395 × 248 mm.

182. THE FIFTH ANGEL SOUNDS HIS TRUMPET; the star with the key of the bottomless pit attached to it falls to earth and opens the pit from which pour the locusts to attack a group of men and women on the L.; another group on the R. is lamenting. (7785)

Rev. viii. 1–10.

348 × 256 mm. This drawing has an absurd (XVIII century (?)) attribution to Cherubino Alberti written on the mount.

Attributed to ANTONIO CAMPI (d. after 1591)

183. A SEATED SYBIL READING A BOOK (4812)

324 × 257 mm. Pen and ink and brown wash over black chalk on blue paper, heightened with white; squared in black chalk.

A.E.P. Attribution in ink at the bottom to the L. to 'Sebastiano del Piombo' in the same hand as No. 335. The drawing shows a definite technical resemblance to this (certainly by Gambara), but I do not think it is by the same hand. It seems to me nearer in style to Antonio Campi, who was Gambara's master, and I would tentatively attribute it to him.

FIG. 42 Cat. No. 184

BERNARDINO CAMPI (1522–after 1584)

184. STUDIES OF A ST. SEBASTIAN BOUND TO A TREE AND OF A ROMAN WARRIOR (*Figure* 42) (0231)

245 × 174 mm. Pen and light brown ink and brown wash over black chalk, the Roman warrior squared in black chalk.

Signed (?) 'b(er)nardino Campi' in ink at the bottom and numbered 21 or 22 in the L. hand bottom corner. The handwriting appears to be the same as that on two drawings in the British Museum of angelic musicians (Malcolm 1895–9–15–746, 747).

185. THE MARRIAGE OF ST. CECILIA TO ST. VALERIAN, the former supported by two women, the latter by two young men. (*Plate* 140) (5110)

178 × 205 mm. Pen and two shades of ink (the three central figures drawn in darker ink) and brown wash over black chalk, squared in red and black chalk.

F.A. Inscribed at bottom in 'deceptive' hand 'Lanini', with whom it has no connection. The relation to the signed drawing (No. 184) already described is unmistakable, and it is the study for one of the four ovals by Bernardino Campi decorating the vault of S. Sigismondo, Cremona (Giulio Ferrari, *Lo Stucco nell'arte Italiana*, Milan n.d., pl. LXI).

186. THE ASSAULT ON A FORTRESS: two commanders are in conversation on the R. in front of a tower, which is being scaled; on the L. a cavalry battle is in progress. (5118)

260 × 245 mm. (torn irregularly at the top). Pen and brown ink and brown wash over black chalk on a cream-coloured ground, squared in black chalk.

A.E.P. Inscribed in the bottom L. hand corner in the 'deceptive' hand 'Castello'. The handling of the drawing is so exactly that of the authenticated drawings by Bernardino Campi described above (Nos. 184 and 185) that it can be confidently ascribed to him.

187. AENEAS AFTER HIS SHIPWRECK ON THE SHORES OF LIBYA (5199)

145 × 221 mm. Red chalk, squared in the same medium, with splodges of yellow.

A.E.P. A comparison with the signed drawing already

FIG. 43 Cat. No. 188

FIG. 44 Cat. No. 189

described (No. 184) makes it probable that the present sheet, though in a different medium, is also by Bernardino Campi. It might conceivably be a sketch for one of the scenes in the Sala di Enea in the Palazzo del Giardino at Sabbioneta (see Dedalo IX (1928), pp. 238–239).

188. A MAN SEEN FROM THE BACK (*Figure* 43) (0221)

257 × 136 mm. Black chalk and wash on blue paper, heightened with white, squared in red.

A.E.P. Attribution in 'deceptive' hand to *Paolo Lomazzo* in bottom R. hand corner. Study for a figure in the cupola of S. Sigismondo, Cremona, painted in 1570 by Bernardino Campi. A similar study in exactly the same style for the adjoining figure of St. Stephen is in the Uffizi (No. 1396E, 270 × 165 mm.).

189. THE MEETING OF JOACHIM AND ANNA; design for an altarpiece with its frame. (*Figure* 44) (0232)

414 × 239 mm. Pen and brown ink and brown wash heightened with white.

Inscribed in the 'deceptive' hand in bottom R. corner 'Giulio Campi'. Though the technique of the actual biblical scene, which differs somewhat from that of the frame, does suggest Giulio, the forms and types are rather those of Bernardino. Bernardino may have adopted a particular, formal technique for a modello-like drawing of this character. In any case the style of the drawing suggests a fairly early date in Bernardino's career. The inscription $\overline{\text{IO}}$ (Johannes) B$\overline{\text{E}}$R (Bernardus) on either side of an escutcheon underneath the frame records, I suppose, the Christian names of the donors.

190. CHRIST DRIVING THE MONEY-CHANGERS FROM THE TEMPLE (*Figure* 45) (0351)

263 × 182 mm. Black chalk and brown wash on blue paper, heightened with white, squared in red chalk.

P.M.R.P. Attribution in 'deceptive' hand, bottom R., to 'parmeggiano'. The style and the types are unmistakably those of Bernardino Campi.

191. THE VIRGIN HOLDING THE INFANT CHRIST, WHO STANDS ON HER KNEES (12069)

940 × 710 mm. Charcoal on very rough paper, heightened with white.

George III 'Inventory A', p. 158, School of Raphael.

A.E.P. Cartoon for a painting.

FIG. 45 Cat. No. 190

After BERNARDINO CAMPI

192. THE VIRGIN SUPPORTING THE DEAD BODY OF CHRIST with four saints, among them on the R., St. Catherine. (0124)

210 × 142 mm. Pen and brown ink and some wash, heightened with white.

Inscribed in an old hand in the bottom R. corner 'Ventura Salimbeni'. The drawing in fact corresponds fairly closely with a picture by Bernardino Campi in the Brera at Milan (Venturi, IX 6, Fig. 564). Its style shows no resemblance to that of Salimbeni, nor does the hand seem to be Bernardino Campi's, though there are considerable differences between the picture and the drawing.

Attributed to BERNARDINO CAMPI

193. THE BODY OF OUR LORD SUPPORTED AT THE FOOT OF THE CROSS BY THE VIRGIN AND ST. JOHN; TWO HOLY WOMEN STANDING ON THE L. (5090)

264 × 200 mm. Brush drawing in pale grey reinforced with pen and ink.

A.E.P. It is more probably a copy after Bernardino Campi than an original drawing. It might alternatively be after Antonio Campi.

194. ALLEGORICAL FIGURE OF PEACE SETTING FIRE TO A PILE OF ARMS AND ARMOUR (0356)

174 × 121 mm. Black chalk.

A.E.P. The attribution to Bernardino Campi is made on grounds of style. It is probably a copy.

Attributed to GIULIO CAMPI (d. 1572)

195. THE ASSUMPTION OF THE VIRGIN; design for an altar-piece with an arched top. (0227)

383 × 255 mm. (torn and cut into at the top). Pen and brown ink and brown wash, heightened with white; apparently once squared in black chalk.

A.E.P. Attribution in 'deceptive' hand to 'Bernardo Campi' in bottom R. hand corner. It would appear to show the characteristics of Giulio Campi's style, and to be a late work by him.

GIROLAMO DA CARPI (1501–1556)

196. *Recto:* BACCHUS DRAWN IN A CHARIOT BY LEOPARDS, ACCOMPANIED BY CUPIDS AND OTHER FIGURES (*Figure* 46)

Verso: A CUIRASS DECORATED IN THE ANTIQUE STYLE AND PART OF A SATYR-LIKE TELAMON (0489)

163 × 226 mm. Pen and brown ink. W. M., crossed arrows.

A.E.P. The old attribution is to Giulio Romano; that to Carpi is made on stylistic grounds. The *recto* is copied from part of a sarcophagus now at Woburn Abbey (S. Reinach, *Répertoire de Reliefs Grecs et Romains*, Vol. II, Paris, 1912, p. 538). The watermark is the same as that found on one of the drawings (Fawkener 5211–53) in the British Museum, which presumably formed part of a sketch book.

197. BACCHIC PROCESSION, FROM THE ANTIQUE (0284)

213 × 415 mm. Pen and brown ink.

The attribution is apparently an old one and may be accepted with confidence, in spite of the resemblance shown in the types of the faces to Giulio Romano. Possibly this may imply that it is copied from a drawing by Giulio. I cannot find any relief with which it exactly corresponds. It is similar to, but not identical with, reliefs in the Campo Santo at Pisa (Reinach, op. cit., III, p. 109), in the Lateran (ibid., p. 274), in the Palazzo Mattei (ibid., p. 292), in the Vatican (ibid., p. 360), and at Verona (ibid., p. 435).

198. A NUDE MAN WALKING TOWARDS THE L. in front of a man seated holding a serpent and a man kneeling on one knee. (0312)

176 × 189 mm. Pen and brown ink on a light brown ground.

The old attribution was to Girolamo or Ugo da Carpi. It is a very characteristic drawing by the former, taken from the R. hand half of a relief now in the Louvre, representing the death of Clytemnestra or Orestes and Pylades (S. Reinach, *Répertoire de la Statuaire Grecque et Romaine*, Vol. I, Paris, 1897, p. 90). It was formerly in the Palazzo Giustiniani, Rome, when it was engraved by P. Santi Bartoli (*Admiranda Romanarum Antiquitatum*, Rome, 1693, pl. 52).

199. FRIEZE OF FIVE WOMEN'S HEADS IN ELABORATE COIFFURES (0349)

79 × 192 mm. Pen and brown ink touched with white.

A.E.P. Attribution in the 'deceptive' hand to Parmigianino; that to Carpi rests largely on an unmistakable resemblance to another frieze of heads, formerly in the collection of Richardson and engraved by C. M. Metz (Weigel 813) as Girolamo da Carpi.

200. MEN AND WOMEN, SOME STANDING, SOME KNEELING AND SOME SEATED, IN FRONT OF A CLOTH, POINTING TO THE R. (5133)

250 × 200 mm. Pen and brown ink and brown wash.

The old attribution was to Ugo da Carpi, an obvious mistake for Girolamo da Carpi, of whom it is a particularly characteristic example. The composition is reminiscent of the *Worshippers of Latona* by Polidoro da Caravaggio on the façade of the Palazzo Milesi, parts of which Girolamo certainly copied.

201. A SAINT OR PROPHET SEATED IN PROFILE TO THE L., HIS R. HAND TO HIS BOSOM (*Plate* 101) (3384)

164 × 205 mm. (corners cut). Pen and grey ink on blue paper, heightened with white.

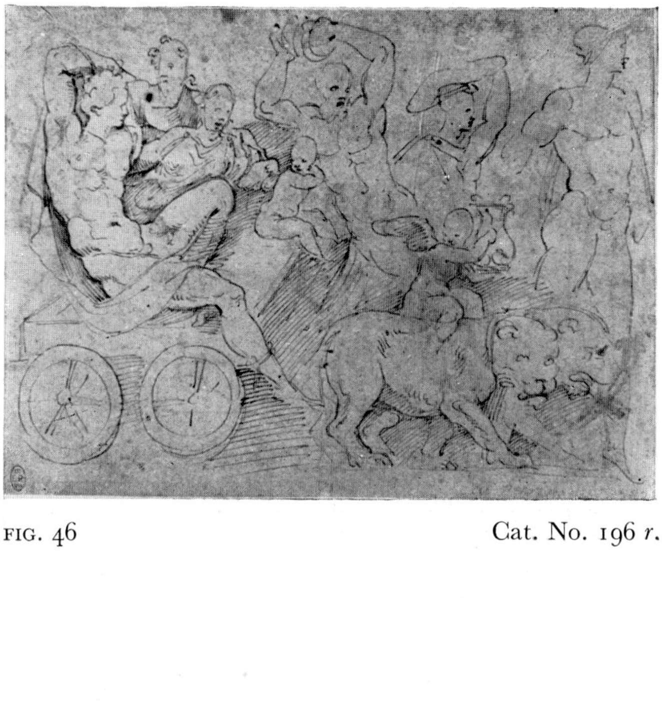

FIG. 46 Cat. No. 196 *r.*

A.E.P. The style of this drawing points to Girolamo da Carpi. It may even be the study for the painting of St. Jerome in San Paolo, Ferrara (Alberto Serafini, *Girolamo da Carpi*, Rome, 1915, Fig. 41).

202. THE ADORATION OF THE SHEPHERDS (*Plate* 102) (0327)

187 × 259 mm. Pen and reddish-brown ink over red chalk, washed with brown, squared with the stylus.

A.E.P. Old attribution 'Rafael' (?) in ink in the L. hand bottom corner. This able and attractive drawing appears to be by the same hand as a drawing in the British Museum (Malcolm, 1895–9–15–582) copied from Garofalo's *Triumph of Bacchus* now in the Dresden Gallery, which there are good stylistic grounds for believing to be by Girolamo da Carpi. On the other hand, the general appearance of the drawing is surprisingly similar to one in the British Museum from the Fenwick Collection attributed convincingly to Giulio Bonasone (Fenwick Catalogue, pl. XXII), but this is so very much weaker in detail that I think Bonasone can hardly be accepted as the draughtsman of the Windsor *Adoration*.

(For other drawings attributed to Girolamo da Carpi, see copies after Polidoro da Caravaggio, Nos. 703, 704, and after Raphael, No. 851.)

Attributed to ALESSANDRO CASOLANI (1552–1606)

203. DESIGN FOR A LUNETTE WITH THE VESTITION OF ST. CATHERINE OF SIENA (?) (5033)

182 × 280 mm. Pen and light brown ink and light brown wash.

F.A. The drawing seems definitely to be by the same hand as one in the British Museum of the *Preaching of a Boy Saint* (1924–5–12–2), with an old attribution to Casolani. The general arrangement of the composition is very similar to that of a frescoed lunette in the ex-Dominican convent of the Cisterna alla Minerva, Rome (ill. Bolletino d'Arte III (1923–24), p. 36), and the scene appears to be the same.

204. STUDIES IN A KITCHEN: on the L. is a child seated on the ground playing with a cat; in the centre, a woman making pastry; on the R. another pouring liquid from a bottle into a basin; further back, two women on their knees, two women at table and two with a cot. (*Plate* 44) (6676)

210 × 259 mm. Black chalk and some pen and ink and wash on blue paper, heightened with white.

P.M.R.P. The attribution to 'Bassano' in pencil in the R. hand bottom corner was no doubt suggested by the domestic character of the scene. I can see no connection in the style of the drawing or in the types with those of the Bassano family. These point to Alessandro Casolani, to whom the drawing can be attributed with some assurance.

Attributed to BERNARDO CASTELLO (1557–1629)

205. THE ASSAULT ON A TURKISH CITY (*Plate* 151) (6337)

170 × 385 mm. Pen and brown ink and brown wash on blue paper heightened with white, squared in black chalk.

A.E.P. The attribution rests on the resemblance in characteristic details between this drawing and the engravings by Agostino Carracci after Castello illustrating the *Gerusalemme Liberata* of Tasso (Genoa, 1590). These resemblances are so close and the mannerisms recur so constantly in the engravings that I feel there is very little doubt. The drawing is perhaps the design for the central compartment of a ceiling in some Genoese Palazzo like that illustrated in Venturi, IX 5, Fig. 494. It might well represent the siege of Jerusalem from the *Gerusalemme Liberata*. A drawing in the Ecole des Beaux-Arts, Paris (Coll. Gatteaux, No. 11974), with an old attribution to Castello, is certainly by the same hand and for the same cycle of decoration.

FIG. 47 Cat. No. 206

206. A COMMANDER RIDING IN TRIUMPH TO THE GATE OF A CITY under a baldachin, the fringes of which are decorated with heraldic lions and fleurs-de-lys; in the background a cavalry engagement is represented and the lion rampant and fleur-de-lys appear on the banners of the combatants. (*Figure* 47). (01196)

457 × 340 mm. Pen and brown ink and brown wash heightened with white, squared in black chalk.

Inscribed in pencil (in the XVIII century ?) on the mount 'DI BERNARDO CASTELLI'. The city, to judge from the banner above the gateway on the L., is presumably Florence. Though the style of the drawing is not exactly that of No. 205, the attribution of which to Castello seems to me certain, it is very near and may represent a different phase of his art.

207. FOUR SMALL GIRLS AND A GROUP OF NUNS KNEELING BEFORE THE ALTAR OF A CHAPEL, on the door of which St. Michael, accompanied by other angels, is knocking. (0157)

187 × 267 mm. Pen and brown ink and pale brown wash.

There is an attribution in pencil on the drawing to 'Ber. Castelli', and though the handling is not very close to that of No. 205, the style of composition is not unlike Castello's, and the attribution may be provisionally accepted.

208. A WARRIOR IN ANTIQUE ARMOUR KNEELS BEFORE A KING, SEATED ON THE L.; SOLDIERS STAND BEHIND EACH (5032)

Circular, diameter 213 mm. Pen and grey ink and grey wash.

A.E.P. The style of this drawing seems to point to Bernardo Castello. The type of composition may be compared with that of the roundels decorating the ceiling of the Palazzo Scassi, Sampierdarena (Venturi, IX 5, Fig. 494).

Attributed to GIOVANNI BATTISTA CASTELLO (IL BERGAMASCO) (About 1510 (?)–1569)

209. S. DOMENICO PRAYS OVER THE DEAD BODY OF THE YOUTH NAPOLEONE, KILLED BY A FALL FROM HIS HORSE; in the background, outside the entrance to the church, men are beating the horse. (*Figure* 48) (5114)

376 × 272 mm. Pen and brown ink and brown wash.

A.E.P. Attributed in the 'deceptive' hand to 'Lorenzo Lotto'. The drawing seems to be by the same hand as a series of four designs of the *Story of Ulysses*, of which two are in the Albertina (Catalogue, III, Nos. 283, 284), one in the Dyce Collection at South Kensington (Catalogue, No. 192), and one in the British Museum (Fenwick Collection, Catalogue, pl. XC, wrongly as Cornelis Teunissen). These drawings are also by the same hand as one in the Uffizi (photo. Braun 76667) with an old inscription, 'Romulo', by which Romolo Cincinnati (d. 1600) is intended. The Vienna drawings (together with the other two *en suite*) and the drawing in the Uffizi show very marked Genoese characteristics and come very close to Luca Cambiaso in style. They have little in common with Florentine drawings of the period, which would be curious in an artist born in that city and trained under Salviati, as was Cincinnati. Nor are they at all clearly by the same hand as the one absolutely authenticated drawing by Cincinnati at Madrid for his painting of the *Martyrdom of St. Maurice* in the Escorial.

The three drawings of the Story of Ulysses seem to me on the other hand to show distinctly the characteristics of Giovanni Battista Castello, an artist who, though he was born near Bergamo, was for long associated with Cambiaso in Genoa. I base this hypothesis on a comparison of the style of a fresco painted on the ceiling of a room in the Palazzo del Governo (formerly Villa Lanzi) at Gorlago near Bergamo, which is illustrated in the Touring Club Italiano Lombardia, Parte Seconda, Milan, 1932, Fig. 48. This fresco, according to F. M. Tassi (*Vite de' Pittori Bergamaschi*, Bergamo, 1793, pp. 156, 157), represents the dispute between Ajax and Ulysses for the arms of Achilles, and was accompanied by twelve small scenes of the life of Ulysses, for which the drawings mentioned above may possibly be the designs.

FIG. 48 Cat. No. 209

210. AN AGED KING, HOLDING A WOMAN BY THE HAND AND PRECEDED BY A WARRIOR, HEADS A PROCESSION of five armed men towards the L.; in the background on the R. is a palace. (5040)

386 × 331 mm. Pen and brown ink and brown wash, squared in pen and ink.

A.E.P. The style of the drawing is definitely Genoese, and nearly approaches that of Cambiaso. It shows so close a resemblance to that of the group of drawings discussed above (see No. 209) that I think it may also be given to G. B. Castello.

GIAMBATTISTA CRESPI (CERANO) (1575/6–1632)

211. A BEARDED MAN, SEATED ON THE GROUND, HOLDING OUT HIS CAP IN HIS L. HAND (*Plate* 147) (5992)

194 × 210 mm. (top corners cut and made up). Red chalk.

A.E.P. Inscribed in pencil 'Procaccino'. The drawing is in fact a study for a figure on the extreme right in Cerano's enormous painting of the *Baptism of St. Augustine* in S. Marco at Milan (ill. Prussian Jahrbuch XLVI (1925), p. 281). The picture is signed and dated, 1618.

212. CHRIST ON THE CROSS WITH ST. MARY MAGDALENE, THE VIRGIN AND ST. JOHN (0187)

320 × 222 mm. Red chalk.

A.E.P. The attribution rests on stylistic resemblances to Cerano's works. The types, especially that of the Magdalene, may be compared with those in the *Crucifixion* in S. Lorenzo Martire, Mortara (ill. Prussian Jahrbuch XLVI (1925), p. 276).

BERNARDINO CESARI. *See* No. 456 (Michelangelo copies)

GIUSEPPE CESARI, Cavaliere D'ARPINO (1568–1640)

213. A WOMAN BEING RAPED BY A SEA-GOD, WHO IS ATTENDED BY THREE SEA-CENTAURS (01257)

347 × 415 mm. (including strips added on all sides except

the L.). Red and black chalk with some wash and heightening in white.
A.E.P. The old attribution was to Giovanni da San Giovanni. It is a most characteristic and unpleasant composition by the Cavaliere d'Arpino.

214. STUDIES OF A WOMAN CARRYING A CHILD, A MAN LOADING A HORSE AND A SOLDIER MARCHING TO THE R. (*Plate* 96) (5219)
232 × 337 mm. Black and red chalk.
Lit.: Catalogue of the Exhibition of 17th Century Art in Europe, London, 1938, No. 350.
Inscribed in bottom R. hand corner 'del Cavallier Giosepp . . .' in ink in a hand of the XVII century. There can be little doubt about the correctness of the old attribution, though the sheet shows a freshness and spontaneity unusual in Cesari.

215. AN ANTIQUE WARRIOR ON HORSEBACK CARRYING OFF A WOMAN; TWO OTHER HORSEMEN TO THE L. (4348)
257 × 360 mm. Red chalk.
A.E.P. From the series of drawings by Carlo Maratta. There can, however, be little doubt about the present attribution. I think it probable that an inscription in the lower R. corner, of which only the tops of the long letters survive, read (like that on No. 214) 'del Cavalliere Gioseppino'.

216. HEAD OF A MAN LOOKING UP TO THE R. (5404)
178 × 149 mm. Red and black chalk.
Old attribution. The head might be a study for that of Lazarus in the painting of his resurrection in the Corsini Gallery, Rome.

217. A NUDE MAN STRIDING TO THE R., BLOWING A HORN (5217)
260 × 175 mm. Red chalk.
Inscribed in the same red chalk as the drawing, perhaps by the artist himself, 'Caure d'Arpino'. There is no doubt that the drawing is by him.

218. STUDY OF A NUDE MAN WALKING TO THE L. LOOKING BACK OVER HIS L. SHOULDER (0174)
257 × 116 mm. Red chalk.
The attribution is old. A more characteristic and less attractive example of the Cavaliere's drawing than No. 214.

Attributed to GIUSEPPE CESARI, Cavaliere d'ARPINO

219. STUDY OF A NUDE MAN ADVANCING TO THE FRONT BUT TURNING, WITH A GESTURE, TO THE R. (0450)
335 × 220 mm. Black chalk.
P.M.R.P. Inscribed in ink at the bottom to the R. 'Danello da Volterra' in a hand of the XVIII century. The style of the drawing and the proportions and type of the figure point, however, to the last quarter of the XVI century and to the Cavaliere d'Arpino.

220. OVAL COMPOSITION: A BISHOP SEATED AT A TABLE ON THE R. EXAMINES SOME PAPERS (PLANS?) BROUGHT HIM BY A BEARDED MAN (6754)
174 × 248 mm. Pen and brown ink and brown wash.
Attribution in pencil on the drawing. This is no doubt correct.

221. STUDY FROM A MODEL OF AN 'ÉCORCHÉ' MAN, FRONT VIEW (0172)
266 × 140 mm. Red chalk.

222. STUDY FROM A MODEL OF AN 'ÉCORCHÉ' MAN, BACK VIEW (0173)
266 × 139 mm. Red chalk.
The attribution of these two studies to Cesari is old. The model is, as pointed out to me by Philip Pouncey, very like Cigoli's statuette in the Museo Nazionale Florence known as 'Lo Scorticato', dating from 1598 (*Il Cigoli*, Piccola Collezione d'Arte, 1922, Fig. 28).

223. TWO STUDIES FROM AN ARMLESS AND HEADLESS 'ÉCORCHÉ' FIGURE SEEN FROM THE BACK (0464)
142 × 169 mm. Red chalk with occasional black.

224. TWO STUDIES FROM AN ARMLESS 'ÉCORCHÉ' FIGURE SEEN FROM THE BACK (0465)
On two pieces of paper, one 165 × 55 mm., the other 165 × 65 mm. Red chalk.
A.E.P. The attribution seems to me a probable, though not a certain, one.

225. HEAD OF A YOUTH IN PROFILE TO THE R. (5386)
210 × 163 mm. Red and black chalk on cream-coloured paper.
George III 'Inventory A', p. 19 (Testi di Diversi Maestri, Tom II).
Apparently a copy after the Cavaliere d'Arpino.

226. HEAD OF A CHILD LOOKING UP, NEARLY IN PROFILE TO THE R. (5397)
160 × 144 mm. Red and black chalk.
George III 'Inventory A', p. 19.
Inscribed in pencil on the mount 'Arpino'. This seems a possible, even a probable, attribution, though it is difficult to be certain about so inconsiderable a sketch.

227. HEAD OF AN OLD BEARDED MAN NEARLY FULL-FACE, LOOKING DOWN TO THE R. (4365)
406 × 263 mm. Red chalk.
A.E.P. From the series of drawings by Carlo Maratta.

228. HEAD OF A MUCH-BEARDED AND MOUSTACHIO'D MAN TURNED THREE-QUARTERS TO THE R. (0321)
387 × 244 mm. Red chalk.
A.E.P. Inscribed in pen and ink in an old hand 'de Rafael'.

BARTOLOMMEO CESI (1556–1629)

229. GOD THE FATHER SEATED ON CLOUDS IN THE ACT OF BLESSING; MUSICIAN ANGELS ON EITHER SIDE (*Plate* 113) (3712)
142 × 226 mm. Red chalk
A.E.P. Study for the upper part of the central panel of the altarpiece in S. Domenico, Bologna (Venturi, IX 6, Fig. 433), below which is the *Adoration of the Magi*. Studies for the musician angels in the same altarpiece are in the British Museum (1943–7–19–30) and in the Gathorne Hardy collection (Catalogue, 1902, No. 20, as Annibale Carracci).

230. CHRIST ON THE CROSS WITH SS. PETER AND ANDREW (?) AND A KNEELING BISHOP (5075)
400 × 267 mm. Pen and brown ink and brown wash.
Inscribed in ink in an old hand 'Cesi'. The attribution seems to be borne out by the style of the drawing, which accords well enough with that of some in the Uffizi (e.g. *Descent of the Holy Spirit*; photo. Gernsheim, No. 12750).

FIG. 49 Cat. No. 231

Attributed to BARTOLOMMEO CESI

231. THE TRINITY SURROUNDED BY ANGELS WITH MUSICAL INSTRUMENTS: design for a cupola. (*Figure* 49) (5524)

375 × 350 mm. Pen and brown ink and brown wash.

A.E.P. The composition may be compared with one painted by Cesi in Sta. Maria dei Bulgari, Bologna (Gaetano Canuti, *Pitture di Bartolommeo Cesi essistenti nella Cappella di Santa Maria dei Bulgari*, Bologna, 1832, pl. 21). In the British Museum is a study from the model (1920–11–16–23, formerly attributed to Zurbaran) which appears to be for the God the Father in this composition. The attitude and fall of the drapery is almost the same, but in the Windsor version the figure is seen more abruptly foreshortened.

POMPEO CESURA DELL' AQUILA (d. 1571)

232. THE MYSTIC MARRIAGE OF ST. CATHERINE (*Figure* 50) (6025)

239 × 195 mm. Pen and brown ink and brown wash, heightened with white, squared in black chalk.

Lit.: H. Bodmer, Thieme-Becker XXIX (1935), p. 371.

A.E.P. 'di Federico Zuccaro' in pencil on the drawing.

Attributed by Bodmer to Sammacchini. It is clearly by the same hand as a drawing of the *Burial of St. Catherine* in the British Museum (Sloane 5223–47) with an old attribution to Pompeo dell' Aquila, which was engraved by Cornelis Cort in 1575, but without the name of the painter being given. The Windsor drawing is closely connected with (i) the painting at Dresden (No. 117) of the same subject attributed to Sammacchini; and (ii) a drawing at Budapest attributed to Bagnacavallo (repr. Schönbrunner-Meder, No. 792). It is quite obviously by the same hand as the last-named drawing. It is possible that its relation to the picture at Dresden is that of a preliminary early design, and that the picture is in fact by Pompeo dell' Aquila.

LODOVICO CARDI, called CIGOLI (1559–1613)

233. TWO MEN STANDING TURNED TO THE R., HOLDING TRAYS (*Plate* 41) (5190)

403 × 246 mm. Brush drawing in grey and white on grey-blue prepared surface.

Lit.: Catalogue of the Exhibition of 17th Century Art in Europe, London, 1938, No. 355.

Attribution in pencil, 'Lodco. detto il Cigoli'.

234. A WOMAN TURNED TO THE L. HOLDING A TRAY (*Plate* 42) (5189)

390 × 265 mm. Brush drawing in grey and white on grey prepared surface (over a document).

Lit.: Catalogue of the Exhibition of 17th Century Art in Europe, London, 1938, No. 361.

Attribution in pencil, 'Lodco. detto il Cigoli'.

The correctness of the apparently old attribution to Cigoli of these two beautiful drawings is attested by the style, which is exactly that of authenticated drawings (e.g. of the study in the Uffizi of the Magdalene for the *Supper at Emmaus* of 1592 in the Doria Gallery, Rome, or the study of a kneeling ecclesiastic in the Ashmolean Museum for the painting of 1605 in the Chiesa dei Cavalieri, Pisa). The studies are obviously for servants waiting at table in such a subject as the *Supper at Emmaus*, and there is an unmistakable resemblance to the two serving men in the Doria picture already cited (*Il Cigoli*, Piccola Collezione d'Arte, 1922, Fig. 10).

Attributed to LODOVICO CARDI, called CIGOLI

235. THREE-QUARTER LENGTH STUDY OF A SAINT OR APOSTLE TURNED TO THE L., THE HANDS CLASPED (0148)

FIG. 50 Cat. No. 232

FIG. 51 Cat. No. 236

253 × 231 mm. Red chalk.

The attribution, written in pencil on the mount, must presumably be traditional. The style of the drawing seems to confirm it. The study might be for a St. John at the foot of the Cross.

236. CHRIST MOCKED (*Figure* 51) (01221)

536 × 405 mm. Pen and brown ink and wash on a pink-tinted ground, heightened with white.

A.E.P. The style of this elaborately finished *modello*-like drawing points to Florence at the very end of the XVI or beginning of the XVII century, and more specifically to Cigoli.

237. THE LAMENTATION OVER THE BODY OF CHRIST (5031)

261 × 186 mm. Black chalk and wash on a brown ground, heightened with white.

F.A. The attribution of this and No. 238 appears to me, if not certain, at any rate probable.

238. PIETÀ. The Virgin, with hands raised, stands behind the body of her Son; on the R. St. Mary Magdalene kneels and holds His hand; on the L. kneels St. Lawrence. (5054)

327 × 242 mm. Pen and brown ink and wash over black chalk, with some white, the outlines indented.

Attributed to NICCOLÒ CIRCIGNANO (IL POMERANCIO (1516 (?)–after 1596)

239. ST. PETER: he is represented half-length in a niche, the keys in his R., a book in his L., hand. (0202)

277 × 210 mm. Pen and brown ink and brown wash over black chalk.

240. ST. PAUL: he is represented half-length in a niche, the sword in his L., a book in his R., hand. (0201)

277 × 207 mm. Pen and brown ink and brown wash over black chalk.

Attribution in pencil on the mount to Niccolò Circignano, also called Pomerancio. I think the style of this pair of drawings points in fact to Circignano rather than to Roncalli, though the two are constantly confused.

GIULIO CLOVIO (1498–1578)

241. THE ADORATION OF THE MAGI (*Figure* 52) (0446)

308 × 215 mm. Finished drawing in grey chalk.

Lit.: J. C. J. Bierens de Haan, *L'oeuvre gravé de Cornelis Cort*, The Hague, 1948, p. 57 (ill. Fig. 9).

Low down on the R. is a 'g' in pen and ink which is probably the beginning of Giulio Clovio's signature. On the *verso*, 'Giulio Clovio' is written in pen and ink in a hand of the XVI century. Engraved in 1567 by Cornelius Cort, with

FIG. 52 Cat. No. 241

an inscription at the bottom, 'Aurum tus myrram regiq hominiq deoq; Dona tulere magi extremis orientis ab oris Ignaros duxit quos stella viaeque; lociq'. The only addition in the engraving, which is in the same direction, is a minute scene of the *Presentation in the Temple* in the rectangular space at the bottom, occurring in the second state.

FIG. 53 Cat. No. 242

242. THE VIRGIN SEATED FEEDING THE INFANT, ST. JOSEPH, ST. JOHN THE EVANGELIST (?) AND TWO WOMEN (*Figure* 53) (0462)
281 × 210 mm. Finished drawing in grey chalk.
The drawing is certainly by Clovio and the background figures are probably his own invention, though the Virgin and Child are based on Michelangelo's *Madonna* in the Medici Chapel at Florence.

243. HEAD OF MINERVA IN PROFILE TO THE L.: she wears the Gorgon's head on her cuirass and a plumed helmet decorated with a battle between a horseman and foot soldiers. (0453)
280 × 197 mm. Finished drawing in grey chalk. Damaged and carefully made up along the R. margin and Minerva's chin. Etched in reverse in 1785 by Charlotte Augusta Matilda, Princess Royal.
A.E.P. Under School of Michelangelo. The attribution rests on the identity of the handling, which is particularly obvious in the subsidiary decorations, with that of authenticated drawings by Clovio, like the *Adoration of the Magi* previously described and the signed *Pietà* in the British Museum (Malcolm, 1895–9–15–645). It also corresponds almost exactly with a small medallion in the margin of the first page of the *Commentaries of Cardinal Marino Grimani on the Epistle of St. Paul to the Romans*. The decoration of this manuscript, now in the Soane Museum, London, was carried out by Clovio between 1528 and 1546 (Bulletin de la Societé Française de reproductions de manuscrits à peinture, IV (1914–20), pl. XLVII).

244. CHRIST, SURROUNDED BY THE APOSTLES, HANDING THE KEYS TO ST. PETER (*Plate* 78) (4814)
362 × 285 mm. Point of the brush and brown wash over black chalk.
George III 'Inventory A', p. 85, Sebastiano del Piombo, 30–34 (?).
P.M.R.P. This very accomplished composition (unfortunately considerably damaged by damp) is the work of an artist who had either very thoroughly absorbed the style of Michelangelo in the *Last Judgment* and the Cappella Paolina, or was actually copying him. It in fact corresponds with a coloured drawing in the Louvre (No. d'ordre 3044) with a different background, there ascribed, no doubt correctly, to Clovio. The rather peculiar technique of the Windsor drawing is paralleled by that of a certainly authentic sheet of Clovio's in the British Museum, Fenwick Collection (Catalogue, p. 50: *The Conversion of St. Paul*; engraved by Cornelius Cort), and less closely by that of the drawing described below (No. 245). I think it may be accepted as Clovio's work, but it may be based on Michelangelo.

245. THE ADORATION OF THE SHEPHERDS (*Figure* 54) (0382)
284 × 199 mm. Pen and brown ink and brown wash over black and red chalk.

FIG. 54 Cat. No. 245

A.E.P. On the *verso* in a hand of the XVII (?) century, 'Rosso Fiorentino'. This has been crossed out and 'Parmesanino' (the reading is not clear) written by another (the 'deceptive'?) hand.

The drawing in fact corresponds closely with a miniature attributed to Giulio Clovio, described as in Austrian Royal possession, of which there is a photograph in the Print Room of the British Museum. There are minor differences between the *Adoration* itself in the drawing and the miniature, and more considerable differences in the respective borders. I find the types singularly like Clovio's, and see no reason for doubting that the drawing is in fact a design by him for the miniature (which, to judge from the photograph is also certainly by Clovio himself). It is one of four of which there are photographs; another has the arms of Cardinal Farnese.

Copies by Giulio Clovio after Michelangelo will be found catalogued under that artist's name, Nos. 457, 459, and a large miniature signed by him in the section of miniatures (No. 43).

ANTONIO ALLEGRI CORREGGIO (1489–1534)

References are given to Corrado Ricci, *Correggio, His Life and Works*, London, 1930; and to Adolfo Venturi, *Correggio*, Rome, 1930.

246. A NUDE WOMAN LYING ASLEEP ON THE GROUND (*Plate* 116) (0594)

170 × 110 mm. Red chalk (top corners cut).

Lit.: Ricci, pp. 170 and 197, pl. CCLVIII; Venturi, *Correggio*, p. 483, pl. 182; Popham, 248, pl. CCIX b.

Inscribed in black chalk on the drawing, 'Del Correggio'. It appears to be, what it has generally been regarded as, the study for the Louvre painting of *Antiope* (Ricci, pl. CLIV). It has distinctly the air of an original drawing, is in the style of those credibly given to Correggio, and differs sufficiently from the picture to exclude the possibility of its being a copy.

247. ADAM, ABRAHAM AND ISAAC, FROM THE CUPOLA OF PARMA CATHEDRAL (*Plate* 118) (0597)

206 × 235 mm. Pen and ink over red chalk.

Lit.: Ricci, pp. 176 and 198, pl. CCLXXVI b.

The three figures correspond fairly exactly with those in the fresco of the cupola at Parma (Ricci, pl. CCXVI). The style is like Correggio's, the drawing intelligent, and I see no reason for not thinking it an original study by Correggio himself. It is very near in manner to the drawing of Eve at Haarlem (Ricci, pl. CCLXXVIII b), which is very possibly a repetition by the artist himself of the drawing in the British Museum (Ricci, pl. CCLXXIX). There are differences in detail between the drawing and the fresco, especially in the preliminary sketch in red chalk, and the hand of the Virgin, which covers part of the figure of Abraham, is not there.

Attributed to CORREGGIO

248. THE VIRGIN AND CHILD WITH ST. JOSEPH AND THE INFANT ST. JOHN (*Plate* 117) (0101)

165 × 188 mm. Red chalk, squared in black chalk.

F.A. According to a note on the mount the drawing was attributed to Sodoma or Ghirlandajo. On the *verso* are 19 lines of a letter, somewhat cut on the R., which Wilde has been so kind as to transcribe for me. There is not much in this to help either in assigning or in dating the drawing. There is a reference to the Duke's having passed on Wednesday the 10th of the month with five carriages and 30 or 40 Lombard horses, and to the 'contino de Linaro' having received a blow with a dagger from 'roberto buzzio', which was not serious. The only reference to a locality is to Castel de Rio, which was the seat of the powerful Alidosi family, and to Cesena. Linaro was also a possession of the Alidosi, and the 'contino de Linaro' is possibly some title in the family, though I can find no mention of it in Litta. The letter seems to point to the writer's having connections with Imola or its neighbourhood and with the Alidosi family.

Antal pointed out a close resemblance in its style to that of the early Correggio. He no doubt had in mind the *Holy Family* in the Museum at Orléans (attributed to Correggio by Longhi, l'Arte XXIV (1921), p. 5), where the type and attitude of the Child especially are extremely similar.

249. STUDY FOR A DANAË (*Figure* 55) (0596)

210 × 158 mm. Red chalk and pen and ink on faded blue paper.

Lit.: Ricci, pp. 180 and 199, pl. CCXCII; Venturi, *Correggio*, p. 485, pl. 188.

Attributed to Correggio and thought to be a study for the *Danaë* in the Borghese Gallery at Rome (Ricci, pl. CCXXXVII), with which it has only the vaguest connection. I have thought of Camillo Boccaccino as the possible draughtsman but, to judge from an anciently attributed drawing, also of Danaë, in the British Museum (Sloane 5223–44), this is hardly possible. The opposite way of the paper and apparently drawn before the Danaë are two studies in pen and ink of angels floating up to heaven.

250. *Recto:* LOVE PELTING A SLEEPING NYMPH WITH FLOWERS (*Figure* 56)

Verso: VARIOUS STUDIES FOR A RAPE OF EUROPA AND FOR A ST. GEORGE (?) ON HORSEBACK (*Figure* 57) (0593 B)

135 × 136 mm. Red chalk. W.M., a cardinal's hat.

Lit.: Venturi, *Correggio*, p. 484, pl. 183 and 184.

Attributed to Correggio, an attribution which is accepted by Venturi. It may be by the same hand as the drawing of Danaë (No. 249), though the *recto* is not nearly so good. The little sketches on the *verso* are however distinctly spirited, and the attribution to Correggio of both *recto* and *verso* does not seem to me out of the question.

After CORREGGIO

251. HEAD OF ST. MARY MAGDALENE (5227)

308 × 246 mm. Red and black chalk.

The head is actually on a much smaller piece of paper measuring 250 × 210 mm., which has been made up all round and the drawing restored. The making up affects the R. eye and line of the cheek and mouth. Inscribed in black chalk at lower L. corner 'Baroccio'. Copy, quite possibly, as seems to have been traditionally believed, by Federico Barocci, of St. Mary Magdalene in Correggio's *Madonna of St. Jerome* in the Parma Gallery (Ricci, pl. CLXII).

252. GROUP OF ANGELS, ONE WITH A MUSICAL INSTRUMENT, ANOTHER HOLDING A LAMB (0217)

337 × 188 mm. Black and red chalk.

Inscribed in ink in lower R. corner, 'Camillo Procaccino, dal Correggio'. Copy, quite possibly by Procaccini as stated, of the group of angels to the R. of St. John the Baptist in the *Coronation of the Virgin* in the apse of S. Giovanni Evangelista, Parma (Ricci, pp. 164–5 and pl. CXXXI). It may have been taken from the original,

FIG. 55 Cat. No. 249

destroyed in 1586, or from Aretusi's copy which replaced it, or from Annibale Carracci's copies now in Naples.

253. THE CORONATION OF THE VIRGIN (0740)

150 × 251 mm. Black and red chalk.

Copy, in reverse, of the *Coronation of the Virgin* in the apse of S. Giovanni Evangelista, Parma. The fresco had by 1608 been replaced by Aretusi's copy, and the drawing no doubt reproduces that copy (Ricci, pl. CXXVII).

254. FOUR APOSTLES WITH ADOLESCENTS ON A BALUSTRADE BEHIND THEM (0741)

189 × 277 mm. Black and red chalk.

Offset from a copy of part of the fresco in the cupola of Parma Cathedral (Ricci, pl. CXXCIII).

255. ST. MATTHEW AND ST. JEROME (0742)

103 × 118 mm. Black and red chalk.

Offset from a copy of the S.E. pendentive of the cupola of S. Giovanni Evangelista at Parma (Ricci, pl. CII).

256. MADONNA AND CHILD (0743)

138 × 116 mm. Black and red chalk.

Copy from the *Madonna of St. Sebastian* at Dresden (Ricci, pl. CLII).

257. THE MADONNA OF ST. GEORGE (0744)

248 × 188 mm. Red and black chalk.

Offset from a copy of the picture at Dresden (Ricci, pl. CCXXVI).

Nos. 253–257 are copies from Correggio probably, to judge from their style, by Frederico Zuccaro, who was in Parma in 1608.

258. HEAD OF AN ADOLESCENT (5423)

216 × 244 mm. Red and black chalk.

Feeble copy of the head of one of the adolescents in the Cupola of Parma Cathedral (Ricci, pl. CCV).

FIG. 56 Cat. No. 250 *r.*

FIG. 57 Cat. No. 250 *v.*

259. THE VIRGIN CARRIED TO HEAVEN (01246)

445 × 350 mm. Red chalk, the outlines indented.

An admirable copy in a style which suggests the Carracci or their school, of a portion of the cupola of Parma Cathedral (Ricci, pl. CCXIV).

260. SOARING ANGELS (01247)

439 × 344 mm. Red chalk.

Copy, obviously by the same hand as, and *en suite* with, No. 259, of another section of the cupola of Parma Cathedral, most of which is illustrated in Ricci, pl. CCXXII.

261. HEAD OF A YOUTH (5147)

158 × 162 mm. Red chalk, with touches of black chalk.

This wretched drawing would appear to be a copy after Correggio, perhaps from the head of the *putto* below the Virgin, immediately to the L. of the angel with the cymbals in the cupola of Parma Cathedral.

DANIELE (RICCIARELLI) DA VOLTERRA (1509 (?)–1566)

262. AN APOSTLE SEATED ON A BENCH (?) (*Plate* 76) (01254)

364 × 347 mm. (cut into on the L. and at the bottom). Grey chalk.

F.A. This study, executed with great precision and attention to detail, is a prototype of the good academic drawing.

A label attached to the back of the mount is inscribed 'Gio. Franc. d° Il Fattore'. This seems to have been traced, no doubt from an inscription on the *verso*, at the time when the drawing was mounted. The attribution to Daniele is based on a comparison with his authenticated drawings (e.g. the study of a standing apostle for Sta. Trinità de' Monti in the British Museum, Fenwick Collection (Catalogue, p. 113, No. 1, pl. LIII)). The Windsor drawing is probably for an apostle looking into an empty tomb in an *Assumption of the Virgin*. P. Totti (*Ritratto di Roma*, 1638, p. 288) and G. B. Passeri (*Vite*, ed. Hess, p. 172) mention a fresco of the subject by Daniele in the Tribuna of Sta. Maria in Via Lata. A work by A. Camassei replaced this in 1642, and no reproduction of Daniele's fresco is known.

263. DRAPED FEMALE FIGURE STANDING IN PROFILE TO THE R. (*Plate* 77) (0443)

367 × 261 mm. Black chalk.

Perhaps identical with George III 'Inventory A', p. 43, Michelangelo, I, 8.

Inscribed on the *verso* in William Gibson's (?) hand, 'Michel Angelo Bonarota 8. I.' (= 8 shillings).

An unsigned pencil note on the mount reads as follows: 'Copy from Daniele da Volterra (fresco S. Trinità, Rome)'. The drawing nevertheless appears to be an original study. It is perhaps for one of the *basamento* figures in the Orsini chapel in Sta. Trinità. The decorations of this chapel have been entirely destroyed, but two pairs of these *basamento* figures were etched in 1771 and 1772 in the Abbé de St. Non's 'Fragmens choisis dans les plus interessans des Palais et des Eglises d'Italie Premiere Suite' (title etching), and in the 'Deuxieme Suite' (unnumbered). The present figure does *not* correspond with any of these four, but the attitude and the character of the work are so similar that it may be presumed to be either a rejected study for one of these or the finished study for another one of them (if there were more than the four). The period, 1540–47, when, according to Vasari, the chapel was being decorated, would fit in well enough with the style of the drawing.

264. HEAD OF A BALD, BEARDED MAN, TURNED SLIGHTLY AND INCLINED TO THE L. (*Figure* 58) (5158)

235 × 166 mm. Black chalk.

Traditional attribution. Apparently the study for a St. Peter.

FIG. 58 Cat. No. 264

265. GANYMEDE: the upper part of his body is bent forward and turned slightly to the L., his head to the R.; his R. leg and R. arm rest on the eagle, which supports him from the L. (0470)

333 × 181 mm. (top corners cut). Black chalk.

Probably George III 'Inventory A', p. 43, Michelangelo, I, 9.

J.W. The attribution is based on the style. Michelangelo's drawing for Cavalieri (see Michelangelo copies, No. 457) must have been known to the draughtsman. There is no record in literary sources of any representation of the subject by Daniele. There is another version of the drawing in red chalk formerly in the Fenwick Collection (Catalogue, p. 13, No. 10). It appears that the early XVII century draughtsman who made the study of a nude woman (Windsor, No. 2076, formerly Annibale Carracci: Popham, No. 297) had this figure of Daniele's in his mind.

After DANIELE DA VOLTERRA

266. THE DEAD BODY OF CHRIST CARRIED BY THREE MEN WITH, ON THE L., THE VIRGIN FAINTING (206)

393 × 278 mm. Drawn with the brush in blue over black chalk on blue paper, heightened with white.

From Vol. V of Domenichino drawings.

Attribution to Niccolò dell' Abbate in pencil on the drawing. It is, as pointed out by Antal, the copy of a painting in the Musée Condé at Chantilly there attributed, apparently correctly, to Daniele da Volterra. The copy is apparently by a Venetian or Veronese.

267. THE DEAD BODY OF CHRIST CARRIED BY THREE MEN WITH, ON THE L., THE VIRGIN FAINTING (7708)

540 × 425 mm. Pen and ink and wash and water colour.

Copy of the XVII or XVIII century from the painting at Chantilly, of which No. 266 is an earlier copy.

Attributed to JACOPO CHIMENTI DA EMPOLI (1551–1640)

268. *Recto:* A BEARDED MAN, WEARING HIS HAT, SEATED IN A CHAIR IN PROFILE TO THE L.

Verso: STUDY OF PART OF A L. LEG (0106)

137 × 95 mm. Red chalk.

The attribution to Empoli of this slight and rather colourless sketch may be accepted provisionally.

269. A PEASANT WOMAN, WEARING A HAT, holding up her apron with her R. hand and pointing to the ground with her L. (6686)

257 × 188 mm. Black chalk on chocolate prepared surface, heightened with white chalk.

A.E.P. The technique, chalk on a dark prepared ground, seems to have been a favourite one with Empoli (see Uffizi, Nos. 919, 942, repr. in the Olschki publication, Second Series I, Empoli, Nos. 2 and 5) and the style resembles his.

270. WHOLE-LENGTH FIGURE OF A ST. JOHN IN A CRUCIFIXION (?) (6029)

396 × 214 mm. Red chalk. Stained by damp.

The attribution to Empoli is due to Dr. H. Bodmer. It is attractive, but it is difficult to be certain about it.

FIG. 59 Cat. No. 271

FIG. 60 Cat. No. 272

PIETRO FACCINI (1562–1602)

271. THE VIRGIN AND CHILD ENTHRONED WITH ST. JOSEPH BESIDE THEM, ADORED BY ST. FRANCIS OF ASSISI, ANOTHER MONASTIC SAINT AND ST. CLARE(?) (*Figure* 59) (2194)
191 × 191 mm. Fine pen and ink and pale brown washes.
A.E.P. The style is unmistakably Faccini's, and the drawing may perhaps be the sketch for the same altarpiece as that represented in a drawing in the British Museum (Malcolm 1895–9–15–698) with an old attribution to Faccini.

272. A BEARDED SAINT IN THE HABIT OF A MONK, KNEELING BEFORE A CRUCIFIX (*Figure* 60) (0602)
214 × 148 mm. Red chalk.
Photo.: Braun 129.
A.E.P. Inscribed in the bottom R. corner in the 'deceptive' hand: 'Coregio'.

273. HEAD AND BODY OF A YOUTH SUFFERING FROM GOITRE (7215)
170 × 117 mm. Black, red and white chalk on blue paper.
A.E.P. From a volume of caricatures formed by Consul Smith and by him attributed to Guercino. The attribution to Faccini is based on the handling and style of the drawing, but seems fairly certain.

274. THE AGONY IN THE GARDEN (5089)
270 × 193 mm. Pen and brown ink and brown wash.
The attribution to Faccini, due to H. Bodmer, may I think be accepted. The technique is absolutely his, though none of his most characteristic types occur.

After ANTONIO FĀNTUZZI (About 1510–after 1550)

275. PORTICO, WITH THREE ENTRANCES, IN THE RUSTIC STYLE (5093)
291 × 420 mm. Pen and ink.
Copy, in the same direction, of the engraving, Bartsch XVI, p. 353, 35, signed: 'ANTo FĀTUZI·DE·BOLOGNA FECIT·AI·D̄M̄·D̄. 45'.

PAOLO FARINATI (About 1524–1606 ?)

The series of drawings by Farinati at Windsor is an important one, certainly the best existing in this country and, most of the sheets never having been exposed to the light, in perfect condition. It was bound in one volume containing 54 drawings, Nos. 4973–5026 (George III 'Inventory A', p. 117). This volume was subsequently broken up and the drawings mounted separately. Of these 54 drawings, at least 10 are not by Farinati and have been placed elsewhere, one, No. 4986, with G. B. Trotti, No. 969, below). However, five drawings will be found catalogued below, which did not belong to this series: Nos. 276, 277, 278, 323 and 324, the attribution to Farinati of the last two being the compiler's. Perhaps a careful study of Farinati's numerous dated paintings still existing in Verona and the district might throw some light on these drawings and their chronology. Only one is connected with a painting of which the reproduction is available, No. 279, with the picture of 1569 in S. Tommaso, Verona, but even in this case it is not at all certain that the drawing is a study for the painting and not a reminiscence of it. Farinati may have produced drawings for sale and gift, and the fact that this one is signed with a snail, which he employed as a signature (like No. 287), suggests that it was a sheet of this character. One drawing, No. 309, has a *ricordo* with the date 1603 on the *verso* and another, No. 292, seems to represent Sixtus V (1585–1590). Perhaps a more careful study than I have been able to give it of Farinati's diary published in Madonna Verona, might throw some light on the chronology of the drawings, but so far the three drawings referred to are the only ones to be dated by any external evidence. I have not therefore attempted to arrange them chronologically and have followed the order of the inventory numbers. Under this arrangement some drawings which are obviously connected have been separated: No. 289, for instance, is a variant of Nos. 297 and 298, and Nos. 305 and 307 are connected. It is probable from the similarity in style that Nos. 299, 300, 301, 303, 304, 305, 306, 307 and possibly 302, are all for the same scheme of decoration, perhaps for a villa, but I have not been able to discover what.

In addition to the nine drawings (Nos. 5018–5026) which are not by Paolo Farinati and seem to have no relation to him, there are some others included about which considerable doubt may be felt. The most interesting of these is No. 288, the *modello* for an important altarpiece. This is certainly Veronese and possibly a very early work by Paolo Farinati. I would, however, tentatively suggest that it might be by Antonio Badile, with whose altarpiece in the Museo di Castelvecchio at Verona (Venturi, IX 4, Fig, 681) it shows considerable similarity. No. 318 is quite obviously not by Paolo but possibly of his workshop, and there are divergencies from the apparently very constant character of Paolo's idiom in Nos. 286, 310 and 313 which suggest a different hand.

276. TWO DOCTORS AND THE VIRGIN WITH ST. JOSEPH from a composition of Christ disputing with the Doctors. (4816)

300 × 177 mm. Pen and brown ink and brown wash over black chalk on blue paper, heightened with white.

277. TWO SEATED AND ONE STANDING DOCTOR from a composition of Christ disputing with the Doctors. (5043)

295 × 215 mm. Pen and brown ink and brown wash on blue paper, heightened with white.

P.M.R.P. This and the preceding drawing, in spite of the separated numbers, must form parts of the same composition. They are no doubt copies, apparently from Paolo Farinati.

278. ALLEGORICAL COMPOSITION: above, a crowned female figure; below, another female supporting the Cross, the upper arm of which is also supported by the Virgin (?) emerging from a cloud; four *putti* precede or hover above the woman carrying the Cross, bearing various objects, and she is followed by Hercules (who seizes Envy, catching hold of the woman's leg, by the hair) and Janus, who carries keys; on the right at the top is part of a band with the signs of the Zodiac. (*Figure* 61) (4827)

527 × 395 mm. Pen and brown ink and brown wash over black chalk on yellow paper, heightened with white.

279. ST. ANTHONY AND ST. ONOFRIO, SEATED AND LOOKING UPWARDS (4973)

255 × 357 mm. Pen and brown ink and brown wash over black chalk on yellow prepared paper, heightened with white.

FIG. 61 Cat. No. 278

FIG. 62 Cat. No. 282

Signed with the snail in the bottom L. hand corner.

Connected with the two saints in the painting of the *Madonna with SS. Anthony and Onofrio* in S. Tommaso, Verona, dated 1569 (Venturi, IX 4, Fig. 729). The attitude of St. Anthony is completely changed in the picture, that of St. Onofrio only slightly.

280. CHRIST CARRYING THE CROSS (4974)

375 × 473 mm. Pen and brown ink and wash on light brown paper, heightened with white.

281. AN ATTACK ON A TURKISH (?) CARAVAN (4975)

368 × 559 mm. Brown wash on lighter brown paper, partly outlined with pen and ink.

The drawing shows very clearly Farinati's method of working; how he drew the subject first in pale washes and subsequently outlined these in pen and ink.

282. PERSEUS AND ANDROMEDA (*Figure* 62) (4976)

408 × 283 mm. Pen and dark brown ink and wash over black chalk on blue paper, heightened with white.

Another study of the same subject by Farinati is in the British Museum, Fenwick Collection (Catalogue, p. 53, No. 2). This latter is the study for part of a wall decoration of which there is a complete sketch in the His de la Salle Collection in the Museum at Dijon (No. 790). The present drawing is possibly an alternative study for the same scheme of decoration.

283. ST. CATHERINE KNEELING, THE BROKEN WHEEL BEHIND HER AND THE EXECUTIONER WITH HIS SWORD STANDING ON THE L. (4977)
350 × 238 mm. Pen and dark brown ink and wash over black chalk on an orange prepared surface, heightened with white.
An inscription in ink on the lower edge has been partly cut away and is illegible.

284. MADONNA AND CHILD WITH ST. MARK AND ST. BERNARD OF CLAIRVAUX (4978)
243 × 165 mm. Pen and brown ink and brown wash over black chalk on yellow prepared paper, heightened with white.

285. THE CRUCIFIED SAVIOUR BETWEEN ST. PETER AND ST. PAUL (4979)
244 × 173 mm. Pen and brown ink and brown wash over black chalk on yellow prepared paper, heightened with white.

286. ST. JOHN THE BAPTIST LED TO PRISON (?) (4980)
408 × 263 mm. Pen and brown ink and wash on blue paper, heightened with white.

287. THE ENTOMBMENT (4981)
408 × 306 mm. Black chalk and pen and dark brown ink and wash on yellow prepared paper, heightened with white.
Coll.: Sir P. Lely (Lugt 2093).
Signed in the lower L. hand corner with the snail.

288. THE VIRGIN AND CHILD ENTHRONED, SURROUNDED BY ANGELS; below, four saints, St. John the Baptist, St. Francis, St. Dominick and St. Andrew (?), look up towards them. (4982)
480 × 300 mm. (arched top). Pen and brown ink and brown wash over black chalk on blue paper, heightened with white.
Presumably the *modello* for an important altarpiece, possibly by Antonio Badile (see Venturi, IX 4, Fig. 681).

289. *Recto:* NEPTUNE STANDING IN HIS CHARIOT DRAWN BY TWO SEA-HORSES
Verso: THE VIRGIN ANNUNCIATE
(4983)
250 × 420 mm. Pen and brown ink and wash on blue paper, heightened with white.
Inscription on the *verso* below the statue or picture in the niche on the church wall: 'Sibilla chumea profeto di la virgine nõciata'. On *recto* in lower R. corner: 'P. Farinato. 5.2.' (= 12/6 in the method of pricing used by William Gibson).
The *recto* is connected with Nos. 297 and 298 below.

290. AN ANTIQUE SACRIFICE: A MAN SLAUGHTERING AN OX (4984)
245 × 352 mm. Brown wash over black chalk on yellow-brown prepared surface.
Inscribed in ink in lower L. corner: 'Paolo Farinata'.

291. A MONK CASTING OUT A DEVIL (4985)
393 × 280 mm. Pen and dark brown ink and wash over black chalk on blue paper, heightened with white.
Inscribed in ink in lower L. hand corner: 'Di P. Farinato'.

292. A POPE KNEELING BEFORE THE CRUCIFIED SAVIOUR; BEHIND HIM A GROUP OF NUNS (4987)
370 × 240 mm. Pen and brown ink and wash on blue paper, heightened with white.
The pope represented is probably Sixtus V (1585–90), which would give an approximate date for the drawing.

293. *Recto:* CHRIST ON THE CROSS, WITH TWO FRANCISCAN SAINTS (ST. FRANCIS AND ST. ANTHONY OF PADUA ?)
Verso: CHRIST TAKEN DOWN FROM THE CROSS
(4988)
270 × 206 mm. Pen and brown ink and wash over black chalk on blue paper. The *recto* heightened with white.
Inscribed on *verso* in ink in lower R. corner: 'P. Farinato. 6.' (the final figure cut off), the system of pricing used by William Gibson.

294. 'POMONA' AND 'CERERE' SEATED ON EITHER SIDE OF THE WINGED AND CROWNED FIGURE OF 'ESTATE': design for a lunette. (*Figure* 63) (4889)
356 × 276 mm. (top corners cut and made up). Pen and brown ink and brown wash over black chalk on yellow prepared paper.

FIG. 63 Cat. No. 294

Inscribed by the artist in ink at lower edge: 'Le sopra ll figure sero circha 3½ epiu secondo vi parera voi che sete sulopera sula infraschedura vi potete sbezerir'.

295. THE VESTAL CLAUDIA DRAWING THE SHIP BEARING THE STATUE OF CYBELE UP THE TIBER (4990)
410 × 280 mm. Pen and brown ink and brown wash on yellow prepared paper, heightened with white.

Inscribed in ink in a hand of the XVIII century in the lower R. corner: 'Di P. Farinati', and in the artist's hand in the lower L. corner: 'Claudia'.

296. BELLONA, GODDESS OF WAR, SEATED AMONG VARIOUS WARLIKE TROPHIES (4991)

273 × 368 mm. Pen and brown ink and brown wash over black chalk on blue paper, heightened with white.

297. *Recto:* NEPTUNE IN HIS CHARIOT DRAWN BY TWO SEA-HORSES AND SURROUNDED BY DOLPHINS, DRIVING TO THE R.

Verso: NEPTUNE AND A DOLPHIN (4992)

210 × 268 mm. Pen and brown ink and brown wash over black chalk on blue paper, heightened with white.

The drawing on the *recto* seems to be an alternative for No. 289 already catalogued and No. 298 *recto* following.

298. *Recto:* NEPTUNE IN HIS CHARIOT DRAWN BY TWO HORSES, DRIVING TO THE L.

Verso: HERCULES OVERCOMING THE DRAGON IN THE GARDEN OF THE HESPERIDES, AND PLUCKING THE APPLES (4993)

270 × 210 mm. Pen and brown ink and brown wash over black chalk on blue paper, heightened with white.

Inscribed on *verso* in the artist's hand: 'Al clarisimo·sor·zuan/memmo'. The *recto* is clearly connected with Nos. 289 and 297 above.

299. A MAN IN CLASSICAL COSTUME, HOLDING THE SHAFT OF A SPEAR IN HIS R. HAND, HIS L. HAND OUTSTRETCHED (4994)

425 × 252 mm. Pen and dark brown ink and wash over black chalk on blue paper, squared in white chalk.

Inscribed 'P. Farinato' in an old hand in ink at bottom R. corner. The features are those of the Emperor Vitellius as represented in a bust of which there are many drawings by Tintoretto.

300. THE EMPEROR VESPASIAN, STANDING IN A NICHE (*Plate* 174) (4995)

394 × 270 mm. Pen and brown ink and brown wash over black chalk on cream-coloured paper, heightened with white.

Inscription in top R. corner: 'INP·CAES·VESPASIA· ·/AUG· P·M·T·R·P·P·P·C·/OS· III'. On the *verso* is the sketch of the reverse of a medal with the inscription 'IVDEA CAPTA SC' and the following writing in Farinati's hand: 'P(er) riverso dila medalia di vespisiano seli fa una palma arbore grāde aqu.../modo una dona asentata tuta pensosa·e ū armado cō le mane ligate de di/[ētro] cone pregiō/il drito dila medalia se li fa: IMP·CAES·VESPA/AUG·COS·III·/Anche se lifa ū altro riverso luna figura cō unasta imano ch afronta ū perchi/cō unalbor di drio la qual figura sia p(er) dito vespisiano caciatore ouer p(er) · · ·/meleagro.'

301. JULIUS CAESAR SEATED (4996)

277 × 384 mm. Pen and brown ink and brown wash over black chalk on yellow surface, heightened with white.

Inscription in centre of lower edge: 'DIVOS·IVLIVS/–Ap riverso la sua medalia unaltra testa di ū zovene c̄o tal litere DIVI E CAESAR' (on the reverse of his medal another head of a youth with the following letters: 'DIVI E CAESAR'. These surround the sketch of the medal referred to).

302. KING DAVID SEATED, HOLDING A LYRE IN HIS R. HAND, HIS L. HAND UPRAISED (4997)

394 × 260 mm. Drawn with the point of the brush and washed in brown over black chalk, on yellowish surface, heightened with white.

He is represented seated on the quoin of an arch.

303. ALEXANDER THE GREAT STANDING HOLDING A BOOK (4998)

413 × 264 mm. Pen and brown ink and brown wash over black chalk, on a greenish-yellow surface, heightened with white.

Inscription in ink at top R. hand corner: 'INP·ALEXANDER·MAGNUS·AUG'.

304. KING SAPOR OF PERSIA STANDING IN A NICHE, HOLDING A SCEPTRE (4999)

424 × 270 mm. Pen and dark brown ink and wash, over black chalk on blue paper, heightened with white.

Inscribed in ink in top L. hand corner: 'Sapore re persiano'.

305. ALEXANDER THE GREAT IN PERSIAN COSTUME WITH CUPID AT HIS FEET, STANDING ON A PEDESTAL (*Figure* 64) (5000)

420 × 276 mm. Pen and brown ink and brown wash over black chalk on blue paper, heightened with white, squared in white chalk.

Inscription in ink at centre of lower edge: 'Alesandro magno con la coraza ai piedi e ū chupido che aquela scherzi in torno labito dalesandro sara longo alla p(er)siana molle e lasivo'. (Alexander the Great with his cuirass at his feet and with a Cupid who plays round it the dress of Alexander is to be long in the Persian fashion soft and effeminate.)

306. ATTILA HOLDING A BROAD SWORD IN HIS R. HAND AND A SHIELD IN HIS L. HAND (5001)

413 × 280 mm. Pen and brown ink and brown wash, over black chalk on blue paper, heightened with white.

An alternative head is drawn on a separate piece of paper hinged over the original head.

Inscription in ink in lower L. corner: 'Atilla in arme re di onghiera' (Attilla in arms King of Hungary).

307. ALEXANDER THE GREAT IN PERSIAN COSTUME standing in a niche with Cupid seated on his cuirass at his feet. (5002)

370 × 216 mm. Pen and dark brown ink and brown wash, over black chalk on a brown prepared surface, heightened with white.

Inscription in ink at lower edge: 'Alesandro magno cō la corazza ai piedi, et con ū chupido che aquella scherzi labito dall' alesandro sara longa ala p(er)siana molle e lasivo'. 'P. Farinato' in pencil. The inscription is almost identical with that on No. 305, of which a translation is given.

308. SOLOMON AND ISAIAH HOLDING TABLETS, AND ANOTHER ROUGHER SKETCH OF SOLOMON. (5003)

253 × 233 mm. Pen and brown ink and brown wash, over black chalk on light blue paper, heightened with white.

Inscription in ink on Solomon's tablet: 'tota pulchra es et macula non est in te,' and on Isaiah's tablet: 'ECCE VIRGO CONCIPIET ET PARIET FILIUM'. Also in lower L. hand corner: 'aciprete di grignan/ceti'.

FIG. 64 Cat. No. 305

309. *Recto:* OVAL COMPOSITION: HERCULES CHAINING CERBERUS (5004)

242 × 189 mm. Pen and dark brown ink and wash on blue paper, heightened with white.

Verso: ADAM AND EVE

Same technique as *recto*, but without white.

Lit.: Giuseppe Fiocco, Madonna Verona X (1916), p. 51. Inscribed on the *verso* in the artist's hand: 'Le None (?) andete a san martin ali. 8. aprile. 1603./insieme co cristofalo e li putini una caroza'. The second line is largely covered by the mount. It is read as above by Fiocco, except that for 'caroza' he reads 'corona', which is clearly wrong.

310. HOPE SEATED, TURNED TO THE L., HOLDING AN ANCHOR (5005)

355 × 264 mm. Pen and brown ink and brown wash, over black chalk on blue paper, heightened with white.

Inscribed 'P. Farinato' in ink in an XVIII century hand in lower R. hand corner.

311. DESIGN FOR A STATUE (?) OF CHARITY, giving money to a child on her R., and bread to another on her L., hand. (5006)

363 × 234 mm. Pen and brown ink and brown wash over black chalk on blue paper, heightened with white.

312. FEMALE FIGURE OF PLENTY HOLDING A CORNUCOPIA trampling on a crouching male figure, whose raised R. arm is without a hand. (5007)

425 × 219 mm. Pen and dark brown ink and lighter brown wash over black chalk on blue paper, heightened with white.

313. VICTORY HOLDING A TUBA ALOFT IN HER R. HAND, A CROWN AND PALM IN HER L.; she stands on a trophy of arms. (5008)

415 × 263 mm. Pen and brown ink and wash on buff-coloured paper over black chalk, heightened with white. An alternative head is shown on a separate piece of paper hinged over the original head.

This may be a very late drawing by Paolo, but I suspect it is by one of his sons.

314. NEPTUNE AND MEDUSA (5009)

423 × 256 mm. Pen and brown ink and wash over black chalk on yellow surface, heightened with white.

Inscribed in the artist's hand in an arc at lower edge: 'netuno e medusa sua diva efu anche sua diva dorida'. (Neptune and Medusa his mistress; Doris was also his mistress.)

315. AFRICA SEATED ON A LARGE LOBSTER, holding in her R. hand a stick on which is a turban surmounted by a crescent; Hercules, holding his club, is seated beside her with his arm on her shoulder, and Cupid is seen behind him on the R. (5010)

275 × 427 mm. Pen and brown ink and grey wash on blue-grey paper, heightened with white.

Inscription in ink at top edge: 'mezo zorno', and on lower edge: 'Africha' and 'erchole'.

In his diary for March, 1581 (Madonna Verona, II (1906), p. 136) Farinati records having painted for Piero Francesco Miniscalcho figures in chiaroscuro and coloured of Europe, Asia and Africa. The house of the Conti Miniscalchi, where this work was carried out, does not survive, but it is possible that the present drawing might have been made for it.

316. MINERVA AND PROMETHEUS: ROUNDEL (5011)

400 × 365 mm. Pen and dark brown ink and wash over black chalk on blue paper, heightened with white.

Inscribed in the artist's hand at the lower edge (partly cut away): '·2· Pezo secondo come minerva cōduse prometo al cielo et deto prometeo tolle il focho dal sole e lo porto . . .' (2 Second piece how Minerva brought Prometheus to the sky and the said Prometheus took the fire from the sun and carried it . . .)

317. *Recto:* IMPRESA: A DOVE HOLDING AN OLIVE BRANCH HOVERS OVER A TREE-TRUNK TO WHICH A YOKE HAS BEEN TIED. An arm in a long draped sleeve on the L. holds a sword, which is cutting the knot. On the R. another arm with a sword is raised.

Verso: TWO SEA-HORSES (5012)

261 × 210 mm. Pen and brown ink and brown wash on blue paper, heightened with white.

Inscribed in ink in lower R. corner: 'P. Farinato' and '3·1·' (= 3/–) the method of pricing used by William Gibson.

318. MADONNA AND CHILD (5013)

321 × 179 mm. Black chalk and brown wash on blue paper, heightened with white.

This feeble drawing can hardly be by Paolo Farinati himself, but it may have been produced in his workshop.

319. CHRIST TAKEN DOWN FROM THE CROSS; St. John kneels on the L. holding the crown of thorns while the Magdalene kneels at His feet; the Virgin Mary looks up to heaven; other figures stand beside her; the sepulchre is seen in the rocks behind. (5014)
353 × 253 mm. Pen and dark brown ink and wash, over black chalk on an orange prepared surface, heightened with white.

320. FRIEZE OF MUSICAL INSTRUMENTS, WITH TWO PUTTI PLAYING AMONGST THEM (5015)

321. COMPANION FRIEZE OF THREE PUTTI with various weapons of war and parts of armour. (5016)
Each 94 × 426 mm. Pen and dark brown ink and wash on cream-coloured ground heightened with white.

322. FRIEZE OF SIX PUTTI BEARING THE CROSS AND THE OTHER INSTRUMENTS OF THE PASSION (5017)
185 × 275 mm. Pen and dark brown ink and wash over black chalk on yellow ground, heightened with white.
Orazio Farinati etched this drawing (Bartsch, XVI, p. 171, 5) in reverse.

323. A GROUP OF RIVER-GODS WITH URNS seated in various attitudes on a rock to the L.; to the R. a swan flies up the river towards them. (5072)
287 × 400 mm. Dark grey wash, heightened with white, on a yellow prepared surface.
A.E.P. I think there can be no doubt that this drawing is by Paolo Farinati, though it does not come from the volume of his drawings. It is in wash only without the characteristic pen-work added.

324. CHRIST CARRYING THE CROSS, THE VIRGIN FAINTING ON THE RIGHT (5079)
283 × 208 mm. Black chalk and washes of brown.
A.E.P. Perhaps the work of one of Paolo's sons. The unusual appearance of the drawing is due to the absence of the pen and ink outlines and shading which Farinati usually added.

Attributed to GAUDENZIO FERRARI (About 1480–1546)

325. HEAD OF A WOMAN WITH LONG HAIR LOOKING DOWN TO THE R. (12820)
269 × 209 mm. Black chalk on coarse, very much faded blue paper.
Photo.: Braun 230 (?).
I do not know whether the attribution of this attractive drawing to Gaudenzio Ferrari is a traditional one. It was photographed by Braun as Leonardo da Vinci. The character of the drawing is unusual—it might be the fragment of a cartoon—and it is difficult to feel any certainty about it, nevertheless the attribution to Gaudenzio seems a possible one, and I have no better suggestion to offer. The head might well be that of a St. Mary Magdalene in an *Entombment* or *Descent from the Cross*.

GIOVANNI AMBROGIO FIGINO (1548–1608)

326. One hundred and twenty drawings mounted in an album measuring 520 × 390 mm. The album, bound in red morocco and elaborately tooled, was made for Consul Smith in Venice. It has an illuminated title page by Antonio Visentini (1688–1782) with the Consul's coat-of-arms at the bottom of the page and another at the top. The latter do not seem to be those of Figino, which are given by Rietstap as *d'azur à un chateau sommé de deux tours d'argent*. Renesse attributed the dexter coat *spaccato d'azzuro e d'argento, al levriere rampante nell' altro* to the family of Romei of Ferrara. The title is as follows:

IOHANNIS AMBROSII / FIGINI / MEDIOLANENSIS, / VIRI AEVVI SVI, ARTE / DELINEATORIA PICTORIAQUE,/NEMINI SECUNDI;/OPVS.

A companion volume, smaller in size, less elaborately tooled and without a title page, has been separated from its fellow and is in the King's Library of the British Museum (*Catalogue of Royal and King's MSS. in the British Museum*, London, 1921, Vol. III, p. 58, King's 323). This contains a number of sonnets and other verses, mostly in Italian, in praise of Figino and his works, by eminent compatriots.
The Windsor album must contain the largest collection of drawings by Figino—at any rate, outside Italy. No doubt a careful study of the numerous paintings by him still existing in Milanese churches would reveal the purpose of many of the sketches in the album, but such a study has not been possible.
The only two definitely connected with any painting of which illustrations are available are No. 54 for the picture of *St. Ambrose expelling the Aryans*, now in the Castello Sforzesco at Milan (Venturi, IX 7, Fig. 285), and No. 45, for the *Ascension of Our Lord*, on one of the organ shutters of the Duomo at Milan (Venturi, IX 7, Fig. 282).
There are, however, whole series of studies for definite compositions, the most important of which are *St. Matthew with the Angel* (No. 69, etc.), the *Agony in the Garden* (No. 6, etc.), the *Lucretia Stabbing Herself* (No. 14, etc.) and the *Vestal Tuccia* (No. 74, etc.). It is a characteristic of Figino as a draughtsman to make numberless small sketches, sometimes as many as twenty or thirty on the same sheet, in which he tries out the arrangement of the whole composition and the attitudes of the individual figures composing it in every variation which occurs to him. His most usual method is to sketch in his composition or his figure in red chalk and then to finish it in very fine pen and light brown ink. He generally makes use of a very thin, creamy-white paper with rather strongly-marked chain-lines and water-marks of a pilgrim in a circle or an escutcheon charged with three shields, but I have not thought it necessary—it is only sometimes possible—to study or to record the water-marks. Figino also employs blue paper, and occasionally prepared grounds and red, and fine grey, chalk. The last is his favourite medium for copies from Michelangelo, of which there are at least 21, and from the antique. These are sometimes heightened with white.
An attempt was made by Consul Smith to arrange the drawings in the album according to subject, and they were numbered accordingly from 1 to 118, beginning with No. 4 (6872), for the first three drawings were added to the album in the XIX century, as appears from a note on the fly-leaf by J. H. G[lover], Royal Librarian, 1836–60, who refers to 118 drawings only (there are now 121), and from the different style of the borders surrounding these first three drawings (mentioned in George III 'Inventory A', p. 117). The order then in which Smith arranged the drawings was roughly as follows:

Nos. 4–18. Studies of limbs.
Nos. 19–35, 39–50. Mostly copies from Michelangelo.
Nos. 36–38, 51–53. Copies from the Laocoon.
Nos. 54–113. Mainly original composition studies by Figino.
Nos. 114–121. Copies of Marcantonio engravings and Michelangelo.

I have not thought it necessary to record in the catalogue the numbering marked on the drawings or the name of Figino and/or Michelangelo, which constantly occur.

Lit.: Bibliotheca Smithiana. Venice, 1755, p. clxxiv (Figinus, J. Ambrosius, Mediolanensis Pictor, Schedae & Experimenta, ms. fol. m. leg. *Corio Turcico rubro deaur.*).

Mentioned in George III 'Inventory A', p. 117.

1. STUDY FOR A COMPOSITION OF CHRIST ON THE CROSS WITH THE FAINTING VIRGIN AT ITS FOOT (*Plate* 142) (6869)

203 × 137 mm. Pen and brown ink and brown wash over red chalk.

2. SLIGHTER SKETCH, WITH VARIATIONS, FOR THE SAME COMPOSITION (*Figure* 65) (6870)

FIG. 65 Cat. No. 326/2

204 × 135 mm. Pen and brown ink over red chalk.

I do not know the picture for which no doubt these studies were prepared.

3. FIVE STUDIES OF APOSTLES, THREE OF WHICH APPEAR TO REPRESENT ST. PAUL, AND FOUR NUDE FIGURES (6871)

199 × 110 mm. Pen and brown ink and brown wash.

A drawing on the *verso* of an apostle holding a book can be distinguished through the backing.

4. ELEVEN STUDIES OF LEGS AND KNEES (6872)

260 × 190 mm. Black chalk.

5. THREE STUDIES OF A L. ARM, five of a L. foot, two of a bird's claw and one of a bent R. arm and part of a head and torso. (6873)

224 × 183 mm. Black chalk.

6. THREE STUDIES OF A L. FOOT, one of a torso seen from the back, and one of a sleeping figure. (6874)

246 × 188 mm. Black chalk on blue paper.

The sleeping figure appears to be for an *Agony in the Garden*, for which there are numerous other studies in the album (326/60, 61, 88, 99, 100, 109).

7. TWO STUDIES OF LEGS BENT AS IF THE FIGURE WERE SEATED, one of the L. leg from the knee down, two of the L. foot—all these are *écorchés*—and one of a bird's claw. (6875)

260 × 166 mm. Red chalk.

Perhaps in part after Michelangelo.

8. FIVE STUDIES OF THE R. LEG SLIGHTLY BENT, one of the R. leg bent double, one of the L. leg standing, and one of the knee. (6876)

257 × 185 mm. Black chalk.

9. TWO STUDIES OF THE R. LEG BENT DOUBLE, one of the R. leg standing and one on the toe, two of the L. leg standing and one of the L. leg bent back. (6877)

257 × 197 mm. Black chalk.

10. STUDIES OF TWO 'ÉCORCHÉ' HUMAN LEGS AND OF THREE HORSE'S LEGS (6878)

267 × 196 mm. Red chalk.

Possibly after Leonardo (see similar studies at Windsor, e.g. Nos. 12633 and 12634).

11. SEVEN STUDIES OF THE L. LEG BOTH BENT AND STRAIGHT, one of the R. leg and one of the knee. (6879)

229 × 290 mm. Red and black chalk (four in each).

The red chalk studies are similar to those on 326/7 and must be from the same model.

12. STUDIES OF TWO HANDS, AN ARM AND TWO SLEEVES (6880)

238 × 185 mm. Black chalk on blue paper.

13. STUDIES OF A L. HAND AND OF A R. ARM BENT as though the figure were supporting something. (6881)

162 × 130 mm. Red chalk on a lighter red prepared surface.

14. STUDIES OF THE DRAPERY OF A SLEEVE AND OF A R. HAND HOLDING A DAGGER (*Figure* 66) (6882)

275 × 197 mm. Red chalk on a lighter red prepared surface.

The hand holding the dagger is probably for a Lucretia (see studies of this subject, 326/67, 80, 81, 84, 85 and 86). The style of this and the preceding drawing seems to imply a conscious imitation of Cesare da Sesto. Figino is in fact recorded by Torre (*Il Ritratto di Milano*, 1674, p. 304) to have copied Cesare da Sesto's *Herodias*.

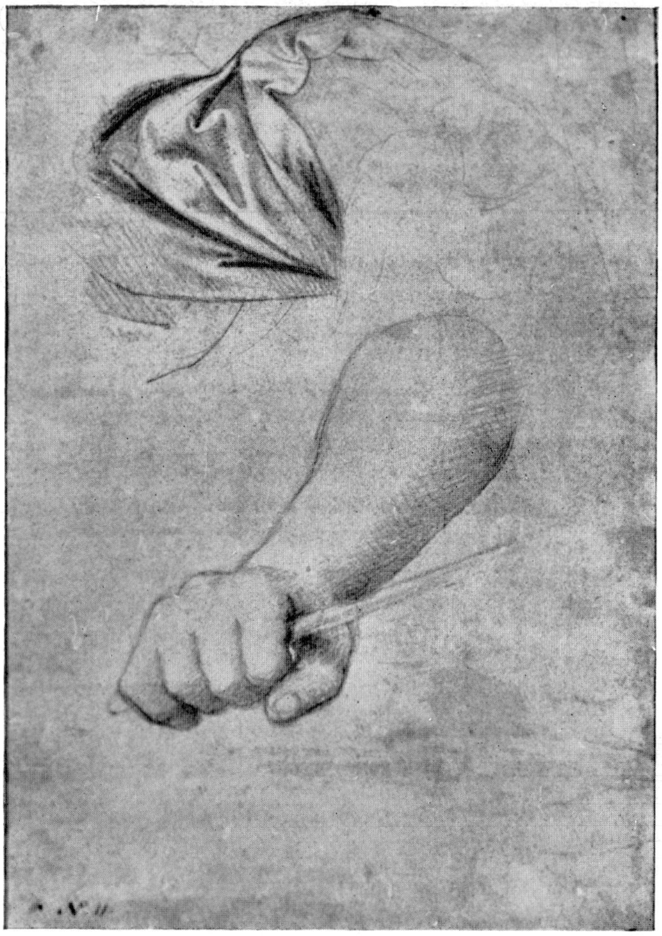

FIG. 66 Cat. No. 326/14

15. STUDIES OF A WOMAN'S ARMS IN THE POSITION OF THOSE OF THE VENUS DE MEDICI AND OF A R. AND L. LEG, BOTH BENT (6883)
210 × 286 mm. Red chalk on a red prepared surface, heightened with white.

16. *Recto:* SEVEN STUDIES OF ARMS BENT AT THE ELBOW AND TWO STUDIES OF BONES

Verso: TWO STUDIES OF A SEATED EVANGELIST HOLDING A BOOK (6884)
230 × 330 mm. Black chalk, except for one study of an arm in red chalk.

17. ELEVEN STUDIES OF ARMS, THREE BENT, THE OTHERS EXTENDED (6885)
335 × 225 mm. Red chalk, except for three in black chalk.

18. *Recto:* EIGHT STUDIES OF ARMS AND ONE OF THE BONES OF THE HAND

Verso: THREE STUDIES OF THE R. ARM (6886)
271 × 191 mm. Black chalk except for one arm on the *verso* in red chalk.

19. TORSO OF A MAN SEEN FROM THE BACK (6887)
270 × 190 mm. Black chalk over an outline in red chalk.
Copy of the figure holding a spear in the L. foreground of Michelangelo's *Crucifixion of St. Peter* in the Cappella Paolina.

20. FOUR STUDIES OF A MALE TORSO: two from the front, one from the back, and one from the side. (6888)
251 × 181 mm. Black chalk.
Another study of a torso seen from the back is visible on the *verso* through the backing.

21. *Recto:* STUDIES OF A MALE FIGURE from the front, another from the side, and three studies of legs.

Verso: EIGHT STUDIES OF LEGS, TWO IN A KNEELING POSITION (6889)
261 × 180 mm. Black chalk.

22. TWO TORSOS (6890)
183 × 238 mm. Red and black chalk.
After the Torso Belvedere.

23. *Recto:* STUDIES OF A NUDE MALE FIGURE WITH HIS R. ARM ABOVE HIS HEAD, six studies of the legs or parts of the legs of the same figure and three studies from Michelangelo's *Night.*

Verso: HEAD OF A MADONNA, MALE NUDE, A L. FOOT, DRAPERY, AND THE LEGS OF A CHILD (6891)
230 × 164 mm. Black chalk.
The male figure on the *recto* resembles Michelangelo's *Slave* in the Louvre (K.d.K. 93), but reversed. The foot and the child's legs on the *verso* are copied from Barocci's *Rest on the Flight Into Egypt* (see 326/82).

24. TWO STUDIES OF MALE NUDES FOR A FLAGELLATION (*Figure* 67) (6892)
230 × 138 mm. Black chalk on yellowish paper.
Perhaps for the same composition as 326/25, 73 and 119.

25. FOUR STUDIES OF A MALE NUDE FOR A FLAGELLATION, a standing male nude pointing to the R. and a larger study of the upper part of his figure, the upper part of a man leaning on his R. arm, and other slight sketches. (6893)
430 × 275 mm. Black chalk on yellowish paper.
The four studies are perhaps for the same composition as 326/24. The nude man in profile to the R. in the act of scourging corresponds with one of the executioners in the *Scourging of Christ* in the Prado by some follower of Michelangelo (ill. Mitteil. des Kunsthistorischen Instituts in Florenz, IV (1932), p. 45).

26. STUDY OF A L. ARM (6894)
192 × 263 mm. Black chalk on blue paper, heightened with white.
From the L. arm of St. Peter in Michelangelo's *Last Judgment.*

27. STUDY OF A L. ARM (6895)
149 × 307 mm. Red chalk on blue paper.

28. STUDY OF A R. ARM (6896)
272 × 190 mm. Black chalk on blue paper, heightened with white.
Copied from the figure above St. Catherine in Michelangelo's *Last Judgment.* See also 326/31.

29. STUDY OF A R. ARM (6897)
280 × 205 mm. Black chalk on blue paper, heightened with white.
Copied from the R. arm of Minos in Michelangelo's *Last Judgment.*

FIG. 67 Cat. No. 326/24

30. STUDY OF A R. LEG (6898)
278 × 176 mm. Black chalk on blue paper.
Copied from the R. leg of the Saviour in Michelangelo's *Last Judgment*.

31. STUDY OF A R. ARM (6899)
388 × 268 mm. Black chalk on blue paper, heightened with white.
Copied from the R. arm of the figure above St. Catherine in the *Last Judgment*. A larger version of 326/28.

32. STUDY OF A R. ARM (6900)
415 × 266 mm. Black chalk on blue paper, heightened with white.
Copied from the figure kneeling on one knee in the L. foreground of the *Last Judgment*.

33. STUDIES OF TWO MEN AND A DEMON (6901)
266 × 207 mm. Red and black chalk on blue paper.
The upper study is from a man in the extreme L. hand corner at the bottom in the *Last Judgment*, the one on the R. from a figure above this, and the demon from a group on the extreme R. of the fresco.

34. A NUDE MAN SEEN FROM BEHIND, LEANING BACK ON BOTH ARMS (6902)
186 × 187 mm. Red chalk.
From a prominent figure in the L. foreground of the *Last Judgment*.

35. HEAD AND ARMS OF A MAN (6903)
206 × 266 mm. Black chalk on blue paper.
From a soaring figure towards the L. in the *Last Judgment*.

36. STUDY FROM THE YOUTH ON THE L. IN THE LAOCOON (6904)
261 × 170 mm. Red chalk.

37. STUDY FROM THE SAME FIGURE IN THE LAOCOON AS 326/36, OF A FEMALE NUDE AND OF A HAND (6905)
268 × 185 mm. Red chalk.

38. STUDY OF THE SAME FIGURE IN THE LAOCOON GROUP AS THE TWO PRECEDING DRAWINGS, and of a man's head in profile to the L. (6906)
262 × 185 mm. Red chalk.

39. HEAD AND SHOULDERS OF A MAN (6907)
171 × 96 mm. Red chalk.
From a figure in Charon's boat in the *Last Judgment*.

40. TWO STUDIES FROM THE SAME FIGURE AS IN THE PRECEDING DRAWING, eleven studies of glasses, a personified wind and a heraldic dragon. (6908)
280 × 207 mm. Pen and brown ink and brown wash.

41. STUDY OF THE HEAD, TORSO AND L. ARM OF A RECLINING FIGURE (6909)
272 × 204 mm. Black chalk on blue paper.
From the figure behind and to the R. of the man stepping out of the ground near the L. of the *Last Judgment*.

42. STUDY OF THE SAME FIGURE AS IN 326/39, of part of the torso and of the R. arm of a man. (6910)
180 × 274 mm. Black chalk.
The second study is from the demon with a man on his back flying above Charon's boat in the *Last Judgment*.

43. STUDIES FROM THE FIGURE OF MINOS, a devil, a devil flying off with a man on his back, and another flying devil. (6911)
243 × 207 mm. Black chalk.
From figures in or near the R. hand bottom corner of the *Last Judgment*.

44. STUDY OF A CLIMBING MAN SEEN FROM THE BACK (6912)
423 × 271 mm. Black chalk on blue paper, heightened with white.
From a figure in the air in the group above Charon's boat in the *Last Judgment*.

45. SHEET WITH, AT THE TOP, A VERY FAINT STUDY OF A NUDE MAN (6913)
420 × 266 mm. Black chalk on blue paper.
This appears to be a study for the painting of the *Ascension of Our Lord* on the organ shutters of the Duomo at Milan (Venturi, IX 7, Fig. 282).

46. STUDY FROM AN ANTIQUE STATUE OF VICTORY (?) AND FROM THE BACK OF A NUDE TORSO (6914)
263 × 187 mm. Red chalk.

47. STUDIES FROM THE GROUP IN THE 'LAST JUDGMENT' WHICH INCLUDES ST. PETER AND THE FIGURES TO THE R. OF HIM (6915)

192 × 202 mm. Red chalk.

48. STUDIES FROM THE GROUP IN THE 'LAST JUDGMENT' WHICH INCLUDES ST. CATHERINE (6916)

100 × 190 mm. (top corners cut). Pen and ink on light brown paper.

49. A SECOND COPY OF THE GROUP WHICH INCLUDES ST. CATHERINE (6917)

96 × 165 mm. Pen and ink on light brown paper.

50. THE GROUP HOLDING THE COLUMN AT THE TOP OF THE 'LAST JUDGMENT' (6918)

154 × 235 mm. Pen and ink.

51. LAOCOON IN THE GROUP OF THAT NAME (6919)

275 × 214 mm. Black chalk on blue paper.

52. ANOTHER VIEW OF THE FIGURE OF LAOCOON (6920)

420 × 253 mm. Black chalk on blue paper.

53. ANOTHER VIEW OF THE SAME FIGURE BUT WITHOUT THE HEAD (6921)

412 × 245 mm. Black chalk on blue paper.

54. ST. AMBROSE EXPELLING THE ARYANS (*Figure* 68) (6922)

124 × 90 mm. Pen and brown ink and brown wash on blue paper, heightened with white.

FIG. 68 Cat. No. 326/54

Study for the painting of the subject now in the Castello Sforzesco, Milan (Venturi, IX 7, Fig. 285).

55. NUDE WOMAN SEEN FROM THE BACK (6923)

330 × 233 mm. Black and red chalk.

Copy from a figure in one of the pendentives of the Farnesina, *Cupid pointing out Psyche to the Graces.*

56. COMPOSITION, ALMOST EFFACED, OF FOUR DANCING ANGELS (6924)

235 × 267 mm. Black chalk on blue paper.

57. ST. VERONICA, KNEELING TO THE L., HOLDING THE SUDARIUM (6925)

185 × 267 mm. Oil on chocolate-coloured ground.

Apparently an original study by Figino for some composition of *Christ carrying the Cross.*

58. STUDY OF THE DRAPERY OF A FIGURE KNEELING TO THE L. (6926)

198 × 142 mm. Black chalk on blue paper.

Perhaps for a Christ in an *Agony in the Garden.*

59. DESIGN FOR A LUNETTE WITH FOUR FATHERS OF THE CHURCH AND OTHER SAINTS (6927)

107 × 185 mm. Pen and brown ink over black chalk.

60. STUDY FOR A KNEELING CHRIST IN AN AGONY IN THE GARDEN (6928)

267 × 196 mm. Black chalk on blue paper.

A sketch for the whole composition in which this figure occurs will be found under 326/99; other studies for it will be found listed under 326/6.

61. SHEET WITH FOUR STUDIES OF A SLEEPING APOSTLE AND A GROUP OF COMBATANTS (6929)

227 × 173 mm. Black chalk on blue paper.

The apostles are studies for the composition already referred to of the Agony in the Garden (see 326/6).

62. THREE STUDIES OF THE DRAPED BODY OF A WOMAN ADVANCING TOWARDS THE SPECTATOR (6930)

230 × 376 mm. Faint black chalk on blue paper, heightened with white.

Apparently from the antique.

63. FIGURE OF A DRAPED MAN (6931)

247 × 135 mm. Black chalk on blue paper.

64. TWO STUDIES OF DRAPED FIGURES (6932)

210 × 207 mm. Black chalk on blue paper.

These two drawings are so faint as to be hardly distinguishable.

65. STUDY FOR AN ANNUNCIATION AND A SEPARATE STUDY OF THE VIRGIN (6933)

240 × 380 mm. Black chalk on blue paper.

66. THE ARCHANGEL MICHAEL EXPELLING THE REBEL ANGELS (*Plate* 143) (6934)

418 × 285 mm. Pen and ink on chocolate prepared surface, heightened with white.

Other studies of the Archangel Michael are 326/67, 70, 87, 91 and 97.

67. *Recto:* FIVE STUDIES OF A LUCRETIA, two of a woman running, one of a woman with a sieve, and one of the Archangel Michael.

Verso: VARIOUS STUDIES OF FIGURES and one of Prosperpina being carried off by Pluto. (6935)

202 × 128 mm. Pen and brown ink over red chalk.

For other studies of Lucretia, see 326/14; for the Archangel Michael, see 326/66.

68. FIVE COMPLETE STUDIES FOR A COMPOSITION OF THE VIRGIN ADORING THE INFANT CHRIST AND SEPARATE STUDIES OF THE VIRGIN (6936)
131 × 197 mm. Pen and ink.

69. VARIOUS FIGURE STUDIES on two pieces of paper fitted together: on the L. hand portion two nude studies and an angel of the *Annunciation*; on the R. hand portion seven studies for a *St. Matthew with the angel.* (6937)
124 × 180 mm. Pen and brown ink and red chalk.
There are numerous other studies for this St. Matthew: see below, 326/97, 100, 101, 102 and 106. They are perhaps for the painting in St. Raffaelle, Milan, mentioned by Torre (*Il Ritratto di Milano*, 1674, p. 359).

70. SHEET OF STUDIES WITH A WOMAN'S PORTRAIT AND A NUMBER OF SMALL NUDE FIGURES, TWO OF WHICH ARE FOR A ST. MICHAEL (6938)
200 × 200 mm. Pen and brown ink and red chalk.
For other studies of St. Michael, see 326/66.

71. *Recto:* NUMEROUS STUDIES, THREE OF WHICH ARE FOR AN ANNUNCIATION
Verso: VARIOUS STUDIES, MOSTLY OF NEPTUNE DRIVING TWO SEA-HORSES (6939)
280 × 198 mm. Pen and brown ink, in most cases over red chalk.
There are a number of other studies for the Neptune, 326/75, 77, 81 and 84.

72. *Recto:* THE ENTOMBMENT: COMPOSITION SKETCH
Verso: THREE-QUARTER LENGTH NUDE WOMAN, HER HANDS CLASPED IN PRAYER (6940)
236 × 200 mm. Indian ink over red chalk.

73. *Recto:* ABOUT SEVENTEEN SMALL STUDIES FOR AN ENTOMBMENT OR A PIETÀ, ONE FOR AN 'ECCE HOMO' AND ONE FOR A FLAGELLATION (the last on a separate piece of paper).
Verso: FOUR COMPLETE STUDIES FOR AN 'ECCE HOMO' (6941)
211 × 272 mm. Pen and brown ink, in a few instances over red chalk.
For other studies for a *Flagellation*, see 326/24; for the *Ecce Homo*, see 326/77 and 99.

74. *Recto:* THREE STUDIES OF A WOMAN CARRYING A SIEVE (THE VESTAL TUCCIA), five studies of figures running, a study of two warriors fighting, and two seated figures.
Verso: SIX STUDIES OF A HOLY FAMILY, AND TWO OTHER FIGURES (6942)
272 × 200 mm. Pen and brown ink over red chalk.
Other studies for the *Tuccia* are 326/74, 87, 92.

75. *Recto:* A MAN ON HORSEBACK WITH A SPEAR PRECEDED BY A MAN WITH A TORCH, THE VESTAL TUCCIA, NEPTUNE, SIX MALE FIGURES AND ONE SEATED WOMAN
Verso: THREE STUDIES OF THE VESTAL TUCCIA, PSYCHE AWAKENING THE SLEEPING CUPID, HERCULES WITH HIS CLUB (?), A MAN WITH A TORCH TWO, RUNNING FIGURES AND OTHER STUDIES (6943)
278 × 210 mm. Pen and brown ink over red chalk, and red chalk alone.
Other studies of the *Psyche* are 326/76, 92, 93; for others of the *Tuccia*, see 326/74, and of the *Neptune*, 326/71.

76. SHEET WITH THREE COMPLETE STUDIES OF THE ANNUNCIATION, two separate studies of the angel Gabriel and two of the Virgin Annunciate. (6944)
242 × 188 mm. Pen and brown ink over red chalk (except in the case of three figures) on blue paper.

77. *Recto:* STUDIES OF A R. HAND HOLDING A VASE, FOUR GROUPS OF NEPTUNE with his trident driving two sea-horses and four separate studies for this composition.
Verso: LARGE STUDY OF PSYCHE AWAKENING CUPID, two for a Christ in an *Ecce Homo*, a nude woman, Cupid flying away from Psyche (?) and a seated figure. (6945)
280 × 211 mm. Pen and ink, sometimes over red chalk, and red and black chalk (for the hand).
For other studies of the *Neptune*, see 326/71; for the *Psyche awakening Cupid*, 326/75; and for the *Ecce Homo*, 326/73.

78. *Recto:* SEVEN STUDIES OF GALLOPING CENTAURS AND TWO OTHER FIGURES
Verso: SIX COMPLETE OR PARTIAL STUDIES OF GALLOPING CENTAURS, in one case carrying off a woman. (6946)
194 × 136 mm. Pen and brown ink over red chalk.
For other studies of centaurs, see 326/81 and 84.

79. THREE COMPLETE STUDIES OF ST. JOHN BAPTIZING OUR LORD, a number of separate studies for one or the other of these figures, and a three-quarter length figure of a man for a different composition. (6947)
238 × 180 mm. Pen and brown ink.
For another study of the same subject, see 326/102 *verso*.

80. STUDIES OF A SEATED LUCRETIA, OF A FEMALE FIGURE, OF A HURRYING MAN AND OF ST. MARY MAGDALENE (AFTER TITIAN) (6948)
133 × 200 mm. Pen and brown ink over red chalk.
For other studies of Lucretia, see 326/14.

81. *Recto:* SIX STUDIES OF GALLOPING CENTAURS, one of Neptune with two sea-horses, one of a seated Evangelist, one of a Lucretia (?), and other compositions.
Verso: THREE STUDIES OF GALLOPING CENTAURS, three of horses (one winged), two complete compositions of Lucretia, a figure of Minerva or Bellona, and other studies. (6949)
200 × 281 mm. Pen and brown ink over red chalk.
For other studies of centaurs, see 326/78 and a sheet in the Fogg Museum (Mongan and Sachs, *Drawings in the Fogg Museum of Art*, Cambridge, Mass., 1940, No. 571, as School of Fontainebleau); for studies of Lucretia, see 326/14; and for others of Neptune, see 326/71.

82. *Recto:* COPY OF PART OF BAROCCI'S REST ON THE FLIGHT INTO EGYPT (Vatican Gallery, Venturi, IX 7, Fig. 492). (6950)
285 × 242 mm. Black chalk on blue paper.
Verso: STUDIES OF TWO TORSOS
Black chalk, heightened with white.
Barocci's composition is reversed and Figino was therefore probably copying from an engraving. Copies of part of the same composition are on 326/23.

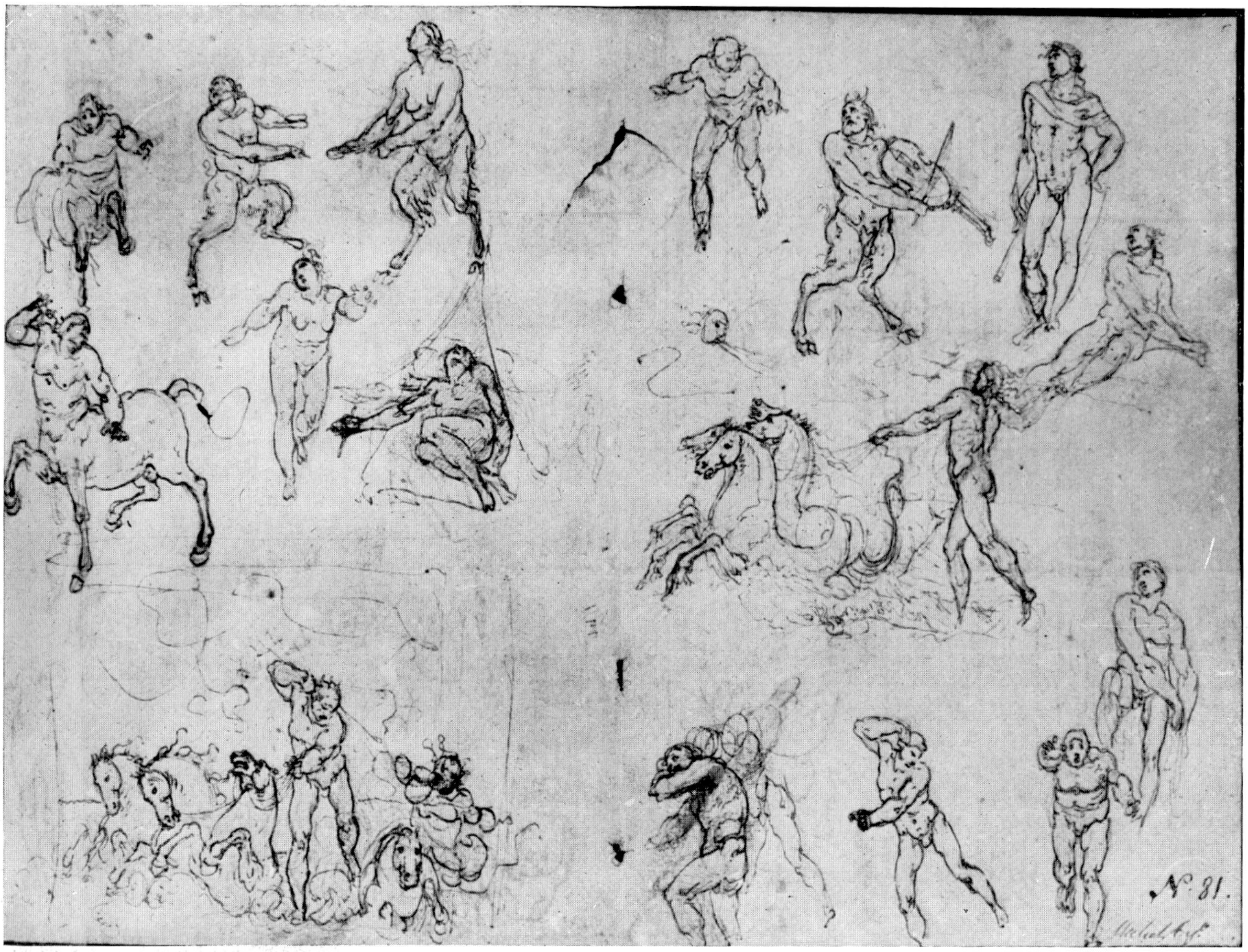

FIG. 69 Cat. No. 326/84 r.

83. CHRIST ON THE CROSS WITH THE VIRGIN MARY AND ST. MARY MAGDALENE BELOW; separate studies of a St. John (?) and of a Virgin lamenting. (6951)
242 × 182 mm. Red chalk and some pen and ink.

84. *Recto:* TWO STUDIES OF NEPTUNE DRIVING HIS SEA-HORSES, two of centaurs, one of a Lucretia, two of satyrs, one of a satyress, and various other single figures. (*Figure* 69)

Verso: THREE STUDIES OF A LUCRETIA, one of the Rape of Europa, one of Hercules attacking a serpent, one of a dog and a bull, one of a lady in XVI century costume and other studies. (6952)
201 × 185 mm. Pen and brown ink over red chalk.
For other studies of Neptune, see 326/71; of Lucretia, 326/14; and of centaurs, 326/78.

85. *Recto:* STUDIES FOR A LUCRETIA, for a St. Jerome being summoned by an angel (?), Perseus and Andromeda, a man with a galloping horse and other figures.

Verso: PORTRAIT HEAD OF A LADY, profile of a Caesar, *putti*, etc. (6953)
282 × 219 mm. Pen and brown ink, mostly over red chalk.
For studies of Lucretia, see 326/14.

86. *Recto:* VARIOUS STUDIES, INCLUDING A MAN ON A GALLOPING HORSE, a Lucretia, a Hercules, and other figures.

Verso: TWO STUDIES FOR A COMPOSITION OF THE ENTOMBMENT, a man on horseback and other single figures. (6954)
200 × 283 mm. Pen and brown ink mostly over red chalk.
For studies of Lucretia, see 326/14.

87. *Recto:* STUDY OF AN ANNUNCIATION, a woman with a vessel (Tuccia ?), two studies of a St. Michael and other figures.

Verso: STUDIES OF VARIOUS FIGURES, MALE AND FEMALE, AND OF A HORSE (6955)
278 × 209 mm. Pen and brown ink, mostly over red chalk.
For other studies of the *Tuccia*, see 326/74, of the Archangel Michael, 326/66.

88. TWELVE STUDIES OF A MADONNA AND CHILD TRAMPLING ON THE DRAGON, and a number of studies for sleeping apostles. (6956)
410 × 270 mm. Pen and brown ink over black chalk.
The studies of the Madonna are perhaps for the painting in S. Antonio, Milan, described as follows by Torre (*Il Ritratto di Milano*, 1674, p. 44): 'Sulla Porta del Cimitero quel quadro, che osservate con ornamento di Cornice, ove stassi la Vergine col Bambino premendo con un piede il capo a mostruosa Vipera dipinse Ambrogio Figino'.
For other studies of sleeping apostles in the *Agony in the Garden*, see 326/6.

89. STUDY FOR A COMPOSITION OF THE VIRGIN AND CHILD WITH THE INFANT ST. JOHN (6957)
410 × 270 mm. Pen and pale brown ink and red and black chalk.

90. *Recto:* STUDY FOR A COMPOSITION OF THE VIRGIN AND CHILD WITH THE INFANT ST. JOHN
Verso: STUDY FOR A ST. MARY MAGDALENE IN PENITENCE AND A NUDE FIGURE BEFORE A BRAZIER (6958)
270 × 201 mm. Pen and ink over red chalk.

91. *Recto:* VIRGIN AND CHILD, ST. MICHAEL, SEATED NUDE WOMAN AND A NUDE MAN
Verso: STUDY FOR A HOLY FAMILY, ETC. (6959)
272 × 200 mm. Pen and brown ink over red chalk.
For other studies of St. Michael, see 326/66.

92. *Recto:* TWO STUDIES OF THE VESTAL TUCCIA, AND PSYCHE AWAKENING CUPID
Verso: VIRGIN AND CHILD AND THE INFANT ST. JOHN (6960)
274 × 207 mm. Pen and ink over red chalk.
For other studies of the *Tuccia*, see 326/74; of *Psyche awakening Cupid*, 326/75.

93. *Recto:* ONE LARGE AND TWO SMALLER STUDIES OF PSYCHE AWAKENING CUPID, and separate studies of Cupid, of Psyche, etc.; sketch of Titian's *Venus* in the Uffizi.
Verso: VIRGIN AND CHILD WITH THE INFANT ST. JOHN AND ST. JOSEPH (6961)
281 × 215 mm. Pen and ink over red chalk.
For other studies of *Psyche awakening Cupid*, see 326/75.

94. THREE STUDIES OF A MAN ON A GALLOPING HORSE; ANTIQUE PROFILE (6962)
181 × 144 mm. (square cut out bottom R.). Pen and brown ink over red chalk.

95. *Recto:* SIX STUDIES OF GALLOPING HORSES; A LIONESS; A MAN ON A GALLOPING HORSE, AND A MAN RUNNING
Verso: TWO STUDIES FOR AN EQUESTRIAN PORTRAIT OF A GENTLEMAN IN ARMOUR; TWO GALLOPING HORSES (6963)
198 × 174 mm. Pen and brown ink and red chalk.

96. TWO STUDIES FOR A MUCIUS SCAEVOLA, AND A GALLOPING HORSE (6964)
200 × 123 mm. Pen and brown ink and wash over red chalk.

97. *Recto:* STUDY FOR A COMPOSITION OF THE TRANSFIGURATION, for studies for a *St. Matthew*, three for the *Archangel Michael expelling Lucifer*, a *Pietà*, horses, etc.
Verso: EIGHT STUDIES FOR A ST. MATTHEW, ONE FOR A ST. JEROME, HORSEMEN AND HORSES, ETC. (6965)
213 × 292 mm. (including a rectangular bit inserted in top L. corner). Pen and brown ink and some brown wash over red chalk.
For other studies of *St. Matthew*, see 326/69; of the *Archangel Michael*, 326/66.

98. *Recto:* FIVE STUDIES OF A FIGURE OF FAME SEATED ON A GLOBE blowing a trumpet and others of her standing; study for a composition of the *Clemency of Scipio*, running figures, etc.
Verso: STUDIES FOR THE LABOURS OF HERCULES combating the hydra, the Lernian bull, shooting at Nessus carrying off Dejanira, etc. (6966)
292 × 217 mm. Pen and brown ink, in many cases over red chalk.

99. *Recto:* ONE COMPLETE COMPOSITION STUDY FOR THE AGONY IN THE GARDEN, very numerous studies for the sleeping apostles in this, the *Conversion of St. Paul*, etc.
Verso: THREE STUDIES FOR THE VIRGIN AND CHILD ON THE CRESCENT, studies for the *Agony in the Garden*, for an *Ecce Homo*, and for the *Adoration of the Kings*. (6967)
276 × 218 mm. Pen and ink and some wash over red chalk.
For other studies for the *Agony in the Garden*, see 326/6; for the *Ecce Homo*, see 326/73.

FIG. 70 Cat. No. 326/100 *r.*

100. *Recto:* STUDIES FOR THE AGONY IN THE GARDEN (*Figure* 70)
296 × 220 mm. Pen and brown ink.
Verso: STUDIES FOR THE SAME, FOR A ST. MATTHEW AND FOR A HORSE (6968)
Pen and ink over red chalk.
For other studies for the *Agony in the Garden*, see 326/6; for *St. Matthew*, 326/69.

101. STUDY FOR THE ST. MATTHEW AND COPY FROM ONE OF RAPHAEL'S PROPHETS IN STA. MARIA DELLA PACE (6969)
233 × 171 mm. Pen and brown ink in part over red chalk.
For other studies for the *St. Matthew*, see 326/69.

102. *Recto:* NUMEROUS STUDIES FOR THE ST. MATTHEW
Verso: Further studies for the *St. Matthew*; study for a composition of the *Baptism of Our Lord* and a copy from Parmigianino's etching of *Judith.* (6970)
196 × 330 mm. Pen and ink partly over red chalk.
For other studies of the St. Matthew, see 326/69.

103. *Recto:* VARIOUS STUDIES OF SINGLE FIGURES, OF HORSES, OF LIONS AND OF SPHINXES
Verso: COPY FROM ONE OF RAPHAEL'S SIBYLS IN STA. MARIA DELLA PACE; studies of executioners, of horses, and of other figures. (6971)
218 × 200 mm. Pen and brown ink over red chalk.

104. *Recto:* STUDIES OF FIGURES BLOWING TRUMPETS, of archers, of St. Christopher, of a Venus and Cupid, and of an armed warrior. (*Plate* 145)
Verso: FURTHER STUDIES OF MEN BLOWING TRUMPETS, three studies of lovers, studies for a Visitation, of a David with the head of Goliath, of Apollo (from the Stanza della Segnatura), etc. (6972)
273 × 207 mm. Pen and brown ink, partly over black chalk.

105. FRIEZE (IN TWO ROWS) OF SEA-CENTAURS WITH NYMPHS RIDING ON THEIR BACKS (6973)
143 × 215 mm. Pen and brown ink over red chalk.

106. *Recto:* STUDIES OF GALLOPING HORSES, of centaurs, of single figures, of *St. Matthew with the angel*, of a group from the *School of Athens*, etc.
Verso: STUDIES OF HORSES, OF A LION, OF THE FARNESE HERCULES, OF A DRAGON, ETC. (6974)
171 × 234 mm. Pen and brown ink partly over red chalk.
The dragon is copied from that in Federico Zuccaro's *Calumny of Apelles* (probably from the engraving of it by Cornelis Cort, 1572). For other studies of *St. Matthew*, see 326/69.

107. NUMEROUS COMPOSITION STUDIES OF BIBLICAL SUBJECTS: the *Fall of Man*, the *Expulsion from Paradise*, the *Creation of Eve*, *Cain killing Abel*, the *Sacrifice of Abel*, *God the Father*, the *Nativity*, etc. (6975)
282 × 420 mm. Pen and brown ink on light brown paper, in some cases heightened with white.

108. *Recto:* FISHERMEN HAULING IN A DRAG-NET
Verso: A WOMAN MOUNTED ON A GOAT, A HERM AND A CUPID (6976)
218 × 176 mm. Black chalk.
Both *recto* and *verso* are copied from Giulio Romano.

109. *Recto:* EIGHT STUDIES FOR A COMPOSITION OF A BISHOP (ST. AMBROSE ?) enthroned between St. Catherine of Alexandria and another female saint.
Verso: STUDIES FOR AN AGONY IN THE GARDEN, with separate studies for the sleeping apostles and the angel. (6977)
207 × 276 mm. Pen and brown ink, in some cases over red chalk.
For other studies for the *Agony in the Garden*, see 326/6.

FIG. 71 Cat. No. 326/118

110. VENUS, CERES AND JUNO (FROM RAPHAEL'S FRESCO IN THE FARNESINA) (6978)
233 × 171 mm. Black chalk outline.

111. STUDIES OF FOUR NUDE MALE FIGURES, ONE OF WHOM IS BLOWING A TRUMPET (6979)
238 × 186 mm. Black chalk on blue paper.

112. STUDIES OF FOUR MALE NUDES, A CHILD AND A LION; two of the studies are for Jupiter hurling his thunderbolt. (6980)
Black chalk on blue paper.
258 × 379 mm.

113. TWO STUDIES OF THE *Virgin lamenting over the dead body of Christ*, three of *Christ appearing to St. Mary Magdalene* and one for a *Descent from the Cross.* (6981)
265 × 195 mm. Pen and two shades of brown ink and some wash, partly over red chalk.

114. CAREFUL COPIES FROM MARCANTONIO'S ENGRAVINGS of *Joseph and Potiphar's Wife* (Bartsch XIV, p. 10, 9 copy), of *Lucretia* (Bartsch 187), of *Les cinq saints* (Bartsch 113), of the proconsul Sergius from the *Blinding of Elymas* by Agostino Veneziano (Bartsch 43), and a figure of Minerva, which seems to be original. (6982)
269 × 195 mm. Pen and brown ink and wash over red chalk.

115. COPIES OF THE TWO HALVES, DRAWN ONE ABOVE THE OTHER, OF MARCANTONIO'S ENGRAVING OF THE MARTYRDOM OF STA. FELICITÀ (Bartsch XIV, p. 104, 117). (6983)

270 × 192 mm. Pen and ink and wash over black chalk.

116. COPIES OF THE TWO HALVES, DRAWN ONE ABOVE THE OTHER, OF MARCANTONIO'S ENGRAVING OF THE MASSACRE OF THE INNOCENTS (Bartsch XIV, p. 19, 18). (6984)

269 × 195 mm. Pen and ink and wash.

117. COPY OF MARCANTONIO'S ENGRAVING OF GALATEA (Bartsch XIV, p. 262, 350). (6985)

416 × 285 mm. Pen and ink and wash.

118. OUR LORD IN THE TRANSFIGURATION (*Figure* 71) (6986)

380 × 250 mm. Point of the brush and wash on blue paper, heightened with white.

Copied from Sebastiano del Piombo's figure in S. Pietro in Montorio.

119. *Recto:* STUDIES FOR A FLAGELLATION OF OUR LORD AND FOR A CHRIST CARRYING THE CROSS

Verso: COPY OF PART OF RAPHAEL'S 'MADONNA OF FRANCIS I' IN THE LOUVRE (6987)

234 × 141 mm. Black chalk.

For other studies for a *Flagellation*, see 326/24.

120. TWO STUDIES FOR A COMPOSITION OF THE HOLY FAMILY IN THE 'REST ON THE FLIGHT INTO EGYPT' (6988)

215 × 140 mm. Red chalk, squared in black chalk.

121. A DEVIL CARRYING OFF A DAMNED SOUL (6989)

209 × 140 mm. Red and black chalk.

From Michelangelo's *Last Judgment.*

After GIACOMO FRANCIA (before 1487–1557)

327. ST. PETRONIUS, A FEMALE SAINT HOLDING A ROUND PICTURE OF THE VIRGIN, ST. PROCULUS, AND ST. FRANCIS OF ASSISI (0697)

248 × 199 mm. Pen and brown ink.

Inscribed 'Raffelle' crossed out, and 'Francia'. It is in fact a feeble copy of the signed engraving by Giacomo Francia. (*Hind, B. M. Catalogue*, p. 544, No. 1, ill.; Bartsch XV, p. 456, 1).

Attributed to GIACOMO FRANCIA

328. THE RESURRECTION: FRAGMENT OF A DESIGN FOR AN ALTARPIECE WITH AN ARCHED TOP (0297)

413 × 182 mm. (irregular). Finished drawing in brown wash on a cream-coloured prepared surface, heightened with white; very much rubbed, torn and damaged.

A.E.P. The technique is characteristic of the Bolognese Raphael imitators. The angel carrying the cross appears with minor variations and reversed in an anonymous

FIG. 72 Cat. No. 332

undescribed engraving of the *Vision of St. Helena* in the British Museum (1895–6–17–46). The style is so close to that of Giacomo Francia that it is legitimate to attribute the drawing to him.

BATTISTA FRANCO (About 1510 (?)–1561)

329. BEARDED MAN, TURNED TO THE L. with his arms raised over his head, holding a flail; a second figure, lightly sketched in behind him. (*Plate* 171) (048)

404 × 224 mm. Red chalk.

Study, in reverse, for the man on the extreme L. in Franco's etching of the *Flagellation* (Bartsch XVI, p. 122, 10). This etching was believed by Hans Tietze (*Tizians Leben und Werke*, Vienna, 1936, text p. 227, plates p. 314) to be from a lost painting by Titian, a theory which is disproved by this drawing, so clearly a detail study and so clearly Franco's.

330. CORIOLANUS PERSUADED BY HIS MOTHER VETURIA AND HIS WIFE VOLUMNIA TO SPARE THE CITY OF ROME (0381)

250 × 405 mm. Pen and light brown ink and wash, squared in black chalk.

The subject is explained by notes added by the artist himself (?). 'Vetturia madre di Corioloa' and 'la moglie li mostra i figliuoli'. At the top and bottom are sketches of part of the frame, presumably a carved wooden one in the Venetian style. The drawing apparently dates from Franco's Venetian period, 1554–61, and may have been intended for the decoration of a villa.

331. SCENE BEFORE THE CASTELLO AND PONTE SANT' ANGELO. In the centre foreground a woman with her back towards the spectator looking down towards a child; on the R. a bearded river-god leaning on his L. arm; on the L. a group of women moving towards the L.; other women in the background. (0384)

213 × 399 mm. Pen and brown ink and brown wash, squared in black chalk.

At the bottom in the centre is a slight sketch of part of the ornamentation of the frame, as in the drawing previously described, with which it may very probably be *en suite*, the ornaments being approximately the same. In this case the subject may be Veturia, Volumnia and the Roman matrons leaving the city to persuade Coriolanus to spare it.

332. FIGURES BRINGING TRIBUTE TO A WOMAN ENTHRONED (*Figure* 72) (5463)

286 × 423 mm. Pen and brown ink and wash. The drawing has been cut in half, and has faded, particularly on the L.

The drawing probably dates from Franco's Venetian period, 1554–61, and the subject may represent tribute offered to Venice.

After BATTISTA FRANCO

333. COPY OF NO. 332 (5462)

263 × 426 mm. Pen and brown ink and wash over black chalk.

There is another copy of this drawing in the Louvre (No. 8509) ascribed to Passarotti.

334. A WOMAN WITH THE HEAD OF A DOG PURSUES A GROUP OF MEN AND WOMEN AND A CHILD; behind, on the L., is a group of three men. (5064)

Circular, diam. 175 mm. Pen and brown ink and brown wash. The drawing is feeble and probably a copy, but the design must have been Battista Franco's; it may perhaps have been for majolica.

LATTANZIO GAMBARA (1530–1574)

335. TWO PROPHETS SEATED ON CLOUDS (*Figure* 73) (4811)

337 × 250 mm. (all four corners made up). Pen and brown ink and brown wash on faded blue paper, heightened with white, squared in black chalk.

FIG. 73 Cat. No. 335

A.E.P. Inscribed in an old hand: 'Di Sebastiano del Piombo'. The figures in fact correspond with two in the nave of the Duomo at Parma, which Gambara painted in fresco between 1567 and 1571 (ill. Laudedeo Testi, *La Cattedrale di Parma*, Bergamo, 1934, p. 46).

Attributed to GAROFALO (BENVENUTO TISI) (1481–1559)

336. A BEARDED PROPHET SEATED ON THE GROUND HOLDING A LARGE BOOK: DESIGN FOR A LUNETTE (*Plate* 100) (5069)

116 × 202 mm. Pen and Indian ink and grey wash on a brown ground, heightened with white.

P.M.R.P. The style of the drawing and the disposition of the figure within the lunette are closely paralleled in a drawing in the Louvre (No. 9070), which is the study for the signed fresco dated 1544 now in the Pinacoteca at Ferrara.

BERNARDINO GATTI (IL SOJARO) (About 1495–1575)

337. THE REST ON THE FLIGHT INTO EGYPT (*Plate* 139) (0599)
202 × 160 mm. (the top R. hand corner torn away). Red chalk, pen and brown ink and some brown wash and white, squared in red chalk.
Photo.: Braun 126.
A.E.P. Attributed to Correggio. The style of the drawing, the pipe-like folds of the drapery and the types connect this sheet with a whole series, which there is good reason for assigning to Bernardino Gatti. A typical example of such a drawing is the *Mystic Marriage of St. Catherine* in the British Museum (Cracherode Ff. 1–78), which is patently by the same hand. A painting corresponding fairly exactly with the Windsor drawing was in the Coesvelt Collection in 1836, when it was engraved by Joubert.

338. FLYING ANGELS (5499)
213 × 165 mm. (top corners cut and made up). Red chalk, heightened with white.
A.E.P. The attribution is obvious on comparison with the drawing previously described. A drawing in the Uffizi (No. 1955F, attributed to Correggio) is clearly by the same hand and forms a pendant to this.

339. THE HOLY FAMILY (*Figure* 74) (01232)
393 × 308 mm. Pen and brown ink and brown wash over red chalk on pinkish paper, heightened with white, the outlines indented; damaged by damp.
A.E.P. Though on a much larger scale, in fact a small cartoon, this is undoubtedly by the same hand as No. 337 and the other drawings of the same group. A drawing in

FIG. 74 Cat. No. 339

FIG. 75 Cat. No. 340

the Uffizi (No. 1957F, attributed to Correggio) is connected with the same composition.

Attributed to BERNARDINO GATTI

340. STUDIES FOR AN INFANT ST. JOHN THE BAPTIST AND OF A FIGURE PRAYING (*Figure* 75) (0595)
193 × 137 mm. Black chalk, the background washed with pale blue.
A.E.P. Inscribed in ink in the bottom L. corner, 'Coregio'. The type of the child's head seems characteristic of Gatti (see that in the *Rest on the Flight into Egypt*, No. 337, and that in the picture in the Cathedral at Pavia (Venturi, IX 6, Fig. 493)).
See also No. 371 below.

GIROLAMO GENGA (About 1476–1551)

341. FRAGMENT OF A MYTHOLOGICAL COMPOSITION (*Figure* 76) (0473)
305 × 195 mm. Pen and brown ink; much damaged, with a number of holes.
Coll.: N. Lanière (Lugt 2885).
Lit.: Rev. B. B. Woodward, Fine Arts Quarterly Review, I (1863), p. 165.
Inscribed in an old hand (Lanière's?) in bottom L. hand corner, 'H. Groinger', which may perhaps be a corruption of 'H. Genga'.
The other half of the composition is in the Ambrosiana, Milan (photo. Braun 216), and a photograph of this is mounted with the drawing. The complete drawing would

FIG. 76 Cat. No. 341

appear, from the indications in the corners here and in the Ambrosiana fragment, to have been circular with a diameter of about 450 mm., but both portions have been very much cut. The subject is obscure. A number of nude men, most of them armed with thunder-bolts, led by a standard-bearer, swarm over the naked body of a monstrous recumbent woman, under whose weight many have been crushed. One man has climbed up by the woman's hair and is aiming a blow at her face. In the foreground to the L. a colossal nude man reclines holding a cornucopia and an urn (the woman also leans on an urn). In the background on the L. a group of nude men kneel and receive an object from a man, also nude, who stands facing them and holds in his R. hand a many-headed serpent.

I do not know to whom the attribution to, or rather the elucidation of the old inscription as, Genga is due. Neither portion of the drawing is catalogued by Fischel in his *Zeichnungen der Umbrer*. It seems to me that the style accords very well with that of the small cartoon by Genga in the Uffizi (Fischel, op. cit., pl. 333) for the predella of the altarpiece of 1513 at Bergamo.

Attributed to GIAMPIETRINO
(working first decades of XVI century)

342. HEAD OF A YOUNG WOMAN (12809)

235 × 225 mm. Black chalk with some touches of red chalk.

Photo: Braun 253.

A note on the mount (by Müller-Walde ?) suggests that the drawing is an early copy from an unknown subject by Leonardo of the period of the *Last Supper*, and that it may be by the same hand as a drawing at Weimar of *St. John* (that ill. in Archive Storico VII (1894), opp. p. 45 ?). The attribution to Giampietrino is Venturi's, but this artist's figure as a draughtsman is very indistinct. The type of head is not unlike that of the *Nymph Egeria* belonging to the Marchese Brivio at Milan (W. Suida, *Leonardo und sein Kreis*, Munich, 1929, pl. 276). There is a very similar head at Rennes, drawn in black chalk, attributed to the school of Leonardo da Vinci (photo. Gernsheim 506). The present drawing is reproduced by Clark who, however, in his catalogue entry (p. 192) describes another drawing (No. 12808) which is catalogued by me above as No. 32.

After GIORGIONE (GIORGIO BARBARELLI)
(About 1478–1510)

343. THE ADORATION OF THE SHEPHERDS (*Plate* 162) (12803)

227 × 194 mm. (upper L. hand corner made up). Drawn with the point of the brush and washed on blue paper over black chalk, heightened with white.

Lit.: Hadeln, *Hochrenaissance*, p. 32 (pl. 1); Tietzes A 719 (with bibliography regarding this much-discussed drawing).

The Tietzes have fairly summed up the opinions previously held on the drawing. They conclude that it is a copy of some picture earlier than the Allendale *Adoration of the Shepherds* (with part of which it corresponds), and that the Allendale panel was based on this earlier picture. There may be something in this as the appearance of the drawing is more primitive than that of the painting. The technique and 'look' of the drawing come very close indeed to Carpaccio, two of whose drawings in the British Museum (Hadeln 40 and 43) I have been able to place beside it. I should think it might equally well be a translation of the Allendale picture into his own more archaic idiom by a draughtsman of an older generation.

Attributed to GIOVANNI DA UDINE (About 1487–1564)

344. DESIGN FOR THE DECORATION OF A CEILING IN THE GROTESQUE STYLE (6829)

395 × 480 mm. Pen and brown ink and brown wash over black chalk.

Attributed, like most drawings of the type, to Giovanni da Udine. Its obvious mastery, its style and its date (about 1539–40) seem in this case to justify the attribution. Perhaps five drawings, Nos. 10870 and 10879 to 10882 in a volume of 'Architectural Ornaments' (A. 18), are by the same hand. The design is for the quarter of the complete ceiling, and is no doubt to be repeated in the other three quarters.

After GIOVANNI DA UDINE

345. FOUR DESIGNS FOR PAINTED PILASTER DECORATIONS (047)

402 × 259 mm. Pen and brown ink and brown wash.

Attribution to Giovanni da Udine in pencil on the mount. Feeble copies of pilaster decorations in the *Loggie* of the Vatican.

FIG. 77 Cat. No. 349

GIROLAMO DA TREVISO (About 1497–1544)

346. VIRGIN AND CHILD IN THE CLOUDS, surrounded by cherubs with musical instruments; below St. Jerome, an angel with a lute, and a bishop. (5457)
339 × 213 mm. (upper part, above the Virgin, made up). Drawn with the point of the brush on grey prepared paper, liberally heightened with white.
Lit.: Hadeln, *Hochrenaissance*, p. 39, pl. 54; Tietzes 746.
The attribution of this drawing to Girolamo da Treviso due, I think, to Hadeln, is absolutely convincing.

347. THE ENTHRONEMENT OF A BISHOP BEFORE AN ALTAR, with, above in clouds, the Virgin and Child, St. Catherine of Alexandria and another saint. (*Plate* 99) (5456)
348 × 264 mm. Pen and ink and point of the brush on brown paper (once blue ?), heightened with white.
A.E.P. Not catalogued by Hadeln or the Tietzes. The attribution rests on the unmistakable similarity in style and technique to the drawing previously described. The method of composition also shows a very close resemblance to that of Girolamo da Treviso's series of the life of St. Anthony of Padua in S. Petronio, Bologna.

GIULIO ROMANO (1499–1546)

348. STUDY OF A NUDE MAN, SEEN FROM THE BACK, HURLING A ROCK (*Plate* 75) (0339)
390 × 124 mm. (torn on the r. hand side).
George III, 'Inventory A', p. 51, Raffaello d'Urbino e Scuola 36.
Lit.: J. D. Passavant, *Raphael d'Urbin*, Paris, 1860, Vol. II, p. 494, q; Ruland, p. 324, xx.
Photo.: Thurston Thompson, 1857.
It is possible, as has been suggested, that this is a study for a figure in Raphael's tapestry of the *Stoning of St. Stephen* (K. der K. 150), but the style of the drawing seems to me to point to a later date. It has the appearance of having been used to make an offset from, and the R. arm has perhaps been touched up, though probably by the artist himself. It would seem to be by the same hand and probably from the same model as the drawing at Oxford for the *Battle of Constantine* (Robinson 143; Vasari Society, 2nd Series XIII, No. 5) which Robinson, and more recently Clark, have claimed as the work of Raphael. Robinson pointed out that this model was used by Raphael himself in the studies for the *Resurrection* at Oxford, Windsor, and elsewhere (see below, Raphael, Nos. 798 and 799). This certainly appears to be the case, but Giulio Romano used the same model in his picture of the *Stoning of St. Stephen* of 1523 in S. Stefano, Genoa, so the model in question may have passed on, with the rest of Raphael's effects, to his heirs. It is possible that this is a rejected study by Giulio for the Genoa picture, on which he obviously lavished great pains.

349. APOLLO AND PAN (*Figure* 77) (0495)
234 × 199 mm. Pen and light brown ink over black chalk.
An admirable original drawing by Giulio Romano. I do not know for what purpose it was made. It has nothing to do with the *Contest of Apollo and Pan* in the Palazzo Torelli at Mantua (drawing in the Albertina, Cat. 100).

FIG. 78 Cat. No. 350

350. OMEN OF THE GREATNESS OF AUGUSTUS (*Figure* 78) (0308)
371 × 240 mm. (top R. corner cut). Pen and light brown ink and light brown wash over black chalk, squared in black chalk.

Lit.: Ruland, p. 163, No. VI.

As observed by Ruland, the drawing forms the R. hand portion of a composition engraved by Giulio Bonasone (Bartsch XV, p. 155, 174). The L. hand portion, in the Albertina, is described by Passavant (*Raphael d'Urbin*, Paris, 1860, Vol. II, p. 446*c*). This drawing is not described in Wickhoff's catalogue, as far as I can discover, nor in the recent catalogue of Stix, but there is a photograph of it in the Raphael collection at Windsor.

Jonathan Richardson (*An Account* . . ., p. 31) refers to this or to a similar drawing in the Bonfiglioli Palace at Bologna: '*Giulio*. Five Figures and a Cradle; two pointing up to a Boy lying on a Ruin, Other Figures in the Sky, the same as one Dr. *Mead* has of this Master, and that of *Biaggio Bolog*. my Father has.'

The subject, which eluded Bartsch, has been explained by Ruland by reference to the following passage in Suetonius (Book II, ch. 94, 6): 'Infans adhuc (Augustus), ut scriptum apud C. Drusum exstat, repositus vespere in cunas a nutricula loco plano, postera luce non comparuit diuque quaesitus tandem in altissima turri repertus est jacens contra solis exortum.'

The present drawing appears to be an original by Giulio Romano.

351. THE PRISONERS (0483)
274 × 420 mm. Pen and brown ink and brown wash, heightened with white (oxidised), squared in black chalk; very much torn and damaged.

George III 'Inventory A', p. 52, 5 or 6.

Inscribed at the bottom in the centre: 'Julio Romano' in an old hand. The drawing corresponds fairly closely with the lunette of the subject painted in the Sala delle Medaglie, Palazzo del Tè. It is still nearer, however, to the engraving by Giorgio Ghisi (Bartsch XV, p. 412, 66), which is rectangular like this, and in which the position of the man's head appearing through the floor also corresponds.

352. A ROMAN FEAST (*Plate* 74) (01367)
375 × 553 mm. (top corners cut; the sheet has been folded across the centre and the paper here has partly perished). Pen and light brown ink over black chalk.

Coll.: Sir P. Lely (Lugt 2092).

George III 'Inventory A', p. 52, 9.

This drawing is a first study, with many variations, for one of the series of tapestries of the history of Scipio Africanus (presumably No. 11 of the inventory, quoted by F. Reiset, *Notice des Dessins . . . du Louvre*, Paris, 1866, p. 243, representing the feast given by Scipio to the Roman tribunes sent to Sicily to enquire into his conduct). The finished cartoon or 'petit patron' according to Hartt is in the Musée Condé at Chantilly, of which there is a copy in the Louvre published by d'Astier in *La Belle Tapisserie du Roi*, 1907.

According to Reiset, op. cit., p. 241, the tapestries are those on account of which Primaticcio was paid two hundred crowns for a journey into Flanders on January 17, 1534. The cartoons must in that case date from 1533 or earlier. This tapestry was also engraved by Antonio Fantuzzi (Bartsch XVI, p. 349, 28).

353. TWO RIVER-NYMPHS AND A BEARDED GOD AMONG CLOUDS (*Figure* 79) (0304)
150 × 272 mm. Pen and brown ink and brown wash on light brown ground, heightened with white, squared in black chalk.

The drawing, which is certainly an original by Giulio, is a finished composition, and the fact that it is squared looks as if it was carried further. It bears a close resemblance to a drawing at Chatsworth (No. 110), which is a study for a section of the ceiling of the Camerino dei Cesari in the Castello at Mantua (ill. Bolletino d'Arte VII (1927–28), p. 622). It is possible that this drawing is the design for another section, which is not illustrated.

354. ST. BIAGIO. He is kneeling facing to the front, his crozier leaning against him, two boy angels kneel on either side holding the instruments of his martyrdom. (0508)
360 × 258 mm. Pen and light brown ink and brown wash, with some *pentimenti* in white, squared in black chalk.

The drawing belongs to Giulio's latest Mantuan period, and its character almost suggests a connection with the contemporary epigram of Matthaeus Faetunus:

> *Imago D. Blasii quaeritur de rudi pictore.*
> Me gemini lacerant alterna cuspide dentes
> Sed magis artificis laedit inepta manus.

355. EUROPA CARRIED OFF BY THE BULL (0300)
181 × 228 mm. Pen and reddish-brown ink and wash of the same colour.

George III 'Inventory A', p. 52, 12.

The figure is entirely characteristic of Giulio Romano, and the drawing appears to be original.

356. LARGE BOWL RICHLY DECORATED WITH A DESIGN OF SWANS (5453)
175 × 235 mm. Pen and brown ink and brown wash over black chalk.

A.E.P.

Copies of known originals by GIULIO ROMANO

357. PART OF THE DECORATION OF THE SALA DI COSTANTINO IN THE VATICAN, WITH POPE FELIX III (0486)
391 × 267 mm. (top R. corner torn). Pen and brown ink and brown wash, heightened with white.

Coll.: Sir P. Lely (Lugt 2093).

The drawing comprises the portion of the wall to the L. of the window on the L. of the *Donation of Constantine*. To judge from the outline engraving of G. Camilli (1838), the only reproduction available to me, there are very considerable and numerous differences between this drawing and the fresco. It must presumably then be a copy from a drawing by Giulio Romano. The style of the copyist is distinct from Giulio's.

358. THE BIRTH OF ST. JOHN THE BAPTIST (01358)
455 × 322 mm. (arched top). Pen and brown ink and brown wash on blue paper, heightened with white.

Inscribed in L. hand bottom corner: '. . . IL CORº' (perhaps altered from IULIO Rº), and in centre in the 'deceptive' hand: 'Benvenuto Garofalo'. As noted on the mount by Frederick Hartt, the drawing is a copy from the Giulio Romano composition engraved by Diana Ghisi (Bartsch XV, p. 443, 26).

FIG. 79 Cat. No. 353

359. THE CLEMENCY OF SCIPIO (01359)
405 × 585 mm. Pen and brown ink and brown wash on blue paper, heightened with white; much faded and injured by damp; with a number of holes.
The subject, according to a note by Frederick Hartt on the mount, belongs to the same series of tapestries as No. 352 above. It is however a copy. It is presumably No. 6 of the inventory quoted by Reiset. The original cartoon in the Louvre is, according to Hartt, more probably by Luca Penni than by Giulio Romano.

360. A ROMAN TRIUMPH (01411)
367 × 478 mm. Pen and brown ink and brown wash on light brown paper, heightened with white.
George III 'Inventory A', p. 52, 7 (?).
The subject, according to a note by Frederick Hartt on the mount, belongs to the same series of tapestries as Nos. 352 and 359 above, and is copied from one of the cartoons for these in the Louvre. It is presumably for the tapestry No. 16 in the inventory published by Reiset, which is described as showing the horses on Monte Cavallo, which seem to be represented in the background on the R. in this drawing.

361. THE CHARIOT OF THE SUN (0301)
296 × 220 mm. Pen and ink and brown wash on brown ground, heightened with white.
Coll.: N. Lanière (Lugt 2886).
George III 'Inventory A', p. 52, 3 (?).
One of the very numerous copies of part of the ceiling of the Sala del Sole in the Palazzo del Té at Mantua.

362. JUPITER HURLING HIS THUNDERBOLTS AT THE GIANTS, JUNO AT HIS SIDE (0343)
280 × 400 mm. (top corners cut and made up). Pen and ink and brown wash on light brown ground, heightened with white.
George III 'Inventory A', p. 52, 2.
Copy from part of the fresco of *Olympus* on the Vault of the Sala dei Giganti in the Palazzo del Té.

363. A GIANT CRUSHED UNDER A ROCKY MOUNTAIN (0305)
272 × 177 mm. Pen and brown ink and brown wash heightened with white, squared in black chalk.
Copy from one of the giants in the Sala dei Giganti, Palazzo del Té.

364. A FAMILY MEAL ('IL CONVITO') (0283)
246 × 416 mm. Pen and brown ink and brown wash, the outlines later gone over in pencil.
Copy from the subject painted in the Casino della Grotta, Palazzo del Té (engraved in d'Arco, *Istoria della vita e delle opere di Giulio Pippi Romano*. Mantua, 1838). According to Hartt, the original drawing for the subject is at Würzburg. What looks like an excellent original is in the National Gallery at Budapest (Schönbrunner-Meder 1223).

365. A FAMILY MEAL ('IL CONVITO') (0306)
223 × 390 mm. Pen and brown ink and brown wash.
A copy of the XVIII century, apparently from the drawing already described (No. 364), rather than from the fresco or one of the other drawings.

366. MEN, CATTLE, AND A DOG SLEEPING IN THE OPEN AIR (0504)
191 × 413 mm. Pen and brown ink and brown wash, partly squared in black chalk.
George III 'Inventory A', p. 52, 4.
Copy of part of the lunette fresco in the Casino della Grotta,

Palazzo del Té. The subject is engraved in d'Arco (*Istoria della vita e delle opere di Giulio Pippi Romano*. Mantua, 1838, pl. XXX). According to a note on the mount by Frederick Hartt, Giulio's original drawing may be that in the Teyler Museum, Haarlem.

367. PROCESSION OF SOLDIERS, MANY ARMED WITH SLINGS, AND OF CHILDREN, MOVING TO THE RIGHT (0487)
226 × 436 mm. Pen and ink.
As already noted by Frederick Hartt on the mount, this and No. 368 are connected with the stucco frieze of a Roman Triumph (generally incorrectly called the *Triumph of the Emperor Sigismund*) in the Sala degli Stucchi in the Palazzo del Té. The present drawing corresponds with pl. 5 of the set of engravings from the frieze by Antoinette Bouzonnet Stella published in 1679. It can only be regarded as a tracing or copy from a drawing by Giulio Romano, not as an original.

368. A WAGGON, DRAWN BY A HORSE AND A DONKEY, loaded with armour and armourer's tools, moving to the R.; other men on horseback and on foot carrying tools behind. (0488)
27 × 43 mm. Pen and ink.
Corresponds with plate 23 of the engravings by Antoinette Bouzonnet Stella. This section of the frieze was also engraved by an artist of the School of Fontainebleau (Bartsch XVI, p. 412, 90).

369. VENUS FAINTING IN THE ARMS OF JUPITER ON HEARING OF THE DEATH OF ONE OF HER FAVOURITE TROJANS (01233)
372 × 487 mm. Pen and ink and wash on blue paper heightened with white, varnished.
Copy of the fresco in the Sala di Troja in the Castello at Mantua.

370A. THE GODS ON OLYMPUS: Cybele with her castellated crown and two lions is conspicuous on the l., Hercules with his club in the centre. (01236)
358 × 570 mm. (on two pieces of paper joined about 100 mm. from the R. side). Pen and ink and brown wash on brown ground, heightened with white, the outlines indented.

370B. THE GODS ON OLYMPUS: Mars seated, to whom Venus, accompanied by Cupid, flies in alarm. (01238)
396 × 556 mm. Pen and brown wash on brown ground, heightened with white, the outlines indented.
The two drawings are copied from portions of *Olympus* on the vault in the Sala dei Giganti, Palazzo del Té.

371. ST. GEORGE AND THE DRAGON, THE PRINCESS KNEELING IN THE BACKGROUND ON THE RIGHT (01225)
460 × 357 mm. Pen and ink and brown wash on brown ground, heightened with white.
Inscribed in the 'deceptive' hand: 'Bernardino Gatti'. The drawing is in fact based on a composition by Giulio Romano preserved in Bonasone's engraving (Bartsch XV, p. 132, 77) which is inscribed 'IVLIO ROMANO. IN. VENTORE 1574'. The drawing is in the same direction as the engraving, and is very possibly copied from it. It does, however, correspond more exactly, in the town in the background for example, with a painting by Bernardino Gatti in the Madonna di Campagna at Piacenza (Venturi, IX 6, Fig. 494), so that the attribution by the 'deceptive' hand to Gatti is in all probability correct.

372. HYLAS AND THE NYMPHS (01239)
293 × 559 mm. Pen and brown ink and grey wash on blue paper, heightened with white.
One of many copies of a composition by Giulio known both by the reversed engraving of Pietro Santi Bartoli and the anonymous print of the School of Fontainebleau (Bartsch XVI, p. 405, 76).

373. HERCULES STRANGLING THE LION (0298)
212 × 130 mm. Pen and ink and grey wash on blue paper, heightened with white.
Engraved in the same direction by Adam Ghisi (Bartsch XV, p. 423, 21). It is the same group, seen from the back instead of from the side, as in the anonymous chiaroscuro woodcut (Bartsch XII, p. 118, 17). It would appear from the style that the originals of this and Ghisi's engraving are Giulio Romano's. The present drawing might well be by Adam Ghisi.

374—377. FOUR SMALL CARTOONS CORRESPONDING WITH THE FRESCOES ON THE FOUR WALLS OF THE SALA DEI GIGANTI IN THE PALAZZO DEL TÉ, MANTUA (01106–01109)
Each about 600 × 930 mm. Careful drawings in black chalk on light brown ground, washed with brown and heightened with white.
George III 'Inventory A', p. 158.
According to 'Inventory A' these drawings were given by Giulio Romano to Baldassare Castiglione. They are not squared and can hardly have served as the small cartoons for the work, with which they correspond very exactly. They seem rather to be copies from it done in Giulio's studio, but hardly from his own hand. The tradition that they were given by the artist to Castiglione may nevertheless be authentic.

Copies from compositions believed to be by GIULIO ROMANO

378. CUPID SEATED ON A BENCH SHARPENING AN ARROW (0295 A and B)
170 × 132 mm. Pen and brown ink and brown wash on blue paper, heightened with white.
The drawing is rather a good copy from, than, as stated by Frederick Hartt on the mount, an original by, Giulio Romano. Attached to it on the R. is a drawing of the second half of the century of apostles or disciples possibly in a *Raising of Lazarus*, which seems to be of the school of Paolo Veronese.

379. THREE PUTTI AMONG VINES; the centre one is seated on a branch eating a bunch of grapes. (0485)
205 × 317 mm. Pen and brown ink and brown wash.
W. M. An anchor in a circle.
The drawing seems to me to be a careful copy. It may be connected with the series of Gonzaga tapestries of playing children.

380. JUPITER AND SEMELE (0496)
148 × 213 mm. Pen and brown ink and brown wash on light brown ground, heightened with white.
Inscribed on the *verso* in William Gibson's (?) hand: 'Julio Romano 4. 3.' (= 20/–).
A copy from a characteristic composition by Giulio Romano. There is another version of this composition in the British Museum, Fenwick Collection (Catalogue, p. 62, No. 20).

FIG. 80 Cat. No. 384

381. ST. MICHAEL AND THE OTHER ARCHANGELS DEFEATING THE REBEL ANGELS (5122)
278 × 214 mm. (a large irregular piece missing from the top R. corner). Pen and brown ink and brown wash, heightened with white, much damaged.
The composition, not otherwise known to me, is very characteristic of Giulio Romano. The drawing, which is careful and finicking, is certainly not his.

382. ST. JEROME. He is seated in profile to the right, writing in a book propped against a crucifix; the lion crouches between his feet. (5080)
207 × 160 mm. Pen and light brown ink and light brown wash.
The drawing is obviously a copy, but the design, not otherwise known to me, is certainly Giulio Romano's.

383. THE ADORATION OF THE MAGI: the three kings advance from the R.; through an opening behind camels and an elephant are seen. (0294)
265 × 205 mm. Pen and brown ink and brown wash on blue paper, heightened with white.
The composition, which bears some resemblance to that of the *Adoration of the Magi* in the series of tapestries 'della scuola nuova', shows clearly the characteristics of Giulio's style. The drawing equally clearly is not his; its technique approaches that of the drawings given to Biagio Pupini. It must be a copy by some artist of that type. There is another version of this composition in the Uffizi (Santarelli 486, attributed to G. F. Penni).

School of GIULIO ROMANO

384. BACCHUS TRANSFORMING INTO TREES THE THRACIAN WOMEN WHO HAD MURDERED ORPHEUS (*Figure* 80) (5030)
273 × 523 mm. Pen and ink and wash on light brown paper, heightened with white. A number of holes, notably in Bacchus's L. leg, have been made up.
Signed by the draughtsman on the base of Bacchus's seat: 'I BAPTISTA C F'.
The subject is taken from Ovid's *Metamorphoses*, Book XI, lines 1–84, and it would be natural to connect the drawing with the series of tapestry cartoons of the *Metamorphoses*, for which Battista Dossi received 140 ducats in 1545 (one tapestry from the Musée des Gobelins is reproduced in the Catalogue of the Ferrara Exhibition, 1933, No. 211 bis). There is obviously also some relation between these tapestries and the decorations of the Villa Imperiali at Pesaro attributed by Patzak to the Dossi (one ill. by Venturi as Francesco Menzocchi IX 5, Fig. 387), but what exactly this relation is, I am not able to determine. It is therefore tempting to suppose the signature to be that of Battista Dossi, but I cannot in that case explain the 'C' following 'BAPTISTA': the 'F' is presumably for 'FECIT'. The style of the drawing besides connects it rather with Mantua and the following of Giulio Romano than with Ferrara and the Dossi. I cannot find any mention of a pupil of Giulio Romano who would fit. A certain Giovanni Battista Giacorollo, who is thought to have been a pupil of Lorenzo Costa the younger, Giulio's pupil, seems too late, and we should also have to assume that he spelt his name Ciacorollo. A drawing of Silenus seated at table in the open air under a tree directing the gathering and pressing of grapes is by the same hand as the Windsor drawing and apparently *en suite* with it. I only know this drawing from an old photograph which I have seen in the Estense Galleria at Modena, but I presume the drawing itself is also in that collection.

385. WINTER: DESIGN FOR A PENDENTIVE (0484)
186 × 230 mm. Pen and brown ink and brown wash.
The drawing is by a pupil of Giulio Romano's, who was responsible for a drawing in the British Museum of the *Feast of the Passover* (5210–76), which is the design for a tapestry of the subject bearing the Gonzaga arms and the name of Guglielmo, Duke of Mantua.

386. VENUS, VULCAN AND CUPID (0302)
250 × 210 mm. (the sheet is narrower towards the top). Pen and brown ink and brown wash, squared in black chalk.

Attributed to Giorgio Vasari, this fragment shows clearly the influence of Giulio Romano and must be by an able pupil. It is doubtless a design for a fresco to be painted over a fireplace.

387. THE INFANT BACCHUS REMOVED FROM THE THIGH OF JUPITER (0307)
Octagonal, 200 × 190 mm. Pen and brown ink and brown wash heightened with white.
Coll.: N. Lanière (Lugt 2886).
'Bertano' in pencil at lower edge. I do not know whether the attribution to Bertano is founded on any tradition. It is probably merely an inference drawn by some connoisseur, who did not believe the drawing to be by Giulio Romano himself. It is certainly by a close follower of his, but in the present state of our knowledge of the school of Giulio Romano at Mantua, it is impossible to attribute it to any individual artist. It may be by the same hand as No. 388 below.

388. GOD THE FATHER IN A CIRCLE, WITH THE SYMBOLS OF THE FOUR EVANGELISTS (6001)
286 × 370 mm. Pen and brown ink and brown wash on light brown paper, heightened with white.
Obviously the work of a close pupil of Giulio Romano, perhaps by the same hand as No. 387 above.

389. THE CALLING OF THE SONS OF ZEBEDEE (Mark I, 20) (5082)
231 × 385 mm. Pen and brown ink and brown wash on light brown ground, heightened with white, squared in black chalk.
A feeble drawing, whether a copy after Giulio Romano or an original production by a scholar, it is difficult to say; probably the latter. It is in the style of No. 387 only feebler.

390. THE ADORATION OF THE SHEPHERDS: the Virgin kneels on the L. in profile to the R. in front of the Child Who sits up; the shepherds approach from the R. (5105)
270 × 220 mm. Pen and ink and brown wash on blue paper, heightened with white.
The drawing is the work of some close but feeble follower of Giulio Romano. The type of the Virgin is not exactly the master's, and I doubt whether it is the copy of a composition by him.

391. THE ENTOMBMENT (0408)
263 × 374 mm. Pen and ink and grey wash on cream-coloured paper, heightened with white.
This odd and provincial-looking composition seems to be by a follower of Giulio Romano.

Attributed to FRANCESCO GRANACCI (1477–1543)

392. THE VIRGIN AND CHILD WITH THE INFANT ST. JOHN (*Figure* 81) (12743)
139 × 121 mm. Metal-point on buff prepared surface, heightened with white.
Coll.: Bonfiglioli; Sagredo; Consul Smith.
George III 'Inventory A', p. 49, Raffaello d'Urbino e Scuola 8.
Lit.: J. D. Passavant, *Raphael d'Urbin.* Paris, 1860, Vol. II, p. 490, No. 428; Ruland, p. 92, XXIII; Crowe and Cavalcaselle, *Raphael, His Life and Works*, London, 1885, Vol. II, pp. 477–78; O. Fischel, *Raphaels Zeichnungen*, Berlin, Text, pt. III, p. 136 (ill. p. 137).
Photo.: Thurston Thompson, 1857.
P.M.R.P. The composition, as Fischel has suggested, may be based on a drawing of Raphael's Florentine period, but

FIG. 81 Cat. No. 392

it is certainly not the work of Raphael himself, to whom the older writers attributed it. Fischel thought of Franciabigio as the possible author, but the style is much nearer to that of Francesco Granacci.

INNOCENZO DA IMOLA (1494–1550)

393. THE VIRGIN AND CHILD WITH ST. ANNE, ST. JOHN THE BAPTIST AND ST. JOSEPH (?) (0411)
333 × 246 mm. Pen and brown ink and brown wash, heightened with white.
George III 'Inventory A', p. 50, Raffaello d'Urbino e Scuola 13.
Lit.: F. Antal, O.M.D. XIV. (1939–40), p. 51 (pl. 48).
Photo.: C. Thurston Thompson, 1857.
F.A. On the *verso* is a mark 'h l' in pen and ink. In the George III 'Inventory A' it was regarded as a first idea by Raphael for the *Madonna del Baldacchino* in the Pitti Gallery (K. der K. 103). Antal was the first to connect the drawing with Innocenzo da Imola. The Virgin and Child, the *putti* holding the baldachin and the angel on the steps of the throne in fact repeat a small altarpiece formerly in the Crespi collection (Venturi, IX 4, Fig. 295).

Attributed to INNOCENZO DA IMOLA

394. PART OF A LARGE COMPOSITION REPRESENTING THE MIRACLE OF THE LOAVES AND FISHES (0736)
263 × 380 mm. (injured round the edges by damp). Finished drawing in brown on a brown prepared ground, heightened with white.
A.E.P. The technique and character of this fragment point to the Bolognese imitators of Raphael. A comparison with the drawing previously described, and even more with Innocenzo's frescoes of 1542 in the Villa della Viola, Bologna (ill. Berlin Jahrbuch XXIX (1908), pp. 175, 177), makes the attribution to him most probable.

PIRRO LIGORIO (About 1510–1583)

395. *Recto:* UNEXPLAINED ALLEGORICAL SUBJECT (*Figure* 82). (5073)

FIG. 82 Cat. No. 395

270 × 364 mm. Pen and ink and grey wash over black chalk on a brown prepared surface, heightened with white.

Verso: STUDY OF A SEATED APOSTLE OR PROPHET, PART OF WHOSE HEAD IS CUT OFF
Black chalk.

In the bottom R. hand corner on the *verso* is a fragmentary inscription (William Gibson's price mark): '7.1.' (= 7/–) and 'Pirr . . .'. Presumably, therefore, the attribution to Ligorio dated from at least the end of the XVII century. Though the drawing is much more careless, the style is not inconsistent with that of a signed (?) drawing at Chatsworth (No. 127) of the *Holy Family* or with the fresco of the *Dance of Salome* in S. Giovanni Decollato, Rome (Venturi, IX 5, Fig. 456). I think the old attribution can be accepted.

396. A POPE CROWNING AN EMPEROR (*Figure* 83) (0111)

255 × 398 mm. Pen and brown ink and brown wash over red chalk.

Inscription in pencil on the drawing: 'Pirro Ligorio', presumably going back to an older source. A comparison with the drawing previously described bears out the attribution.

FIG. 83 Cat. No. 396

397. A TELAMON IN THE FORM OF A SATYR HOLDING A CUDGEL (19263)

400 × 223 mm. Pen and brown ink and grey wash.
Coll.: Cassiano del Pozzo, Albani.

398. A CARYATID IN THE FORM OF A SATYRESS HOLDING A PAN-PIPES (19264)

402 × 222 mm. Pen and brown ink and grey wash.
Coll.: Cassiano del Pozzo, Albani.

A.E.P. The attribution to Ligorio of this and its companion drawing, No. 397 above, is based on their style and character.

399. ALLEGORICAL SUBJECT: Minerva (?) seated on the R. distributes chains to a group of old men, who approach from the L.; three women, a child, an old man and other figures are grouped round Minerva. (01234)

367 × 489 mm. Pen and brown ink and brown wash, on brown paper, heightened with white. Repaired top centre.

F.A. The attribution to Ligorio seems almost certain by comparison with the drawing No. 395 already described. The style also shows resemblances to that of the more finished, signed (?) drawing at Chatsworth (No. 127) and forms a link between the two groups.

Attributed to PIRRO LIGORIO

400. A ROMAN GENERAL, ACCOMPANIED BY A KING, POINTS TO A YOUNG MAN WHO STANDS NEXT TO TWO BOYS (5461)

304 × 260 mm. Pen and light brown ink and wash.

A.E.P. A suggested attribution to Tibaldi written on the mount by Sir J. C. Robinson can, I think, be dismissed. I think the actual handling of the drawing points to Pirro Ligorio, but it might well be copied from a fresco by Polidoro da Caravaggio. The subject may be Camillus and the schoolmaster of Falerii, but the presence of the king would need to be explained.

401. BACCHIC PROCESSION AMONG TREES: Silenus, mounted on a lion, is on the L.; on the R. is a woman sacrificing to Priapus. (5464)

258 × 320 mm. Pen and brown ink and brown wash.

A.E.P. The drawing, presumably copied from an antique relief, which I have not been able to identify, was attributed to Giulio Romano.

402. THE VIRGIN AND CHILD WITH ST. JOSEPH (0325)

130 × 149 mm. (irregular on the L.). Pen and light brown ink.

A.E.P. The style of this wretched drawing seems sufficiently close to a sheet of studies of the *Madonna and Child* in the British Museum (1885-5-9-39), certainly by Pirro Ligorio, to justify its attribution to that often very feeble draughtsman.

JACOPO LIGOZZI (1547–1626)

403. THREE ROMAN WARRIORS AND THREE OTHER MEN IN CONVERSATION (4809)

395 × 268 mm. (on two pieces of paper joined irregularly down the centre). Pen and ink and wash on brown oiled paper, heightened with white oil colours.

Inscribed in an old, perhaps contemporary, hand: 'Jacomo ligozza di Verona'. This is an unusual type of drawing for Ligozzi both in technique and in the handling, which is much bolder than usual, but the types and the general effect confirm the correctness of the old attribution to him.

Attributed to JACOPO LIGOZZI

404. UNEXPLAINED ALLEGORICAL SUBJECT (*Figure* 84) (6322)

256 × 264 mm. Pen and ink and brown wash on blue paper, heightened with white (oxidised).

FIG. 84 Cat. No. 404

A.E.P. Though the style of this elaborately finished drawing may at first sight suggest the period and circle of the Dossi, I think there can be little doubt that it is in fact much later and perhaps one of Ligozzi's archaistic productions.

For a copy after Raphael, possibly by Ligozzi, see No. 817.

GIAN PAOLO LOMAZZO (About 1538–1600)

405. THE FEAST OF QUADRAGESIMA (*Plate* 144) (5138)

288 × 470 mm. Pen and ink and wash over black chalk, on brown paper, heightened with white.

F.A. The drawing was identified by Antal as Lomazzo's sketch for his vast fresco of 1567 in the Refectory of the Convent of S. Agostino at Piacenza (Venturi, IX 7, Figs. 278 and 279), with which it seems closely to correspond. There is a slight composition sketch for the same fresco at Christ Church, Oxford (No. DD 3).

Attributed to GIAN PAOLO LOMAZZO

406. A GIRL MOUNTING THE STEPS OF AN ALTAR AND OPENING A RELIQUARY ON IT (0218)

280 × 273 mm. (tapering to 170 mm. at the top). Pen and brown ink and brown wash over black chalk, heightened with white.

A.E.P. Attribution in pencil on the drawing to Giovanni Battista Crespi (Cerano), with whose style I can see no connection. It seems to me of considerably earlier date and the technique is so similar to the authentic drawing by Lomazzo just described that I think it may be tentatively attributed to him.

After LORENZO LOTTO (1480–1556)

407. HEAD OF A YOUNG PRELATE, TURNED THREE-QUARTERS TO THE L. (6665)

394 × 290 mm. Black chalk on light brown paper, heightened with white.

Inscribed in ink below in an XVIII century hand: 'Tiziano'. The drawing is a copy from the picture in the Naples Gallery (No. 91) attributed by Berenson to Lotto (*Lorenzo Lotto*, London, 1901, p. 116), and by Suida (*Leonardo und sein Kreis*, Munich, 1929, Fig. 323) to Luini. The copy, of the XVII century, may be by the same hand as No. 1168 below.

AURELIO LUINI (1530–1593)

408. TWO SEATED PROPHETS (*Plate* 148) (4807)

214 × 313 mm. Pen and brown ink over black chalk.

Coll.: A collector's stamp, representing the sun with rays, not in Lugt.

Inscribed on the *verso* in a contemporary hand, perhaps that of the artist: 'd Manno d Aurelio e Lovino pitore d'. This inscription can no doubt be trusted. The style of the drawing is identical with that of another anciently attributed to the artist at Dresden (K. Woermann, *Handzeichnungen des Dresdner Kupferstichkabinetts*, Munich, 1896–1898, VI, 6). The mannerisms of these two drawings are indeed so pronounced, that a whole series, including those next to be described, can with assurance be given to Aurelio Luini.

409. THE LAMENTATION AT THE FOOT OF THE CROSS (5074)

404 × 285 mm. Pen and brown ink.

A.E.P. The identity of the hand with that responsible for the drawing previously catalogued is unmistakable.

410. *Recto:* STANDING FIGURE OF ST. PAUL (0287)

293 × 197 mm. Pen and brown ink on blue paper, heightened with white.

Verso: FOUR STUDIES OF SEATED EVANGELISTS (ONE IS ST. MATTHEW) AND A NUDE FIGURE

Black chalk.

A.E.P. Old attribution in pen and ink, 'Bacio Bandinelli', on the *verso* copied by the 'deceptive' hand on the *recto*.

411. STUDY OF A NUDE MAN SEEN FROM THE BACK, of two hands, a foot, a bearded head, and part of another figure standing in water. (0461)

301 × 182 mm. (including pieces added to make the sheet rectangular). Pen and brown ink, over black chalk.

A.E.P. The method of drawing the hands and knuckles is characteristic and unmistakable.

Attributed to ALESSANDRO MAGANZA (1556–after 1630)

412. THE ADORATION OF THE MAGI: design for an altarpiece with an arched top. (4777)

440 × 320 mm. Pen and brown ink and brown wash on blue paper, heightened with white.

Old inscription of the XVIII or early XIX century: 'Alessandro Maganza', in ink in L. hand bottom corner.

The attribution is supported by the style of the drawing and is likely to have some basis. It seems to be the *modello* for an important altarpiece.

After MARCANTONIO RAIMONDI (About 1480–1527/34)

413. GROUP OF FIVE WARRIORS AND OTHER FIGURES (040)

273 × 325 mm. Pen and brown ink and brown wash.

Copy (or tracing worked up) of parts of Marcantonio's engraving known incorrectly as the 'Triumph of Titus' (Bartsch XIV, p. 173, 213), but more probably representing an allegory on the Punic Wars. The original drawing by Jacopo Ripanda, from which the engraver worked, is in the Louvre (photo. Braun 363).

414. A MUSE, HOLDING A LYRE, IN A NICHE (0746)

130 × 81 mm. Pen and brown ink and grey wash.

Copy of one of the series of Apollo, Minerva and the Muses by Marcantonio (Bartsch XIV, p. 214, 277). On the *verso* is an unfinished copy of another of the series (Bartsch 265).

Attributed to MARCO MARCHETTI DA FAENZA (d. 1588?)

415. A ROMAN COMMANDER RECEIVING TRIBUTE, in the form of sacks of gold, from three barbarians, within a frame flanked by two winged females. (5034)

213 × 180 mm. Pen and brown ink and brown wash, squared in red chalk.

P.M.R.P. The drawing is obviously the work of a professional decorator, who can, I think, be identified as Marco da Faenza. There is a series of drawings attributed to this artist in the Uffizi, which show the same unmistakable mannerisms.

FIG. 86 Cat. No. 419A

FIG. 85 Cat. No. 416

416. THE CONVERSION OF ST. PAUL (*Figure* 85) (6010)

253 × 172 mm. Pen and brown ink and brown wash.

Lit.: F. Antal, O.M.D. XIII (1938–39), p. 37 (pl. 41).

A.E.P. Published by Antal as Taddeo Zuccaro's first idea for his altarpiece in the Frangipani chapel of S. Marcello al Corso, Rome, a composition which he repeated in a smaller version now in the Doria Gallery, Rome (ill. loc. cit., p. 38). The relation of this drawing to the picture seems to me rather that of derivation from, than preparation for. In fact its style is radically and irreconcilably different from that of Taddeo Zuccaro (as shown in his authentic drawings, in this collection for example). It is clearly that of Marco da Faenza, whose mannerisms are here, as always, very easily recognizable.

417. PUTTI CARRYING THE COLUMN OF THE FLAGELLATION (5528)

111 × 125 mm. Pen and brown ink and brown wash.

A.E.P. The drawing, attributed to Parmigianino, shows the easily recognized mannerisms of Marco da Faenza.

After DAMIANO MAZZA (working 1573)

418. THE RAPE OF GANYMEDE (6741)

328 × 247 mm. Red chalk with outlines in black chalk.

Copy from the octagonal canvas of the subject in the

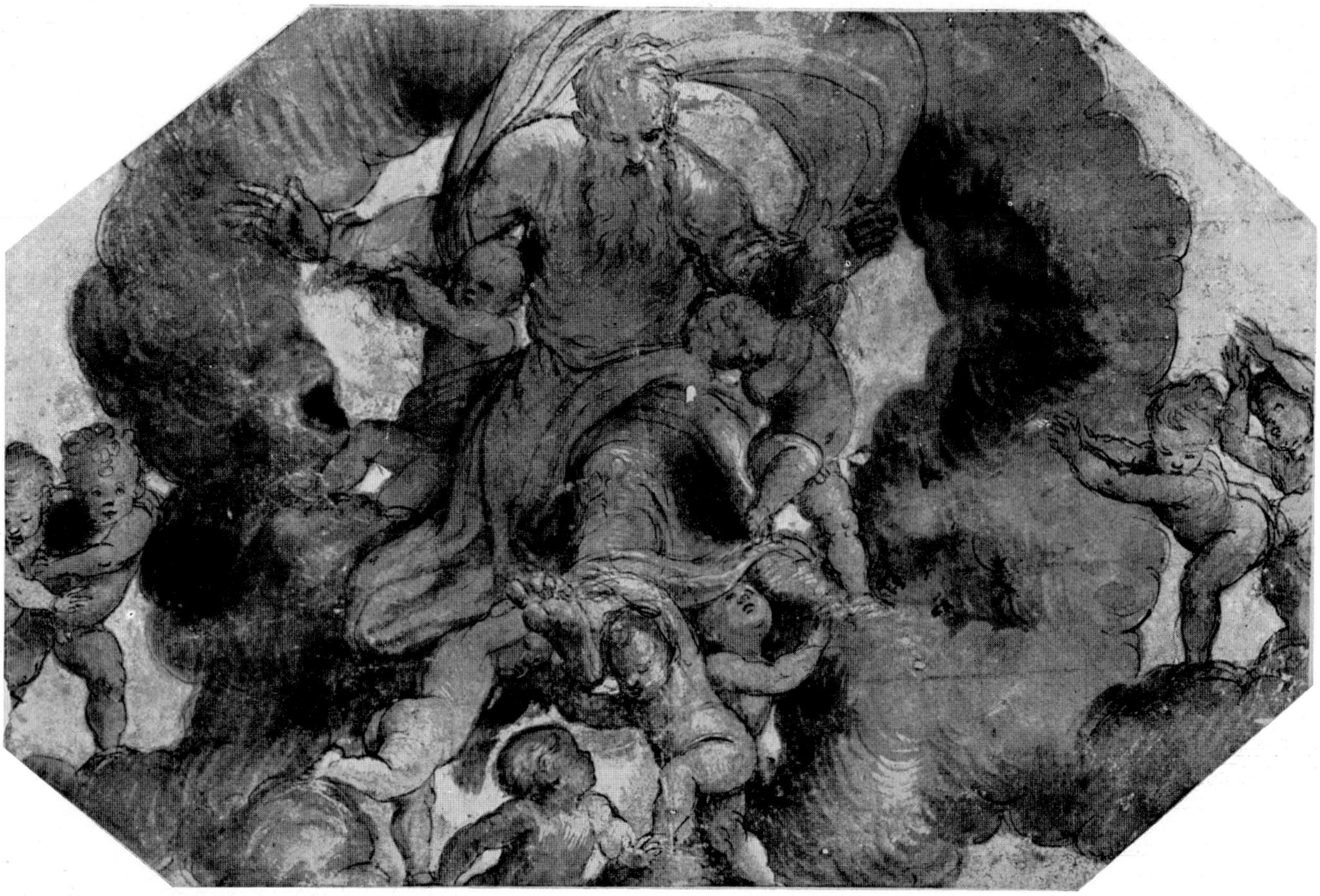

FIG. 87 Cat. No. 420

National Gallery (No. 32) formerly attributed to Titian, but almost certainly the painting by Mazza referred to by Ridolfi (ed. Hadeln, Vol. I, p. 224), as in the Casa Assonica at Padua.

GIROLAMO MAZZOLA-BEDOLI

(About 1500–about 1569)

419A. THE VIRGIN AND CHILD ENTHRONED, with a sainted bishop standing on the L. and St. Francis kneeling on the R. (*Figure* 86) (0353)

190 × 125 mm. Pen and ink and water colour.

Copy from a composition of Parmigianino's, of which the original was presumably that in Zanetti's collection (engraved by him in chiaroscuro, Bartsch 29), with the figure of the sainted bishop substituted for that of St. Jerome (see below Parmigianino, No. 593). The composition is also widened and is without the arched top. The drawing was attributed by Adolfo Venturi on the mount to Mazzola-Bedoli, and the style seems to me to confirm this. It is not at all improbable that he should adapt a drawing by Parmigianino.

419B. HEAD OF A CHILD WITH ITS L. ARM THROWN BACK BEHIND ITS HEAD (2032)

Circular: diam. 64 mm. Pen and ink and grey wash.

Recognized by Dr. R. Wittkower as corresponding with the head of the Infant Christ in Mazzola-Bedoli's painting in the Alte Pinakothek at Munich (Venturi, IX 2, Fig. 578). There are minor differences and the drawing seems to be an original study by the artist.

Attributed to FRANCESCO MENZOCCHI

(1502–1574)

420. GOD THE FATHER SUPPORTED BY CHERUBIM (*Figure* 87) (0377)

237 × 367 mm. (all four corners cut). Pen and brown wash and point of the brush on faded blue paper, heightened with white and some yellow, squared in black chalk.

A.E.P. There is a certain relationship in style to drawings by Girolamo da Treviso, but it does not seem to be by him, and I would tentatively suggest that it is the work of Francesco Menzocchi of Forlì (where Girolamo da Treviso was also at work). The subject may be compared with the God the Father in the upper part of the altarpiece in the Pinacoteca at Forlì (Venturi, IX 5, Fig. 386) and with the corresponding portion of the altarpiece in the church of the Sta. Trinità, Forlì (ill. in the periodical 'Melozzo da Forlì', VII (1939), p. 373).

MICHELANGELO (Michelagniolo di Ludovico Buonarroti-Simoni) (1475–1564)

References in abbreviated form are given as follows:

B.B. = B. Berenson, *The Drawings of the Florentine Painters*, amplified edition, Vols. I–III. Chicago, 1938. (The numbers given are those of the catalogue in Vol. II.)

Brinckmann = A. E. Brinckmann, *Michelangelo Zeichnungen*. Munich, 1925.

Delacre = M. Delacre, *Le Dessin de Michel-Ange*. Brussels, 1938.

Frey = K. Frey, *Die Handzeichnungen Michelagniolos*, Vols. I–III. Berlin, 1909–1911.

Milanesi, Corr. = G. Milanesi, *Les Correspondants de Michel-Ange. I. Sebastiano del Piombo*. Paris, 1890.

Milanesi, Lett. = G. Milanesi, *Le Lettere di Michelangelo*. Florence, 1875.

Robinson = J. C. Robinson, *The Drawings of Michel Angelo and Raffaello in the University Galleries, Oxford*. Oxford, 1870 (the numbers refer to the list of watermarks on pp. 362 ff.).

Steinmann = E. Steinmann, *Die Sixtinische Kapelle*, Vol. II. Munich, 1905 (the numbers given are those of the catalogue of drawings on pp. 587 ff.).

Symonds = J. A. Symonds, *The Life of Michelangelo*, 2 vols. 2nd edition. London, 1893.

Thode = H. Thode, *Michelangelo und das Ende der Renaissance*, 6 vols. Berlin, 1902–1913 (the numbers given are those of the catalogue of drawings in Vol. VI).

Tolnay = C. de Tolnay, *The Medici Chapel*. Princeton, 1948 (the numbers given are those of the catalogue of drawings on pp. 201 ff.).

Woodward = B. B. Woodward, *Drawings of Ten Masters at Windsor Castle*. London, 1870.

The Michelangelo drawings in the Royal Collection, with the exception of No. 433, which bears the collector's mark of N. Lanière, and of No. 434, which bears the price marks associated with William Gibson, and were therefore probably in England in the XVII century, are first recorded in the Inventory of George III. The drawings made for Tommaso de' Cavalieri (see Nos. 429–431) are known to have been in the possession of Cardinal Alessandro Farnese (1520–1590), but their history between that time and their appearance in the Royal Collection is unknown. Cardinal Farnese also probably owned two drawings (Nos. 424 and 427) which had belonged to Giulio Clovio (1498-1578).

The Rev. B. B. Woodward began the rearrangement of the drawings by Michelangelo at some time before 1863 (see Fine Arts Quarterly Review, I (1863), p. 163), when the *versos* of Nos. 421, 426, 427, 430, and 435 were first revealed.

421. *Recto:* MALE NUDE, WITH PROPORTIONS INDICATED (*Plate* 17) (12765)

Verso: MALE NUDE. THE FIGURE PARTIALLY OUTLINED WITH THE STYLUS (*Plate* 18)

289 × 180 mm. Red chalk.

George III 'Inventory A', p. 43, Michelangelo, I, 11.

Lit.: Symonds, I, pl. facing p. 264 (*recto*); B.B. 1607; K. Frey, *Michelagniolo*, I. Berlin, 1907, p. 145, note 3; Thode, 532; E. Panofsky, Zeitschrift für bildende Kunst LXI (1927–28), p. 222, 224, 241 note 7, 242 note 18, p. 226 (ill. *recto*); A. E. Popp, Zeitschrift für bildende Kunst LXII (1928–29), p. 66.

Recto: A: nude man, standing, facing to the front, resting his weight on the R. foot, his head turned towards the R., the L. arm hanging and bent outwards, the R. arm behind his back and clasping the L. B–E: small sketches, two above to the R., and two below to the L. B: a profile, divided into three parts, upon which a hand is superimposed, providing the unit of measurement for A. C: upper arm. D: knee. E: foot, side view. The unit of measurement provided by B is applied to the figure A to the L. The figure is marked off in 6 2/3 such units extending from the base to the waist. Within the lines delimiting the last unit is inscribed 'una', written from the bottom upwards (the peculiar character of the writing is accounted for by the fact that the paper was not turned round for the purpose). Both to the R. and L. straight lines define certain sections of the body. Their measurements are given thus: R. elbow—'terzo d una testa'; from wrist to the fingers—'terzo d una testa'; upper leg—'dua e u(n) terzo a l a(n)guinaia' (= groin); L. ankle—'dua terzi'. Measurements are also given of the anatomical sections sketched in the margins: C (breadth of upper arm)—'2 terzi'; D—'[u]na'; E—'una e 3 quarti'. All the annotations are in red chalk in Michelangelo's autograph.

Verso: F: nude man, standing, facing to the front. The torso is slightly braced back and turned towards the R.; the head turned towards the R.; the R. arm, folded across the chest, is cut off below the elbow; the L. arm is behind the back (at first this arm was also cut off below the shoulder). The modelling is indicated by parallel strokes, but is not carried further.

A copy of the *recto* by the miniature painter Don Giulio Clovio (1498–1578) is thus described in his inventory of 1577: 'Una notomia con tutti le misure di Michelangiolo fatta da D^n Giulio' (A. Bertolotti, *Don Giulio Clovio*. Modena, 1882, p. 14). This copy is still in existence. It was last in the collection of Sir Edward Poynter (Sale, April 24, 1918, lot 82, 'School of Michelangelo'; there is a photograph in the British Museum). Another copy of the *recto* is in the Teyler Museum at Haarlem (A.26). A copy of the *verso* is in the Uffizi (6550E, attributed to Pontormo).

A is an instructional drawing, executed with great care, and is, with the exception of the head, elaborately finished. It thus shows more affinity with Michelangelo's 'presentation sheets' (see Nos. 423, 424, 428–431) than with his preparatory studies and sketches. The drawing displays a man's body in the prime of life, with the poise and harmony of its structure, its muscular formation, and with the relationship of its parts determined by measurements. The figure is therefore carefully constructed. Some guiding lines can still be seen, for example, the straight line which runs through the collar-bone, and a second one at right angles to it which defines the course of the neck muscle and the position of the ear. The unit (B) employed for the measurement of the parts is the length of the face from the chin to the hair, which corresponds to the length of the hand; the word 'testa' is used in the notes in the sense of 'faccia'. (The same usage is to be found in Vasari (I, p. 150 f.) and Borghini (*Il Riposo*, Florence, 1584, pp. 150 f.).) The whole figure is slightly more than 10 units high. This type of figure is called by Lomazzo (*Trattato dell' Arte della Pittura*, ed. Rome, 1844, II, p. 77) the Jupiter type. Another type, of nine face-lengths, was named after Apollo; it is possible that the unfinished drawing on the *verso* was to illustrate this type of figure. It is worth mentioning that the same measurements are inscribed on an anonymous XVI century drawing (now in the L. C. G. Clarke collection, Cambridge), which is a copy after Michelangelo's terra cotta model of a nude male figure in the Casa Buonarroti. This drawing achieved canonical significance, was engraved by Giovanni Fabbri, and has often been reproduced in works on artistic anatomy. A detailed explanation of its measurements can be found in J. Kollmann, *Plastische Anatomie*, Leipzig, 1886, pp. 526 f.

The artist's preoccupation with the problem of proportion is mentioned by Condivi (ed. Frey, pp. 178 f., 192 f.). Further evidence is supplied by a sheet containing drawings of a pupil of Michelangelo's, Antonio Mini (1506–1533), in the Casa Buonarroti (B.B. 1408).

The fine red chalk technique in which A is executed is first found in some sheets of Michelangelo's dating from the end of the Sixtine period, like the study for the Libyan Sibyl in New York (B.B. 1544D *recto*), or the studies for Haman in the British Museum and at Haarlem (B.B. 1690, 1670). The nearest stylistic parallels to the drawing are to be found in Michelangelo's sketches for Sebastiano del Piombo's *Raising of Lazarus* at Bayonne and in the British Museum (B.B. 2474C, 2483; their date is 1516). No. 421 probably belongs to this period too. It is even possible that it was also made for the use of Michelangelo's protégé Sebastiano. The figure of Christ in Michelangelo's first design for Sebastiano's *Flagellation of Christ* in the British Museum (B.B. 2487) reveals a close connection with A, which gives the impression of being a systematic and detailed elucidation of the sketch of the nude in the former. (How much Sebastiano was dependent upon Michelangelo's help in anatomy even in later years is attested by a letter of his of July 15, 1532 [Milanesi, Corr., p. 100].) If this connection is accepted the date of the composition of No. 421 can be fixed as 1516. The character of the writing of the notes fits in well with this date (see, for example, W. Maurenbrecher, *Aufzeichnungen des Michelangelo*, Leipzig, 1938, pl. 3).

The *verso* also was perhaps begun in connection with an intended figure of an executioner in the *Flagellation*, but was abandoned before it was completed. Berenson rightly points out the similarity of motive that exists between this figure and one of the sketches for Slaves on the sheet in the Ashmolean (B.B. 1562; date 1513). The peculiar form of hairdressing occurs also in the Sixtine Ceiling (in the Naason lunette) and in the *Last Judgment* (in one of the angels in the centre).

Both Berenson and Thode see in A and F studies for the Slaves of the Julius Monument from the first phase of Michelangelo's work upon it (1505–6). Panofsky mentions A in connection with No. 423. A. E. Popp rejects this sheet of drawings.

422. *Recto:* UPPER PART OF A RECUMBENT MALE FIGURE, AND A SEATED MONK (*Plate* 23) (12763)

Verso: LOWER HALF OF A STANDING DRAPED FIGURE, AND A PUTTO

266 × 166 mm. Red chalk; pen and ink of a yellowish tinge.

George III 'Inventory A', p. 44, Michelangelo, I, 30.

Lit.: B.B. 1750A (former 1609); Frey 204/205; Thode 534.

It is clear from the *verso* that this is only the R. half of a larger sheet; the bottom and R. hand margins have also been cut. In the upper R. hand corner, in ink: 'n. 76'; on the *verso*, at the bottom: 'Bona Roti'.

Recto: A–C: studies of a recumbent male figure. L. (A), the head only, bent back; below (B), head and upper part of L. arm, the latter hanging; R. (C), the whole of the torso and both arms, the R. across the chest. Above this figure and to the L. of it the outstretched L. arm of a second, apparently female, figure, covered by study D. D (partly drawn over C; the sheet held lengthways): male figure, seated, in profile and turned towards the L., in a voluminous cloak, the head covered by the cowl. The legs are bent back, the L. hand is in front of the chest, the R. supporting the chin. C was drawn first, followed by A and B and, later, D.

Verso: E (in the centre, the sheet held lengthways): the lower half of a standing draped figure, facing to the front, some folds only of the garment lightly shaded. F (L. of E): seated *putto*, facing to the front, the upper part of the body bent far forwards, the arms thrown back, the L. leg drawn up; rapid sketch.

A–C and E are drawn in red chalk; D and F in pen and ink.

The head in studies A–C, which is that of a young man, has a kerchief tied round it; the R. arm in C rests on what is apparently a coverlet. Both these facts exclude the idea of their being studies for a *Pietà*, an interpretation which has been repeatedly advanced. The details of form in A and B appear to be identical with those in C, but seen from slightly different angles. This makes it very probable that the studies were done from a plastic model, and in point of fact the existence of such a model can be proved. It was an antique relief in marble representing Cupid and Psyche, once in the possession of Lorenzo Ghiberti, which under the title of 'The Bed of Polycletus' enjoyed great renown during the Renaissance, but which had disappeared by the first half of the XVII century. (The literary sources dealing with this work have been collected by Julius von Schlosser: Vienna Jahrbuch XXIV (1904), pp. 125 f., and *Ghiberti's Denkwürdigkeiten*, II, Berlin, 1912, p. 172 f.) Christian Huelsen, however, identified a perfectly preserved if crudely executed XVI century copy of the lost original in the Palazzo Maffei in Rome (Jahreshefte des österreichischen archäologischen Institutes XVIII (1915), pp. 130 f.). The studies B and C are better evidence of the quality of the original, as well as being drawn to the same scale. About 1525, the date to which the technical and stylistic character of the drawings point, this antique relief was to be found in the possession of Ghiberti's great-grandchild Vittorio, himself a sculptor, in Florence. Four letters by Vittorio Ghiberti of the years 1520–21, now in the Archivio Buonarroti, bear witness to the close relationship existing between him and Michelangelo (K. Frey, *Briefe an Michelagniolo*, Berlin, 1899, p. 183; C. de Tolnay, *Michelangelo's Youth*, Oxford, 1943, p. 244). Contemporary with these studies there is also a rapid sketch by Michelangelo of the composition of the whole relief on a sheet in the Casa Buonarroti (B.B. 1664). Several of his works bear testimony to the deep impression which the motive of the sleeping youth had made upon him; see, for example, the helpless son carried by his father in the *Deluge* of the Sixtine Ceiling; the design for Sebastiano del Piombo's *Ubeda Pietà* in the Louvre (B.B. 1586); the Christ in the *Pietà* in Florence Cathedral. Huelsen has shown how 'The Bed of Polycletus' was utilised in Raphael's workshop as well as by Titian. The composition was also used as a decorative motive in Tribolo's design for the mosaic floor of the Library of S. Lorenzo (repr. in Zeitschrift für bildende Kunst LXI (1927–28), p. 10).

It is not known for what purpose the studies D–F were intended. From the point of view of technique D should be compared with the Sibyl in the British Museum (B.B. 1482 *recto*); and the form of the drapery in E with Michelangelo's *Noli me tangere* of 1531 (see Venturi, IX 6, Fig. 154).

I agree with Thode in believing all the drawings on this sheet to be by Michelangelo, but not in his dating of them in the period of the Sixtine Ceiling. Frey only allowed Michelangelo's authorship in the case of the two pen and ink sketches, whereas Berenson saw even in the latter the work of a pupil who was supposed to have been active about 1525–30.

423. THREE LABOURS OF HERCULES (*Plate* 19) (12770)

272 × 422 mm. (slightly cut into on all sides). Red chalk; surface rubbed, especially in the centre and to the R.

George III 'Inventory A', p. 45, Michelangelo, II, 1.

Lit.: B.B. 1611; Frey 7; Thode 536; Brinckmann 53; Popham 224. Discussion on the authenticity of the sheet: A. E. Popp, Belvedere VIII (1925), Forum, p. 74; Zeitschrift für bildende Kunst LXI (1927–28), pp. 11 f.; LXII (1928–29), pp. 54 f.; E. Panofsky, *Festschrift für J. Schlosser*, Vienna, 1927, p. 157; Zeitschrift für bildende Kunst, LXI, pp. 221 f.; LXII, p. 179 f.; K. Clark, Burlington Mag., LVI (1930), p. 181; Tolnay, p. 185.

On undulating ground, L.: *The Killing of the Nemean Lion* (First Labour). Hercules, a beardless young man, facing to the front, stands astride the neck of the lion and rends its jaws. A lion skin swings from his shoulders behind. Above the group, in red chalk, is written: 'questo e il seco(n)do leone ch(e) ercole/am(m)azzo'.

R., further back than the first group on the L.: *The Fight with the Lernean Hydra* (Second Labour). The hero, bearded and powerfully built, the lower part of his body towards the R., his torso turned to the front and his head to the L., places his R. knee upon the body of the hydra and throttles one of its seven necks with his outstretched R. arm. His L. arm is poised to strike with the club. A second of the hydra's heads hangs down dead while those remaining attack Hercules from all sides. There are obvious *pentimenti*, notably in the drawing of the L. arm.

In the centre, still further back: *Hercules wrestling with Antaeus* (not one of the twelve canonical Labours, but the subject of a widely diffused legend). Hercules, in profile to the L., clasps against his chest with both arms the doubled-up body of his opponent head downwards. A mantle hangs from his shoulder. Definite *pentimenti* are to be observed, more particularly in the drawing of Hercules' R. leg.

The drawings on this sheet form a unity, the groups following a well-defined scheme of composition. The choice of the three typical views of the human figure, frontal, profile, and three-quarters profile, is no doubt deliberate. Equally the drawing must be considered as finished. (Alterations in a red chalk drawing cannot be concealed, as the medium is indelible). The degree of sharpness in the rendering of forms varies according to the spatial position of each group. The L. hand group, where stippling is extensively used, shows a degree of perfection one associates with a painting: only in Michelangelo's lost *Leda* of 1530 could the *chiaroscuro* have been more richly graduated. The style of the drawing points to a connection with this picture; the study for the head of Leda in the Casa Buonarroti (B.B. 1401), the first datable example of the employment of stippling by Michelangelo, shows the same fineness of surface modelling. A corroboration of this approximate date is provided by the connection of motive between the Hydra group and the Samson model of 1528 (only known through copies), a connection which however emphasizes the differences between plastic and graphic design. The *Labours of Hercules* must have been drawn as a gift for a friend, a small masterpiece complete in itself, rather than as a design for sculpture.

In all three groups Michelangelo has borrowed motives from earlier works of art. In connection with the group on the L. it is to be noted that the motive of the rending of the lion's jaws is peculiar to the story of Samson (Judges xiv. 6). According to the legend, Hercules first fought the Nemean lion with his club and then strangled it: contrast with this the representation of the Old Testament hero either in Israhel van Meckenem's engraving (Bartsch 3), or Dürer's early woodcut (Bartsch 2). The transfer of the Samson motive to Hercules had already been made before Michelangelo, as may be seen from Cosimo Tura's drawing in the Koenigs Collection (Popham 146), and in a finished design from the Mantegna workshop at Christ Church (C. F. Bell, *Drawings . . . in the Library of Christ Church, Oxford*, 1914, pl. 68). Two engravings go back to the latter drawing: one by Giovanni Antonio da Brescia (Bartsch 11), and another from the workshop of Marcantonio (Bartsch XIV, p. 221, 291). Doubtless we have in the latter engraving the prototype used by Michelangelo. The changes which he has made clearly indicate the direction of his thought. The note above the group gives the *raison d'être* for the lion's skin which the hero is wearing (in the prototype it is a mantle), by drawing attention to the legend according to which Hercules had already slain a lion—the Cithaeronian—in his youth. The group on the R. appears to have been influenced, both in its subject and form, by the late-antique group of Laocoon, which ever since its discovery in 1506 had excited the admiration of Michelangelo. The influence of this statue on a representation of *Hercules with the Hydra* can be found even earlier than Michelangelo: see Baldassare Peruzzi's fresco in the *Stanza del Fregio*, Villa Farnesina, Rome. Although Michelangelo's reproduction is less exact, it nevertheless retains more of the spirit of the Hellenistic prototype. The motive of the central group has been transferred from classical representations of the strangling of the Nemean lion to the struggle with Antaeus (see, for example, S. Reinach, *Répertoire de Reliefs*, III, Paris, 1912, p. 303, 4; and for Renaissance copies, Victoria and Albert Museum, *Catalogue of Plaquettes*, London, 1924, p. 35, pl. VII). This very attractive variation is an original addition by Michelangelo to his own representations of the subject in the traditional manner; see his three sketches of 1524–25 for a sculptural group of Hercules and Antaeus on the sheets in the British Museum and the Ashmolean (B.B. 1490, 1712). A small plastic model by Michelangelo with the same theme (Vasari, VII, p. 258) has disappeared.

A copy of the group on the L. in pen and ink is in Venice (G. Fogolari, *I Disegni della R. Galleria dell' Accademia Venezia*, Milan, 1913, pl. 79). Bandinelli used the whole sheet as a model for a large drawing (a facsimile is given in C. M. Metz, *Imitations*, 1789, London, Weigel 153).

Critical opinion on No. 423 has been remarkably varied. Of the virtuosity displayed in the handling of the red chalk Berenson wrote in 1903: 'I cannot readily conceive anything closer to perfection'. Twenty-five years later the drawing becomes for A. E. Popp the concoction of a forger of the late XVI century. A. E. Popp's criticisms of the construction of the groups and of the composition of the whole sheet may be considered as refuted by E. Panofsky, who deals with the subject exhaustively. But even Panofsky finds 'serious and indubitable weaknesses of draughtsmanship' in parts of the drawing. According to him the whole sheet, as it exists at present, together with the inscription, must be considered a copy of a lost original by Michelangelo, made by his pupil Antonio Mini (1506–1533). I cannot subscribe to this thesis. Drawings which are indisputably by Mini—they are authenticated by his handwriting (the copies in red chalk in B.B. 1502; and B.B. 1731, 1408)—and numerous other drawings similar to these, which can reasonably be attributed to him, are so inferior in quality that one cannot for a moment credit this youngster (who had finally left Michelangelo's studio at the age of twenty-five) even with the capacity to understand a masterpiece of the rank of No. 423. But every theory propounded in favour of its being a copy ignores the existence of the significant *pentimenti* in the drawing. Finally, if we consider the sheet as it should be considered, i.e. as an independent work of graphic art, without comparing it with sketches and preparatory studies, the alleged 'weaknesses' are seen in part as evidences of a slow, careful, sometimes even laborious, preparation by the draughtsman. In part, too, they point to a stylistic break which can be observed in *all* the drawings by Michelangelo from about 1530. In spite of the opinion of two experts in handwriting cited by Panofsky, I am convinced that even the inscription is from the hand of Michelangelo and not from that of Mini. Sir Kenneth Clark, in 1930, rightly protested against the 'condemnation' at the hand of modern critics of this and many other of the Windsor drawings by Michelangelo.

424. ARCHERS SHOOTING AT A HERM (*Plate* 20) (12778)
219 × 323 mm. (slightly cut into on all sides). Red chalk.
W.M., a cross-bow in a circle (or oval ?).

Coll.: Don Giulio Clovio; Cardinal Alessandro Farnese; George III 'Inventory A', p. 45, Michelangelo, II, 2.

Lit.: Vasari, V, p. 431; Woodward, p. 30 f.; Symonds, I, p. 296 f.; B.B. 1613; Frey 298; Thode 538; Brinckmann 52; A. E. Popp, Belvedere VIII (1925), Forum, p. 75; E. Panofsky, Zeitschrift für bildende Kunst, LXI (1927–28), p. 243 note 34, Fig. E on p. 243 (repr. of memorandum); A. E. Popp, Zeitschrift für bildende Kunst LXII (1928–29), p. 64 f., ill. fig., p. 61 (*recto*), p. 58 (repr. of collector's note); C. de Tolnay, Thieme-Becker, XXIV (1930), p. 522; Popham 223; Tolnay 121, Fig. 157.

On the subject and the connection of its representation with antique art, see: A. Conze, Jahrbuch für Kunstwissenschaft I (1868), p. 359 f.; F. Wickhoff, Mitteilungen des Instituts für österreichische Geschichtsforschung II (1882), p. 435; A. Michaelis in H. Egger, *Codex Escurialensis*, I, Vienna, 1906, p. 70; F. Wickhoff, Kunstgeschichtliche Anzeigen, 1907, p. 49 f.; K. Borinski, *Die Rätsel Michelangelos*, Munich, 1908, pp. 63 f.; F. Weege, Jahrbuch des deutschen archäologischen Instituts XXVIII (1913), p. 179; R. Förster, Neue Jahrbücher für das klassische Altertum XXXV (1915), p. 578 f.; H. Sponsheimer, Neue Jahrbücher, etc., XXXVII–VIII (1916), p. 304; A. Farinelli, *Michelangelo e Dante*, Turin, 1918, pp. 143 f.; E. Panofsky, Wiener Jahrbuch für Kunstgeschichte I (1921–22), Buchbesprechungen, col. 47 f.; A. Hekler, Wiener Jahrbuch, etc., VII (1930), p. 222; E. Panofsky, *Studies in Iconology*, New York, 1939, pp. 225 f.

Upon raised ground is a crowded group of naked youthful figures—two female and seven male—flying, running, kneeling or crawling in a whirl of excitement, all of them surging forward in the direction of a Herm which stands to the R. of the raised ground and frames the R. side of the drawing. Mingled with the figures are two flying *putti*. With the exception of two which have thrown themselves down in front, the figures are all imitating the actions of archers, drawing the bow and aiming at a target (the Herm), without however having weapons in their hands. Popham drew attention to the fact that they were all, with one exception, left-handed. Above and behind the group to the L. a flying satyr bends his bow. Below, to the L. and behind the group are two kneeling *putti*, one of them blowing a bundle of faggots into a blaze, the other holding a second bundle in readiness. In the fire are laid three arrows with their heads; nearby, on the ground, a goblet. To the R. and below, the group is completed by the figure of a winged Cupid resting on a bundle and sunk in deep sleep, with his bow lying across his lap and a quiver full of arrows near him. The Herm is represented as a handsome youth; he is armless, and from his R. shoulder hang an oval shield and a short mantle. Four arrows have hit the shield, two the pedestal, and one has pierced the mantle. (The arrows thus correspond to the number of archers.) The best guide to the appearance of the sheet before its margins were cut is Bernardino Cesari's exact copy in the Royal Collection (No. 456; repr. in A. Venturi, *Michelangelo*, Rome, 1926, pl. 161, from a photograph by Braun). Beatrizet's engraving (Passavant VI, p. 120, 116) is reversed, in some parts free and rather feeble. For other copies, see Thode, V, p. 366. On the *verso*, at a height of about a third of the leaf from the bottom and at right angles to the obverse side, the following memorandum is written in ink: 'andrea · quaratesi venne · quj a di/12 · di · ap[r]ile · 1530 · ed ebbe · α 10· [i.e. ten ducats; the amount was then cancelled in the same ink] p(er)man[d]/ are · a suo · padre · a pisa.' In the centre of the *verso* also in ink, but in a hand of the late XVI century: 'D. Giulio Clouio copia di/Michiel Angelo'. The latter, a collector's inscription, makes it clear that the sheet was once in the possession of Don Giulio Clovio (1498–1578). In the inventory of Clovio's important art collection taken a few days before his death, it is described as follows: 'Il saggittario di Michelangiolo fatto da D. Giulio' (A. Bertolotti, *Don Giulio Clovio*, Modena, 1882, p. 14). It was probably on this occasion that the inscription came to be written on the sheet. (A. E. Popp suggests that this was done by Clovio's pupil, C. Masserolli da Caravaggio). The majority of the drawings in the possession of Clovio were inherited by Cardinal Alessandro Farnese (1520–1590), in whose service this artist had been employed. Ten years later the cardinal also acquired the Michelangelo drawings owned by Tommaso de' Cavalieri (see Repertorium für Kunstwissenschaft XXIX (1906), p. 506). Bernardino Cesari, who executed the good copy of the *Archers* already referred to (No. 456), also saw and copied the Cavalieri drawings in the Farnese collection. The view, which at one time gained general acceptance, that No. 424 was executed for Cavalieri, is ruled out by its having been in Clovio's possession. We do not know to whom Michelangelo presented the drawing.

Both the inscription and Clovio's inventory are at one in describing the sheet as a copy made by this artist from Michelangelo, an error that has long since been corrected. The drawing is an original by Michelangelo. As in the *Labours of Hercules*, every stroke betrays his hand. In both cases we are dealing with a 'presentation sheet'. But in the present drawing the execution is carried yet a stage further and is more minute, in harmony with the smaller size of the sheet and the smaller scale of the figures. The stippling is handled with the virtuosity of a professional engraver, and the gradations of light and shade are infinite. The figures on the L. which are exposed to the full light show the same fineness of surface modelling as the highly polished statues of *Night* and *Dawn* in the Medici Chapel. That contemporaries should have studied a work of this kind under the magnifying glass was thoroughly justified (see Vittoria Colonna's letter to Michelangelo in the British Museum, Add. 23139, fol. 10: Steinmann-Wittkower, *Michelangelo Bibliographie*, Leipzig, 1927, pl. 14). We do well to follow their example, and by so doing are enabled to discover a series of characteristic *pentimenti* which may serve to satisfy those who desire manifest proofs as an argument for originality. As for Clovio, one glance at his copies of Michelangelo's drawings in this collection (Nos. 451, 454, 459) is sufficient to establish that he—even with such models before him—could not belie the practices of the school to which he belonged.

A study by Michelangelo for the figure of the satyr on the L. is in the Louvre (B.B. 1591).

The memorandum on the *verso* is, to say the least, a proof

that the sheet came out of Michelangelo's *house*. It was written by a house-mate of the artist's in the following circumstances: At the time of the siege of Florence by the Imperial army in 1529–30, Michelangelo's aged father and the orphan children of his brother Buonarroto stayed, like many other refugees, in Pisa. The banker Riniero Quaratesi, father of Michelangelo's young friend Andrea, also happened to be residing there. The artist and his brothers managed to transmit money from Florence to their dependants, a proceeding that was not only forbidden but was difficult to carry out owing to the siege. In February, 1530, Giovansimone, Michelangelo's brother, sent an initial ten ducats (see Repertorium für Kunstwissenschaft XXIX (1906), p. 396 f.). Then Michelangelo himself sent a like sum. This second remittance is confirmed by an autograph memorandum of the year 1531 by Michelangelo in the Archivio Buonarroti which begins: 'Dieci ducati mandai a mio padre a Pisa per Giovanni Quaratesi . . .' (Gotti, *Vita di Michelangelo*, II, Florence, 1875, p. 81; Münchener Jahrbuch, N.S. V (1928), p. 441, n. 56). Giovanni Quaratesi was Andrea's elder brother (see Frey III, p. 135 note 4: Andrea's letter to Michelangelo of November 24, 1530). The memorandum on the *verso* of No. 424 is an entry of this transaction made at the time; the cancellation of the sum probably signifies that the money was then handed over not to Andrea, but to his brother Giovanni.*

The date of the memorandum on the *verso* of No. 424 also applies approximately to the drawing. The ideal of physical beauty is here the same as in the sketch (mentioned in the footnote) for the Christ in the *Noli me tangere* cartoon of 1531 (repr. in Münchener Jahrbuch, N.S. V (1928), p. 442), and as in a second study for the same figure in the Casa Buonarroti (B.B. 1666).

The allegorical significance of the *Archers* has not yet been definitely explained, although certain features of the representation are quite comprehensible. The underlying theme would appear to be that passionate, blind striving cannot achieve its real aim; the presence of the accompanying figures seems to show that this striving is to be identified with a species of 'love'. (That the archers have no weapons and merely mimic the action of shooting *may* be explained on purely aesthetic grounds: see the archer in the *Battle of the Centaurs*, one of Michelangelo's early works). It has, however, been accepted with good reason that the composition was based upon some definite literary source. Conze, Thode, and Panofsky brought forward texts in support of this view. Each of these texts undoubtedly explains some of the details, but none of them elucidates the subject as a whole. Panofsky's reference to Pico della Mirandola's Platonic distinction between two kinds of the 'desire for beauty'—*il desiderio naturale* and *il desiderio con cognizione*—may rightly define a train of ideas to which expression may have been given in a source so far undiscovered. As the probable source for the compositional *scheme* Michaelis cited a stucco relief, once in the Golden House of Nero, which we know from a watercolour by Francisco de Hollanda (repr. in *Codex Escurialensis*, Text, pl. 3).

The majority of critics see in No. 424 one of Michelangelo's masterpieces. A. E. Popp did not however believe the drawing to be an autograph and decided in favour of the inscription on the *verso*. Panofsky, while repudiating the attribution to Clovio, finally (1939) saw in the drawing a good copy of a lost original. This opinion is also held by Tolnay.

* In this connection I may be permitted to correct a biographical date which one encounters right through the Michelangelo literature. The artist's father Lodovico did not die in the summer of 1534, but was already dead in 1531. The above memorandum of Michelangelo's in the Archivio Buonarroti makes further references to the expenses incurred by the artist on behalf of his father after the latter's return from Pisa (after September 30, 1530), including, among other things, *burial costs*. As two payments to Antonio Mini appear later in the document, and as Mini left Michelangelo's house and Florence for good at the end of November, 1531, the death must have occurred *before* this time. Lodovico was probably dead at the beginning of 1531, so that his last existing letter to his famous son, dated January 15 of that year (Repertorium für Kunstwissenschaft XXIX (1906), p. 398), was in fact his farewell letter. The study for the figure of Christ in Michelangelo's cartoon *Noli me tangere* on the *verso* of the sheet in the Archivio Buonarroti tallies with the established date of the memorandum, for the artist, as we know, had been working on the cartoon at this time. The erroneous date of Lodovico's death rests exclusively on a passage in Michelangelo's elegy upon the death of his beloved brother Buonarroto (d. July 2, 1528) and his father (Frey, *Dichtungen*, No. LVIII). In the elegy the poet says that his father (who was born on June 11, 1444) was 90 years old at the time of his death. This can only be ascribed to poetic licence or to ignorance of his exact age. Twenty years later Michelangelo told Condivi that his father had died at the age of 92 (see Condivi, ed. Frey, p. 176).

425. *Recto:* GROTESQUE HEAD (*Figure* 88) (12762)

Verso: FRAGMENT OF A RECUMBENT MALE NUDE

248 × 119 mm. (part of a larger sheet, as shown by the *verso*). Black and red chalk.

George III 'Inventory A', p. 47, Michelangelo, III, 1.

Lit.: Robinson, p. 69; B.B. 1610; Steinman II, Fig. 228 (study A repr. full-scale); Frey 212A/213B; Thode 535; A. E. Popp, *Medici-Kapelle*, Munich, 1922, p. 156, pl. 67 (*recto*); Delacre, p. 383, 463, Fig. 216, 289A; Tolnay 93, Fig. 134 (*recto*).

Recto: A (above): male mask, full face, with rolling eyes, pointed ears, tongue put out, and a tall elaborate head ornament; the natural forms stylized into patterns merging into one another. The face was first sketched in red chalk and lightly shaded, the whole being then drawn in black chalk. B (below to the R.): the L. half of a similar mask, lightly sketched in black chalk.

Verso (the sheet held lengthways): C: a nude male figure lying on its L. side, the R. leg crossing the L. and drawn up; cut at the top below the R. knee and, to the R., not far from the groin. Red chalk. Inscribed in ink in the R. lower corner in a XVI century hand: 'michel Angelo Bona . . .'

Study A is generally assigned to the period of the Medici Chapel, and treated by most critics as a sketch for the friezes on the base of the tombs of the Medici dukes. Apart from the lack of resemblance of the two types of masks which appear in these friezes, there are also chronological considerations which tell against this identification. The frieze containing the masks on the Lorenzo monument had already been executed in marble in the second half of the year 1524 (see Milanesi, Lett., p. 596); but the style and the technique of the study point to about 1530. This grotesque shows a far greater resemblance to the central mask on the breast-plate of Giuliano, or that on the diadem of Leah on the Julius monument, than to the masks in the frieze. We know that the statue of Giuliano was not quite completed by July, 1533 (Milanesi, Corr., p. 108); and the statue of Leah was probably conceived by Michelangelo in 1532–33 (see text to No. 430 *verso*). On the other hand, the drawing might equally well be independent of these works and have been designed for another purpose altogether. A sheet by Michelangelo in the Fogg Museum in Cambridge, Mass.,

FIG. 88 Cat. No. 425 *r.*

with models for small plastic works (B.B. 1623D, catalogued as belonging to the School of Michelangelo), though perhaps somewhat earlier, provides the nearest basis of comparison within the work of the artist. Thirty years later Michelangelo remembered study A and had his giant mask in the lunette of the Porta Pia chiselled from it.

As Robinson has already noted, C is part of an unfinished copy made by a pupil of Michelangelo from the large sheet in the Ashmolean representing *Samson and Delilah* (B.B. 1718; 270 × 395 mm., red chalk). This 'presentation drawing' corresponds completely in style to the *Labours of Hercules* (No. 423) and belongs no doubt to the same period. The copyist was perhaps Antonio Mini (1506–1533). Another contemporary copy of the Oxford drawing, with its outlines pricked for transfer, is in the British Museum (Fenwick Collection, Catalogue, p. 65, No. 3). Berenson considers the sheet in the Ashmolean to be a copy by Antonio Mini from a lost drawing of Michelangelo's and says of C: 'This one is closer to M[ichelangelo], but scarcely his own'. Tolnay does not exclude the possibility of A also being a copy.

426. *Recto:* THE VIRGIN AND CHILD WITH ST. JOHN (*Plate* 26) (12773)

Verso: DRAPED FEMALE FIGURE

317 × 210 mm. (cut on the L. and at the top). Black and red chalk.

George III 'Inventory A', p. 45, Michelangelo, II, 8.

Lit.: Chamberlaine, pl. 63 (facsimile of the *recto* under the name of Michelangelo, by F. C. Lewis); Woodward, pp. 24 f.; F. Wickhoff, Prussian Jahrbuch XX (1899), p. 204 f.; B.B. 2504; Frey, text to No. 34; P. d'Achiardi, *Sebastiano del Piombo*, Rome, 1908, p. 320, 323; Thode 549; O. Fischel, O.M.D. XIV (1939–40), p. 28, pl. 2 (*verso*); L. Dussler, *Sebastiano del Piombo*, Bâle, 1942, p. 179 f., Figs. 94, 95; R. Pallucchini, *Sebastian Viniziano*, Milan, 1944, p. 82, 180, pl. 102A (*recto*).

Recto: A: the Virgin, seated, three-quarter profile to the L., the R. leg raised higher than the L., thus providing a support for the Child; the Child, standing in her lap, puts His arms round her neck, as she holds Him with both hands; R., the boy John with legs and arms crossed, leaning against the Virgin's seat. Completely finished study in black chalk, in an excellent state of preservation.

Verso: B: draped female figure in profile, turned to the R., the R. hand in the hand of a second person (of whom nothing more is visible); the figure cut off at the shoulders. Lightly sketched in black chalk and delicately drawn in red chalk.

The details of form and technique in study A point to a date about 1532. In recent literature Thode alone maintained the traditional attribution of the drawing to Michelangelo, an opinion which in my view is perfectly correct. Wickhoff assigned the study to Sebastiano del Piombo, and linked with that name other drawings by Michelangelo. Berenson greatly enlarged this group. More recently Fischel considered the attribution of these Michelangelesque drawings to Sebastiano as problematic, but accepted No. 426 as being his.

Study B, whose authenticity Thode did not recognize, differs considerably in character from A and is certainly not by Michelangelo. Wickhoff, who considered it to be a study for a *Visitation*, attributed it also to Sebastiano, in which all later authors have followed him. Berenson (in his amplified edition) considered the drawing was derived from an Attic funeral stele of the IV century B.C. Woodward's note seems to have been overlooked; it reads: 'The original was a bas-relief in terra-cotta, of which two examples may be seen in the Musée Napoleon III; one of them is represented in Tavola LX of the "Museo Campana", where it is called *Nozze di Peleo e Teti.*' In fact, this prototype, a Roman work of the first century B.C. now in the Louvre (see H. von Rohden, *Die antiken Terrakotten*, II–2, Berlin [1911], pl. 11), was copied by the anonymous draughtsman in B with an almost archæological accuracy.

427. *Recto:* THE RESURRECTION (*Plate* 22) (12767)
Verso: STUDIES OF A SHOULDER

240 × 347 mm. (slightly cut into on all sides). Black chalk. On the *recto* some red chalk offset from another sheet.

Coll.: Don Giulio Clovio; George III 'Inventory A', p. 45, Michelangelo, II. 4.

Lit.: B.B. 1612; Frey 19, 224; Thode 537; A. E. Popp, *Medici-Kapelle*, Munich, 1922, p. 97, 162, pl. 56 (*recto*); C. de Tolnay, Münchener Jahrbuch, N.S. V (1928), p. 438 f.; A. E. Popp, Zeitschrift für bildende Kunst LXII (1928–29), p. 65 (*verso* ill.); Popham 219 (*recto*); C. Gamba, *La pittura di Michelangelo*, Novellara, 1945, p. XXXII, pl. 97 (*recto*); Tolnay 109, Fig. 145 (*recto*).

Recto: A: Christ bursting forth from the tomb, His face and arms raised towards heaven. L. six, R. seven soldiers, some of whom are asleep, others awake or taking to flight. The open cave provides the framework to the whole group. Christ on a substantially larger scale than the soldiers; all the figures nude, except for a shroud behind Christ. Three of the figures, in the background, are only sketched in outline, but all the rest are finished uniformly, although full of alterations and exhibiting other traces of swift, passionately concentrated work.

Verso (in relation to the *recto* this side of the sheet is upside down): three studies of a male R. shoulder. B (above to the L.): front view. C (below B): view from above. D (in the centre): in profile ; here the whole arm is shown also. In both B and C the joint is indicated by a line. Little more than the outlines and indications of the chief muscles are given, drawn in very soft chalk. On the lower margin, upside down, is written in ink: 'D. Giulio Clouio,' in the same hand as the inscription on the *verso* of No. 424.

The Louvre possesses a rapid sketch in red chalk for study A (B.B. 1580). It contains fewer figures, but the essential elements of the composition are well established, amongst them the figure of Christ. The subject appears to have occupied the artist's mind for a long time, for there exist in the British Museum two further representations of the *Resurrection*, differing from each other in both content and composition (B.B. 1507, 1507A). The workmanship of the first is as finished as that of No. 424. In addition, Michelangelo has left us several drawings containing single representations of the *Risen Christ* which should be considered as a parallel series (see No. 428). There are various grounds, both external and internal, for connecting all these sheets with the years 1532–33, and they were perhaps intended as gifts or as designs for gifts. A, and the sketch for it in the Louvre, probably belong to the late summer of 1532. The fact that a sheet closely analogous to that in the Louvre, the sketch by Michelangelo for a *Christ in Limbo* in the Casa Buonarroti (B.B. 1407), can be shown to have originated in May or June of 1532, speaks in favour of this dating. An interesting sketch for the soldier in A clinging to the lid of the tomb, which Berenson (1406), Frey (139), and Thode (32) associate with the *Last Judgment*, is in the Casa Buonarroti.

In a picture of the Resurrection, now in the Fogg Museum, Cambridge, Mass., Marcello Venusti (*c.* 1515–1579) has combined groups copied from A with figures copied from B.B. 1507 (see C. de Tolnay, Art in America XXVIII (1940), pp. 169 f.).

The rapidly executed sketches B–D are perhaps demonstrations made by Michelangelo for one of his pupils. They are very likely contemporary with the *recto*.

Whereas the genuineness of study A has never been in doubt, its dating in the literature has oscillated between 1525 and 1535. A. E. Popp considered the sketch in the Louvre to be later than the more elaborate version, while Panofsky suggested that it was the work of Antonio Mini (Zeitschrift für bildende Kunst LXII (1928–29), p. 182). One of the drawings in the British Museum—B.B. 1507A—is condemned by A. E. Popp and Tolnay as a *pastiche*.

As regards the purpose of the *recto*, A. E. Popp formulated the theory that it represents a design for a fresco which Michelangelo had projected for the lunette of the entrance wall of the Medici chapel. We possess no evidence of such a plan. Moreover, the four extant compositions of the *Resurrection* differ considerably from each other in shape, and not one of them could have easily been fitted into a semi-circle. C. Gamba suggests that B.B. 1507 in the British Museum and A had been designed for a fresco in the Sixtine Chapel (to the L. and above the entrance door) to replace one by Domenico Ghirlandajo which had been damaged in 1522. The fresco in question was later executed by Hendrick van den Broeck from a different design.

The three studies on the *verso* were attributed by A. E. Popp to Giulio Clovio, in whose possession the sheet had once been.

428. THE RISEN CHRIST (*Plate* 25) (12768)

373 × 221 mm. (slightly cut on the L. and top). Black chalk. George III 'Inventory A', p. 45, Michelangelo, II, 5.

Lit.: B.B. 1616; Frey 8; Thode 541; A. E. Popp, *Medici-Kapelle*, Munich, 1922, p. 162 f.; Brinckmann 49; A. E. Popp, Belvedere VIII (1925), Forum, p. 75, and Zeitschrift für bildende Kunst LIX (1925–26), p. 172; C. de Tolnay, Münchener Jahrbuch, N.S. V (1928), p. 445 note 60; Popham 220; Tolnay, p. 188.

Christ rises out of His tomb, front view, His face and arms raised towards heaven; behind Him a flowing shroud. Fully finished, except the R. hand. The major *pentimenti*, notably in the drawing of the R. lower leg and the L. ankle, have been carefully erased (a similar erasure was begun on the R. arm, but discontinued).

In Michelangelo's compositions of the *Resurrection* containing many figures (see No. 427), Christ is invariably drawn on a substantially larger scale than the soldiers. In a parallel series of drawings of the same period, only the isolated figure of the Risen Christ is shown. The earliest of these representations appears to be B.B. 1413 *verso* in the Casa Buonarroti, showing the first stage of execution (a sketch for this, in the Archivio Buonarroti, published by Tolnay, loc. cit., Fig. 54, appears on the back of a letter which the artist had received in Rome on September 19, 1532). In this drawing the figure is a free variant of that of Christ in No. 427. The present drawing starts from the same point (the torso), and combines with it the motive of the legs in the sketch on the *verso* of No. 429 (done at the end of 1532). The result is a new, wholly organic form, one of the most magnificent in Michelangelo's work. A third drawing, unfinished, entirely different in the treatment of the subject, exists in the British Museum (B.B. 1523). Each of these three figures occupies a whole folio sheet. Further sketches by Michelangelo connected with this series are: B.B. 1713 *verso* in the Ashmolean (the *recto* contains a ground-plan which was demonstrably drawn in October, 1532); B.B. 1667, and 1665A *recto* and *verso*, in the Casa Buonarroti (the *verso* of B.B. 1665A has remained unpublished). A lost drawing which also belonged to this series is known from a contemporary copy (B.B. 1676A), now in the Boymans Museum at Rotterdam (No. I.20).

A. E. Popp (in 1925) did not accept No. 428 and the sheet in the British Museum as genuine, and Tolnay delivered the same verdict on B.B. 1413 *verso* in the Casa Buonarroti.

In addition, A. E. Popp rejects the sketches B.B. 1667, 1665A *recto*, and Tolnay that on No. 429 *verso*. I can find no argument to justify these verdicts. On the contrary, the three large sheets here referred to, in combination with the compositions of the *Resurrection of Christ* containing many figures, seem to offer an unique opportunity of following the supremacy of Michelangelo's genius in his powers of imagination and construction.

429. *Recto:* TITYUS (*Plate* 21) (12771)
Verso: SKETCHES FOR A RESURRECTION OF CHRIST (*Figure* 89)

190 × 330 mm. (slightly cut into on the L. and at the top). Black chalk.

Coll.: Tommaso de' Cavalieri; Cardinal Alessandro Farnese; George III 'Inventory A', p. 45, Michelangelo, II, 6.

Lit.: Vasari, 1550, p. 986; 1568, ed. Milanesi, V, pp. 374, 431, VII, p. 271; Woodward, p. 25 f.; B.B. 1615; Frey 6, 219; Thode 540; A. de Rinaldis, Rassegna d'Arte XVIII (1918), p. 203 f.; E. Panofsky, *Handzeichnungen Michelangelos*, Leipzig, 1922, 12–13; A. E. Popp, *Medici-Kapelle*, Munich, 1922, p. 162 f.; Brinckmann 54 (*recto*); W. Slomann in Burlington Mag. XLVIII (1926), p. 10 f.; Popham 222 (*recto*); E. Panofsky, *Studies in Iconology*, New York, 1939, p. 212 f.; Tolnay 115, Fig. 155 (*recto*).

Recto: A: the young giant Tityus lies upon a slab of rock, to which his R. arm and R. leg are chained; the vulture, with wings outspread, perches behind him gnawing at his liver. In the foreground a stream of Hades; to the R. a tree stump with claw-like roots and a branch forming the profile of a terrifying monster. (Tityus, son of Gaea, who dared to offer violence to Leto and was slain for it by her children, was doomed to have his ever-renewing liver devoured by a vulture in the underworld: Metamorphoses IV, 456 ff.).
Verso: B (in the centre): the Risen Christ, standing on the edge of the sarcophagus and its lid, the R. arm pointing downwards and the L. raised towards Heaven. Torso, head, L. upper arm and R. thigh have been traced from the figure of Tityus in A by holding the sheet against the light, and are consequently reversed. The head was afterwards altered and turned upwards, and the R. arm has been tried out in three different positions. C (R.): a squatting figure, front view, the arms raised, the head turned to the L. The R. half of the figure has been cut away. A has the degree of finish one associates with an engraving; B and C are hardly more than outlines.

Vasari records that Michelangelo designed the *Tityus* for his friend Tommaso de' Cavalieri. Michelangelo made the acquaintance of the young Roman nobleman* in the autumn or winter of 1532, and at once conceived the warmest friendship and respect for him. This friendship only ended with the artist's death. Michelangelo addressed the young man in poetical epistles, celebrated him in poems and made him presents of drawings. The list of such drawings given by Vasari embraces four mythological-allegorical compositions: the *Ganymede*, the *Tityus*, the *Fall of Phaethon* and the *Children's Bacchanal*. In addition there is a representation of *Cleopatra*, and, finally, a life-size half-length portrait of Cavalieri. The drawings, with the exception of the *Cleopatra* which Cavalieri presented to Duke Cosimo I in 1562 (see Vasari V, p. 81, and Gualandi, Lettere, III, p. 22 f.), passed into the possession of Cardinal

FIG. 89 Cat. No. 429 *v.*

Alessandro Farnese (1520–1590). We do not know what happened to them afterwards. Woodward refers to a tradition according to which the *Ganymede* had entered the collection of E. Bouverie, Delapré Abbey, Northampton, and had subsequently perished by an accident; and we meet the other three allegorical sheets soon after 1760 in the collection of George III. They (Nos. 429–431) are among the chief glories of the Royal Library.

These four drawings (for the lost *Ganymede* see the excellent copy in this collection, No. 457), outstanding examples of Michelangelo's art, were done during the first year of his friendship with Cavalieri, apparently in the order given in Vasari's list. Shortly before the end of 1532 the artist wrote for the first time to his young friend who was then ill. His letter, which no longer exists, was accompanied by two drawings. After promising that he would visit Michelangelo after his recovery, Cavalieri, in his reply of New Year's Day, 1533, speaks as follows of the drawings: 'In questo mezo mi pigliaro al manco doi hore del giorno in contemplare doi vostri disegni che Pierantonio [Cecchini, a sculptor, who delivered the letter] mi a portati, quali, quanti piu li miro,

* It is not known when Cavalieri was born. In his first letter to Michelangelo, of January 1, 1533, he calls himself 'un giovane appena nato al mondo'. He died in 1587.

tanto piu piacciono; et appagero il mio male, pensando alla speranza che 'l detto Pierantonio mi a data di farmi vedere altre cose delle vostre' (Symonds, II, p. 400). Everything points to these two drawings having been the *Ganymede* and the *Tityus*. Both in their content and composition they are companion pieces, and were so treated from the beginning; see the cameos engraved after them by Giovanni Bernardi. While the *Fall of Phaethon* was only completed in August, 1533, and the *Children's Bacchanal* probably some months later, the two companion pieces had already become generally known in Rome in the summer of the same year; see Sebastiano del Piombo's letter of July 7 (Milanesi, Corr., p. 104) and Cavalieri's letter of September 6 (Symonds, II, p. 401 f.).

Through such mythological themes the artist gave expression to Platonic ideas which we also meet in his contemporary poems. 'The Ganymede, ascending to heaven on the wings of an eagle, symbolizes the ecstasy of Platonic love, powerful to the point of annihilation, but freeing the soul from its physical bondages and carrying it to a sphere of Olympian bliss. Tityus, tortured in Hades by a vulture, symbolizes the agonies of sensual passion, enslaving the soul and debasing it even beneath its normal terrestrial state. Taken together, the two drawings might be called the Michelangelesque version of the theme: 'Amor sacro e profano'. In both compositions the traditional allegorical interpretation of a mythological subject was accepted, but it was invested with the deeper meaning of a personal confession, so that both forms of love were conceived as the two aspects of one essentially tragic experience' (Panofsky, *Iconology*, p. 218). With regard to the form, the dependence of the drawings upon the antique is also evident. The figure of Tityus lies upon the rock as on a pedestal; the recumbent Hellenistic statues, like the *Fallen Giant* at Naples, influenced this composition. Both drawings were much admired by contemporaries and succeeding generations and were copied in various media; see Thode, V, pp. 351 f., 356 f. Two copies of the *Tityus* are in the Royal Collection (Nos. 458, 459).

Before Michelangelo parted with this sheet he made use of the back for sketches for a composition which at that time had long been exercising his mind (see text to No. 427). The figure of the Risen Christ (B) is a peculiar variant of the Tityus figure, being developed from a partial tracing of the latter. Further variants of this figure of Christ are provided by the *Resurrection*, B.B. 1507B, in the British Museum, and by No. 428. His habit of trying out motives from every angle is characteristic of Michelangelo's method of work at all times. And there is certainly at least one more example of tracing figures through paper held against the light: the sheet in the British Museum (B.B. 1536) with sketches for the *Last Judgment*. A variant of the figure of the soldier (C) is to be found in the *Resurrection* in the British Museum mentioned above (B.B. 1507A).

Tolnay considered sketch B to be a *pastiche*. But the graphic abbreviations used in it can be found in a whole series of drawings by Michelangelo dating from the early 1530's.

430. *Recto:* THE FALL OF PHAETHON (*Plate* 29) (12766)
413 × 234 mm. (slightly cut on all sides). Black chalk.
Verso: FEMALE HALF-LENGTH FIGURE (*Figure* 90)
Red chalk.

Coll.: Tommaso de' Cavalieri; Cardinal Alessandro Farnese. George III 'Inventory A', p. 45, Michelangelo, II, 7.

Lit.: Vasari, V, p. 431: VII, pp. 17, 271; B.B. 1617; Frey 58 (*recto*); Thode 542; E. Panofsky, *Handzeichnungen Michelangelos*, Leipzig, 1922, 11 (*recto*); A. E. Popp, *Medici-Kapelle*, Munich, 1922, p. 147 f., pl. 49 (*recto*); Brinckmann 56, 58; A. E. Popp, Belvedere VIII (1925), p. 20, 11; W. Slomann, Burlington Mag., XLVIII (1926), p. 10; Panofsky, *Studies in Iconology*, New York, 1939, p. 218 f.; Tolnay 119, fig. 153 (*recto*).

Recto: A: Zeus, riding his eagle, hurls his thunderbolt with his R. hand against Phaethon who falls headlong together with the four horses of the sun; below the river-god Eridanus, the three wailing Heliades, and Cycnus transformed into a swan; behind the group a large urn from which water pours, and a boy carrying an amphora. A completely finished drawing; the major *pentimenti* carefully erased (e.g. the arms of the sister of Phaethon on the R. were originally raised towards Heaven).

Verso: B: female half-length figure, front view, but slightly turned towards the L.; in her R. hand she holds the end of a plait of her hair, in her L. a round mirror. The bust and arms are only slightly sketched, the head is more elaborated, but also unfinished. Originally the gaze was straight to the front, but this was altered so that the eyes turn in the direction of the mirror. C (top R.): another drawing of the L. ear from B, but on a larger scale.

FIG. 90 Cat. No. 430 *v.*

A follows closely Ovid's account of the Phaethon legend (Metamorphoses, I, 750 f.). The drawing brings together in one scene three moments in the story, each separated from the other by an interval of time: the punishment of Phaethon's *hubris*, the lament of Phaethon's sisters, and the punishment of Phaethon's brother Cycnus for his lamentations. Here, too, as in the case of *Ganymede* and *Tityus*, the legend is used as the vehicle for a symbolic expression of the artist's feelings for Cavalieri.

It is clear from Cavalieri's letter of January 1, 1533 (its text is given in the entry to No. 429), and from Michelangelo's reply of the same day (Milanesi, Lett., p. 462 f.), that on sending the *Ganymede* and the *Tityus* to his young friend he had held out to him the prospect of receiving further drawings. No. 430 is one of these. Cavalieri confirms the receipt of this sheet in a letter of September 6, 1533, written to Michelangelo in Florence: 'Forse tre giorni fa io ebbi il mio Fetonte assai ben fatto; e allo visto il papa, il cardinal de Medici, e ugnuno, io no so gia per qual causa, sia desiderato di vedere' (Symonds, II, p. 401). The phrase 'il mio Fetonte' appears to confirm the view that Cavalieri was already acquainted with the drawing. We may infer from this that when Michelangelo had to return from Rome to Florence at the end of June, 1533, he took the unfinished sheet with him in order to complete it there. Judging by the technical quality, it is natural to assume that the execution of the drawing must have taken a considerable time. The work is the result of an intense absorption by the artist with the problem of representation. We possess two more versions of the *Phaethon* by him. The smaller, in the British Museum (B.B. 1535), a sort of *modello*, bears a note from which it is clear that the artist had submitted the drawing to his friend Cavalieri for an opinion before finishing it. This drawing must therefore have been made in Rome. The second version, in Venice (B.B. 1601), which is as large as No. 430, has only the central portion of the composition (the chariot, the four horses and Phaethon) half finished, the rest being only sketched in. It must thus be a rejected version. (This sheet, unfortunately in a very bad state of preservation, also bears a note from Michelangelo to Cavalieri which it has not been possible to decipher completely). Innumerable copies of the final version of the *Phaethon* bear witness to the deep impression which it made both upon Michelangelo's contemporaries and later artists; see Thode, II, p. 361 f.

The artist undoubtedly used the *verso* of the sheet before the *recto*. To judge from the attribute of the mirror, the half-length figure stands for a personification of either Prudence or the Active Life in the form of Leah. As she appears to be adorning herself before the mirror—like Leah in Dante's well-known verses (Purgatorio, 27, 97 f.)—the latter interpretation is the more probable. And, moreover, the figure shows a startling resemblance to the Leah of the Julius Monument. In a petition to the Pope in July, 1542, this statue was mentioned by Michelangelo as being far advanced (Milanesi, Lett., p. 486). It might very well have been conceived in 1532–33, possibly as one of those new statues for the Monument for which the artist at that time wanted to prepare full-size clay models (see Sebastiano del Piombo's letter of July 15, 1532; Milanesi, Corr., p. 98 f.). The close connection between the drawing and the statue would thus be easily explained.

Berenson and A. E. Popp considered study B as the work of a pupil ('Andrea di Michelangelo' and Antonio Mini respectively; the latter, it should be noted, had already settled in France by the end of 1531). I can see no adequate reason for such a judgment. The drawing seems to have been abandoned before completion, and the half-finished state of the head makes a somewhat unsatisfactory impression, more particularly because of the *pentimento* in the pupils of the eyes. Compared however with the authenticated drawings of Michelangelo of this time, it shows no difference of technique. The lightly sketched lower portion invites comparison with the similar details in the *Fall of Phaethon* in Venice, or in the two versions of the *Resurrection* in the British Museum (B.B. 1507, 1507A).

431. A BACCHANAL OF CHILDREN (*Plate* 28) (12777)

274 × 388 mm. (the edges slightly cut and a few small holes restored). Red chalk.

Coll.: Tommaso de' Cavalieri; Cardinal Alessandro Farnese; George III 'Inventory A', p. 45, Michelangelo, II, 3.

Lit.: Vasari, 1550, p. 986; 1568, ed. Milanesi, V, p. 431, VII, p. 271; Robinson, p. 65 f.; Symonds, II, pl. facing p. 144; B.B. 1618; Frey 187; Thode 543; E. Panofsky, Zeitschrift für bildende Kunst LXII (1928–29), p. 180; C. de Tolnay, Thieme-Becker XXIV (1930), p. 522; E. Panofsky, *Studies in Iconology*, New York, 1939, p. 221 f.; R. W. Lee, Art Bulletin, XXII (1940), p. 245; Tolnay 120, Fig. 156.

The scene is a cave, the upper portions of whose side walls are visible, and over whose opening hangs a broad curtain. The rocky ground rises in tiers, upon which five groups are disposed on two diagonals intersecting in the centre. To the R., in front, a young man sunk in deep slumber; near him four *putti* sitting and standing. One of them holds a wine goblet: sleep is thus represented as a phase of drunkenness. In front, to the L., a female satyr sits with two *putti*, one of them asleep in her lap, the other suckling at her breast. Near this group are the remains of a meal on a cloth. On the first ledge of the rock, in the centre, seven *putti* carrying the carcass of a red deer. These figures are on a larger scale and more plastic than all the others and therefore form the chief group. (The specific meaning of the carcass is not clear.) Upon a second ledge to the L., nine *putti* are busy round a large cauldron in which meat is boiling. A swine's head and a dead hare hang above them. Above to the R., upon a third ledge, eight unruly *putti* surround a wine butt. Owing to the edges having been cut away, half of the R. hand figure is missing; for this see the XVI century engravings of the composition: Enea Vico, 1546 (Bartsch 48); N. Beatrizet (Bartsch 40); Anonymous, ed. Lafreri, 1553.

It is not known whether this representation is based upon any text. The actions of the groups have however all one meaning: these thirty *putti* and two adults represent the functions of life at its lowest level. Analogies may be found for some of the motives in late-antique sarcophagus reliefs, but these are used quite freely. There is a notable likeness between the two lower groups and representations of related themes in the Sixtine Ceiling (the *Drunkenness of Noah* and the paintings on the spandrels).

Vasari mentioned the *Children's Bacchanal* last among the compositions which Michelangelo sent to his friend Cavalieri. Actually this sheet appears to have originated in Florence, before the artist had returned to Rome at the end of October, 1533. We find some of the figures copied on one of the Florentine sheets by Raffaello de Montelupo in the Ashmolean (B.B. 1716 *recto*), and it is known that Montelupo entered the service of Michelangelo late in the summer of 1533. The connection of No. 431 with the *Fall of Phaethon* is quite close; compare, for example, the figure of the sleeper with the river god. Technically, the *Bacchanal* represents the highest point of achievement in this series of 'presentation sheets'. It shows to a high degree the consistency and transparent texture of an engraving, and to perfection the closely-knit structure of a painting. Foreground and background are given the same amount of care as the figures, and there are practically no blank spaces left in the drawing. Vasari (ed. 1550) noted the extraordinary fineness of the *chiaroscuro*: 'col fiato non si farebbe più d'unione'. Nevertheless, Tolnay considered this drawing to be no more than a copy. The series of the four Cavalieri sheets, of which the existing three are in the Royal Collection, appears to form a unity and an effective sequence both in style and content. Panofsky (*Iconology*, p. 223) sums up their Platonistic aspect in these words: 'If the flight of Ganymede symbolizes the enraptured ascension of the Mind, and if again the punishment of Tityus and the fall of Phaethon exemplify the fate of those who are incapable of controlling their sensuality and imagination, the Children's Bacchanal, which is entirely devoid of amorous tension, might be the image of a still lower sphere: the sphere of a purely vegetative life which is as much beneath specifically human dignity as the Mind is above specifically human limitations.'

432. *Recto* and *verso:* SKETCHES AND STUDIES FOR THE 'LAST JUDGMENT' (*Plate* 27 and *Figure* 91) (12776)
277 × 419 mm. A new piece of paper, roughly the shape of a flattened triangle, has been inserted at the bottom to the R. Black chalk, rubbed in places.
George III 'Inventory A', p. 46, Michelangelo, II, 13.
Lit.: B.B. 1620; Steinmann 80; Frey 188–189; Thode 545; C. de Tolnay, Thieme-Becker XXIV (1930), p. 522; Art Quarterly III (1940), p. 127; Art Bulletin, XXII (1940), p. 128 note 4.
On the *verso*, L., in ink: 'di Bona Roti'.

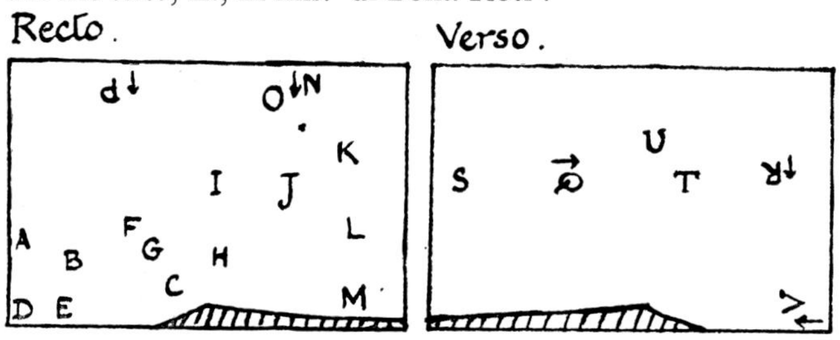

A detailed description of all the sketches on the *recto* and *verso* and a demonstration of their connection with the finished work in all its particulars would require too much space here, and is perhaps not really necessary. All the drawings are for one limited section of the fresco: the L. half and centre of the lowest horizontal strip, representing the resurrection of the dead and the mouth of hell. The sketches are in the nature of single figures or groups of figures for this section and belong to the preparatory stage of the final *modello*. By interweaving the groups A, B and C the artist was able to obtain the composition of practically the whole of this section. What is new in the fresco is the figure on the L. border and the emphasis given to the centre by another standing figure. The *verso* contains sketches for these two figures: Q and R. D is a special sketch for the figure raising himself in front of the man standing in the centre; in the fresco this sketch was used reversed. E deals with a smaller group, F–H with single figures in various stages of resurrection (I is partly drawn over H). The *recto* contains eight detailed sketches of the resurrected figure carried by two angels, upside down, with a devil pulling him back to hell by his hair: I–P (three of these, N–P, are drawn the opposite way up on the sheet). In addition to the sketches Q and R already mentioned, the *verso* was also used for four detail studies (S–V). Three of these are for the risen man whose hovering body is supported under the armpits by an angel, while he is being pulled back by a devil with the help of a serpent's coils. S shows the lower part of this body, T the R. forearm hanging down, U the R. hand of the devil, pulling. V is a study for the L. arm of the risen man in the immediately adjoining group on the R., the one for which the *recto* has eight sketches. Although these four studies of details are not identical with

FIG. 91 Cat. No. 432 *v.*

the corresponding forms in the fresco, they come so close to them that they must have immediately preceded the final design for this section. S is a good example of the accuracy with which the artist in studies of this kind reproduced the muscular structure of the human body. In the fresco the same forms are more summarily rendered.

No. 432 and a sheet in the British Museum containing sketches for the groups of the Martyrs and the Deadly Sins (B.B. 1536) form the most important sources from which we can gain an insight into Michelangelo's preparatory work upon his *final* plan for the *Last Judgment.* It was only with this plan that the extension of the fresco over the whole altar-wall of the Sixtine Chapel was projected. The two sheets served to build up certain sections of this plan, such sections forming in the mind of the artist separate units of the whole composition. (Michelangelo's other existing drawings for the *Last Judgment* are connected either with earlier, more restricted plans, or with single figures for the final cartoons). The *modello* of the whole work was built up from a number of such preparatory drawings. This preparatory work took place—if I understand the sources correctly—in 1534. The execution of the painting itself (which naturally involved the making of full-size cartoons for all the parts) was begun in the autumn of 1536 and lasted five years. The unveiling of the work took place on October 31, 1541.

In common with the four catalogues (op. cit.) all the drawings, both on *recto* and *verso*, are here assigned to Michelangelo. On the other hand, Tolnay, in his general elucidation of the drawings for the *Last Judgment*, included No. 432 among the apocryphal works, and expressly declared study S to be 'a feeble copy . . . executed after the fresco'. Yet the sketches on both sides of the sheet are completely identical in style and technique with the sketches for groups on the sheet in the British Museum previously mentioned, about which no one has expressed any doubts. Moreover, inner criteria as, for example, the manner of their relationship to the fresco, provide evidence of their genuineness. As regards the four studies of detail (S–V on the *verso*), it is difficult to believe that a later hand would have made copies after that section of the fresco to which the genuine sketches on the same sheet correspond, and partly even actually over these genuine sketches. The arrangement of these four studies on the sheet also follows precisely the method used by Michelangelo. The studies themselves—they are delicate and spirited, in no way weak—reveal characteristic differences from the corresponding forms in the fresco.

Recently Tolnay published a sketch by Michelangelo of a L. leg in the Huntington Library, San Marino, California, which he claimed had been made for the figure corresponding to the studies S and T on No. 432. In this sketch the leg is somewhat more extended and its position is approximately vertical. Following upon this, C. E. Gilbert brought forward proofs to show that a draft of a poem in Michelangelo's hand, found on the sheet in the Huntington Library, belonged to the year 1546 (Art Bulletin XXVI [1944], p. 48 f.).

433. *Recto:* SKETCH AND STUDIES FOR A PIETÀ (*Plate* 30)
Verso: ARCHITECTURAL STUDIES (*Figure* 92) (12769)

257 × 221 mm. (cut into on the L. and R.). Black and red chalk.

W.M., Robinson 20.

Coll.: N. Lanière (Lugt 2885); George III 'Inventory A', p. 46, Michelangelo, II, 24.

Lit.: B.B. 2506; Frey 206/207; Thode 551; P. d'Archiardi, *Sebastiano del Piombo*, Rome, 1908, p. 324; E. Panofsky, *Festschrift für J. Schlosser*, Vienna, 1927, p. 161 note 22; C. de Tolnay, Prussian Jahrbuch LI (1930), p. 45 note 1; L. Dussler, *Sebastiano del Piombo*, Bâle, 1942, p. 199 f.; R. Pallucchini, *Sebastian Viniziano*, Milan, 1944, p. 180.

Recto: A (extending over the whole sheet): rapid sketch, in faint outline only, for a *Pietà*. To the L., the Virgin, sitting on the ground, holds in her lap the head and shoulders of her Son (the rest of His body having been sacrificed when the sheet was cut down). Her L. hand is raised as she looks up to St. John, who approaches her on the R. and bends forward in her direction. Behind the Virgin are two women, one turned towards her, the other looking towards Heaven. B (in the centre): a kneeling male figure, clad in close-fitting clothes, in profile to the L.; a finished study. C (R. of B): an outstretched R. arm, cut off at the shoulder; carefully executed. D (to the R., drawn over A, B and C): the shaft of a column, drawn with a ruler. C in red chalk; all the others, including those on the *verso*, in black chalk. The very faded sketch A can be studied more easily with the help of a not much later copy of the sheet in the British Museum (Fawkener 5211–75; on the *verso* a fragment by the same hand after Michelangelo's study of the *Crucifixion* in the Seilern Collection, London). The copyist was able to see more than we can to-day, and he omitted C and D.

Verso (the other way up). E (above): ground plan of a portal, in front of which is a railing of seven balusters. F (below E): section of pillared structure with half-oval niche, the columns flanking it on each side being recessed

FIG. 92 Cat. No. 433 *v.*

into the wall to a third of their depth. G (below L.), H (centre R.), I (below H): elevation sketches of a portal, with various designs for frame and pediment. J (R. of F): detail sketch for F, section of the wall columns. K (R. of H): section of an entablature.

A is the sketch for a *Pietà*, for which a different and more elaborate compositional study exists in the British Museum:

the famous drawing from the Warwick Collection (B.B. 2486). On the other hand, the interdependence of the two sheets is obvious from the fact that B and C are finished detail studies for the Warwick *Pietà*: B for the figure of St. John, C for the R. arm of the figure supporting the head of Christ. These drawings which constitute our only documentary source for an important project of Michelangelo's were, according to all appearances, designed for a painting. We do not know whether this painting was to have been executed by the master himself or by somebody else, e.g. Sebastiano del Piombo. Technical and stylistic considerations point to the middle of the fourth decade of the XVI century as the probable date of the drawings.

In recent literature the traditional attribution of these sheets to Michelangelo was only supported by Thode. Berenson first gave both to Sebastiano, then withdrew this attribution in respect of No. 433. This latter sheet suggested to Frey the hand of Michelangelo's pupil Antonio Mini. Panofsky ascribed both drawings to Daniele da Volterra.

As for the sketches E–K on the *verso*, Michelangelo's authorship has never been subjected to any doubt. They were undoubtedly done many years later than the drawings on the *recto*. According to Thode, they are closely connected with the designs which group themselves round the Porta Pia, and Tolnay included G–I amongst the sketches for the Porta Pia itself. Michelangelo undertook this work at the wish of Pius IV (elected to the papacy on December 26, 1559); the builder's contract was concluded on July 2, 1561. F occurs again on the margin of a large drawing in the Casa Buonarroti (Frey 294); the sketch here seems to deal with a detail (the surrounding pillars) of the ground-plan of S. Giovanni dei Fiorentini, executed on the same sheet. Michelangelo's plans for this church were made shortly before November 1, 1559. We do not know with what work E is connected. I should like to suggest, with all due caution, that it may be for the chapel for Cardinal Ascanio Sforza in Sta. Maria Maggiore. This was still in course of construction at the time of the founder's death (October 7, 1564). Later its entrance was reconstructed, but it originally had a monumental portal and was railed off by a balustrade (see V. Fasolo, *La Cappella Sforza di Michelangelo*, in Architettura e Arti Decorative III (1924), p. 433 f.).

434. *Recto:* HEAD OF A YOUNG WOMAN (*Plate* 24)
Verso: THE SAME (*Figure* 93) (12764)

212 × 142 mm. (the top corners cut). Black chalk.

George III 'Inventory A', p. 43, Michelangelo, I, 2.

Lit.: B.B. 1608; Steinmann 56; Thode 533; E. Panofsky, *Handzeichnungen Michelangelos*, Leipzig, 1922, 6; Vasari Society, 2nd Series V (1924), 5; Brinckmann, text to No. 20; A. E. Popp, Belvedere VIII (1925), Forum, p. 74; K. Clark, Burlington Mag., LVI (1930), p. 181; Popham 215.

On the *verso*, in the lower R. corner, in W. Gibson's (?) hand: 'MAngolo. 1.4'.

Recto: A: head of a young woman, front view, slightly turned towards the R., looking down. Unfinished study, the outlines of the head and shoulders barely indicated, the face and neck delicately shaded, but the form nowhere finally fixed.

Verso: B: head similar to A, turned towards the R., but with a shorter neck. In the first stage of execution, the sharply-pointed chalk having scarcely left any trace on the paper. It seems possible that the sheet was originally much larger and that A had been designed for a representation of the Virgin. The veil which starts over the forehead is characteristic of almost all Michelangelo's Virgins, and the form

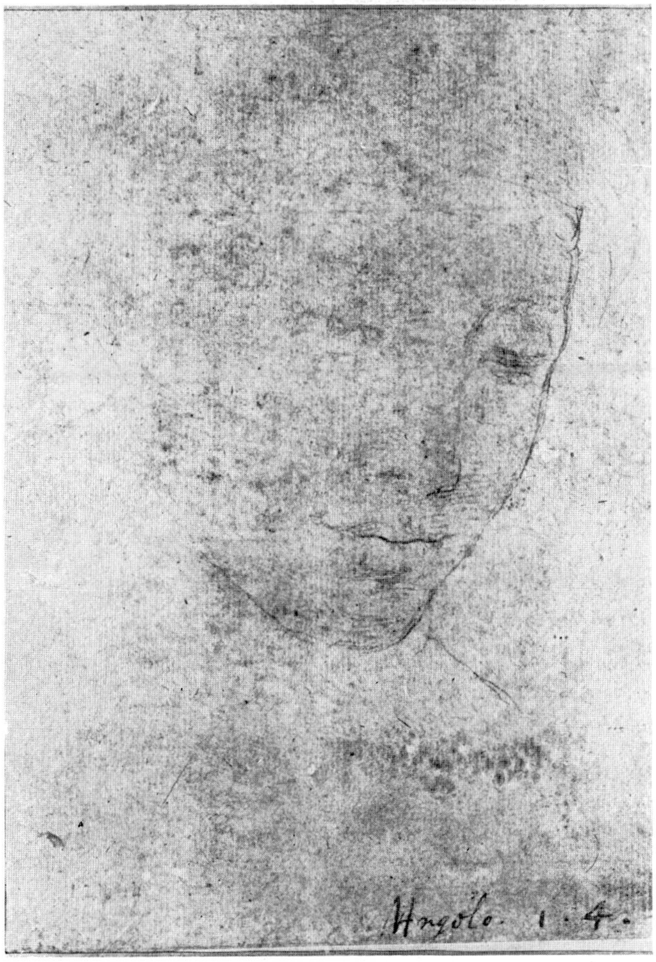

FIG. 93 Cat. No. 434 *v.*

of the veil cap is the same as in the two *Annunciations* painted by Marcello Venusti from Michelangelo's drawings about 1550, and in the studies for these compositions in the British Museum (B.B. 1519, 1534 *recto*). The type itself, the rather long oval of the face and the long, but not exactly slender neck, was already known in Florentine art about 1540: see Bronzino's *Holy Family* in Vienna (Venturi, IX 6, Fig. 32). In style and technique the drawing can scarcely belong to an earlier time.

In A we have also perhaps a drawing which may have been intended as a gift for Cavalieri. The passage where Vasari speaks of Michelangelo's friendship for the young Roman (VII, p. 271) begins as follows: '[Michelagnolo] infinitamente amò, piu di tutti, messer Tommaso de' Cavalieri . . . quale essendo giovane e molto inclinato a queste virtù [i.e.: arti], perchè egli imparassi a disegnare, gli fece molte carte stupendissime, disegnate di lapis nero e rosso, di teste divine'. Cavalieri himself mentions his own attempts at drawing, and the fact that they were praised by Michelangelo, in his letter of January 1, 1533 (Symonds, II, p. 400). Moreover, in a sheet which, after passing through a number of famous English collections, now belongs to Sir Kenneth Clark (B.B. 1694), the Windsor head appears as that of a half-length Madonna. It is on a smaller scale and is obviously the work of a pupil, for the rest of the figure also seems to be copied from Michelangelo, as well as the other three studies on the same sheet, one of which seems to reproduce a lost sketch by Michelangelo for the *Conversion of St. Paul*, of 1542. There are, furthermore, indications that

FIG. 94 Cat. No. 435 *r.*

the faint sketch B, on the *verso* of No. 434, derives from the same pupil's hand. Should we see in these modest, but by no means unpleasing, drawings exercises by Cavalieri? This hypothesis, and the suggestion that the drawing A was a gift by Michelangelo to Cavalieri, is not wholly impossible. In the older literature A was assigned to the period of the Sixtine Ceiling or dated even earlier; it was Thode who first established its correct date. A. E. Popp saw in it only a copy of a lost original by Michelangelo, and Sir Kenneth Clark thought it was possibly the work of Michelangelo's friend Giuliano Bugiardini (1475–1554). Thode, on the other hand, also ascribed (with one exception) the sketches on the sheet in the Clark Collection to Michelangelo himself. Berenson is the only author to notice B; he thought that it was 'done by some such artist as Sogliani'.

435. *Recto:* THE VIRGIN AND CHILD (*Figure* 94) (12772)
Verso: DRAFT OF A POEM

225 × 194 mm. (including a strip 15 mm. wide on the R., first cut off the sheet, then added to it again. Upper and lower edges cut, as may be seen from the *verso*). W.M., Robinson 3. Black chalk, partly over a preliminary sketch in red chalk. The ground was later covered with gold paint, most of which was, however, with the exception of a few slight traces, washed off again.

George III 'Inventory A', p. 47, Michelangelo, III, 16.

Lit.: B.B. 2505; Frey 34/35B; Thode 550; P. d'Achiardi, *Sebastiano del Piombo*, Rome, 1908, p. 323 f.; C. de Tolnay, Thieme-Becker XXIV (1930), p. 524; L. Dussler, *Sebastiano del Piombo*, Bâle, 1942, p. 199; R.

Pallucchini, *Sebastian Viniziano*, Milan, 1944, pp. 83, 193.

Recto: the Virgin, turned slightly towards the L., sits on a low block; she clasps the Child with both her arms as He sits astride her R. leg. The Child, turning round, presses His head against His mother's face. To the R. side of the sheet and at right angles to the bottom margin, some very faded lines in Michelangelo's hand may be deciphered (the top line is covered by the drawing): 'altiera e fera/al core s appressa amore/ donna altiera/i[n] me passar puo pro/li ochi al core/passar po li ochi al core'. They are disconnected phrases of a poem jotted down.

Verso (the other way up): 28 lines of a poem by Michelangelo. Faded brown ink, later partially written over by Michelangelo himself (with the exception of the sixth line) in a darker ink, and partly crossed out. This makes it very difficult to read. As the metrical form indicates, the poem consisted originally of six strophes, six lines each. The whole of the first strophe and the last two lines of the poem were sacrificed when the sheet was cut down. The poem is experimental in form. The verses are hendecasyllabic, ending in a word of two syllables (Phalaecean metre). The words with which each line of the first strophe ended recur in various successions in all the subsequent strophes, in such a way that the word with which the sixth line of the strophe ends is repeated at the end of the first line in the following stanza. (The following transcription diverges in some places from that given by Frey.)

[. . . . . arme]

. . . fuor del mie propio c ogni altr arme
difender posso ogni mie cara cosa
altra spada altra lancia u(n) altro scudo
fuor delle propie forze ch(e) so(n) nulla
tant e la trista usa(n)za ch(e) m a tolta
la gratia ch(e) l ciel pioue in ogni loco

Qual uecchia serpe p(er) istrecto loco
passar poss io lasciando le uecchie arme[1]
e dal costume rinnouata e tolta
sie l alma in uita e d ogni umana cosa
coprendo se co(n) piu securo scudo
ch(e) tucto el mo(n)do a morte e me(n) ch(e) nulla

Amore i sento gia di me far nulla
natura del pechato in ogni loco
spoglia di me me stesso e col tuo schudo
colle pietose tuo uere e dolci arme
difendimi da(m)me[2] c ogni altra cosa
e come no(n) istata in brieue tolta

Mentre c al corpo l alma no(n) e tolta
ora ch(e) l uniuerso puo far nulla
factor gouernator re d ogni cosa
poco ti fia auer dentra me loco
come cosa mortal queste fie(n) l arme
chi sie tuo seru . . . sempre . . . scudo

De rompi espera(n)za el . . . ch(e) targa e scudo
dal qual sol[3] p(er) me la tuo gratia e luce tolta
ch(e) do ogn uomo ueril so(n) le uere arme
senza le quali ogn uo(m) diue(n)ta nulla
[. . . . . loco]
[. . . . . cosa]

[1] above the line the variant 'ogni uechi arme'
[2] Followed by 'cogli', which is crossed out.
[3] Followed by 'la tuo', which is crossed out.

The proper appreciation of the drawing on the *recto* is rendered difficult by an optical distortion. The former gilding of the background was not in all places carried right up to the outlines of the figures, but left, particularly to the L., an aureole of varying width around them. What remains of the gold now produces a second—and false—silhouette which perforce overweighs the original one. The drawing itself is partly rubbed, but has not been worked over by later hands.

R. Duppa (*Life of Michelangelo*, London, 1807, p. 331) mentioned and reproduced a painting by Marcello Venusti, then in the possession of R. Cosway, which introduced the same group in an interior setting. (The present whereabouts of this picture is unknown to me.) The Roman painter Marcello Venusti (c. 1515–1579) acquired great renown among his contemporaries by his pictures based on designs by Michelangelo. The corresponding designs were mostly made by Michelangelo specifically for this purpose, but in some cases Venusti used drawings by the master dating from an earlier period. As far as we know this collaboration started shortly before 1550 at the latest. But it may very well have begun earlier, as Venusti is already mentioned in 1541 as the best of the artists copying the *Last Judgment* (Pastor, *History of the Popes*, XII, p. 660). Judged by its style, the present drawing would seem to belong to a period round about 1545. It may well have followed, after an interval, upon the completion of Michelangelo's drawings for Vittoria Colonna. The only one of the latter drawings preserved in the original, the *Crucifixion* in the British Museum (Thode 353), offers the nearest technical and stylistic parallel to it.

Berenson's attribution of No. 435 to Sebastiano del Piombo was shared only by P. d'Achiardi; all the other critics stoutly maintained Michelangelo's authorship. But the dating of the sheet has fluctuated widely, partly perhaps because of its unsatisfactory state of preservation. Berenson dated the drawing about 1514–15; Frey and Thode, 1520–30; and Tolnay, 1556–60.

436. CHRIST ON THE CROSS BETWEEN THE VIRGIN AND ST. JOHN (*Plate* 32) (12775)

382 × 210 mm. (L., R., and top margins cut). Black chalk.

George III 'Inventory A', p. 47, Michelangelo, III, 2–4.

Lit.: B.B. 1622; Frey 130; Thode 548; C. de Tolnay, Repertorium für Kunstwissenschaft XLVIII (1927), p. 201 f.; R. Wittkower, Burlington Mag., LXXVIII (1941), p. 159 f.

The dead Christ upon a T-shaped cross, His head turned towards the R. and sunk on His breast, the body curved outwards towards the R., the R. foot over the L. On the L. the Virgin, slightly turned to the R., arms folded across her breast, with the R. hand supporting her head and the L. clasping her headdress. To the R. St. John, slightly turned to the L., his hands raised in front of his chest and his face turned towards Christ. The figures beneath the cross are almost completely finished. The actual figure of Christ is only given in outline and has been achieved as the result of a long succession of alterations. Behind it we can see traces of former versions, more particularly three different pairs of arms. The artist covered over the first outlines of the body of Christ with white wash and drew his final version over this surface, which has since to a large extent oxidised. In the final version the figure of Christ is on a smaller scale than the other two figures.

See note on No. 437.

437. *Recto:* CHRIST ON THE CROSS BETWEEN THE VIRGIN AND ST. JOHN (*Plate* 31) (12761)

Verso: A L. LEG (*Figure* 95)

405 × 218 mm. All the margins cut. (Note that the uneven cutting has disturbed the balance of the sheet, the vertical axis now inclining towards the L.) W.M., Robinson 16. Black chalk.

George III 'Inventory A', p. 47, Michelangelo, III, 2–4.

Lit.: B.B. 1621; Frey 129, 220; Thode 547; Brinckmann 72 (*recto*); Popham 226 (*recto*); R. Wittkower, Burlington Mag. LXXVIII (1941), p. 159 f.

Recto: A: Christ hanging dead on a Y-shaped cross, His head sunk on His L. shoulder, the lower part of the body bending markedly outwards to the L., the L. foot over the R. The two arms of the cross joined at the top by a cross-piece. To the L. the Virgin, the upper part of her body slightly turned towards the R., her L. hand raised to her head and her R. forearm across her bosom. To the R. St. John, slightly turned towards the L., the upper part of his body bent a little forward, the arms folded across his chest. There is a third figure, front view, kneeling behind the cross and embracing it, which is either a first idea for St. John, or a sketch for the figure of Mary Magdalen. The figures beneath the cross are only slightly sketched in, that of Christ—over two outlined versions in which the cross was T-shaped—is fully finished.

FIG. 95 Cat. No. 437 *v.*

Verso: B (occupying the R. side of the sheet turned horizontally): a male L. leg, front view, the upper part strictly vertical, the lower bent. Scarcely more than the outlines.

The late series of representations of Golgotha by Michelangelo—with the dead Saviour on the Cross and the Virgin and St. John below—embraces, in addition to Nos. 436 and 437, two sheets in the British Museum (B.B. 1529, 1530), and a sheet each in the Ashmolean and the Louvre (B.B. 1574, 1583). A seventh drawing can be reconstructed from fragments and copies; see Thode, V, p. 468 f. The single studies of the *Crucifixion* in the Louvre (Thode 503) and in the Seilern Collection, London (repr. Burlington Mag. LXXVIII (1941), pl. facing p. 160), also belong to the same series. Preparatory studies are on No. 437 *verso* and on a sheet in the Ashmolean (B.B. 1547 *recto* and *verso*). These representations of Golgotha appear to belong to the same class of drawing as the sheets for Tommaso de' Cavalieri and Vittoria Colonna: they are independent works of graphic art. Of the existing drawings in the series not one is, however, completely finished: the subject spurred the artist on to ever fresh variations. Critics have suggested dates for the composition of this series, which fall within two decades: 1538 to 1557. But stylistic considerations and the appearance of similar ideas in Michelangelo's poems appear to point—as R. Wittkower has emphasized—to the last five years of this period. The difficult problem of the probable sequence of these leaves cannot here be discussed. The figure of St. John in No. 437 appears to be a later version of that in the seventh drawing above mentioned (see the fragment in the Louvre, B.B. 1582). The latter drawing, with the addition of the figures of mourning angels from Michelangelo's earlier *Crucifixion* drawn for Vittoria Colonna, was carried out as a painting by Marcello Venusti.

The study on the *verso* of No. 437 is, in its strict frontality and its suggestion of depth, a fine example of Michelangelo's mastery of figure drawing in his latest period. This study perhaps belongs to the figure of St. John in the sheet in the Louvre (B.B. 1583). It might then have been used by a pupil for the figure of the Magdalene in the marble group of the *Pietà* from Sta. Rosalia, Palestrina.

SCHOOL OF MICHELANGELO

See also: Michelangelo No. 425 *verso*, 426 *verso*, 434 *verso*.

438. NUDE YOUTH IN PROFILE WALKING TO THE R. He holds a lighted torch in his L. hand and shields the flame with his R. (*Figure* 96) (0340)

380 × 168 mm. Black chalk over a faded sketch in pen and ink.

George III 'Inventory A', p. 51, Raffaello d'Urbino e Scuola, 34.

The draughtsman, a pupil or follower of Michelangelo's, copied a figure on a sheet of studies at Chantilly (B.B. 1397; about 1503–4). The original sketch in pen and ink corresponds exactly, except that in it the arms are omitted; when he completed it in black chalk the draughtsman worked with more independence. Copies of the same figure and of a second figure on the sheet at Chantilly by a different draughtsman are in the Albertina (B.B. 2502 *verso*).

FIG. 96 Cat. No. 438

439. 'ÉCORCHÉ' OF A MALE TORSO (0624)
282 × 206 mm. Red chalk, with traces of a surrounding line in red chalk.

George III 'Inventory A', p. 47, Michelangelo, III, 7–15: 'Anatomical Studies', without further particulars. The present sheet and the four following are probably included under this heading.

Above to the L. is the letter 'f'; to the R. '26'; on the *verso* at the bottom to the L., 'di Michel Angelo Buona Roti' is inscribed in an old hand.

The torso is represented turned three-quarters to the L., cut off above the knee; the head is twisted round a little to the R. and bent back; only the shoulder of the hanging L. arm is included and not even this part of the raised R. arm. The weight of the body rests on the L. leg, the R. leg is slightly behind. On the R., near a line pointing to the shoulder joint, is the word 'braco'; to the R. at the bottom, 'culo'—both in the same red chalk as the drawing.

440. 'ÉCORCHÉ' OF A MALE TORSO (0802)
281 × 208 mm. (cut into at top and bottom). Red chalk. At the top on the L. 'M', on the R. '28'; at the bottom to the L. 'di Michel Angelo Buona Roti', and above this 'n° 45'. The torso is the same as is No. 439 but seen from the back.

441. 'ÉCORCHÉS' OF A MALE LEG: on the L., a R. leg, extended, seen from the inside; on the R., the same leg seen from the back. (*Figure* 97) (0803)
282 × 207 mm. (cut into at top and bottom). Red chalk. At the top on the L.: 'R'; along the R. edge, 'n° 44'; on the *verso* at the bottom in the centre: 'di Michel Angelo Buona Roti'. The separate muscles are marked in red chalk with letters, sometimes on the drawing, sometimes outside it.

Nos. 439–441 are certainly the work of the same practised draughtsman. A fourth sheet belonging to the same series

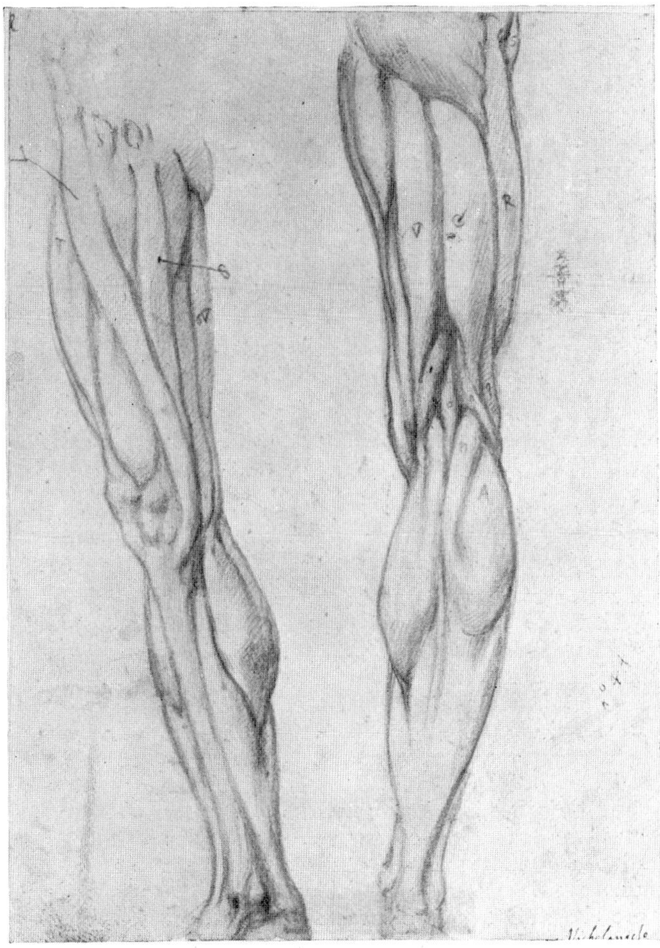

FIG. 97 Cat. No. 441

with two studies of a L. arm and two of a L. shoulder on the *recto*, and four studies from different points of view of a L. leg on the *verso* is in the Teyler Museum at Haarlem, Frey-Knapp 333 and 334 (see Frey, *Michelangelo*, I, 1907, p. 148 note). As shown by the identical character of the inscriptions, the four sheets were at one time together in the same collection. Three lines of a madrigal written on the Haarlem sheet in Michelangelo's own hand indicate their provenance from his studio.

The method of expression and the technique likewise point clearly to a Michelangelesque origin. A drawing of a male figure seen from the back in the Albertina (B.B. 1603 *verso*) shows a connection in the attitude of the figure with Nos. 439 and 440. Berenson and Thode (No. 526) regard it as an original study for the cartoon of the *Bathers*; Tolnay (*Michelangelo's Youth*, Fig. 285), as the copy of such a study; and A. E. Popp (Zeitschrift für bildende Kunst LIX (1925–26), p. 173) as the work of a pupil. There are a number of holes in the sheet and it has been extensively restored. Whatever opinion is held as to its originality, there is no question about its Michelangelesque stamp or any doubt that the drawing on the *verso* is by Michelangelo himself. Further, the figure is repeated in reverse on a sheet in the Louvre (B.B. 1597 *recto*), also originating from Michelangelo's studio, and at one time in the same collection as the four *écorchés* under discussion. Now these three red chalk drawings at Windsor, as well as the one at Haarlem, represent portions of the same plastic model as the study in the Albertina, but in the same direction as the drawing in the Louvre, and *écorché*. The material available is not sufficient to allow any hypothesis for explaining the relationship of these studies to be formed. There can, however, be little doubt that the studies in red chalk formed part of a book of anatomical studies, or copies of such studies, used as models in Michelangelo's studio. Sebastiano del Piombo seems to be asking for models of this sort when he writes to Michelangelo on July 15, 1532 (Milanesi, Corr., p. 100), as follows: 'Pregovi a recordatevi di portarmi qualche cossa: figure o ganbe o corpi o brace; che tanto tempo le ho dessiderate, come vui sapete . . .'. Condivi (ed. Frey, p. 192) definitely says that Michelangelo repeatedly had in mind the preparation of a treatise on the human body for the use of artists. And finally mention may be made of the fact that, according to Bottari (*Vita di Michelangelo*, Rome, 1760, p. 172, No. 23), the Florentine academicians possessed a wax model which was called 'la notomia di Michelagnolo'.

FIG. 98 Cat. No. 443

442. STUDIES OF 'ÉCORCHÉS': A, male torso in profile to the L., the parts under the arm; B, male figure in profile to the R., from the shoulder to below the knee; C, male torso seen from the back. (0474)

283 × 190 mm. Pen and brown ink.

Inscribed at the top on the R.: 'n° 39', and under this, '36'.

443. STUDIES OF 'ÉCORCHÉS'. *Recto:* A–D, studies of knees; E, male head and bust from the front; F, joints of the hand; G, hanging R. arm from the front; H, L. leg seen from the inside. (*Figure* 98) (0475)

Verso: I, hanging L. arm seen from the back; J, male torso in profile to the R.; K, bones of the hand; L–N, studies of legs.

278 × 203 mm. Pen and brown ink.

Inscribed on the *verso:* 'Michel Anglo [sic] Buona Roti' and 'n° 43'.

Nos. 442 and 443 are by the same draughtsman. They also formed part of the same old collection as Nos. 439, 440 and 441, and partly reproduce other aspects and details of the same plastic model. They may therefore be copies of sheets from the same book of anatomical studies to which the studies in red chalk once belonged.

444. *Recto:* FIVE SLIGHTLY VARIED VIEWS IN PROFILE OF A SHARPLY FLEXED L. ARM, the hand of which holds a stone; whole length figure of Hercules to the front; the head of the same figure on a larger scale. (0467)

Verso: TWO MORE VIEWS OF THE BENT L. ARM

406 × 244 mm. Black chalk (the studies of arms), some gone over with pen and ink; the figure the same; the head first sketched in red chalk.

George III 'Inventory A', p. 46, II, 23.

Inscribed at the bottom on the L.: 'Michelangelo'.

The studies of arms are from a plastic model taken from Michelangelo's *David*. The L. forearm of the David was broken off in 1527 and was not replaced until 1543 (see A. Lensi, *Palazzo Vecchio*, Milan, 1929, p. 109). Possibly the model of the arm was made on the occasion of the restoration. The draughtsman was apparently a Florentine of the second half of the XVI century.

445. KNEELING DEMON, SEEN FROM THE FRONT, THE R. LEG STRETCHED OUT (0448)

371 × 255 mm. (upper corners cut). Black chalk.

George III 'Inventory A', I, p. 43, 10.

Lit.: B.B. 1750.

Inscribed on the *verso* in William Gibson's (?) hand: 'Michel' Angolo. 5·2'. Berenson believes the drawing is perhaps the enlargement of an original sketch by Michelangelo for one of the figures of demons in the *Last Judgment*. The connection with the fresco is, however, of the vaguest. The resemblance to the Triton on one of the walls of the former villa of the Buonarroti at Settignano (B.B. 1462A) is closer. The draughtsman, a Florentine, may well have been working in the second half of the XVI century.

446. *Recto:* STUDIES OF TWO FIGURES OF DEMONS IN THE 'LAST JUDGMENT'; three studies of an *écorché* male leg, two of the bust, and one of the head. (0215)

Verso: SKETCH OF A 'SACRA CONVERSAZIONE' (cut into at the top), including four female saints, among them St. Lucy and St. Agatha kneeling.

264 × 203 mm. (cut into on all sides). Red chalk.

Apparently the work of a Roman draughtsman about 1600.

447. PORTRAIT OF MICHELANGELO, WEARING A HAT, BUST, THREE-QUARTERS TO THE R. (12806)

207 × 167 mm. Red and black chalk.

Acquired in 1875.

Lit.: E. Steinmann, *Porträtdarstellungen des Michelangelo*, Leipzig, 1913, p. 39, pl. 33.

The portrait is based, if indirectly, on Jacopino del Conte's painting in the Uffizi which was taken from life. The same costume and hat are to be found in certain portrait miniatures (Steinmann, pl. 32). Roman or Florentine, about 1600.

MICHELANGELO. Copies after (A) Drawings

See also Michelangelo, No. 425, *verso*.
School of Michelangelo, No. 438.
Pupini, No. 785, *verso*.

448. THE SOLDIER IN THE CENTRE OF THE CARTOON OF THE 'BATHERS' (*Figure* 99) (5317)

165 × 182 mm. Red chalk.

FIG. 99 Cat. No. 448

An early and artistically valuable study from the figure in the centre of the lost cartoon, the last great creation of the artist's youthful period (1504–05). Hitherto the figure was only known from Michelangelo's preparatory study in the Albertina (B.B. 1604 *recto*) and from the stylistically different copy of the finished cartoon at Holkham Hall. No. 448 is certainly a more accurate copy than the latter.

449. THE 'IGNUDO' TO THE R. ABOVE THE PERSIAN SIBYL on the Sixtine Ceiling, and studies of detail. (0441)

390 × 235 mm. Red chalk.

Inscribed underneath in red chalk: 'Del Buona Rota'; on the *verso:* 'Michel' Angelo. 3.3.' (= 15/–) in the hand of William Gibson (?). Copied from two sheets of Michelangelo's with studies for the figures of the two *ignudi* above the Persian Sibyl and for the *Creation of Adam*, both in the Teyler Museum, Haarlem (B.B. 1465, 1466). The academically trained copyist combined in No. 449 studies for the *ignudo* on these two different sheets.

Brinckmann, Panofsky and C. de Tolnay regard B.B. 1465 and 1466 as nothing but copies from the frescoes.

450. *Recto:* THE FIGURE OF HAMAN AND THREE STUDIES OF DETAIL (0435)

Verso: OUTLINES OF THE FIGURE AND OF ONE OF THE DETAILS TRACED THROUGH FROM THE RECTO

390 × 222 mm. W.M., three lilies on a shield. Red chalk.

Lit.: Brinckmann 96 (*recto*); Delacre, p. 474 f. (Fig. 304–5).

Photo.: Braun 120.

Copy from Michelangelo's study in the British Museum (B.B. 1690 *recto*) for the fresco in the Sixtine Chapel. The copyist—perhaps a Dutch artist—was an excellent and careful draughtsman, even if he betrays the period in which he worked, the late XVI century. Another work of his hand is a copy in the Uffizi (Steinmann 46) of Michelangelo's study for the Libyan Sibyl (New York, B.B. 1544D *recto*), including the copy of a lost original study for the R. foot of the figure. Brinckmann transposes the relation between the original in the British Museum and No. 450, seeing in the latter a copy from the completed fresco. Delacre attributes No. 450 to Michelangelo himself.

451. THE FLAGELLATION OF OUR LORD (*Figure* 100) (0418)

200 × 182 mm. (the upper corners cut). Red chalk over a slight sketch in black chalk.

FIG. 100 Cat. No. 451

Inscribed in ink on the *verso* in the centre: 'Julio Clouio da M. Angelo Bon.t', in the same hand as the inscription on No. 459.

The miniature painter Don Giulio Clovio (1498–1578) was a great admirer of Michelangelo, a collector and untiring copyist of his drawings, and also, according to Vasari (ed. of 1550, p. 905), a close friend of Sebastiano del Piombo. No. 451 is thus described in the inventory of Clovio's effects: 'Un Xpo alla colonna in lapis rosso con tre figure di Michelangiolo fatta da D. Giulio' (A. Bertolotti, *Don Giulio Clovio*, Modena, 1882, p. 14). (There is a fourth executioner on the L., but he is summarily indicated and largely covered by the foremost figure. With the exception of the executioner in the back row on the R. all the figures are unclothed.) This drawing of Clovio's provides the answer to a question which has been much debated. Vasari (ed. of 1550, p. 898; that of 1568, ed. Milanesi, V, p. 569) says that the basis for Sebastiano del Piombo's masterpiece, the *Flagellation* in S. Pietro in Montorio, Rome, was a 'piccolo disegno' of Michelangelo's. This drawing, as Michelangelo's correspondence shows (see Frey, *Briefe an Michelagniolo*, Berlin, 1899, p. 31 f.), was made in August, 1516. From Sebastiano's possession it later entered that of Tommaso de' Cavalieri (Vasari, VII, p. 272), but has subsequently disappeared. Vasari's statement has for this reason been very variously interpreted. Now No. 451 is, to all intents and purposes, a very accurate copy of Michelangelo's lost drawing. It shows us that Vasari's statement is to be taken *literally*. Vasari further says that Sebastiano for the preparation of his cartoon made a number of larger studies from Michelangelo's 'piccolo disegno'. One of these studies is in the British Museum (B.B. 2488).

452. DANCING FAUN (0425)
308 × 176 mm. Hard black chalk.
Lit.: B.B. 1749; E. Panofsky, Zeitschrift für bildende Kunst LXI (1927–28), p. 240 f.; Delacre, p. 180 f. (Fig. 89, reversed).
Photo.: Braun 110.

On the *verso* is a monogram composed of the letters RDF, which is, according to L. van Puyvelde, the signature of the Antwerp painter David Ryckaert I (1560–1607), and also the number '13'.

Copied from Michelangelo's red chalk study in the Louvre (B.B. 1581) representing a dancing satyr with a tambourine surrounded by three *putti*, which dates perhaps from about 1520. The copyist, very probably a Netherlander, only reproduces the main figure in an empty style which attempts at the same time to 'prettify' the original. (The outlines were traced from the original with the stylus.) L. Demonts and Brinckmann doubt the genuineness of the Louvre drawing; Panofsky ascribes it to Michelangelo's pupil Antonio Mini, and postulates for it and for No. 452 a lost original by Michelangelo.

453. *Recto:* A 'DAMNED SOUL' (01365)
Verso: MALE TORSO (*Figure* 101)
262 × 213 mm. (cut on the L. and at the top). Black chalk.
W.M., like Robinson 16.
George III 'Inventory A', p. 43, I, 3.
Lit.: B.B. 1619 and Vol. I, p. 230; Steinmann 77 (Fig. 79 *recto*); Thode 544; Delacre, p. 177 f. (Fig. 87 *recto*). (The reproductions of *recto* given in Steinmann's and Berenson's books are reversed.)

The drawing on the *recto* is the copy of a drawing in the Uffizi (B.B. 1628). This has at the top the inscription: 'GHERARDVS: DE PERINIS:', at the bottom to the R.: 'MICHELAÑ. BONAROTI FACIEBAT', with, under it, three intersecting circles—that is, the stonemason's mark by which the blocks of marble quarried for Michelangelo were habitually marked. The writing shows that the Uffizi drawing was one of the three which, according to Vasari (ed. of 1550, p. 986; that of 1568, ed. Milanesi, VII, p. 276 f.), Michelangelo gave to his young friend Gherardo Perini, and which after the latter's death came into the possession of the Medici. (A second one of these drawings is B.B. 1627, a third perhaps B.B. 1626.) Pietro Aretino hints at these presents to Perini in his well-known defamatory letter of November, 1545 (Gaye, *Carteggio Inedito*, II, Florence, p. 334). Otherwise we know very little of Perini. There are three letters of his from the year 1522 in the Archivio Buonarroti (Frey, *Dichtungen des Michelangelo*, Berlin, 1897, p. 504 f.). Michelangelo's answer to the first of these letters is signed with an angel's head and the three intersecting circles instead of with his name (Milanesi, Lett., p. 418). The writing on the Uffizi drawing is therefore perhaps Perini's. The drawing may well date from about 1525, and is apparently a physiognomical representation of terror. It early became known, and A. Salamanca (d. 1562) made an engraving from it. Milanesi mentions an engraved gem after it by Giovanni Bernardi (Vasari, V, p. 374, note 2), and Benvenuto Cellini used it in his relief of Perseus and Andromeda. Michelangelo himself adapted it for the head of the devil to the L. behind Minos in the *Last Judgment*. Other copies of the head are in the Uffizi (No. 18738E) and in the former Vaughan collection (photograph in the British Museum).

The torso on the *verso* is a study by the same draughtsman from Michelangelo's fragmentary model of a river-god in the Florentine Academy. It represents the model as it was (wrongly) exhibited in 1589. (The manner in which it is set up at present is also wrong: the figure originally lay on its R. side leaning on its R. forearm.) This date is apparently a terminus post quem for the drawing. The more or less contemporary study by a different draughtsman from the same model in the British Museum (B.B. 1489) has been generally regarded, like No. 453, as an original.

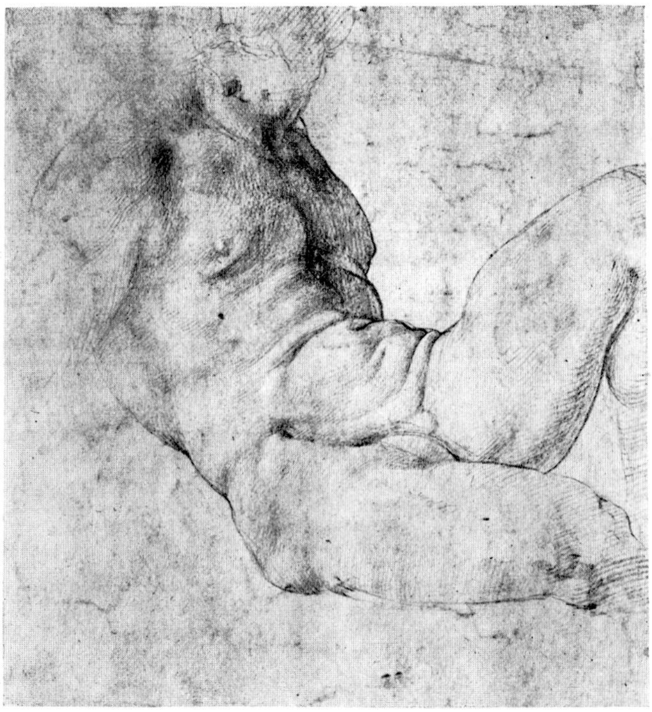

FIG. 101 Cat. No. 453

Berenson believes that the Uffizi drawing (B.B. 1628) is a weak copy of the *recto*, which he ascribes to Michelangelo. The study on the *verso* he likewise regards as an original study for the *Last Judgment*. Later writers have followed Berenson.

454. 'ZENOBIA' (0419)
305 × 237 mm. Hard black chalk.
Lit.: Thode, V, p. 344.
Photo.: Braun 119.
The original is in the Uffizi (B.B. 1626). It is possibly one of the drawings which Michelangelo in the 1520's presented to his young friend Gherardo Perini (see note to No. 453). The traditional name for the subject can hardly be right: 'Venus, Vulcan and Cupid' is a more probable interpretation. Recent critics, with the exception of Thode, attribute the Uffizi drawing to an assistant of Michelangelo's or see in it the copy of a lost original. No. 454 plainly reveals the hand of that tireless copyist of Michelangelo, Don Giulio Clovio. The fact that the original was in Florence suggests that the copy dates from the period of Clovio's stay in that city, 1551–53. It is apparently to be identified with the drawing described as follows in Clovio's inventory: 'Il combattimento di Marte e Venere fatto da D° Giulio et inventione di Michelagnolo' (A. Bertolotti, *Don Giulio Clovio*, Modena, 1882, p. 12).

455. IMAGINARY FEMALE HEAD (0432)
332 × 235 mm. Hard black chalk.
George III 'Inventory A', p. 43, I, 6.
Lit.: Frey, text to No. 289; Thode, text to No. 344; Delacre, p. 148 f. (Fig. 71).
Photo.: Braun 118.
Inscribed in ink on a label stuck on below on the R.: 'Michel. Angello Buonaroti. 2.4.' (= 40/- in William Gibson's method of pricing).
The original is Michelangelo's drawing of about 1525–28 in the British Museum (B.B. 1689 *recto*), which recent critics, with the exception of Thode, regard as a school drawing or the copy of a lost original. No. 455 is a relatively late copy, but made before the original was cut into at the top.

456. 'THE ARCHERS' (*Figure* 102) (0412)
257 × 372 mm. Red chalk.
Lit.: Thode, p. 366; Frey, text to No. 298; A. Venturi, *Michelangelo*, Rome, 1926, pl. 161; E. Panofsky, *Studies in Iconology*, New York, 1939, p. 225 (Fig. 166).
Photo.: Braun 124.

FIG. 102 Cat. No. 456

Inscribed on the *verso* in ink in a hand of the XVII century: 'M.B.C. Ap^{n}' and 'Copiato da Berardino Cesari'.
The original is in this collection, No. 424. The copyist, the Roman painter Bernardino Cesari, who died young in 1614, was the pupil and assistant of his brother, the Cavaliere d'Arpino. Baglione (*Vite*, 1642, p. 147) informs us that Bernardino copied some of the drawings which Michelangelo had given to Tommaso de' Cavalieri, and adds: 'Bernardino li fece tanto simili, e sì ben rapportati, che l'originale dalla copia non si scorgeva'. The same judgment would have been passed by contemporaries on No. 456, which in fact aims at being a *facsimile*. Its chief value for us lies in the fact that it reproduces the original before the edges were cut.

457. THE RAPE OF GANYMEDE (*Figure* 103) (13036)
192 × 260 mm. Black chalk.
George III 'Inventory A', p. 43, I, 20.
Lit.: Vasari, ed. of 1550, p. 986; that of 1568, ed. Milanesi, V, p. 431, VI, p. 575, VII, pp. 271 and 567 f.; Woodward, p. 24; B.B. 1614; Frey 18; Thode 539; Brinckmann 88; Tolnay, Thieme-Becker, XXIV (1930), p. 522; E. Panofsky, *Studies in Iconology*, New York, 1939, p. 212 f.; Tolnay 118, Fig. 154.

FIG. 103 Cat. No. 457

Photo. Braun 117.
Until a short time ago generally identified with the drawing which Michelangelo—together with the *Tityus*—gave his young friend Tommaso de' Cavalieri towards the end of 1532 (see text to No. 429). Berenson and Frey had already expressed doubts regarding it, but Brinckmann was the first definitely to put forward the view that the drawing could be nothing more than a copy of the original, which was so much admired by contemporaries. According to a tradition referred to by Woodward, the original had been in the Bouverie Collection and had perished by an accident. Woodward also mentioned No. 457 as a copy made by Giulio Clovio, perhaps on the ground of an inscription on the back not now visible. In fact, Clovio's inventory of 1577 lists a copy of the *Ganymede* by this artist (A. Bertolotti, *Don Giulio Clovio*, Modena, 1882, p. 14).

458. TITYUS (0471)
212 × 327 mm. Hard black chalk.
George III 'Inventory A', p. 43, I, 18 or 19.
Inscribed at right angles to the top margin, 'le ungie'; at the bottom to the R., 'Del . . .'

FIG. 104 Cat. No. 459

The original is in this collection, No. 429. The copyist, an Italian of the second half of the XVI century, in spite of his striving after accuracy, has failed to conceal his mannerist training.

459. TITYUS (*Figure* 104) (0472)
203 × 290 mm. (top corners cut). Hard black chalk.
On the *verso* in a XVI century hand: 'Julio Clovio d MAngelo Buonarottj'.
The original is in this collection, No. 429. This copy of Clovio's gives the group in statuesque isolation. The curved outlines, varying in breadth, are characteristic alike for the artist's original drawings and for his other copies after Michelangelo, Nos. 451 and 454.

460. THE DEAD SAVIOUR ON THE CROSS (*Figure* 105) (12774)
246 × 124 mm. (cut on the L. and at the top). Hard black chalk on parchment.
George III 'Inventory A', p. 47, III, 2–4.
Lit.: Frey, text to No. 129; Thode 546; Delacre, p. 315 (Fig. 172).
The original has disappeared. A study for it by Michelangelo, regarded by recent critics, with the exception of Thode, as apocryphal, is on a sheet in Haarlem (B.B. 1675 *recto*; Thode 269) dating from about 1535–40. There is another copy of the lost original in the Louvre (Thode 495).

461. *Recto:* HEADLESS MALE NUDE; slighter repetition of the same nude to the L.; to the R. the pelvic bones; below to the L. a seated child.
Verso: THE BONES OF THE HAND (0433)
333 × 267 mm. Pen and brown ink with, on the *verso*, wash.
George III 'Inventory A', p. 44, I, 32.
Lit.: B.B. 1749A.
The original of the nude is in the Louvre (B.B. 1590 *recto*). It is an early study by Michelangelo, going back perhaps to his first period in Rome. The copy is a late one and by a weak hand. The other studies are no doubt also copies, but not after Michelangelo.

462. A PROPHET (0409)
413 × 282 mm. Pen and brush and brown ink.
On the *verso:* 'Michelangelo Bonarotti' and, covered by the mount, an indication of price (by William Gibson ?).
The original is in the British Museum (B.B. 1486). It dates from about 1508–10 and is partly used in the figure of Isaiah. This feeble copy dates from the late XVI century. To the R. at the top is a partial copy of a drawing in Haarlem (B.B. 1468 *recto*); below this, a L. leg.

463. A STANDING WOMAN PRAYING (0459)
227 × 74 mm. Pen and brown ink.
Fascimile-like copy of the central figure in a drawing of a group in Haarlem (B.B. 1474 *recto*), of which the dating is disputed.

464. THE DEAD CHRIST ON THE LAP OF HIS MOTHER, WITH TWO ANGELS LAMENTING (0424)
328 × 206 mm. Pen and brown ink, washed with blue and heightened with white.
George III 'Inventory A', p. 43, I, 21.
Weak and relatively late copy of the drawing which Michelangelo made at the request of Vittoria Colonna (Condivi, ed. Frey, p. 202). The copy is not from the lost original but from some reproduction of this, and seems to be by a Venetian or Veronese artist.

FIG. 105 Cat. No. 460

MICHELANGELO Copies after (B) Frescoes

See also School of Michelangelo, No. 446 *recto*.
R. da Montelupo, No. 417 *verso*.
Agostino Carracci (Steinmann, II, Fig. 204–5)

THE CEILING OF THE SIXTINE CHAPEL

465. THE SECTION OVER THE ALTAR (01368)
410 × 563 mm.
Steinmann, II, Fig. 208.

466. THE CENTRAL SECTION; the figure of Ezekiel and the subject pictures omitted. (01370)
420 × 556 mm.

467. A SECTION WITH THE DELPHIC SIBYL AS THE CENTRE; the subject pictures omitted. (01369A)
263 × 372 mm.

468. A SECTION WITH THE PROPHET JOEL AS THE CENTRE (01369B)
268 × 372 mm.
Pen and brown ink and brown wash. George III 'Inventory A', p. 46, II, 36–39 ('imitated by Carracci').
Inscribed on the *verso* of each: 'Di Polidoro doppo Michelangelo Buonarota'. The draughtsman (who is *not* Polidoro Caldara) intended to reproduce the whole of the ceiling in these four drawings (Tolnay, *Sistine Ceiling*, Oxford, 1945, Figs. 258–261). He never completed his task; there are gaps and the execution is of varying degrees of sketchiness. The draughtsman must have worked before 1535, for No. 465 includes the two lunettes of the altar wall (and the arms of Julius II), which were sacrificed to the *Last Judgment*. (See also No. 492.) In this connection the sheet is a valuable source. No. 467 also reproduces the *ignudo* to the L. above the Delphic sibyl, which was almost completely destroyed in the explosion of 1797 (see also No. 471).

469. THE 'IGNUDO' TO THE L. ABOVE THE CUMAEAN SIBYL (0634)
244 × 168 mm.

470. THE 'IGNUDO' TO THE L. ABOVE EZEKIEL (0635)
244 × 168 mm.

471. THE 'IGNUDO' TO THE L. ABOVE THE DELPHIC SIBYL (*Figure* 106) (0636)
243 × 171 mm.

472. THE 'IGNUDO' TO THE L. ABOVE JOEL (0637)
246 × 169 mm.

473. THE 'IGNUDO' TO THE R. ABOVE JEREMIAH (0638)
246 × 170 mm.

474. THE 'IGNUDO' TO THE R. ABOVE DANIEL (0639)
253 × 168 mm.

475. THE 'IGNUDO' TO THE L. ABOVE THE PERSIAN SIBYL (0640)
250 × 171 mm.

476. THE 'IGNUDO' TO THE L. ABOVE JEREMIAH (0641)
248 × 170 mm.

477. THE 'IGNUDO' TO THE L. ABOVE THE ERYTHREAN SIBYL (0642)
241 × 169 mm.

FIG. 106 Cat. No. 471

478. THE 'IGNUDO' TO THE L. ABOVE DANIEL (0643)
228 × 162 mm.
Numbered '18' above to the R.

479. THE 'IGNUDO' TO THE R. ABOVE THE ERYTHREAN SIBYL (0644)
247 × 170 mm.

480. THE 'IGNUDO' TO THE L. ABOVE ISAIAH (0645)
243 × 168 mm.

481. THE CENTRAL PORTION OF THE FLOOD (0632)
257 × 197 mm.

482. THE FATHER WITH HIS DEAD SON FROM THE FLOOD (0633)
252 × 182 mm. Pen and brown ink and brown wash on a light brown ground, heightened with white.
George III 'Inventory A', p. 46, II, 40–53 ('imitated by Carracci').
All fourteen (Nos. 469–482) are the work of the same draughtsman. The copies of the *Ignudi* were used by Adam Ghisi for his engravings (Bartsch XV, p. 426, 2 f.). The *Ignudo* in No. 474 is drawn over a figure of Hercules in black chalk, which corresponds with Giorgio Ghisi's engraving (Bartsch XV, p. 422, 16). No. 471 is the best copy hitherto known of the figure which was almost entirely destroyed in 1797 (see also No. 465).

483. TORSO AND L. ARM OF NOAH'S SON ASTRIDE A RAM IN THE SACRIFICE OF NOAH (0213)

144 × 151 mm. (cut into at the top and bottom, the upper corners made up). Red chalk.
Inscribed underneath in red chalk in the hand of the draughtsman, 'el finira'. Early and careful study from the fresco, imitating the technique of Michelangelo's red chalk studies for the ceiling.

484. JUDITH AND HER MAID WITH THE HEAD OF HOLOFERNES (4320)
247 × 165 mm. Black chalk.
Unfinished copy from the fresco. From the series of Maratta copies, but not apparently by him. It is certainly by the same hand as the series of ten copies from Raphael's frescoes in the *Loggie* (Nos. 835–844).

485. ESTHER AND HAMAN (0649)
229 × 373 mm. Black chalk, pen and dark brown ink and wash on brown paper, heightened with white (oxidised).
Copy of moderate quality lacking in detail.

486. THE LIBYAN SIBYL (0431)
388 × 248 mm. Hard black chalk.
Bottom R. corner cut.

487. THE ERYTHREAN SIBYL (0625)
430 × 286 mm. Hard black chalk.

488. THE DELPHIC SIBYL (0626)
375 × 251 mm. Black chalk, pen and dark brown ink.
Inscribed at the bottom to the R. on a label, 'Michel Angelo Buona Rota'. Studies of the sibyls are mentioned in George III 'Inventory A' (I, p. 44, 41–46), but it is not possible to identify them. The first two copies are relatively early, the third is by the Bolognese B. Passarotti (1529–1592).

489. THE PROPHET EZEKIEL (0627)
362 × 267 mm. Black chalk, washed with grey.
Inscribed underneath in the 'deceptive' hand, 'Raffaello'.

490. THE PROPHET JONAH (0628)
436 × 326 mm. Grey wash.

491. THE PROPHET JONAH (01363)
402 × 413 mm. Grey wash.
Inscribed underneath in ink twice, 'Michiel Angelo'. A number of studies of prophets are mentioned in George III Inventory A (I, 41–46, 48, 49; II, 15–17), but it is not possible to identify them individually.
The first two drawings are of moderate quality, the third is very detailed and accurate.

492. FIGURES FROM TWO DIFFERENT LUNETTES (0646)
195 × 320 mm. Black chalk on yellow prepared surface, heightened with white. W.M., a crossbow within a double circle.
Inscribed in pencil to the L. at the bottom, 'del Buona Rota'. On the L. is a copy of the lunette with Amminadab; on the R. one of the L. half of the destroyed lunette on the altar wall with Pharez, Hezron and Aram (see No. 465). By a Florentine working before 1535.

493. SOLOMON, FROM THE LUNETTE WITH DAVID AND SOLOMON (0650)
253 × 186 mm. Washed in brown and pink, heightened with white (much oxidised).
Apparently by a North Italian.

THE LAST JUDGMENT

See also Bartolommeo Passarotti, No. 666.

494. THE WHOLE COMPOSITION (0420)
32 × 232 mm. Pen and brown ink over black chalk.
George III 'Inventory A', p. 46, II, 24 ('seems to be drawn for the print by Martin Rota').
Copy of moderate quality, but one which shows the fresco in its original state, that is before the over-paintings made by Daniele da Volterra from 1558 onwards. This date is not, however, to be taken necessarily as a terminus ante quem for the drawing, which might quite well have been copied from an engraving. The note in the George III Inventory refers to Martin Rota's well-known engraving of 1569, which is itself based on an original of earlier date. Above in the centre, in place of the prophet Jonah, are two seated figures with a board between them.

495. THE MOTHER AND DAUGHTER TO THE L. AMONG THE BLESSED (0458)
402 × 252 mm. Red chalk.
Moderate copy of about 1600.

496. THE TWO SEATED FIGURES IN THE MIDST OF THE BLESSED ON THE R. (0451)
333 × 228 mm. Red chalk.
George III 'Inventory A', p. 43, I, 16.
Good copy of the second half of the XVI century.

497. THE L. HAND HALF OF THE GROUP OF THE MARTYRS (0422)
397 × 276 mm. Hard black chalk.
Early copy.

498. THE L. HAND HALF OF THE GROUP OF THE MARTYRS (0423)
155 × 126 mm. Hard black chalk.
Weak.

499. *Recto:* THE RESURRECTED SOUL CARRIED UPWARDS BY AN ANGEL ON THE L.
Verso: THE GROUP OF RESURRECTED SOULS BELOW ON THE L. (01364)
305 × 242 mm. Hard black chalk. W.M., Robinson 13.
Accurate copy in the style of the Cavalieri drawings, made before the additions by Daniele da Volterra.

500. THE RESURRECTED SOUL BELOW ON THE EXTREME L.; the head of St. John the Baptist; an extended R. arm. (0436)
402 × 246 mm. Hard black chalk.

501. THE RESURRECTED SOUL IN FRONT IN THE CENTRE (0631)
335 × 255 mm. Black chalk on blue paper, heightened with white.
Inscribed underneath on the L., 'M.A. Buona Rota'. Good copy of the second half of the XVI century.

502. MINOS (0629)
370 × 255 mm. Pen and brown ink, washed with brown and pink.
George III 'Inventory A', p. 46, II, 14.
In the manner of Federico Zuccaro (1542/43–1609).

503. *Recto:* MINOS (0421)
Verso: GOD THE FATHER APPEARING TO ABRAHAM (from the ceiling of the Stanza d'Eliodoro); a kneeling angel with a cross.
357 × 205 mm. Red chalk.

Inscribed underneath to the L., 'M. del Buonaroti'; above in the centre, '200'; and at the bottom, 'duecento'. An unknown collector was in the habit of numbering his drawings in this manner.
After 1600.

CONVERSION OF ST. PAUL

504. CHRIST AND THE GROUP OF ANGELS ON HIS L. (01362)
445 × 594 mm. Black chalk.
Inscribed underneath on the R., 'Studi di Michelangelo'.

505. THE THREE SOLDIERS ON THE R. OF THE HORSE (0647)
413 × 330 mm. Black chalk.
Inscribed as above. Nos. 504 and 505 are fragments of the same cartoon, composed of numerous pieces stuck together, which must have reproduced the whole fresco in outline. The copy was made before the partial over-painting of the angels.

MICHELANGELO. Copies after (C) Sculptures.

See also School of Michelangelo, No. 444.
Copies after Drawings, No. 453 *verso*.

506. THE PIETÀ IN ST. PETER'S (0426)
298 × 235 mm. Hard black chalk.
George III 'Inventory A', p. 43, I, 22.
Elaborate copy of the late XVI century.

507. CHRIST FROM THE PIETÀ IN ST. PETER'S (0630)
318 × 254 mm. Hard black chalk on blue paper, heightened with white, the outlines indented.
George III 'Inventory A', p. 43, I, 13.
Coll.: N. Lanière (Lugt 2885).
A good study of the beginning of the XVII century.

508. THE 'DAWN' FROM THE MEDICI CHAPEL (0428)
265 × 381 mm. Hard black chalk.
George III 'Inventory A', p. 44, I, 27 or 28.
Lit.: Delacre, p. 347 (Fig. 191).
Good academic copy of about the middle of the XVI century.

509. THE 'DAWN' (0429)
238 × 378 mm. Hard black chalk.
George III 'Inventory A', p. 44, I, 27 or 28.
In the manner of Bronzino.

510. THE 'NIGHT' (0430)
276 × 397 mm. Hard black chalk.
Photo.: Braun 122.
Good copy in the manner of Daniele da Volterra.

511. *Recto:* THE 'DAY' (0445)
Verso: STUDY OF LEGS
310 × 232 mm. Red chalk.
George III 'Inventory A', p. 44, I, 26.
Coll.: N. Lanière (Lugt 2885).
Inscribed underneath to the L. in Lanière's (?) hand: 'Michel Angelo'. The figure is seen at an angle from the L. Copy of the second half of the XVI century.

512. THE 'DAY' (0427)
270 × 227 mm. Black chalk.
George III 'Inventory A', p. 43, II, 18.
The back of the figure seen from the L. Of moderate quality.

FRANCESCO MONTEMEZZANO (About 1540–after 1602)

513. TWO LADIES AND A DWARF CARRYING A MONKEY, UNDER A PORTICO (043)
278 × 196 mm. Pen and brown ink and wash on blue paper, heightened with white.
Coll.: N. Lanière (Lugt 2886).
Lit.: Hadeln, *Spätrenaissance*, p. 21 (pl. 66); Tietzes, No. 810.
The drawing has an old attribution in pen and ink to 'P. Veronese', and another, not unintelligent one, to Pozzoserrato is recorded on the mount. Hadeln, who first attributed the drawing to Montemezzano, gave no reasons. It was presumably owing to the general resemblance of the design to that of the fresco from the Palazzo Regazzoni, now in the Dresden Gallery (No. 248A). The Tietzes accept the attribution, but the resemblance in style to the autographed *modello* in the Kupferstichkabinett at Darmstadt (Hadeln 64) is not to me very striking.

PIER FRANCESCO MORAZZONE (1571–1626)

514. THE PRESENTATION OF THE VIRGIN (*Figure* 107) (4819)
372 × 190 mm. Pen and ink and brown wash over black chalk on blue paper, heightened with white, squared in black chalk.
Lit.: E. Tietze-Conrat, Critica d'Arte III (1938), pp. 68, 69 (pl. 45).

FIG. 107 Cat. No. 514

Inscribed in the 'deceptive' hand, 'Moranzon'. Identified by Mrs. Tietze as a study for the painting of the subject in the Cappella del Rosario, Basilica di S. Vittore, Varese (G. Nicodemi, *P. F. Mazzucchelli detto 'Il Morazzone'*. Varese,

FIG. 108 Cat. No. 515

1927, p. 47). There are various differences in detail, notably in the nude man on the R., which make it certain that this is in fact the original sketch and not a derivative.

515. THE PRESENTATION IN THE TEMPLE (*Figure* 108) (0292)
300 × 222 mm. Pen and brown ink and brown wash over black chalk on faded blue paper, heightened with white, squared in black chalk.
A.E.P. The absurd old attribution was to Garofalo. That to Morazzone rests on the resemblance in the types and style of composition to the authenticated drawing, No. 514 above. The old woman on the R., for example, is extraordinarily like the one behind the high priest in that drawing. The proportions of this figure are characteristic and the bunched drapery in front is exactly paralleled in that of the Delphic Sibyl, Cappella della Buona Morte, S. Gaudenzio, Novara (G. Nicodemi, op. cit., pl. 80). The arrangement of the composition is curiously similar to that in the drawing by Paris Nogari (No. 523 below), but this is probably rather the result of a common tendency than of direct imitation. Nogari's composition is certainly the earlier.

516. A MONASTIC SAINT KNEELS BELOW IN ADORATION OF THE VIRGIN AND CHILD, who, surrounded by angels, appear above the altar. (5113)
312 × 200 mm. (bottom L. hand corner cut and made up). Pen and brown ink and brown wash, with touches of red chalk, on faded blue paper over black chalk.
Inscribed bottom L. in the 'deceptive' hand, 'Moranzon'. This attribution seems to me quite a convincing one.

517. CHRIST WASHING THE FEET OF HIS DISCIPLES (6680)
177 × 220 mm. (oval). Pen and brown ink and brown wash.
A.E.P. Attribution in pencil on the drawing to Palma (Giovane), with whose manner it has no connection. The attribution to Morazzone rests on the resemblance in style to the authenticated drawing No. 514 above, as well as on the general similarity of the composition to the ovals painted by Morazzone in the Capella del Rosario, Basilica di S. Vittore, Varese (ill. Nicodemi, op. cit., pl. 31, etc.). A large and elaborate drawing for one of these, the *Agony in the Garden*, is in the Uffizi (photo. Braun 795 as G. B. Moroni). The difference in technique and general appearance between this and the Windsor drawing may be explained by the former being a finished *modello*. There seems to me to be no essential difference in style between the two.

GIROLAMO MUZIANO (1528–1592)

518. STUDY OF A MAN SEATED TO THE FRONT; HIS HEAD IN PROFILE TO THE R. (*Plate* 81) (0440)
390 × 276 mm. Red chalk. W.M., a shield bearing crossed keys surmounted by a fleur-de-lys.
The attribution of this fine drawing is apparently traditional. The figure in fact corresponds, with some modifications in the drapery and in the position of the left hand, with that of St. Jerome in the painting of *St. Jerome and St. Romuald* in S. Maria degli Angeli, Rome, Muziano's last work, left unfinished at his death in 1592 (Venturi, IX 7, Fig. 257). There is an almost identical and equally authentic study for the same figure in the Louvre (photo. Braun 415).

FIG. 109 Cat. No. 519

519. THE ASCENSION (*Figure* 109) (5142)
302 × 208 mm. Red chalk, squared in the same medium.
F.A. The drawing is a study for the picture of the *Ascension* in Sta. Maria in Vallicella, Rome (Venturi, IX 7, Fig. 254).

520. A SEATED EVANGELIST OR FATHER OF THE CHURCH (0439)
429 × 273 mm. Black chalk, squared in red chalk.
A suggestion on the mount that the drawing is by the same hand as No. 518, Girolamo Muziano's, seems right.

BATTISTA NALDINI (1537–1591)

521. THETIS RECEIVING FROM VULCAN THE SHIELD OF ACHILLES (?) with the forge of the Cyclops in the background. (0163)
355 × 283 mm. Pen and ink and brown wash on brown paper, heightened with white (damaged on the L. by damp).
A.E.P. Attribution to 'Salviati' in pencil on the drawing. Antal suggested a connection with the decorations of the Sala degli Elementi in the Palazzo Vecchio at Florence (see Venturi, IX 5, Fig. 376), and thought that Cristofano Gherardi might be the draughtsman. I think, however, on comparison with authentic drawings by Naldini (the two studies of *Christ carrying the Cross* in the British Museum, 1856–7–12–9 and 10, for example) there can be little doubt that it is by this other assistant of Vasari. The rather unusual colour of the ground, the very *staccato* method of laying on the whites and the mannerisms of the drawing (particularly in the background figures) are all identical.

FIG. 110 Cat. No. 522

FIG. 111 Cat. No. 523

BARTOLOMMEO NERONI (RICCIO) (d. 1571)

522. THE NATIVITY (*Figure* 110) (5491)
305 × 226 mm. Pen and brown ink and brown wash, squared in black chalk.
George III 'Inventory A', p. 53, 10.
A.E.P. Old inscription, 'Baldassar di Siena', in red ink in the bottom R. hand corner. The attribution to Neroni is based on the unmistakable similarity of the types to those in Neroni's paintings (cf. Venturi, IX 5, Fig. 292).

PARIS NOGARI (About 1536–1601)

523. THE CIRCUMCISION (*Figure* 111) (0162)
417 × 246 mm. Pen and brown ink and brown wash over black chalk on faded blue paper, heightened with white.
Lit.: F. Antal, O.M.D. XIII (1938–9), p. 40 (pl. 42).
As discovered by Antal the drawing is a study for the painting of the subject in S. Spirito in Sassia, Rome, and I would refer the student to his article for a discussion of the drawing and of Nogari.

After PARIS NOGARI (?)

524. CHRIST TEACHING IN THE SYNAGOGUE (Matthew xiii. 54). (3629)
197 × 165 mm. Pen and ink and wash over black chalk.

525. CHRIST DISPUTING WITH THE DOCTORS (Luke ii. 46). (6325)
181 × 163 mm. Pen and brown ink and brown wash over black chalk.
A.E.P. These two drawings are obviously by the same hand, though the first has an old inscription on the *verso* (visible through the backing), 'del licarci' (?), interpreted as Carracci, and the second is attributed to Bononi (in pencil on the drawing). Both in fact correspond with paintings on the vaulting of the *Loggie* of Gregory XIII in the Vatican, No. 524 with one in the sixth arcade, No. 525 with one in the first arcade. Baglione only names the painter of one of the subjects in the former, the *Raising of the Widow's Son of Naim*, which he says is by Jacopo Sementa. Jacob Hess in his article on the *Loggie* in Illustrazione Vaticana (February 16–29, 1936, p. 164) suggests that the *Christ Teaching in the Synagogue* is by a follower of Raffaellino da Reggio, possibly Paris Nogari. If this is right the drawing can hardly be by him, as a comparison with the authenticated study already discussed makes clear. Indeed the colour indications suggest that it is copied from a painting rather than is a study for one. Hess does not make any attribution for the subject of *Christ Disputing with the Doctors* in the first arcade, but it contains, on the L., a foreground figure almost identical with one in the *Teaching in the Synagogue*, is composed in the same manner and may be attributed to the same painter, who we may tentatively identify as Paris Nogari. It should perhaps be stated that No. 525 differs from the fresco in being an upright instead of an oblong, a difference which it is not easy to reconcile with the theory that it is copied from it. It may perhaps be taken from a drawing.

NOSADELLA (GIOVANNI FRANCESCO BEZZI) (d. 1571)

526. THE VISITATION WITH, ON THE L. ST. PETRONIUS, AND ON THE R. TWO KNEELING WOMEN (*Plate* 114) (5502)
191 × 255 mm. Pen and brown ink and brown wash.
A.E.P. The drawing is clearly by the same hand as that in the University Collection, Göttingen, published by Elisabeth Valentiner in Mitteilungen des Kunsthistorischen Instituts in Florenz, IV (1933), p. 132, which has an old attribution to Nosadella, and as two unpublished drawings at Chatsworth, also anciently attributed. One representing *Jupiter and Antiope* (No. 394) is particularly similar in handling. The style of the picture authenticated as from Nosadella's design (though finished by Prospero Fontana) in Sta. Maria Maggiore, Bologna (ill. Mitteil. des Kunsthistorischen Instituts in Florenz, III (1919–1932), p. 452), seems to me also convincingly the same.

FIG. 112 Cat. No. 527

PIER PAOLO OLIVIERI (1551–1599)

527. THE YOUTHFUL ST. JOHN THE BAPTIST KNEELING IN THE WILDERNESS; OVAL COMPOSITION (*Figure* 112) (5061)
214 × 290 mm. Pen and brown ink and brown wash over red and black chalk.
Inscribed on a scroll on which St. John kneels: 'CAR. EMANVELLI DVCI SABAVDIE P. PAV. OLIVERIVS ROMANVS D.D 1516'. (The date must be a slip or it must have been altered from 1596; Charles Emanuel the Great was Duke of Savoy from 1580 to 1630). It seems probable that the drawing is a design for sculpture. I can find no reference to Olivieri's having worked for the Duke of Savoy.

LELIO ORSI (1511 (?)–1587)

528. PIETÀ (*Plate* 135) (4836)
174 × 245 mm. Outlined in brown ink and elaborately finished with the brush and Indian ink and heightened with white, on faded blue paper.
A.E.P. On the R. is a faint sketch in black chalk of another mourning woman. If it is not actually a study for, it at any rate shows a very close stylistic resemblance to, the painting in the Estense Gallery at Modena of the *Dead Christ between Justice and Charity* (Venturi, IX 6, Fig. 380). A drawing in pen and ink in the Uffizi (No. 2001: ill. Correggio Exhibition Catalogue, p. 167) shows the body of Christ in almost the same position as in the painting, but with mourning Maries behind and without the allegorical figures.

529. A CROSSBOWMAN: he is represented standing on a pedestal firing down at the spectator. (*Plate* 134) (4791)
252 × 198 mm. Drawn with the brush over black chalk on paper washed with yellow, heightened with white; the pedestal in pen and ink.
A.E.P. Study for the central figure of the decoration of the façade of a house, probably Orsi's own. An elaborate drawing of the whole façade including this figure is at Chatsworth, No. 351. It has a coat of arms with two bears, which, Dr. Walter Friedländer has suggested, is probably that of Orsi himself. The Chatsworth drawing is perhaps the copy of one formerly in Crozat's collection mentioned by Mariette (*Abecedario*, ed. de Chennevières and de Montaiglon, Paris, 1851–60, IV, p. 64). Another version of the upper part of the design is in the Estense Collection at Modena (No. 1265).

530. DESIGN FOR PART OF THE FAÇADE OF A HOUSE (*Figure* 113) (10899)
391 × 523 mm. Pen and brown ink and brown wash.
A.E.P. Detached in 1944 from an album of architectural and decorative drawings (Vol. 192). The drawing is for part of the decoration of the first and second stories of a house or hall, resting on an open arcade. The upper parts of two and part of a third of the arches of this arcade are included. Above each of the arches are windows flanked by columns and surmounted by pediments, and above these are feigned attic windows. In the centre of one of these an old man is seen threatening his young wife with his fist and interrupting a conversation between her and a young gallant who looks out of the attic window on the L. In the half window on the R. a young woman is seen reading a book. In the spaces between the three attic windows sheep-shearing and wool-beating are represented.

FIG. 113 Cat. No. 530

Below each of these scenes, between the pediments of the three windows, are escutcheons on which bales of wool are shown, with wreaths and supporters. Below them on the L. the washing of the wool is shown, on the R. the carding. A frieze runs along under the windows with representations of the tools of the same craft, and in the angles of the arches below are men weighing wool, counting bales, a woman with a distaff, etc.

The style leaves no doubt that the design of this and the drawing next to be described is Orsi's, but the question of the actual execution, excellent as this is, might be called in question. An inscription on a similar drawing at Chatsworth (No. 351) reads 'al viso del vero f.', which seems to imply a copy. Orsi is known to have painted various façades of houses, but none of these apparently survives.

The decoration of the present house front suggests that it was the residence of an eminent wool merchant, or more probably the hall of the 'Arte della Lana' in Reggio d'Emilia or Novellara or some neighbouring town.

531. DESIGN FOR PART OF THE FAÇADE OF A HOUSE (*Figure* 114) (10900)
257 × 388 mm. Pen and grey ink and grey wash.
A.E.P. Detached in 1944 from an album of architectural and decorative drawings (Vol. 192). The drawing is for the decoration of the first floor of a house. Part of the lower story built *alla rustica* is shown. Above this is a frieze decorated with different coloured marbles in geometrical patterns. Above the frieze two windows and part of a third are shown. A wider space between two windows is occupied by a niche containing a statue of Vulcan (?). A frieze (interrupted by the niche), divided into panels, runs above the windows. It is decorated with figures, whose legs terminate in foliage, variously occupied.

The drawing is obviously by the same hand as No. 530, but for a different house, the occupier of which might have been a smith.

532. DESIGN FOR DECORATION (10897)
180 × 152 mm. Fine pen and brown ink and brown wash.
A.E.P. Detached in 1944 from an album of architectural and decorative drawings (Vol. 192). The attribution to Orsi rests on the close resemblance to authenticated decorative drawings by him, like that in the Uffizi (No. 1004E, repr. in the Alinari Series of Uffizi Drawings 'Ornato').

533. A PORTICO WITH ONE LARGE CENTRAL AND TWO SMALLER LATERAL OPENINGS (*Figure* 115) (5091)
237 × 288 mm. Pen and brown ink and brown wash over lines ruled with the stylus.
A.E.P. The attribution to Orsi, whose style here is unmistakable, needs no explanation.

534. APOLLO DRIVING THE CHARIOT OF THE SUN, WITH AURORA IN FRONT SCATTERING FLOWERS (0224)
197 × 300 mm. Pen and brown ink and brown wash, with *pentimenti* in black chalk, squared in black chalk.

FIG. 114 Cat. No. 531

Inscribed in ink at the bottom to the L. in an old hand, 'Di Lelio Orsi da Novellara'. The figures and animals are seen foreshortened from below advancing on the spectator. The group is contained within a half circle beyond which the heads of two of the horses and the head and shoulders of Apollo protrude. Outside this circle and partly concealed by it are a lion, the head of a woman, part of a pair of scales and the claw of a lobster, obviously the signs of the zodiac, and, to R. and L., two decorated half-escutcheons each with a cross.

FIG. 115 Cat. No. 533

There is another version of this drawing, on a slightly larger scale, in the Ambrosiana at Milan (photo. Braun 119 as Giulio Romano). In this the escutcheons on either side are omitted. The technique of the Ambrosiana drawing looks in the photograph more characteristic of Orsi than that of the Windsor version, though in some ways the latter is the better. Some version was in all probability in the Crozat Collection (P. J. Mariette, *Description . . . du Cabinet Crozat*, Paris, 1741, lot 376, 'Vingt [by Lelio Orsi] dont Apollon dans son char précedé de l'Aurore').

535. TWO CARYATIDS AND THE VISITATION (0225)
210 × 101 mm. Pen and ink and brown and grey wash.
The Caryatids are on a different piece of paper and quite distinct from the *Visitation*. The former are more obviously by Orsi than the latter, but it seems to me likely that this too is his work. The attribution, apparently an old one, seems to apply both to parts.

536. ENVY (0226)
228 × 149 mm. (top corners cut and made up). Pen and brown ink and brown wash.
The attribution to Lelio da Novellara, in pencil on the drawing, is apparently based on some older source and is, I think, correct.

537. ENVY OR FURY (5132)
238 × 182 mm. Pen and brown ink and brown wash.
A.E.P. The figure is a study for a composition known in a drawing in the Albertina attributed to Salviati (photo. Braun 64), but which is apparently by Orsi. (Another version in outline is in the Uffizi, Santarelli No. 779 as Taddeo Zuccaro). In this the figures to the R. and L., who are

being pushed by Fury, are nude men each chained by one leg; one has a cannon and the other a torch.

Attributed to LELIO ORSI

538. ALLEGORICAL COMPOSITION (*Figure* 116) (5084)
253 × 175 mm. Fine pen and ink and grey wash over red chalk, squared in black chalk. The corners made up.
A.E.P. The attribution rests on general stylistic resemblances. The design and the types are very similar to those of a drawing in the British Museum of *Neptune surrounded by Marine Deities* (1852–10–8–9).
The shape suggests that it is for the decoration of the hood of a chimney-piece. Vulcan is represented at the top forging arrows for Cupid. Below is the god of love ('amor' is inscribed above his head); he is casting a gauntlet into the flames where other arms are being consumed; on the R. stands Mars, and on the L. a bearded man who seems to be clipping Cupid's wings.

539. JUPITER DESTROYING THE GIANTS WITH HIS THUNDERBOLT (*Figure* 117) (6012)
245 × 295 mm. Pen and brown ink and brown wash.
A.E.P. Inscribed 'Zuccaro' in red ink at the bottom to the R., an attribution which is out of the question. The type of Jupiter and the manner of modelling the flesh with faint washes seems to me definitely Orsi's.

540. FANTASTIC SCENE WITH VARIOUS WILD BEASTS AND MONSTERS AMONG ROCKS; on the R. silhouetted

FIG. 116 Cat. No. 538

FIG. 117 Cat. No. 539

against an opening in the rocks, is a satyr attacking a dragon with a club. (5208)
196 × 303 mm. Red chalk.
A.E.P. It was given by Antal to Andrea Boscoli, who composed somewhat similar fantasies, but whose style is different. Though I have thought of Ligozzi as possibly the draughtsman (and it is not always as easy as it might appear to distinguish between the two) I think it is rather the work of Orsi.

NICCOLÒ PAGANELLI (1538–1620)

541. THE PRESENTATION OF OUR LORD IN THE TEMPLE (0182)
194 × 124 mm. Pen and light brown ink and brown wash over black chalk, much faded and partly re-drawn.
A.E.P. Inscribed in pencil on the drawing, 'del Samacchini'. It is however the study for a picture in the Pinacoteca at Faenza (ill. in the periodical 'Melozzo da Forlì', April, 1939, p. 347) which is apparently signed by Niccolò Paganelli, an obscure painter of Faenza. Though the differences between the drawing and the painting are very considerable, the main lines of the architecture, the subject and the beggar in the foreground on the L. are the same, and there can be no doubt about the connection. A drawing in the Uffizi (Santarelli 777) is clearly by the same hand.

JACOPO PALMA (GIOVANE) (1544–1628)

The drawings by and after Palma Giovane are listed together in the order of the inventory numbers.

542. STUDY OF A WOMAN SEATED TO THE L., of the head of a man wearing a cap looking down, and of the head of a woman looking down in profile to the L. (2204)
257 × 188 mm. Red and black chalk.
A.E.P. From the Carracci series but attributed by Bodmer to F. Zuccaro, which is quite out of the question. The style is unmistakably that of Palma Giovane. There is a fragmentary inscription in pen and ink at the bottom to the L.

543. THE VIRGIN SEATED HOLDING THE CHILD, WHO LEANS TOWARDS A MONK KNEELING TO THE R. (3634)

138 × 118 mm. Pen and brown ink and brown wash over black chalk.
A.E.P. On the *verso* is part of a characteristic pen and ink sketch of a nude figure, visible through the backing.

544. THE AGONY IN THE GARDEN AND A STUDY OF CHRIST SUPPORTED BY AN ANGEL (3635)
146 × 135 mm. Pen and brown ink and brown wash over black chalk.
On the *verso* is the other half of the sketch on No. 543.

545. ONE OF THE ACTS OF MERCY: TENDING THE SICK; design for a lunette. (3812)
167 × 309 mm. Pen and brown ink and brown wash, over black chalk.
A.E.P.

546. THE THREE FATES, TO WHOM MERCURY FLIES DOWN (4799)
240 × 225 mm. Pen and Indian ink and grey wash on green prepared paper, heightened with gold.
Inscribed in ink in an old hand, 'Del Palma'. I do not know other drawings of this type, but it was presumably a special one prepared as a gift. It is certainly from the artist's hand and dates from after 1600.

547. CHRIST APPEARING TO A KNEELING DOGE, AROUND WHOM ARE THREE ALLEGORICAL FIGURES (4800)
193 × 238 mm. Pen and ink and two shades of brown wash, over black chalk.
Coll.: N. Lanière (Lugt 2886).
Lit.: Tietzes, No. 1246 (pl. CLXXIV 2).
Inscribed in ink in an old hand (Lanière's ?), 'Jac° Palmo'. As ascertained by the Tietzes the drawing is a preliminary sketch for the painting in the Sala del Senato of the Ducal Palace at Venice representing the Doge Pasquale Cicogna, attended by St. Mark, pointing out the Saviour to the Venetians (Venturi, IX 7, Fig. 132). Cicogna was doge from 1585 to 1595. The Tietzes illustrate two further sketches for the same composition, in Copenhagen (No. 881) and in the Uffizi (No. 922).

548. THREE COMPOSITION SKETCHES: A PRESENTATION, A PIETÀ, AN ASSUMPTION OF THE VIRGIN, AND OTHER STUDIES (4801)
180 × 230 mm. Pen and brown ink and brown wash.
Coll.: N. Lanière (Lugt 2886).
Lit.: Tietzes, No. 1247.
Inscribed in ink in a later hand, 'Palma'. A characteristic late drawing by the artist.

549. COMPOSITION SKETCH FOR CHRIST AND THE WOMAN TAKEN IN ADULTERY, and separate studies of two of the figures. (4802)
167 × 266 mm. Pen and brown ink and brown wash.
Coll.: N. Lanière (Lugt 2886).
Lit.: Tietzes, No. 1248.
Inscribed in ink in an old hand (Lanière's ?), 'Giaco^mo Palma'. Dated by the Tietzes about 1600.

550. STUDIES OF FIGURES, the most finished of which is a man seen from the back holding a (?) standard. (4803)
272 × 179 mm. Pen and light brown ink.
Lit.: Tietzes, No. 1249.
Inscribed at the top in a different ink, 'palma'. Dated by the Tietzes at the end of the century. The two sketches on the R. are from figures in Michelangelo's *Last Judgment*.

551. OLD MAN'S HEAD IN PROFILE AND SLIGHT SKETCHES (4804)
102 × 69 mm. Pen and brown ink and some wash.
Lit.: Tietzes, No. 1250.

552. TWO HEADS OF OLD MEN, THE FOREMOST CLEAN-SHAVEN IN PROFILE TO THE L. (4805)
162 × 130 mm. Pen and brown ink.
Lit.: Tietzes, No. 1251.

553. TWO HEADS OF BEARDED APOSTLES LOOKING UP TO THE L. (4806)
167 × 137 mm. Pen and brown ink over black chalk.
Of these three drawings mounted together, No. 552 is certainly by Palma, No. 551 less certainly so, in fact distinctly doubtful; and No. 553 (apparently condemned by the Tietzes) probably an XVIII century copy after Palma.

554. OTTO IS GIVEN PERMISSION BY POPE ALEXANDER III TO VISIT HIS FATHER, FREDERICK BARBAROSSA, WITH A VIEW TO TREATING FOR PEACE (6034)
247 × 204 mm. Pen and brown ink and wash with some water colour, the architectural background in black chalk.
Copy of the painting by Palma Giovane in the Sala del Maggior Consiglio of the Ducal Palace, Venice (Venturi, IX 7, Fig. 102).

555. THE VIRGIN ENTHRONED WITH ST. JEROME KNEELING ON THE L., ST. GEORGE STANDING ON THE R., a bishop and St. Anthony (?) behind: design for an altarpiece with an arched top. (6368)
253 × 150 mm. Pen and brown ink and brown wash over black chalk.
A.E.P. From the volume of drawings by the Sirani. The style is definitely Palma Giovane's.

556. THE BAPTISM OF OUR LORD (*Figure* 118) (6674)
435 × 321 mm. Pen and brown ink and brown wash over black chalk; the figure of the Baptist is repeated in a different form on a piece of paper hinged over the original.
A.E.P. Though the drawing is certainly from Palma's immediate *entourage*, it is not quite certain that it is from his own hand. The large foreground figures especially are unusual for him. If it is not by Palma it is by an artist who has to a remarkable extent absorbed not only his style but his technique of drawing.

557. THE THREE CROSSES (6684)
348 × 300 mm. (damaged and irregular on the L.). Pen and brown ink and brown wash.
A.E.P. The drawing, obviously a copy from a picture, is rather after Palma Giovane than Tintoretto, to whom it was attributed.

558. DESIGN FOR AN ALTARPIECE WITH AN ARCHED TOP: THE MYSTIC MARRIAGE OF ST. CATHERINE, with SS. Catherine of Siena and Francis kneeling on the L., St. Cecilia on the R.; God the Father and the Holy Spirit above. (6744)
206 × 122 mm. Pen and brown ink and brown wash over black chalk.
A.E.P.

559. THE DEAD BODY OF OUR LORD SUPPORTED BY JOSEPH OF ARIMATHEA ON THE TOMB; the mourning Virgin stands behind on the R. (6760)
274 × 255 mm. Pen and brown ink and brown wash.
A.E.P. The attribution is not certain.

560. THE BRAZEN SERPENT: SKETCH FOR AN OBLONG COMPOSITION (6781)

136 × 288 mm. Pen and brown ink and brown wash over black chalk.

Inscribed in pencil at the bottom: 'Giacomo Palma Giovane'. A characteristic composition sketch perhaps dating from the nineties.

561. THE MARTYRDOM OF ST. BARTHOLOMEW (6782)

272 × 185 mm. Pen and light brown ink and wash on porridge-coloured paper, heightened with white.

A characteristic late drawing by Palma of exactly the type of many of those in the British Museum album, mostly dating from the twenties of the XVII century.

562. THE TRINITY ADORED BY SAINTS AND PATRIARCHS (6809)

303 × 234 mm. Pen and brown ink and brown wash on porridge-coloured paper, heightened with white.

Dated 1614 (?) in L. hand bottom corner by the artist. The style in any case points to that period. Inscribed on the *verso* in an old hand (visible through the backing): 'Giacomo Palma'.

563. STUDIES OF FOUR HEADS: those of a bearded man, of a woman looking up and of two youths, and the study of a foot. (0578)

100 × 63 mm. Drawn with the point of the brush in grey. A.E.P. Attributed to Parmigianino, with whose style it has little in common. It seems rather to be by Palma Giovane.

FIG. 118 Cat. No. 556

PARMIGIANINO (FRANCESCO MAZZOLA) (1503–1540)

Occasional references are given to Giovanni Copertini, *Il Parmigianino*, 2 vols., Parma, 1932 (quoted as Copertini), and to L. Fröhlich-Bum, *Parmigianino und der Manierismus*, Vienna, 1921 (quoted as Fröhlich-Bum).

I have gone more thoroughly into a number of questions relating to Parmigianino in my catalogue of the larger and more representative series of his drawings in the British Museum, and I would refer the reader to this work, which should appear in the not too distant future.

The greater number of the drawings attributed to Parmigianino in the collection were contained in four miniature books, described as follows in George III 'Inventory A', p. 132:

> Four small Pocket Books of Drawings by Parmegiano.
> Tom. I. Contains Twenty-four Drawings.
> Tom. II. Twenty-two Drawings with Black lead Pencil on a Coloured Pasteboard, the lights are given by a Pointed Instrument in scraping through the upper surface.
> Tom. III. Fourteen Drawings, as in the second volume, except the lights, which are touched with a pencil.
> Tom. IV. Thirty Drawings in Various manners.
> Pencil note: 'The originals of Two engravings in Metz are not to be found in these books now. Several are not engraved.'

These four 'Pocket Books' are apparently identical with four enumerated in the 'List of the Drawgs in ye Cabinet in His Majtys Lower Apartment' (B.M. Add. 20,101, fol. 28) drawn up after (probably shortly after) 1735:

> No. 20. Another of Defferent Figures.
> No. 21. Another by Parmesano.
> No. 22. Another by the same hand.
> No. 23. Another by the same hand.

Three of these little books are preserved, though the drawings were taken out of them and mounted at some period in the XIX century.

Tom. I of 'Inventory A', oblong, 97 × 74 mm., bound in calf with a brass clasp, has on the fly-leaf the inscription in pen and ink: '24. desegni del Parmigiano' and the price mark '7 2' (= 17/6) in the hand supposed to be William Gibson's. This is presumably No. 20 of the earlier inventory.

Tom. II of 'Inventory A', 124 × 87 mm., has an elaborate blind-tooled decoration on the covers and engraved silver clasps. It has inscribed in ink on the cover: 'PARMESANE TOM. IV No. 30', and on a label attached to the back, '4' written over 'No. 21'. It now contains thirteen loose sheets of card or thick parchment coated with a cream-coloured preparation for metal-point. The leaves are blank and show no signs of having had drawings attached to them. This is to be identified with No. 21 of the earlier inventory.

Tom. III of 'Inventory A', oblong, 80 × 115 mm., with silver filigree corners, centre-piece and clasps, was apparently composed of paper and metal-point leaves arranged alternately, but all of the latter except three have been removed. There are still 14 leaves of paper. On the last of these 'FRANc PARMENSs 1533' is inscribed in Indian ink. On the last metal-point leaf is some scribbling and the inscription: 'ce livre appartien a WVaillant pintre . . . WVaillant esté aupres le lecteur le 5 decemb. 1655'. This has a label pasted on the back inscribed 'No 22' and '3' and is to be identified with No. 22 of the earlier list.

Tom IV of 'Inventory A' appears to be lost.

The contents of two of these 'Pocket Books' can be identified with certainty. Those contained in Tom. II (Nos. 01330 to 01340) have nothing to do with Parmigianino, but are apparently Dutch or German of the beginning of the XVII century. They have been placed with the anonymous drawings of the former school, to be catalogued later. Those contained in Tom. III (which differed from the other two in the fact that the drawings were on the pages of the book itself, not attached to them) are catalogued below under copies after Parmigianino (Nos. 605 to 612). It seems possible that they were the work of the engraver Wallerant Vaillant, who inscribed his name and the date 1655 on one of them, though in that case the statement by Henry Reveley (*Notices illustrative of the Drawings and Sketches . . .* London, 1820, p. 43) that the four little volumes had belonged to Charles I can hardly be true of this one.

Tom. I probably contained most of the minute drawings, which I believe to be copies of originals in the Arundel collection made in the XVII century.

A large number of the drawings were engraved in facsimile by C. M. Metz (*Imitations of Drawings by Parmegiano in the Collection of His Majesty*. Engrav'd and Publish'd by Conrad Martin Metz London MDCCLXXXIX and MDCCXC). The plates in this work are not numbered, but I have numbered them in the copy in the Department of Prints and Drawings in the British Museum and quoted this numbering. I cannot however be certain that the arrangement of the plates in this copy is the normal one.

All the drawings engraved by Metz are still in the Royal Collection with the exception of No. 6 (Nativity in a circle), No. 10 (St. Catherine in a circle) and No. 32 (two old men in profile to the R.). I do not know the present whereabouts of No. 6, but drawings corresponding with Nos. 10 and 32 are now in the British Museum. Both of these (Pp. 2–132 and Pp. 2–147) were bequeathed by Richard Payne Knight in 1824. One cannot however be certain that these are the identical drawings engraved by Metz: they may equally well be copies of them or, alternatively, the drawings engraved by Metz may have been the copies.

Of the remaining 71 drawings engraved by Metz, 19 are from the little pocket book referred to above (Tom. II of 'Inventory A'). Out of the remaining 52, 12 are from Tom. III of 'Inventory A', and are described below under copies and 23 more are also copies, presumably of the XVII century from originals then in the Arundel collection, leaving 17 original drawings. But to these 17—some of them of very high quality, though others are not above suspicion—must be added a number not included by Metz, most of which are of even greater interest. These were in all probability added to the collection after Metz had engraved his series (first published August 1, 1789), or he would have been likely to have included at least some of them.

One original drawing by Parmigianino (a woman holding a crucifix. No. 2336; pen and brown ink and brown wash with some heightening in white, 200 × 100 mm.) will be catalogued later with the drawings by Lodovico Carracci, who added to it a most elaborate frame (described by Richardson, *An Account . . .* London, 1722, p. 33, as in the Bonfiglioli Palace).

I have arranged the originals in as near chronological order as was possible without remounting and re-arranging the whole series. The copies are arranged according to size, beginning with the two metal-point sketch books and working upwards to the larger copies. Some of these copies are, as will be seen, of some interest to the student of Parmigianino's art.

564. HEAD OF A BEARDED MAN IN PROFILE TO THE R. WITH ANOTHER HEAD BEHIND (0527)

25 × 23 mm. Red chalk.

The fragment is for the heads of Daniel and the angel in an oval composition of *Daniel in the Lions' Den*, of which versions exist in the British Museum (three studies on two sheets), in the Staedel Institut at Frankfort and elsewhere. Another version, now in the Gallery at Parma, was engraved by Benigno Bossi (Weigel 5786), and there are two further studies of the head of Daniel in the British Museum. The purpose of this oval is unknown to me.

565. BUST OF A BEARDED MAN IN PROFILE TO THE R. (0528)

115 × 81 mm. Red chalk.

On the *verso* are studies of a man's R. knee and of another subject, which is not clear.

The head may be intended for that of a Greek or Roman philosopher or poet. It shows some resemblance to the heads on the sheet at Parma with a dead mouse and studies for the National Gallery picture of 1527 on the *verso*, and it may be of that date or earlier.

566. FULL-FACE PORTRAIT OF A YOUTH WEARING A CAP (*Plate* 123) (0529)

107 × 76 mm. Red chalk. Damaged at bottom and made up.

I think there can be little doubt that this is a self-portrait by Parmigianino drawn at an early age, about the same time as the portrait of himself painted from a convex mirror (now at Vienna), which, according to Vasari, he took with him to Rome (about 1524).

567. A KNEELING CHILD LOOKING OUT FROM UNDER A CURTAIN (0566)

65 × 35 mm. Pen and brown ink and brown wash, over black chalk.

Engraved by Metz, No. 22.

It is possible that this charming little sketch was made for

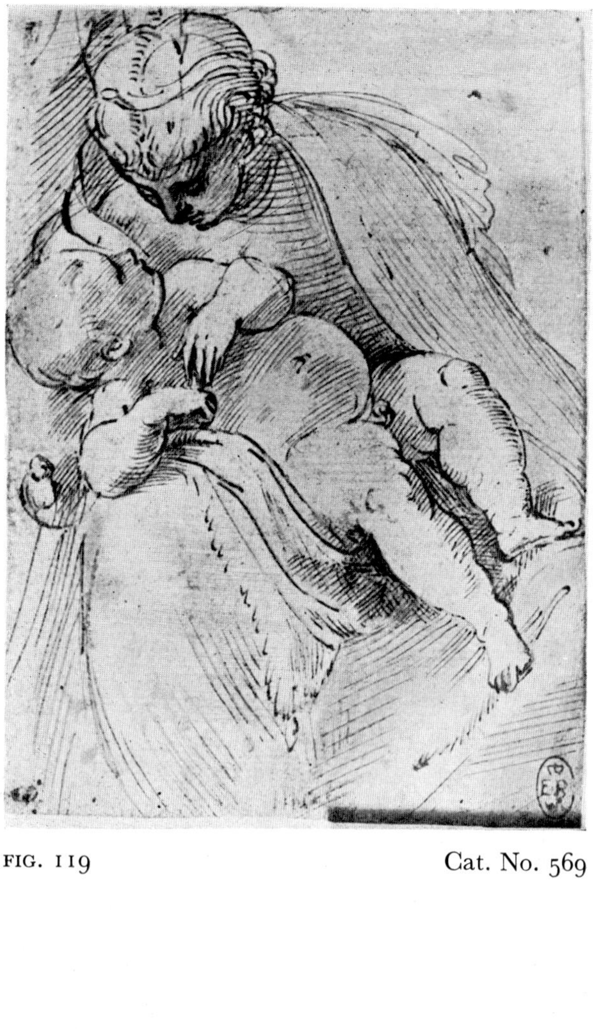

FIG. 119 Cat. No. 569

the decoration of the vault of the Steccata, for one of the spaces between the lozenges in the 'sottarchie', like Nos. 588, 590 and 591, though the octagonal frames round the lozenges are not here indicated. I am not quite confident that this is an original. It may be a copy of the time of Vorsterman.

568. TWO PUTTI EMBRACING AND ADVANCING TOWARDS THE FRONT (0567)
110 × 65 mm. Pen and brown ink and some wash; oil stain bottom R. corner.
Engraved by Metz, No. 39.
On the *verso* is part of a slight sketch in red chalk, apparently of a human figure. I do not know the purpose of the sketch on the *recto*. It is apparently of Parmigianino's Roman period.

569. THE VIRGIN BENDING OVER TO LOOK AT THE CHILD, WHO LIES ON HER LAP (*Figure* 119) (0568)
110 × 79 mm. Pen and Indian ink and a little wash.
Engraved by Metz, No. 37.
I do not know that this is a study for any particular composition. It is very near in feeling to the midwife bending over the Infant Christ in the *Adoration of the Shepherds* engraved by Caraglio in 1526 (Bartsch XV, p. 68, 4). It is almost certainly of the Roman period. There is also some resemblance to a drawing of the Virgin and Child in red chalk in the British Museum (Pp. 2–137), which is certainly early, perhaps pre-Roman.

570. STUDY OF A NUDE MAN SEEN FULL-FACE (1835)
106 × 40 mm. Pen and brown ink on pink-tinted paper.
A.E.P. Formerly mounted with five small drawings by the Carracci, the present unimportant sketch seems nevertheless to be certainly Parmigianino's and to be connected with a series of anatomical drawings now in the Parma Gallery (Copertini II, pl. 2).

571. GROUPS OF WOMEN WITH DEAD OR WOUNDED MEN IN FRONT OF AN ENCAMPMENT (*Figure* 120) (1960)
110 × 115 mm. (Cut on the R. and at the bottom). Pen and brown ink on paper tinted pink.
A.E.P. The style of the drawing makes the attribution to Parmigianino certain, although it formed part of the Carracci series. Another drawing by Parmigianino apparently of the same subject is in the National Gallery at Melbourne, Australia. The presence of the tents in the Windsor drawing makes the interpretation of the subject as the *Death of Orpheus* (that suggested for the Melbourne composition) improbable.

572. TWO CUPIDS STANDING, the one on the L. in profile to the R., the one on the R. seen from behind. (2309)
240 × 149 mm. Pen and brown ink over black chalk.
A.E.P. Though on an unusually large scale for Parmigianino and rather weak, the style points definitely to him. The drawing comes from the Carracci series and was attributed by Bodmer to Agostino, which seems to me out of the question. It would seem to belong to the Roman or Bolognese period of Parmigianino's activity.

573. *Recto:* A MAN HOLDING THE BODY OF CHRIST ON THE EDGE OF THE TOMB AND A WEEPING MARY (*Plate* 121) (0539)
197 × 142 mm. Pen and brown ink on paper tinted pink.

FIG. 120 Cat. No. 571

Verso: HEAD AND BUST OF A WOMAN holding her R. hand to her breast, probably intended for a Cleopatra. Red chalk.
The sketch on the *recto* is apparently for the composition of the *Entombment*, which was etched by H. van der Borcht when in the Arundel collection, and which had previously been engraved by Enea Vico in 1543 (Bartsch XV, p. 284, 6). The relative positions of Christ and of the man supporting Him are the same, though their attitudes are changed. This composition may date from Parmigianino's Bolognese period, 1527–1531, or it may be rather earlier.

574. DECORATIVE FRIEZE (*Plate* 122) (0534)
137 × 285 mm. Pen and brown ink and brown wash on grey paper, heightened with white.
Inscribed in the bottom L. hand corner in the 'deceptive' hand: 'Parmeggiano'. This is rather an unusually large and largely designed drawing for Parmigianino, but there can be no doubt that it is from his hand. I should suppose it to be of his Roman period, 1524–1527. It was engraved in reverse by Giulio Bonasone (Bartsch XV, p. 173, 354).

575. *Recto:* FRIEZE OF A PUTTO STANDING BETWEEN TWO WINGED LIONS; below, a man holding a violincello (?). (*Figure* 121) (0537)
188 × 137 mm. Pen and ink (for the frieze) and pen and ink and wash heightened with white (for the man).
Verso: TWO WARRIORS HOLDING THEIR SHIELDS ABOVE THEIR HEADS (*Figure* 122)
Red chalk.
Coll.: N. Lanière (Lugt 2886).
The studies on the *verso* are for the soldiers in the foreground on the L. in the etching of *Christ Rising from the Tomb* (Bartsch XVI, p. 9, 6). I cannot connect the drawings on the *recto* with any particular work. There is a copy of the frieze of the *putto* between winged lions at Dresden (photo. Braun 178).

FIG. 121 Cat. No. 575 *r.*

FIG. 122 Cat. No. 575 *v.*

576. THE ADORATION OF THE SHEPHERDS (*Plate* 127) (0535)
249 × 200 mm. Black chalk.
This drawing (or a copy from it) was engraved by Francesco Rosaspina at the end of the XVIII century (British Museum, Rosaspina Album, No. 355). It represents a version, nearly the final version, of the composition which Parmigianino himself etched (Bartsch XVI, p. 7, 3), but shows the foreground figures full-length and in addition the ox and the ass. It will be observed that the sheet was folded across at the height of the woman's L. hand, as if the artist were already contemplating curtailing the composition. It is not possible here to go into the complicated question of this composition and of those connected with it, for which numerous drawings exist. It probably dated from Parmigianino's Roman period, 1524–1527. It is possible that this drawing is the same as 'La natività di N.S. del *Parmegiano* di lapis nero' in the collection of Alfonso d'Este (G. Campori, *Cataloghi ed inventarii inediti*, Modena, 1870, p. 56).

577. HEAD OF A BEARDED MAN WEARING A WREATH IN PROFILE TO THE R.; from the antique. (0579)
99 × 74 mm. Pen and Indian ink on blue-grey paper.
This, as pointed out to me by Dr. Otto Kurz, is copied from an antique cameo of Hercules in Florence, which was also engraved by the Master HB (G. Habich, *Die Medaillen der ital. Renaissance*, Stuttgart and Berlin [1924], pl. LXXVI, 15).

578. MAN'S HEAD IN PROFILE TO THE L.; from the antique. (0580)
102 × 74 mm. Pen and brown ink.
A copy (by Lucas Vorsterman ?) of another study from the same head, turned more to the front, is in the British Museum (Pp. 2–180), and a third drawing of the head from a slightly different angle is described below with copies (No. 652).

579. HERCULES, WHO HAS JUST DISCHARGED AN ARROW FROM HIS BOW, STANDING IN PROFILE TO THE R. (0582)
111 × 80 mm. Fine pen and Indian ink.
Engraved by Metz, No. 57.
This seems to be an original drawing by Parmigianino in the finished, engraver's style, which he employed occasionally throughout his career. The head is based on the antique, the same model as No. 577. There is another version of this drawing at Chatsworth (No. 789B), which is imperfect on the R. It is on the back of a drawing of the *Canephorae* on the vault of the Steccata, which may give an indication of its approximate date, but it seems to be somewhat inferior in quality to the Windsor drawing.

580. *Recto:* A HORSE'S HEAD IN PROFILE TO THE R.; from the antique. (0581)
111 × 80 mm. Pen and brown ink.
Verso: UPPER PART OF THE HEAD OF A WOMAN; from the antique.
Black chalk.

581. THE VIRGIN SEATED ON THE GROUND, ROCKING THE CHILD IN HIS CRADLE, with two *putti* holding the ox by the horns on the background on the R. (*Plate* 124) (0346)
135 × 98 mm. Red chalk over a sketch with the stylus.

On the *verso* are some slight anatomical drawings in pen and ink.

This is probably a first idea for the panel of the *Holy Family with the Infant St. John* at Naples (Copertini, pl. XLVIII). The position of the Child is almost exactly the same in reverse with His leg projecting over the side of the cradle, and the Virgin has the same drooping hand, which Parmigianino used again in the *Madonna della Rosa*. The picture at Naples seems to be generally assigned to Parmigianino's Bolognese period (1527–1531). There is a copy of this drawing in the Albertina (photo. Braun 316).

582. *Recto:* STUDIES OF A WOMAN'S PROFILE AND OF CHILDREN'S HEADS (*Plate* 126) (0345)
Verso: TWO STUDIES OF CHILDREN
134 × 92 mm. Red chalk.
The profile on the L. may be the study for the head of St. Margaret in the *Madonna di S. Margherita* in the Bologna Gallery, painted about 1529 for the nuns of the church of St. Margaret in Bologna (Copertini, pl. L). The other sketches on the *recto* and *verso* of the sheet do not show any close resemblance to other parts of the picture, and the connection can only be regarded as probable.

583. VENUS (?) ASLEEP AGAINST THE TRUNK OF A TREE, ATTENDED BY TWO 'AMORINI' OVAL COMPOSITION (*Figure* 123) (0546)
109 × 79 mm. Pen and brown ink and some brown wash.
Engraved by Metz, No. 58.
Etched in reverse by H. van der Borcht, when in the Arundel Collection.
I do not know the purpose of this composition or of any other drawings connected with it. It may date from the Bolognese period, 1527–1531.

FIG. 123 Cat. No. 583

FIG. 124 Cat. No. 584

584. DIANA AND A NYMPH HUNTING (?); LIONS FIGHTING ON THE R. (*Figure* 124) (0583)
60 × 110 mm. Pen and brown ink and brown wash on slate-coloured prepared surface, heightened with white.
Engraved by Metz, No. 74.
The subject of this exquisite little drawing is obscure. It is apparently fairly late, probably after 1531.

FIG. 125 Cat. No. 585 *r.*

585. *Recto:* APOLLO OR ORPHEUS SEATED UNDER A CLUMP OF TREES, PLAYING THE LYRE, WITH A DOG BESIDE HIM (*Figure* 125) (0584)
Verso: A SIMILAR COMPOSITION IN REVERSE PARTLY TRACED THROUGH; the dog is omitted and the trees are different.
68 × 100 mm. Pen and brown ink.
Apparently late, probably after 1531.

586. *Recto:* A MUSE PLACING A WREATH ROUND THE NECK OF PEGASUS (*Figure* 126) (0563)
110 × 81 mm. Pen and brown ink and brown wash, heightened with white.
Verso: THE FIGURE OF THE MUSE TRACED THROUGH FROM THE *recto*
Pen and ink.
Engraved by Metz, No. 53.
Etched in reverse by a XVII century artist (Lucas Vorsterman ?). Etched in the same direction by *J*, 1808.

FIG. 126 Cat. No. 586 *r.*

FIG. 127 Cat. No. 587

587. A MUSE PLACING A WREATH ON THE HEAD OF PEGASUS (*Figure* 127) (0564)
109 × 78 mm. Pen and Indian ink and grey wash, with some white.
Engraved by Metz, No. 54.
Etched in reverse by Andrea Schiavone, Bartsch XVI, p. 66, 70.
Engraved in the same direction by an anonymous XVI century engraver (impression in the British Museum, Sloane W.2–61).
Etched in reverse by H. van der Borcht (?) (impression in B.M., Sloane W.2–101).
An almost exactly similar drawing is represented by a copy by Lucas Vorsterman in the British Museum (Pp. 2–135), the only difference being that the horse turns his head inwards towards the muse and has a wreath round his neck. The purpose of this and the preceding drawing, a variant of the same composition, is not known to me. Perhaps they were intended to be engraved or etched. There are still other variants of the subject, a drawing in the Louvre (Copertini, Vol. II, pl. 136), another drawing known from the copy by Vorsterman in the British Museum (Pp. 2–136), and a painting known from the engraving by B. Lepicié. In these three versions the muse is naked. It is difficult to be quite certain among this large number of replicas and reproductions, but the Windsor versions appear to me to be originals.

588. DECORATIVE DESIGN OF TWO CONFRONTED NUDE YOUTHS, HOLDING DRAPERY ABOVE THEIR HEADS (*Plate* 130) (0547)
80 × 67 mm. Pen and light brown ink and wash, heightened with white.
Engraved by Metz, No. 70.

589. A WOMAN SEATED IN PROFILE TO THE L. WITH A CHILD; WITHIN AN OVAL SURROUNDED BY AN OCTAGONAL FRAME (*Plate* 131) (0548)
85 × 63 mm. Pen and brown ink and brown wash over black chalk, heightened with white.
Engraved by Metz, No. 103.

590. NUDE YOUTH, SEATED, WITH HIS FEET ON PART OF AN OCTAGONAL FRAME, SUPPORTING ANOTHER FRAME ABOVE HIS HEAD (*Plate* 128) (0549)
92 × 70 mm. Pen and brown ink and brown wash, heightened with white.
Engraved by Metz, No. 61.

591. SEATED WINGED WOMAN WITH HER FEET ON PART OF AN OCTAGONAL FRAME, SUPPORTING ANOTHER FRAME (*Plate* 129) (0550)
95 × 65 mm. Pen and brown ink and brown wash, heightened with white.
Engraved by Metz, No. 63.
Nos. 588–591 are studies for the decoration of the two 'sottarchie' (ribs) of the vaulting of the Steccata. The arrangement was subsequently simplified, and the decoration finally only consisted of an interlacing pattern with Adam and Eve, Moses and Aaron, at the two ends of each rib. The original scheme comprised five ovals within octagonal frames containing various figure subjects on each of the two 'sottarchie'. No. 589, apparently a sibyl, is the design for one of these. The spaces between the octagonal frames were filled by decorative supporting figures, for which Nos. 588, 590 and 591 are alternative designs. The scheme is shown in a drawing of half the vault in the British Museum (Cracherode, Ff. 1–86; ill. Copertini, pl. LXVI)

FIG. 128 Cat. No. 593 *r.*

FIG. 129 Cat. No. 594

and in a drawing of details of the ribs in the Victoria and Albert Museum (No. 4898). I do not feel quite certain that these four drawings are originals.

592. HEAD OF A WOMAN (0541)
Oval, 49 × 36 mm. Pen and brown ink on pink-tinted paper.
This is certainly a drawing of Parmigianino's later period, and is probably for the head of the *Madonna del collo lungo* in the Uffizi, commissioned in 1534.

593. *Recto:* A BEARDED SAINT STANDING TO THE R., READING FROM A BOOK (*Figure* 128) (0589)
112 × 74 mm. Pen and brown ink and grey wash on blue paper, heightened with white.
Verso: STUDY OF A TABERNACLE
Pen and brown ink.
Recto engraved by Metz, No. 71.
The study on the *recto* is for a St. Jerome, who appears on the L. in a drawing in the Albertina (S.L. 70, water colour, 190 × 99 mm.; ill. Fröhlich-Bum, Fig. 136). The Vienna drawing is apparently the copy of one by Parmigianino, formerly in the collections of A. M. Zanetti (who made a chiaroscuro woodcut from it, Bartsch 29) and Antonio Armano (when it was engraved in facsimile by F. Rosaspina). There is no reason for Mrs. Fröhlich-Bum's attribution of this composition to Mazzola-Bedoli. It is certainly Parmigianino's of the period of the *Madonna del collo lungo.* Another version of the Vienna (or Zanetti) drawing, with a bishop substituted for the St. Jerome, is in this collection (No. 419). This *is*, I believe, by Bedoli, and it is discussed under that name.

594. A STANDING PROPHET; in an oval. (*Figure* 129) (0592)
Oval, 130 × 60 mm. Pen and brown ink and brown wash on pink-tinted paper.
This is probably a design for one of the five ovals, which Parmigianino originally projected for each of the 'sottarchie' of the Steccata vault (see above, Nos. 588 to 591). It shows the influence of Correggio's somewhat similarly placed figures under the arches of the cupola of S. Giovanni Evangelista, Parma.

595. TWO WOMEN WITH AMPHORAE ON THEIR HEADS, HOLDING HANDS (0565)
82 × 80 mm. Pen and Indian ink and grey wash on brownish paper.
Engraved by Metz, No. 21.
Study for two of the Virgins on the vault of the Steccata, differing considerably from the final version. Certainly an original drawing.

596. *Recto:* THE VIRGIN AND CHILD ON CLOUDS WITH, BELOW, ST. STEPHEN, ST. JOHN THE BAPTIST AND A DONOR (*Figure* 130) (0590)
Verso: PART OF THE SKETCH OF A CHIN AND NECK and the old inscription 'fco parmigio'.
105 × 67 mm. Pen and grey ink.
Recto engraved by Metz, No. 38.
This appears to be a first idea for the picture of the *Madonna and Child with St. Stephen and St. John the Baptist* in the Dresden Gallery (No. 160). The picture was painted for

FIG. 130 Cat. No. 596 *r.*

the church of S. Stefano at Casalmaggiore, where Parmigianino had taken refuge after 1539. The fragment on the *verso* is probably for the chin of St. John the Baptist, who in the picture is beardless.

597. *Recto:* DESIGN FOR THE DECORATION OF AN APSE: THE CORONATION OF THE VIRGIN (*Plate* 132)

Verso: Various studies. Those in the same ink as the studies on the *recto*, which are drawn across the sheet, comprise: (1) Two studies of the infant St. John with a lamb (?). (2) A bearded man, seated, bound with his hands behind him to a tree. (3) A nude youth standing, turned to the R., and a partial study of the same figure. In a lighter brown ink at the bottom of the sheet are: (4) three figures with picks. (5) Two studies of a Madonna and Child (the opposite way). (*Plate* 133) (2185)

187 × 183 mm. Pen and grey ink and grey wash on faded blue paper, heightened with white.

The study on the *recto* is for the apse of the church of the Steccata, which Parmigianino was commissioned to paint in a contract of May 10, 1531. He had already by that date submitted a sketch to the Confraternity, which is usually identified as that now in the Biblioteca ex-Reale at Turin (Copertini, pl. LXIV). The present sketch corresponds in general arrangement with that at Turin, except that the position of the Virgin is altered. Copies of two other studies, one for the complete composition (No. 633) and another for the figure of the Virgin alone (No. 640) are catalogued below. The present sketch is by far the most elaborate of the studies for the apse of the Steccata known to me. (Another study, for the figure of Christ under the guise of Jupiter, etched in reverse by Vorsterman, when in the Arundel collection, is now in the Museum at Poitiers, 402–1341).

Of the studies on the *verso*, Nos. (2) and (3) are from some version of an antique gem of *Apollo and Marsyas* formerly belonging to Lorenzo di Medici (see Victoria and Albert Museum, *Catalogue of Plaquettes Italian*, London, 1924, p. 13 and pl. I). These studies would certainly seem to have been drawn with the oval design of the *Contest between Apollo and and Marsyas* now in the Pierpont Morgan Library (*Drawings by the Old Masters*, IV, 44) in view. This drawing was the original of the chiaroscuro woodcut (Bartsch XII, p. 123, 24). Of the L. hand of the two sketches of an infant St. John the Baptist (No. (1)) there was another drawing differing in some particulars, but unmistakably the same figure, in the Arundel Collection (etched, presumably in reverse, by H. van der Borcht). The studies of the Madonna and Child seem to be connected with the composition of the *Mystic Marriage of St. Catherine*, known in various versions (Copertini, pl. XXXIX), though this composition is no doubt considerably earlier in date, and the picture for which the present studies were intended did not, as the indication of the rectangle enclosing one makes clear, include a St. Catherine. I do not know for what purpose the figures with picks were drawn. They suggested the men destroying the bridge in some composition of Horatius Cocles, but no such composition by Parmigianino is known to me.

The sheet is closely connected stylistically with that of the *Bathing Nymphs* in the Uffizi (for the chiaroscuro woodcut, Bartsch XII, p. 122, 22). It would seem to belong to the beginning of Parmigianino's work on the Steccata, about 1531, and not to a later phase.

598. *Recto:* COPY FROM RAPHAEL'S 'SCHOOL OF ATHENS' (*Figure* 131) (0533)

235 × 415 mm. (edges covered). Pen and brown ink and brown wash over black chalk.

Verso: VARIOUS SLIGHT SKETCHES as follows (taken from L. to R.): (1) The lower halves of two floating angels, which might be an impression of the angels on the L. at the top of the *Disputà*. (2) A male nude reclining with his head to the R. in the attitude of a river-god. (3) A circle divided into eight segments. (4) A globe (?). (5) Sketch for the decoration of a cupola divided by spokes into six segments: figures recline along the circumference and outside it clouds are indicated.

Pen and ink.

Lit.: K. T. Parker, O.M.D. XIV (1939–40), p. 41, pl. 38; Passavant, *Raphael d'Urbin*, Paris, 1860, II, p. 493k, No. 1; Ruland, p. 190, No. 85; Crowe and Cavalcaselle, *Raphael, His Life and Works*, London, 1885, II, p. 74, note 1.

Photo. Thurston Thompson, 1857.

I cannot agree with K. T. Parker's dismissal of the old attribution to Parmigianino (O.M.D., loc. cit.). I think the style of the drawing is quite definitely Parmigianino's and no one else's. Without wishing to be dogmatic on the point, I should further suggest that the style is not that of Parmigianino's Roman period (1524–1527), but rather that of his second Parma period (1531–1539). Its handling is very close indeed to that of the drawing of the *Circumcision* in the British Museum (1910–2–12–34), which was probably designed for one of the apses of the Steccata and the composition of which is, in fact, based on that of the *School of Athens*.

K. T. Parker has pointed out (loc. cit.) that this drawing resembles Raphael's cartoon of the *School of Athens* in the Ambrosiana, in the absence of the figure of Heraclitus to the L., while it differs from it in the inclusion of the relief of Philosophy in the architecture to the R. It is not easy to explain either the omission or the addition. There must presumably have been in existence a *modello* of the *School of*

FIG. 131 Cat. No. 598 r.

Athens distinct from the cartoon, to which Parmigianino had access.

The recumbent male nude on the *verso* seems to be an impression of Michelangelo's *Dream of Human Life* (drawing formerly at Weimar, ill. A. E. Brinckmann, *Michelangelo-Zeichnungen*, Munich, 1925, pl. 59: it is immaterial whether this is the original or not), though the position of the head and of the L. arm is altered. This is one of the Cavalieri drawings of 1532–33, which would seem to be an additional reason for dating Parmigianino's drawing late. I cannot suggest for what purpose the cupola sketch was made.

Richardson (*An Account* . . ., 1722, p. 32) saw in the Bonfiglioli palace at Bologna a framed drawing, which he describes as follows: '*Parmeggiano, School of Athens*, most exquisitely copy'd, and perfectly well preserved: Pen, Wash. one Foot and a half long, one Foot broad: 'tis in the same manner, lightly touch'd with a small Pen, as the *Venus*, *Mars*, &c. which my Father has.' It is tempting to identify the Bonfiglioli drawing with that now at Windsor, in spite of the difference in the measurements ($8\frac{3}{4} \times 16\frac{1}{2}$ in.). Perhaps Richardson included the frame.

599. HEAD OF A BOY, IN PROFILE TO THE L., WEARING A CAP (0530)

109 × 77 mm. Pen and brown ink.

This is rather an uninteresting drawing in Parmigianino's formal, engraver-like technique. Though its quality is poor, I think it would be unwise to dismiss it as a copy. If it is by him it is likely to date from his Roman or Bolognese periods.

600. HALF-LENGTH OF A WOMAN TURNED TO THE L. BUT LOOKING BACK TO THE R. (0525)

124 × 69 mm. Pen and dark brown ink.

Coll.: Earl of Cholmondeley (Lugt 1149).

The drawing may well be a study for one of the virgins on the vault of the Steccata, 1531–1539, though the position of the arms is different. The style seems to me very late—I should place it as near 1539 as possible—and by that date the attitudes of the virgins must have been fixed in their final form. The connection is therefore doubtful, but the arrangement and style of the drapery is extraordinarily close.

601. FOUR WOMEN'S HEADS IN PROFILE TO THE L. (*Plate* 125) (0526)

88 × 105 mm. Pen and Indian ink.

The head on the R., to which the others seem to have been added as an afterthought, might well be a study for that of one of the virgins on the R. on the vaulting of the Steccata, or a reminiscence of one of these. The date is fixed by an inscription on the *verso*, in the artist's hand. It reads: '1537 · a · 22 · d · decenb io dete duj schudj dor a M4 damiano' (dec. 22 1537 I gave two gold scudi to Messer Damiano). The Messer Damiano in question is no doubt the architect Damiano de Pleta (b. 1498), who together with Francesco Bojardi stood surety for Parmigianino's carrying out the terms of the renewed contract for the paintings in the Steccata made on September 27, 1535.

602. TWO HEADS OF SATYRS IN PROFILE TO THE L. (0544)

106 × 78 mm. Red chalk on faded blue paper, heightened with white.

Engraved by Metz, No. 62.

If this drawing is by Parmigianino, which I think probable, it must date from his pre-Roman period.

603. LUCRETIA ADVANCING IN PROFILE TO THE R. AND STABBING HERSELF (0562)

111 × 78 mm. (a rectangular piece cut from the bottom R. corner). Pen and brown ink and brown wash, heightened with white.

The drawing was etched in reverse by a hand which looks like that of H. van der Borcht II, but without any inscription (impression in British Museum, Sloane W.2–107). If the drawing is by Parmigianino, of which I am not entirely convinced, it must date from his Roman period, 1524–1527. It has nothing to do with the *Lucretia* engraved by Enea Vico or with the half-length painting at Naples, both of which are late in style.

604. A DRAPED FEMALE FIGURE STANDING IN A NICHE, HOLDING A SPEAR (0545)
111 × 52 mm. Pen and Indian ink and grey wash on blue paper, heightened with white.
Engraved by Metz, No. 69.
This is quite dissimilar in handling and technique from any genuine drawing by Parmigianino known to me. If it were by him it would have to be very early, of his pre-Roman period. I think it more likely to be by Mazzola-Bedoli—compare the figure of the Virgin in the picture by him of the *Immaculate Conception* in the Parma Gallery, dating from 1533—though it seems almost too spirited. As it was engraved by Metz as Parmigianino's it is perhaps better to leave it under that name.

Copies from PARMIGIANINO

SERIES OF EIGHT LEAVES OF A METAL-POINT SKETCH-BOOK DRAWN ON BOTH SIDES (Nos. 01341 to 01346, Nos. 01348 and 01401)
109 × 71 mm. Metal-point on light brown prepared surface (except No. 607 *verso* and No. 612 *verso*, which have a blue surface), in some cases heightened with white.

605. *Recto:* VIRTUE VICTORIOUS OVER VICE (01341)
Corresponding in reverse with the etching marked 'F.P.' (Bartsch XVI, p. 24, 17).
Engraved by Metz, No. 51.
Verso: DIANA SHOOTING WITH BOW AND ARROW
Corresponding in reverse with an undescribed etching attributed to 'F.P.' (impression in the British Museum). A drawing of the subject was etched by H. van der Borcht II, when in the Arundel collection. A certainly original sketch for the figure is on a sheet in the Uffizi (Copertini, pl. CVII). Another copy, also in the Uffizi, was etched by Mulinari (Weigel 5740).

606. *Recto:* A PHILOSOPHER (ARCHIMEDES?) SEATED, POINTING TO A BOOK STANDING OPEN BEFORE HIM ON THE R. (01342)
There are innumerable versions of this subject, including one formerly in the collection of C. A. Armano engraved in reverse by C. C. M. Gini (Weigel 5684).
Engraved by Metz, No. 55.
Verso: HOUNDS PURSUING A STAG
Corresponding in reverse with the etching marked 'F.P.' (Bartsch XVI, p. 24, 16) and the chiaroscuro woodcut (Bartsch XII, p. 113, 10).

607. *Recto:* A WOMAN, FOLLOWED BY ANOTHER AND PRECEDED BY A CHILD, STRETCHING OUT HER HAND TO AN ALTAR (01343)
Corresponding in reverse with the etching marked 'F.P.' (Bartsch XVI, p. 24, 18).
Engraved by Metz, No. 68.
Photo. Braun 146, II.
Verso: HOPE (?): A NAKED WOMAN ON WHOM RAYS FROM THE SUN, INSCRIBED 'SPERAN', DESCEND
Corresponding in reverse with an undescribed etching marked 'F.P.' (impression in British Museum).
Engraved by Metz, No. 50.

608. *Recto:* A WINGED WOMAN HOLDING A SWORD IN EITHER HAND, A VIOLIN ON THE GROUND BEHIND HER (01344)
The subject was etched in reverse by H. van der Borcht II when in the Arundel collection. Another version in the Uffizi etched by Mulinari (Weigel 5788).
Engraved by Metz, No. 49.
Verso: DIANA WITH HER HOUNDS
Corresponding in reverse with the etching marked 'F.P.' (Bartsch XVI, p. 25, 21) and (in the same direction) with the chiaroscuro woodcut (Bartsch XII, p. 112, 10). Another version on a sheet of red chalk studies formerly in the collection of G. A. Armano etched by F. Rosaspina (Weigel 5750).
Engraved by Metz, No. 52.

609. *Recto:* MUTIUS SCAEVOLA (01345)
There are innumerable versions of this drawing, including one formerly in the collection of G. A. Armano engraved by C. C. M. Gini (Weigel 5691), and one at Chatsworth (No. 796C), which is probably original. The present drawing is reversed as Mutius Scaevola is putting his *left* hand into the flames.
Engraved by Metz, No. 67.
Verso: HERCULES AND CERBERUS
Corresponding in reverse with the etching marked 'F.P.' (Bartsch XVI, p. 23, 15). The original is probably the drawing at Chatsworth (No. 795C). There is another in the Louvre (?) etched in reverse by Caylus (Weigel 5395).
Engraved by Metz, No. 56.

610. *Recto:* A WOMAN ADVANCING TO THE R. HOLDING A WREATH IN BOTH HANDS (01346)
Inscribed bottom R., 'F.P.'. Corresponding in reverse with the etching marked 'F.P.' (Bartsch XVI, p. 26, 23).
Engraved by Metz, No. 33.
Verso: A PHILOSOPHER SEATED IN PROFILE TO THE R.
Corresponding in reverse with the etching marked 'F.P.' (Bartsch XVI, p. 24, 19). There is a drawing at Chatsworth (No. 795A) which is probably the original.
Engraved by Metz, No. 45.

611. *Recto:* FORTITUDE (01348)
Inscribed at bottom L., 'F.P.'. Corresponding in reverse with the etching marked 'F.P.' (Bartsch XVI, p. 23, 14). The original is probably the drawing at Chatsworth (No. 795B *recto*).
Engraved by Metz, No. 34.
Verso: A WOMAN CONTEMPLATING AN ARMILLARY SPHERE
Inscribed to the R., 'EDIMEON'. Corresponding in reverse with the etching marked 'F.P.' (Bartsch XVI, p. 25, 20). The original is probably the drawing at Chatsworth (No. 795B *verso*).
Engraved by Metz, No. 44.

612. *Recto:* THE CENTAUR NESSUS CARRYING OFF DEJANIRA (01401)
Corresponding in reverse with the undescribed etching marked 'F.P.' (impression in the British Museum). The original is probably the drawing at Chatsworth (No. 791A).
Verso: MINERVA OR BELLONA
Corresponding with the chiaroscuro woodcut (in the same direction) (Bartsch XII, p. 122, 23). The original is probably the drawing at Chatsworth (No. 791B).

With the seven sheets of this sketch-book was associated an eighth (No. 620), a playing card with a prepared surface of the same character, but 5 mm. wider. This was blank on one side, but had on the other the profile of a young woman lightly sketched. The type suggests the period of Rubens, and I have no doubt that it is Dutch or Flemish and perhaps, as an inscription on another leaf suggests, by Wallerant Vaillant. With the seven sheets (Nos. 613–619) from J. P. Heseltine's collection purchased in 1935 was an eighth (No. 612), which certainly belonged to the series of seven originally in the royal collection, and it has been mounted with these. It had been in the collection of the elder Richardson, and must therefore have been separated from its companions as early as the beginning of the XVIII century. As will have been noticed all the subjects except No. 605 *verso* and No. 606 *verso* (and of course the additional sheet, No. 612) were engraved in facsimile by C. M. Metz in 1790 as Parmigianino's. Most of the subjects (12 out of 16) are represented by etchings in reverse marked 'F.P.'. I assume that both the engraver and the draughtsman of Nos. 605–612 had access to the same set of drawings by Parmigianino. They correspond very closely indeed. Good as the Windsor drawings are, there can be no question of their being by Parmigianino himself: they show a quality of drawing different from his. Nevertheless this particular series is the most widely reproduced of all Parmigianino's compositions, and without a careful study of all these drawings in the original it would be rash to be dogmatic. The originals would seem to have dated from Parmigianino's Roman or Bolognese periods, and it seems a possible hypothesis that they were intended by the artist for reproduction in engraving or etching and formed part of the series stolen from him in Bologna by Antonio da Trento (see Vasari, V, p. 227).

The type of sketch-book and the elaborate metal-point ground suggests an artist from the Netherlands or Germany. Certainly Goltzius and Jacob de Gheyn used playing cards prepared in this sort of way for metal-point sketches (see J. Meder, *Die Handzeichnung*, Vienna, 1919, p. 97), and I know of no example of the use of such sketch-books in Italy.

SERIES OF SEVEN LEAVES OF A METAL-POINT SKETCH-BOOK DRAWN ON BOTH SIDES (EXCEPT NOS. 618 AND 619) (Nos. 01397 to 01400 and Nos. 01402 to 01404)

95 × 62 mm. Metal-point on playing cards prepared with a cream-coloured surface, heightened with white.

Coll.: Sir T. Lawrence (Lugt 2445); J. P. Heseltine (Lugt 1508; Sale, Sotheby's, May 28, 1935).

613. *Recto:* MINERVA OR BELLONA (01397)
Corresponding with the drawing described above, No. 612 *verso*.

Verso: THE CENTAUR NESSUS CARRYING OFF DEJANIRA
Corresponding in reverse with an etching marked 'F.P.' (undescribed: impression in the British Museum) and with the drawing already described, No. 612 *recto*.

614. *Recto:* A WOMAN CONTEMPLATING AN ARMILLARY SPHERE (01398)
Corresponding with the drawing already described, No. 611 *verso*, and, in reverse, with the etching marked 'F.P.' (Bartsch XVI, p. 25, 20).

Verso: A WOMAN ADVANCING TO THE R., HOLDING A WREATH IN BOTH HANDS
Corresponding with the drawing described above, No. 610 *recto*, and in reverse with the etching marked 'F.P.' (Bartsch XVI, p. 26, 23).

615. *Recto:* DIANA SHOOTING WITH BOW AND ARROW (01399)
Corresponding with the drawing described above, No. 605 *verso*, and with the undescribed etching marked 'F.P.'.

Verso: VIRTUE VICTORIOUS OVER VICE
Corresponding with the drawing described above, No. 605 *recto*, and in reverse with the etching marked 'F.P.' (Bartsch XVI, p. 24, 17).

616. *Recto:* HOPE (?) (01402)
Corresponding with the drawing described above, No. 607 *verso*, and with an undescribed etching marked 'F.P.'.

Verso: A WINGED WOMAN HOLDING A SWORD IN EITHER HAND
Corresponding with the drawing described above, No. 608 *recto*.

617. *Recto:* FORTITUDE (01400)
Corresponding with the drawing described above, No. 611 *recto*, and in reverse with the etching marked 'F.P.' (Bartsch XVI, p. 23, 14).

Verso: A SEATED PHILOSOPHER (ARCHIMEDES?)
Corresponding with the drawing described above, No. 606 *recto*.

618. A WOMAN STRETCHING OUT HER HAND ABOVE AN ALTAR, WITH OTHER FIGURES (01403)
Corresponding with the drawing described above, No. 607 *recto*, and in reverse with the etching marked 'F.P.' (Bartsch XVI, p. 24, 18).

619. DIANA WITH HER HOUNDS (01404)
Corresponding with the drawing described above, No. 608 *verso*, and in reverse with the etching marked 'F.P.' (Bartsch XVI, p. 25, 21).

620. HEAD OF A GIRL LOOKING DOWN TO THE R. (01347)
Perhaps by Wallerant Vaillant (*not* forming part of the Heseltine sketch-book).

---

621. A NUDE MAN, CARRYING A WEIGHT ON HIS SHOULDERS, STRIDING FORWARD (0585)
90 × 53 mm. Pen and brown ink and brown wash.
Engraved by Metz, No. 30.

622. A NUDE MAN, CARRYING ANOTHER ON HIS BACK, STRIDING FORWARD (0586)
81 × 52 mm. Pen and brown ink and brown wash.
Engraved by Metz, No. 29.
A copy by Lucas Vorsterman from the same original is in the British Museum (Pp. 2–150).
Nos. 621, 622 might be studies for a composition of the Sack of Troy. No. 622 is the copy of a drawing formerly in the Denon collection (lithograph in *Monuments Denon*, Weigel 5818), and previously, it is to be presumed, in the Arundel collection. The Denon sheet contained a second study of a man carrying another on his shoulders, but not the man with the weight, No. 621. Perhaps this obviously cognate study was on the *verso*.

623. ST. JEROME IN PENITENCE: ROUNDEL (0593)
96 × 86 mm. (diam. of circle, 86 mm.). Pen and ink on pink ground, heightened with white.
This comes very near to Parmigianino, but is hardly good enough.

624. HEAD OF A BEARDED MAN IN PROFILE TO THE R., THE FACE IN SHADOW (0542)
70 × 48 mm. Pen and brown ink.
Copy of a study for the head of the man on the extreme L. in Parmigianino's etching of the *Entombment* (Bartsch XVI, p. 8, 5). What was presumably the original was etched in reverse by N. Lanière in his series after Parmigianino dated 1636.

625. HEAD OF AN ELDERLY WOMAN, WEARING A HEADDRESS, IN PROFILE TO THE L. (0543)
77 × 58 mm. Pen and brown ink.
Engraved by Metz, No. 31.
This appears to be a copy of the same period, but not by the same hand, as Nos. 621 and 622. The original (ill. G. Copertini, *Nuovo Contributo di Studi e Ricerche sul Parmigianino*, Parma, 1949, Fig. 9), now in the Biblioteca ex-Reale, Turin, was etched in reverse by N. Lanière in his series of 1636.

626. HEAD OF A BEARDED MAN IN PROFILE TO THE R. (0540)
51 × 40 mm. Pen and brown ink.
Engraved by Metz, No. 12.
Copy, of the time of Vorsterman, of an original otherwise unknown to me.

627. ST. JEROME IN PENITENCE, KNEELING IN PROFILE TO THE L. (0588)
80 × 56 mm. (top corners cut). Pen and brown ink and brown wash, over black chalk.
Engraved by Metz, No. 59.
A copy of the Vorsterman type.

628. KING DAVID, HIS HARP BEFORE HIM, KNEELING TO THE R. (0587)
75 × 50 mm. Pen and brown ink and brown wash.
Inscribed on *verso* in an old hand 'parmigiano'. This is a copy from a drawing in the British Museum (Pp. 2–134), or from the original from which that was copied.

629. ST. FRANCIS RECEIVING THE STIGMATA (0591)
88 × 59 mm. Pen and grey ink, over black chalk.
Engraved by Metz, No. 60.
The character of the paper and the handling point clearly to a copy of the time of Vorsterman from a drawing, presumably that once in Denon's collection (lithographed in *Monuments Denon*, Weigel 5543).

630. A MAN WALKING TO THE R. WITH HIS CLOAK BLOWN OUT BEHIND HIM (0551)
79 × 59 mm. Pen and brown ink.
Engraved by Metz, No. 9.
This drawing, or more probably the original from which it was copied, was etched by F. Rosaspina when in the collection of G. A. Armano.

631. APOLLO PURSUING DAPHNE: LARGER OVAL (0552)
72 × 55 mm. Pen and brown ink.
Engraved by Metz, No. 48.
This, drawing, or more probably the original from which it was copied, was etched by F. Rosaspina when in the collection of G. A. Armano. I believe this original to be the drawing now in the British Museum (Fenwick collection, Catalogue, p. 79). A version of the subject, also in an oval, but differing from this and from No. 634, is in the Berlin Kupferstichkabinett (Fröhlich-Bum, Fig. 75). They are possibly designs for medallions to be worn in the hat.

632. TWO SHEPHERDS, WITH A RAM, KNEELING TO THE R. (0553)
60 × 54 mm. Pen and Indian ink.
Engraved by Metz, No. 4.
This must be a XVII century facsimile, though it is of much better quality than Nos. 635 and 636. It is drawn on the same heavily-ribbed paper. It was clearly for an *Adoration of the Shepherds*, like that in the Hermitage (Fröhlich-Bum, Fig. 83).

633. THE CORONATION OF THE VIRGIN (0554)
58 × 80 mm. Pen and brown ink over pencil or black chalk.
Engraved by Metz, No. 11.
This is copied from a study for the *Coronation of the Virgin* designed for the apse of the Steccata. There is an alternative study for the design of the whole apse at Turin (Copertini, pl. LXIV), a study of part of the composition described above (No. 597), and another copy of a study for the figure of the Virgin (No. 640).

634. APOLLO PURSUING DAPHNE: SMALLER OVAL (0555)
58 × 49 mm. Pen and brown ink.
Engraved by Metz, No. 47.
A slightly varied version of No. 631. The original is in the Louvre (No. 6406).

635. STUDY OF THE DRAPERY OVER THE BODY OF A WOMAN (0556)
82 × 59 mm. Pen and brown ink and brown wash.
Engraved by Metz, No. 36.
Copy of a study for the *Madonna del collo lungo*, presumably that engraved by F. Rosaspina when in the collection of Gini (B.M. Rosaspina album, No. 500), together with two other studies for the same picture now in the British Museum (1905–11–10–61, 62).

636. THE VIRGIN BATHING THE INFANT CHRIST WITH ST. ELIZABETH (?), TO THE L. (0557)
83 × 61 mm. Pen and brown ink.
Engraved by Metz, No. 35.
The interpretation of the subject becomes clear by reference to a well-known drawing in the Uffizi (Copertini, pl. C), in which the shepherds adore the Child, who is being bathed by the Virgin. I do not know where the original of this, an obvious copy of the Vorsterman type, is to be found.

637, 638, 639. THREE STUDIES OF THE MOSES IN THE STECCATA (0569, 0570, 0571)
70 × 26 mm.; 78 × 24 mm.; 65 × 31 mm. Pen and brown ink and brown wash (No. 637), pen and brown ink (Nos. 638 and 639).
Engraved by Metz, Nos. 16, 15, 14.
Facsimiles, probably by Lucas Vorsterman, from a sheet with nine studies of the Moses and ten studies of the Eve in the Steccata, now in the collection of Captain Bruce Ingram. This sheet belonged to Baron Denon, and was lithographed in reverse in *Monuments Denon* (Weigel 5819). It had previously formed part of the collections of Lord Arundel and of A. M. Zanetti. It might be natural to assume that the Windsor drawings had been cut out of the Denon sheet, but this is chronologically impossible, as this was intact as late as 1829. Of all three there are similar copies in the British Museum (Pp. 2–169 = 637; Pp. 2–166 = 638; Pp. 2–160 = 639).

640. STUDY OF A NUDE WOMAN LOOKING UP TO THE R. AND POINTING TO THE L. WITH BOTH HANDS (0572)
65 × 44 mm. Pen and brown ink and brown wash over black chalk.
Engraved by Metz, No. 7.

The original was apparently the study for the figure of the Virgin in the design for the apse of the Steccata with the *Coronation of the Virgin*, of which there is a drawing in the Biblioteca ex-Reale at Turin (Copertini, pl. LXIV) and another described above, No. 597.

641. JACOB WRESTLING WITH THE ANGEL (0573)
88 × 41 mm. Pen and brown ink and brown wash.
Engraved by Metz, No. 8.
Inscribed underneath to the L., 'Jacob'.
Copy of a drawing, which was once in the Arundel collection, when it was etched by Lucas Vorsterman, and then in that of G. A. Armano, when it was engraved by Rosaspina. The original was probably a study for the Steccata, though the subject was not used there. Another drawing also inscribed 'Jacob' in the Louvre (ill. O.M.D. IX (1934–35), pl. 60) may have been an alternative study. There is another copy from the original of the Windsor drawing in the British Museum (Pp. 2–159).

642, 643, 644, 645. FOUR STUDIES OF THE EVE IN THE STECCATA (0574, 0575, 0576, 0577)
60 × 26 mm.; 77 × 32 mm.; 82 × 28 mm.; 80 × 32 mm. Pen and brown ink (Nos. 642, 644); pen and brown ink and wash (Nos. 643, 645).
Engraved by Metz, Nos. 18, 5, 17, 19.
These four studies are copies from the sheet with nine studies of Moses and ten of Eve formerly in the Denon collection (see above, Nos. 637, 638, and 639). There are similar copies of all four in the British Museum (Pp. 2–155 = 642, Pp. 2–157 = 643, Pp. 2–154 = 644, and Pp. 2–158 = 645).

646, 647, 648. THREE SAINTS: ST. JOHN THE EVANGELIST, ST. PAUL AND ST. JAMES THE LESS (?) (0558, 0559, 0560)
Each 151 × 85 mm. Pen and brown ink and wash.
These drawings correspond on a larger scale with the etchings marked 'F.P.': No. 646 with Bartsch XVI, p. 20, 5; No. 647 with Bartsch 13; No. 648 with Bartsch 10. They are more likely to be copies from drawings than from the actual etchings. Their style suggests Andrea Schiavone, who in fact copied the 'F.P.' etchings (No. 646 = Bartsch XVI, p. 54, 28; No. 647 = Bartsch 37; No. 648 = Bartsch 33).

649. TEMPERANCE (0561)
133 × 75 mm. Pen and brown ink and wash.
This very faded drawing, mounted with the three apostles, may also be after Parmigianino, though I do not know the original.

650. HERCULES AND CERBERUS (0531)
172 × 118 mm. Pen and brown ink and brown wash over black chalk on pink-tinted paper.
Enlarged copy of the composition of this subject represented by the metal-point drawing, No. 604 *verso* and the etching marked 'F.P.', Bartsch XVI, p. 23, 15. The style is impossibly loose for Parmigianino himself and suggests Schiavone.

651. VIRGIN AND CHILD (5977)
172 × 124 mm. Black chalk. Corners cut and made up.
This is obviously a copy from a drawing by Parmigianino not, however, known to me. It may have been a study made in 1527 in connection with the National Gallery *Vision of St. Jerome*. It shows some resemblance to a drawing formerly in Henry Reveley's collection, when it was engraved in facsimile by C. M. Metz (Weigel 5451) and to another etched by Lanière when in the Arundel collection.

652. MAN'S HEAD IN PROFILE TO THE L.; from the antique. (2279)
189 × 143 mm. Pen and brown ink.
A.E.P. From the Carracci series. The head is the same as that represented in No. 578 by Parmigianino himself, seen from a slightly different angle. The present drawing is a little too precise and mechanical for Parmigianino, and must, I think, be a facsimile of a drawing by him.

653. THREE MEN IN CLASSICAL COSTUME WALKING PAST A BUILDING; OTHER FIGURES BEHIND AND A CUPID FLYING ABOVE (0289)
215 × 123 mm. Pen and brown ink.
Lit.: A. Mongan and P. J. Sachs, *Drawings in the Fogg Museum*, Cambridge, Mass., 1940, p. 82, No. 139.
Inscribed on the *verso* in an old hand, 'Sig^r Gio'. What appears to have been the original from which this is copied was engraved in facsimile by F. Rosaspina, when in the collection of the brothers Gio. Angelo and Gabriele Brunetti at Bologna (L. Inig, *Celeberrimi Francisci Mazzola . . Graphides*, Bologna, 1788: Weigel 5825). Another version of part of the composition is in the Fogg Museum, Loeser collection (from the Denon collection: lithographed in *Monuments Denon*, Weigel 5509). This may be the original, and the Brunetti and Windsor drawings copies made from it before it was damaged. The Denon Parmigianinos were unusually good.

654. A NAKED BEARDED MAN BLOWING A CURVED HORN, AND TWO PUTTI (0350)
197 × 133 mm. Pen and brown ink and grey wash.
This is certainly not from Parmigianino's own hand, but it looks like a copy from a drawing by him of the type of those formerly in Zanetti's collection and engraved by Faldoni (Weigel 5656 and 5797). The original was presumably that described in the inventory of Roberto Canonici, 1632, 'Un huomo nudo, che suona una tromba, e ne tiene un' altra in mano, ha duoi putini appresso nudi, e a in mano un cornucopia, del *Parmiggiano*' (G. Campori, *Cataloghi ed inventarii inediti*, Modena, 1870, p. 126).

655. THE VIRGIN AND CHILD WITH THE INFANT ST. JOHN, ST. JOHN THE EVANGELIST AND THREE FEMALE SAINTS (0347)
235 × 165 mm. Pen and brown ink and brown wash on light brown ground, heightened with white. Much faded and wormed.
Inscribed in the 'deceptive' hand, 'parmegiano'. Copy of a composition known from the engraving attributed by Bartsch to C. Reverdino (Bartsch XV, p. 470, 9) and from various other versions.

656. MARS AND VENUS SURPRISED BY VULCAN (0348)
290 × 211 mm. Pen and brown ink.
Photo.: Braun 257.
This is an old facsimile, of the XVII or XVIII century, of the drawing by Parmigianino in the Parma Gallery (Copertini, Vol. II, pl. 8).

657. THE MARRIAGE OF THE VIRGIN (0355)
363 × 229 mm. Pen and brown ink and brown wash on light brown ground, heightened with white.
Copy of the engraving by Caraglio (Bartsch XV, p. 66, I) of the subject. Parmigianino's original drawing from which the engraving was made is at Chatsworth (No. 399).

BARTOLOMMEO PASSAROTTI (1529–1592)

658. THE BODY OF THE VIRGIN MARY LYING ON THE BIER, SURROUNDED BY THE APOSTLES, HER ASSUMPTION AND HER BURIAL (6037)

508 × 347 mm. Pen and brown ink and brown wash over black chalk, squared in black chalk.
On the *verso* in William Gibson's (?) hand: 'Bartolomeo Passerotti', and price 6.3.' (= 30/–). There can be no doubt of the correctness of this attribution. It is one of the comparatively rare drawings by the artist which is obviously the study or *modello* for a picture and in a technique other than pure pen and ink. I cannot find any record of a painting of the subject attributed to him.

659. THE FLAGELLATION (6039)
410 × 515 mm. Broad pen and light brown ink on porridge-coloured paper; the head of one of the executioners is a correction on a scrap of paper pasted on.
Attribution to 'Passarotti' in pencil on the mount. There can be no doubt that it is an original by Bartolommeo and perhaps the study for a picture. It is drawn on inferior paper and there are *pentimenti*, as well as detail sketches to the R., which would seem to imply that it was not intended as a finished drawing for sale or presentation.

660. HERCULES AND CERBERUS (6043)
467 × 353 mm. Broad pen and Indian ink, squared in black chalk.
Inscribed in pen and ink in an old hand to the R., half-way up the drawing: 'del pasaroto vechio'. In the L. hand bottom corner are the figures '1.3.' (5/–), which may be the indication of price used by Gibson.

661. ST. JEROME IN PENITENCE (6044)
470 × 375 mm. Broad pen and brown ink over black chalk.
Inscribed in ink on the *verso* in William Gibson's (?) hand: 'Bartolommeo Passerotto 4.3. (= 20/–) and '1.4.' (also = 20/–). A smaller variant of the same figure is in the British Museum (Malcolm Collection, No. 242). The figure, as noted on the mount by F. Kriegbaum, is derived from a statue of a river-god by Giambologna (1571–3) in the fountain of Oceano in the Boboli Gardens, Florence (Venturi, X 3, Fig. 593). The drawing was attributed in the XVIII century (pencil inscription on mount) to Ventura Passarotti, which may be right, but I should have thought it might well be by Bartolommeo. It is better than the variant in the British Museum.

662. THREE NUDE MALE FIGURES, SEEN FROM BEHIND, RAISING THEIR ARMS IN SUPPLICATION (6041)
392 × 258 mm. Broad pen and dark brown ink.
Old attribution in pencil on the drawing: 'Passarotti'. Presumably by Bartolommeo Passarotti.

663. BUST OF MINERVA (6038)
408 × 260 mm. Broad pen and brown ink.
Coll.: N. Lanière (Lugt 2885).
Inscribed in pencil on the drawing: 'del Passeroti'. Bodmer on the mount attributes it to the school, but the pen-work of the helmet seems to me characteristic of Bartolommeo himself.

664. *Recto:* STUDIES OF A L. FOOT AND THREE SEPARATE STUDIES OF THE TOES
Verso: THREE SIMILAR STUDIES OF A L. FOOT (0401)
310 × 275 mm. Broad pen and dark brown ink.
There can be little doubt that these are by Bartolommeo himself.

665. HEAD OF A DOG AND STUDY OF TWO DOGS LYING DOWN (1976)
224 × 154 mm. Pen and brown ink.
From the Carracci volumes, but the style of the penwork points to Bartolommeo Passarotti, as noted on the mount by H. Bodmer.

666. NUDE MALE FIGURE SEATED WITH HIS R. ARM RAISED ABOVE HIS HEAD; another figure, of which only the leg is finished, is to the R. (6040)
440 × 280 mm. Pen and brown ink over black chalk.
Inscribed in ink in an old hand in lower R. hand corner: 'del Passarotto'. Copy from two of the figures on the R. of St. Paul in Michelangelo's *Last Judgment* in the Sixtine Chapel. Attributed by Bodmer on the mount to the school. It seems to me however good enough to be by Bartolommeo.

Attributed to BARTOLOMMEO PASSAROTTI

667. MERCURY KILLING ARGUS with, in the background, on the R., Mercury charming Argus to sleep; above are Mercury and Jupiter, Jupiter possessing Io, and Juno in her car drawn by peacocks hurrying to the scene. (01249)
366 × 493 mm. Pen and brown ink, the outlines indented.
A.E.P. From the Carracci albums. The figure of Mercury is taken with slight modifications from that of Hercules in Caraglio's engraving of *Hercules and the Lernian Hydra* after Rosso (Bartsch XV, p. 85, 46). There is also a relation between this composition and that of a drawing in the Albertina (Catalogue VI, No. 45) with an old attribution to Lorenzo Sabbatini. This likewise represents incidents in the story of Io, the main one being Mercury charming Argus to sleep, is of approximately the same size (335 × 485 mm.)

FIG. 132 Cat. No. 674

FIG. 133 Cat. No. 675

and format, and shows the same relationship between incidents in the foreground and background. The two drawings cannot, however, be pendants—apart from the difference in technique—as some of the same incidents are reproduced in both. The style of the pen work in the Windsor drawing suggests Bartolommeo Passarotti, but it is not absolutely conclusive.

School of BARTOLOMMEO PASSAROTTI

668. NUDE MALE FIGURE WEARING A HELMET, CROUCHING, TURNED TO THE R. (6045)
415 × 335 mm. Pen and brown ink.
Inscribed in pencil on the drawing: 'del Passerotto'. It is apparently the copy of an almost identical drawing in the Albertina (Wickhoff, Scuola Romana 362: photo. Braun 7 as Bandinelli). Like No. 661, this sheet has an attribution in pencil on the mount to Ventura Passerotti.

669. HEAD OF A BEARDED MAN WEARING A FANTASTIC HEAD-DRESS (5145)
205 × 142 mm. Pen and brown ink.
A.E.P. The type and style of drawing undoubtedly points to Passarotti's school.

670. LIFE-SIZE STUDY OF A LEFT KNEE (2160)
324 × 220 mm. Pen and ink.
The drawing is probably, as suggested by H. Bodmer on the mount, of the school of Passarotti rather than by the master himself.

671. A BEARDED MAN SEATED, FACING TO THE FRONT (0390)
215 × 145 mm. Pen and brown ink.
The figure bears some resemblance to Amminadab in Michelangelo's lunette in the Sixtine Chapel. It is apparently by Bartolommeo Passarotti or his school, though it was formerly attributed to Bandinelli.

672. STUDIES OF SEVEN PUTTI SEATED ON CLOUDS OR ON BRACKETS (6042)
261 × 365 mm. Pen and brown ink.
Old inscription in ink in William Gibson's (?) hand: 'Bartolomeo Passerotti'. The drawing seems to be too mechanical for Bartolommeo and is probably, as suggested by Bodmer on the mount, of his school.

673. AN ANTIQUE SACRIFICE (0400)
265 × 205 mm. Pen and brown ink.
Coll.: N. Lanière (Lugt 2886).
A.E.P. Attribution in pencil on the drawing: 'M. A. Buona Rota'. The figure astride the animal in the foreground is indeed based on a similar figure in Michelangelo's *Sacrifice of Noah* on the ceiling of the Sixtine chapel, but the rest of the composition is more or less original. The attribution is a tentative one. The drawing is hardly by Bartolommeo, but may well be by one of his sons or scholars.

PASSIGNANO (DOMENICO CRESTI) (1558/60–1638)

674. ST. LAWRENCE, HOLDING THE MARTYR'S PALM ALOFT, SURROUNDED BY SIX SAINTS (*Figure* 132) (5980)
427 × 282 mm. Pen and brown ink and pink wash.

FIG. 134 Cat. No. 676

Inscribed in pencil on the drawing: 'del Passignano'. The saints represented are to the L. (standing), St. Francis of Assisi, St. Peter; to the R., St. Anthony Abbot (?), St. Philip (?); kneeling, a bishop (St. Loui ?) and St. Catherine of Alexandria.

675. THE WHEEL, ON WHICH ST. CATHERINE WAS TO HAVE BEEN BROKEN, DESTROYED BY AN ANGEL (*Figure* 133) (5981)
365 × 250 mm. Pen and brown ink and pink wash, corrected in places with white, squared in black chalk.
Inscribed in pencil on the drawing: 'Passignano'. According to Baldinucci (III, p. 439), Passignano painted a *Martyrdom of St. Catherine* for the Badia a Ripoli, Florence.

676. THE VIRGIN AND CHILD ENTHRONED WITH SAINTS (*Figure* 134) (5979)
340 × 245 mm. Pen and brown ink and pink wash, squared in black chalk.
Inscribed in pencil on the drawing: 'del Passignano'. The saints are: on the L., St. Clara and St. Francis of Assisi; on the R., St. Anthony of Padua and a bishop pouring water on a town, who has been identified by an annotator on the mount as St. Prosdocimus, first bishop of Padua, but there is no record in his legend of his having extinguished a fire as his action would seem to imply.
Nos. 674-676 described above were all attributed to Passignano at least as early as the XVIII century, and I have little doubt that the attributions are well-founded. They probably date from early in his career, when he was working with Federico Zuccaro, whose influence the drawings seem to me to show very strongly. An authenticated sheet in the British Museum (1912–2–14–1), which can be dated in 1598 or somewhat later, shows a style of drawing which is much more Venetian in character. I have not been able to find the record of any painting by Passignano for which Nos. 674 or 676 might have served.

FIG. 135 Cat. No. 679

Attributed to PASSIGNANO

677. MIRACLE OF ST. CATHERINE OF SIENA: Our Lord removes half the wafer from the altar where the priest is ministering and places it in the mouth of the saint; in the background the body of St. Catherine lying in state (?). (5086)
300 × 212 mm. Pen and ink and pink wash over black chalk; some heads drawn with the point of the brush in red; squared in red chalk.
A.E.P. The attribution rests on the similarity in style and technique to Nos. 674–676.

678. PROCESSION OF FIGURES, SOME IN ATTITUDES OF PRAYER, MOVING TO THE L. (5051)
128 × 342 mm. Pen and brown ink and brown wash over black chalk.
A.E.P. At the bottom to the L. is an illegible inscription. There is a striking resemblance in style between this and the authenticated drawing in the British Museum (1912–2–14–1) of the entry of Margaret of Austria into Ferrara in 1598.

679. A POPE GIVING THE BENEDICTION FROM A BALCONY (*Figure* 135) (5518)
222 × 166 mm. Pen and brown ink and blue wash on blue ground, heightened with white, squared in black chalk.
A.E.P. Though near in style to Federico Zuccaro, the handling and the odd colouring rather suggest Passignano. There is a striking parallel between the scene as here represented in the XVI century (the pope might be Sixtus V, 1585–90) and a modern photograph of Pius XVI blessing the crown from St. John Lateran on May 18, 1939.

680. THE LAST SUPPER, WITH ANGELS ON CLOUDS ABOVE (5982)
320 × 222 mm. Pen and ink and brown wash on green paper, heightened with white.
Old attribution, 'Del Passignani', on George III mount. I can see little connection between the style of this feeble drawing and those previously described. The general composition and the types are, however, quite like those of Passignano, and it may be his or a copy after him.

LUCA PENNI (d. 1556)

681. THE ENTOMBMENT (*Figure* 136) (0407)
322 × 413 mm. Finished drawing in pen and brown ink and grey wash.
Inscribed in a formal hand, almost contemporary, on the sarcophagus: 'L. Pennis'. The types and style of composition are exactly those of the engravings by Giorgio Ghisi (*Apollo and the Muses*, Bartsch XV, p. 411, 58, and the *Calumny of Apelles*, Bartsch 64) which are inscribed 'L. Pennis', as well as of the various engravings of the school of Fontainebleau believed, no doubt rightly, to be after him. The present drawing, although it is a formal and finished production (perhaps a *modello*) does not give the impression of being a copy and, within the limits of its rather unpleasant formula, is sensitive and expressive. There is a very similar composition of the *Entombment* engraved by Martin Rota as after Luca Penni (Bartsch XVI, p. 251, 11).

682. A GROUP OF MEN LOADING A CAMEL (5094)
294 × 387 mm. Pen and dark brown ink and red wash, the outlines indented.
A.E.P. Inscribed in pencil at the bottom to the L.: 'Primaticcio'. Engraved by the Master L.D. (Bartsch XVI, p. 331, 63), and again, in reverse, by an anonymous engraver of the School of Fontainebleau (Bartsch XVI, p. 412, 92). The inscription on the first of these engravings, 'Bol inventeur a Fontainebleau', implies that the subject was painted in the chateâu. The style and the types are so exactly those of No. 681 that the actual drawing may be ascribed with some confidence to Luca Penni in spite of this contemporary evidence in favour of Primaticcio. Another version is in the Uffizi (No. 1488F).

BALDASSARE PERUZZI (1481–1536)

683. DESIGN FOR AN ORGAN-CASE (*Plate* 66) (5495)
565 × 380 mm. Pen and brown ink and brown wash on cream-coloured paper, heightened with white.
George III 'Inventory A', p. 53, 14 [Peruzzi]: 'A most capital ornamented Architectural drawing for the Front of an Organ for a Church in his native City of Sienna'.
The purpose of the design is indicated by an inscription in the artist's hand in the space in the centre which would be occupied by the organ-pipes: 'E da notare che inquesta faccia vāno le cāne piccole delo organo & di laltra dove vāno le cāne grandi va levata via el collarino segnata · B. preterea sepo volendo tor via el fastigio overo quarto tondo socto ali satyri e qui dare la cornice drjcta ussando el fastigio sup(er)iore Vlterius se po levare luno e laltro fastigio e farlo a modo de arco triumphale.' 'It is to be noted that the small pipes of the organ are on this side and that, on the other, where the large pipes are, the frieze marked . B . is left out. Besides, if it is desired, the pediment or quarter-round underneath the satyrs can be removed and the cornice here left straight, using the upper pediment. Further both pediments can be removed and it can be made in the form of a triumphal arch.'
The organ is surmounted by five statues, the central one of which is Apollo and the other four presumably Muses. There are also, on a level with the quarter-round pediment, seated Muses and four female figures standing in niches below on either side. One other seated Muse and two other standing women in niches are to be seen in perspective on the left, decorating the side of the organ-case, the depth of which apparently corresponds with the space comprising the two pillars and the niches between them on the front. The 'altra faccia' with the big organ pipes referred to in the inscription is, I presume, the back, which would exactly correspond with the front except that the statues would be seen from behind. The number of seated figures above the frieze would then be six, and those in the niches below, twelve. Obviously some of these figures are intended to represent Muses (the seated ones, in front, for example), but it is difficult to make out which nine of this large number are Muses and for what the residue are intended.
In spite of the statement in 'Inventory A' the design is clearly for a secular organ. Its destination is indicated by the escutcheon of the Gonzagas in the upper pediment, and one of their devices in the quarter-round pediment below. This device, in a medallion supported by two *putti* with acanthus-leaf tails, is composed of a mountain, with a spiral road winding round it surmounted by an altar on which there is a fire burning (?) and the word FIDES. This 'impresa' was adopted by the Marquess Francesco II (d. 1519) and continued under his successor. According to Sir G. F. Hill, *A Corpus of Italian Medals*, London, 1930, p. 68, No. 271, the altar with the word FIDES (as well as the Greek inscription ΟΛΥΜΠΟΣ underneath) were added to the arms of Mantua (?) by Charles V in 1523 as a reward for the defence of Pavia against the French in 1522. It is not, however, clear to me whether any inference about the date of Peruzzi's design can be drawn from this 'impresa'.
According to Vasari (IV, pp. 596, 602), Peruzzi designed the organ-case in the Carmine at Siena, and the design of other church organs have been attributed to him.
There is apparently no record connecting Peruzzi with the Court of Mantua, or Isabella Gonzaga, of whom it is natural to think as a noted patroness both of music and of the fine arts. Peruzzi might well have met her in Rome in 1514 when Bibbiena's *Calandra* (the scenery of which, much praised by Vasari, was his work) was performed at the command of Leo X in her honour, or again in 1525–7 when she was resident in Rome. It is, however, tempting to connect this drawing with an alabaster organ described in a letter of 1522 from Baldassare Castiglione in Rome to the Marchioness in Mantua. This Castiglione bought for 600 ducats on her behalf: it was sent to Mantua and placed in the Studio of the Grotta. The letter is referred to in Julia Cartwright, *Isabella d'Este*, London, 1903, p. 207, but I have not been able to consult the original. This alabaster organ was regarded as something of a marvel, and was celebrated in a set of Italian elegiacs by Celio Calcagnini (printed in *Deliciae CC Italorum Poetarum*, 1608, Vol. I, p. 527).

FIG. 136 Cat. No. 681

684. DESIGN FOR THE LEAF OF A DOUBLE DOOR WITH SCENES FROM THE LIVES OF THE VIRGIN AND OF JOSEPH (*Figure* 137) (5492)
500 × 144 mm. Fine pen and brown ink and brown wash over black chalk, washed in brown; unfinished.
George III 'Inventory A', p. 53, 11 [Peruzzi].
The attribution to Peruzzi is certainly correct. The door is divided into three main rectangular spaces, in the top one of which the *Death of the Virgin* is represented. In the centre is the *Visitation.* The scene in the bottom space is only lightly sketched in in black chalk. It may be intended for *Christ disputing with the Doctors.* Above the first scene is a narrow band with *Joseph being sold to the Ishmaelites*; below it another with *Joseph in Prison* and *Joseph and Potiphar's Wife.* There is a space for another such scene below the lowest panel, but this has not been filled in. The drawing is obviously the design for the bronze doors of some important church or cathedral. The scenes represented suggest that this church may have been dedicated to

FIG. 137 Cat. No. 684

the Virgin, as was the case with the Duomo at Siena, and Peruzzi is recorded to have been paid 250 lire and 5 soldi in 1525 'sonno per le sue fadighe di avere lui fatto più disegni delle porti s'ànno a fare di bronzo e per altri designi' for the cathedral. It is tempting to connect the present drawing with this work, but this is no more than a hypothesis. The bronze doors in question do not seem to have been carried out.

685. STUDY FOR A STANDING STATUE OF JUPITER, HOLDING THE THUNDERBOLT (*Plate* 67) (0745)
268 × 165 mm. Pen and light brown ink and brown wash, over black chalk.
George III 'Inventory A', p. 53, 8 [Peruzzi].
Coll.: Sir Peter Lely (Lugt 2092); I. P. Zoomer (Lugt 1511).
Inscribed on the *recto* at the bottom to the R.: 'Di Baldas . . .' and on the *verso*: 'di Baldassare da Siena', both times in ink in a hand (the same ?) of the XVII (?) century. There can be no doubt about the correctness of this attribution. The elongated and rather mannered form suggests a late date.

BERNARDO POCCETTI (BARBATELLI) (1548–1612)

686. TWO MEN WORKING ON THE CROSS (0140)
351 × 238 mm. Red chalk.
Inscribed in ink, 'Del Pozzi,' which is perhaps a misreading of an inscription written on the *verso*, which can be seen from the front and almost certainly reads 'Del B. Poccetti'. I cannot find any painting of *Christ nailed to the Cross* by Poccetti reproduced for which the drawing could have served as a study, but its style is clearly his.

687. HALF-LENGTH STUDY OF A YOUNG MAN WITH HIS HANDS CROSSED ON HIS CHEST, and separate study of the hands. (0368)
210 × 167 mm. Red and black chalk.
A.E.P. Apparently the study for a shepherd in an *Adoration*. A separate study of the hands in much the same position in the Uffizi (Santarelli, No. 1630) is attributed, no doubt rightly, to Poccetti.

Attributed to BERNARDINO POCCETTI

688. THE ISRAELITES ON THEIR WANDERINGS (?) (5195)
150 × 205 mm. (torn irregularly at the top and made up). Pen and brown ink and brown wash over black chalk.
A.E.P. The grouping of the figures and the composition are like Poccetti's as well as the attempt at historical accuracy in the costumes. It shows a certain similarity in style to Allori and is probably rather early in date.

689. DESIGN FOR THE DECORATION OF A WALL, WITH TWO PROPHETS REPRESENTED UNDER ARCHES (5984)
166 × 418 mm. Pen and brown ink and watercolour with some gold, over black chalk.
F.A. The attribution of this drawing to Poccetti seems a reasonable though not a certain one. It bears an old partly effaced attribution to Perino del Vaga.

A copy after Andrea del Sarto, attributed to Poccetti, is catalogued below (No. 912).

POLIDORO DA CARAVAGGIO (1496/1500–1543)

690. A PAINTING OF THE VIRGIN AND CHILD SUPPORTED IN THE AIR BY FOUR ANGELS; below, souls in purgatory with, on the L., St. Peter (?) and on the R., St. Andrew, who intercedes for them; the whole surrounded by a frame with ornamental columns. (*Figure* 138) (0383)

FIG. 138 Cat. No. 690

260 × 206 mm. Pen and brown ink and brown wash with some *pentimenti* in Chinese white. Folded and torn in the centre and on the L.

A.E.P. The attribution to Polidoro rests on the close resemblance in style and types to those of drawings belonging to the artist's Neapolitan or Sicilian period (1528–1543), particularly to drawings in the British Museum (1918 6 15–2 and 1936–10–10–3) and in the sketch-book in the Kunstgewerbe Museum, Berlin (published by B. Kassirer in Berlin Jahrbuch XLI (1920), p. 344 ff.).

What may possibly be a design by Polidoro for the same altar-piece is in the Albertina (Albertina Cat., III, No. 484, as Florentine, second half of the XVI century). This represents souls in purgatory interceding directly, without St. Peter and St. Andrew, to the Virgin, who is, however, painted on the panel and not represented by an ancient and no doubt miraculous picture as in the Windsor drawing. The Vienna drawing has the same bridge and castle in the background and a similar frame with decorated columns.

691. CHRIST CARRIED TO THE TOMB (*Figure* 139) (5433)
244 × 325 mm. Red chalk, heightened and touched up or repaired with white or pink, the outlines pricked.

F.A. A comparison of this with the red chalk drawings by Polidoro in the Albertina (Albertina Cat., III, Nos. 172–187) seem to me to render this attribution quite conclusive. A certain difference in the general effect is due to the heightening with white, all of which may well be later. The composition shows some resemblance to that of the drawing of the *Entombment* in the Albertina (Albertina Cat., III, No. 169), clearly a copy, but no doubt reproducing a composition of Polidoro's. The style may also be compared with that of the drawing in the Louvre of the same subject reproduced by Herman Voss (*Spätrenaissance*, Vol. I, Fig. 11), the outlines of which are pricked in the same way.

692. THE BETRAYAL (*Plate* 70) (050)
212 × 263 mm. Drawn with the point of the brush and washed with grey on blue surface, heightened with white.
Coll.: Paul Sandby (Lugt 2112); Sir T. Lawrence (Lugt 2445); W. Mayor (Lugt 2799: catalogue 1874, No. 63).
Lit.: Voss, *Spätrenaissance*, Vol. I, p. 76 note; E. Kris *Meister und Meisterwerke der Steinschneidekunst*, Vienna, 1929, p. 50 (pl. 63, No. 164).
Engraved in facsimile by C. M. Metz, when in Sandby's collection, as Garofalo (Weigel 2697).
Photo.: Braun 140 (as Garofalo).
Inscribed in ink in a hand of the XVIII or XIX century: 'Benevenuto Garofalo'.

F.A. There can be no question that the old attribution to Garofalo is incorrect. The drawing shows none of this painter's mannerisms. Voss (loc. cit.) attributed it to Perino del Vaga and connected it with a number of other oval drawings of the sort, which are designs for crystal plaques. Nevertheless the style of this drawing with its squat, energetic figures is unmistakably Polidoro's, not Perino's.

It served as the design for an oval crystal plaque engraved by Valerio Belli and now in the Biblioteca Vaticana. This and two corresponding ovals of the *Deposition* and *Christ carrying the Cross* are associated with an engraved crystal cross in the same collection and were, it is thought, originally mounted with this. Valerio Belli was paid 1111 gold ducats for this cross in 1525 (Vasari, V, p. 380, Note 1), and the present drawing must date from a year or two before. Kris (op. cit.) dated the plaques much later on the ground that the Windsor drawing, which he accepts as Perino's, resembles in style drawings by that artist for the Farnese casket ovals of about 1544. He admits the connection between the three Vatican ovals and the Vatican cross, but, as I understand him, denies that the payment of 1525 is for this cross. Zorzi in L'Arte XXIII (1920), p. 184, accepts the dating of 1525 for the cross, and I can see no reason for calling it in question. The Windsor drawing, if by Polidoro, would almost certainly date from before his departure from Rome soon after the sack in 1527.

693A. HEAD OF A BEARDED MAN TURNED TO THE L. (5434)
105 × 78 mm. Red chalk, stained with oil.
Coll.: J. D. Lempereur (Lugt 1740).
The attribution is presumably an ancient one and seems perfectly reasonable. The handling of the red chalk is not dissimilar from that in the series of drawings, presumably from a sketch-book, in the Albertina (Albertina Cat., III, Nos. 172–187) and in the Louvre, which are certainly by Polidoro. The type of head is quite in his manner.

693B. GROUP OF FIGURES: a priest accompanied by an acolyte on the L., three men in voluminous hooded mantles, and other figures. (*Plate* 69) (2349)
205 × 259 mm. Red chalk.
George III 'Inventory A', p. 77, XI.
Inscribed in the 'deceptive' hand 'polidoro', an attribution which, for once, is obviously correct. It appears to be connected in subject, as it certainly is in style (though not in technique) with a drawing in the Louvre (No. 6974) of a priest at the altar with a crowd of worshippers, which was engraved in Crozat's work, No. 71. There is also a close stylistic connection between the Windsor drawing and the sheets of the red chalk sketch-book in the Louvre and in the Albertina.

FIG. 139 Cat. No. 691

FIG. 140 Cat. No. 695

Attributed to POLIDORO DA CARAVAGGIO

694. SCENE FROM ROMAN HISTORY (?) (*Figure* 141) (5438)
215 × 140 mm. Pen and brown ink and point of the brush on blue paper, heightened with white.
The composition corresponds with that painted between the windows, the third from the L., on the façade of the Palazzo Milesi, Via della Maschera d'Oro. The subject is the pendant to another unidentified scene in which a warrior offers his sword to a priest.
The question remains whether this is an original design by Polidoro for this decoration or a particularly intelligent copy by some artist of talent. Though I know of no quite analogous drawing certainly by Polidoro, it does not seem incompatible with drawings by him in a different technique. It is better to give it the benefit of the doubt. If by Polidoro it is of some interest as one of the few drawings, known to me at any rate, which is definitely connected with his work on Roman façades.

695. FRIEZE WITH THE SIBYL POINTING OUT TO THE KNEELING AUGUSTUS THE VISION OF THE VIRGIN AND CHILD (*Figure* 140) (5473)
168 × 147 mm. Pen and brown ink and brown wash on blue paper, heightened with white.
A.E.P. The drawing was attributed for some obscure reason to the sculptor, Nanni di Baccio Bigio (d. 1568). The composition is reminiscent of the subjects painted in chiaroscuro under the windows of the *Loggie* (see Perino del Vaga, Nos. 973, 990 ff.), but it does not occur there. The style of composition is unmistakably that of Polidoro, and it may well be by the same hand as No. 694.

696. DESIGN FOR THE DECORATION OF AN APSE with above, God the Father in a glory of angels and, below, St. Peter receiving the keys in the presence of the apostles. (6324)
229 × 350 mm. Pen and brown ink and brown wash over black chalk, much rubbed and faded.
P.M.R.P. The generally Raphaelesque design points to the period about 1520–30, and the types of the individual figures suggest Polidoro da Caravaggio, but the state of the drawing, which is very rubbed and perhaps partially re-drawn, make any attribution doubtful.

697. ST. PAUL STANDING FACING TO THE FRONT, his L. arm resting on the sword, his R. holding a book; a larger study of the head to the R. (0286)
170 × 90 mm. Pen and brown ink.
P.M.R.P. Attached to the back of the mount is an old label inscribed 'Perino del Vaga', but it shows little connection with his style, and is much nearer to Polidoro da Caravaggio.

Copies after POLIDORO DA CARAVAGGIO

These are nearly all copied from façades of houses in Rome painted by Polidoro and/or Maturino. Those which I have been able to identify as from houses described by Vasari or by other authors I have arranged in alphabetical order of the name of the house or street. Those of which the originals are unknown to me are grouped together at the end.

BUFALÒ, Giardino del

698. WOMAN WALKING TO THE R., GATHERING FRUIT FROM A TREE (5486)
268 × 151 mm. (top corners cut, bottom R. corner torn, and all three made up) Pen and brown ink and brown wash on blue paper, heightened with white.
From the figure of one of the Hesperides gathering fruit in the frieze of *Perseus changing Atlas into a Mountain* and the *Garden of the Hesperides* painted in the Giardino del Bufalò and engraved in reverse by Cherubino Alberti (Bartsch XVII, p. 85, 108, 109).

FIG. 141 Cat. No. 694

GADDI, Palazzo de'

699. PART OF A FRIEZE WITH A NAVAL BATTLE (5481)
155 × 417 mm. Pen and brown ink and brown wash (stained with oil).
Copy of the later XVI century, of part of a frieze painted on the façade of the Palazzo de' Gaddi, now Camuccini, in the Via della Maschera d'Oro, opposite the Palazzo Milesi. The frieze was engraved by Pietro Santi Bartoli in eight sheets.

700. PART OF A FRIEZE WITH A NAVAL BATTLE (5482)
134 × 420 mm. Pen and brown ink and brown wash.
Inscribed in pencil bottom R.: 'Polidoro'. Copy, of the XVI century, of part of the frieze on the Palazzo de' Gaddi (see above, No. 699).

701. PART OF A FRIEZE WITH A NAVAL BATTLE (5483)
126 × 419 mm. Pen and brown ink and brown wash.
Inscribed in pencil, bottom R.: 'Polidoro'. Copy, of the XVI century, of part of the frieze on the Palazzo de' Gaddi (see above, Nos. 699 and 700).

MONTECAVALLO, House in (near S. Agata)

702. HORATIUS COCLES DEFENDING THE BRIDGE (5470)
232 × 383 mm. Pen and brown ink and brown wash and black chalk on blue paper, heightened with white; damaged by damp, especially in the lower half.
This is presumably copied from one of the subjects described by Vasari (V, p. 146): 'Lavorarono [Polidoro and Maturino] in Montecavallo, vicino a Sant' Agata, una facciata . . . e nel' altra facciata doppo il cantone . . . la terribilissima pugna d'Orazio, che mentre solo fra mille spade difende la bocca del ponte, ha dietro a sè molte figure bellisime, che in diverse attitudini con grandissima sollecitudine co' piccioni tagliano il ponte'. The style of the copy, with its sharp contrast of light and shade, recalls Salviati's.

703. CAMILLUS ABOUT TO ADD HIS SWORD TO THE TRIBUTE MONEY PAID BY THE ROMANS TO THE VICTORIOUS GAULS UNDER BRENNUS (5476)
198 × 225 mm. Pen and brown ink and brown wash on blue paper, heightened with white.
Inscribed in pencil: 'Polidoro'. Copied from part of a chiaroscuro, the whole of which is engraved in reverse by P. Saenredam (Bartsch III, p. 230, 32). It was another of the subjects painted on the house in Montecavallo, near Sant' Agata, according to Milanesi in a note to his edition of Vasari (V, p. 146). The style of the copy points to the middle of the century, and it is perhaps by Girolamo da Carpi.

704. THE VESTAL TUCCIA CARRYING WATER IN A SIEVE (5489)
185 × 193 mm. Pen and ink and brown wash.
The whole composition of which this forms a part is represented in a drawing in the British Museum (Sloane 5214–260). A drawing of what appears to be the pendant to this, the Vestal Claudia hauling the ship which bears the statue of Cybele, is in the Uffizi (photo. Braun 477 as Giulio Romano). Vasari (V, p. 146) records that Polidoro and Maturino painted at Montecavallo near S. Agata a façade with many histories, among them 'come quando Tuzia vestale porta del Tevere al tempio l'acqua nel crivello, e quando Claudia tira la nave con la cintura', and it seems reasonable to connect the drawings with this façade, which also included the subjects of Horatius Codes and Camillus (Nos. 702, 703). In spite of its look of spontaneity I do not think this is an original study but a sketch from the fresco by Girolamo da Carpi. The style may be compared with that of another copy, anciently and certainly rightly given to Girolamo da Carpi, from part of the Niobe frieze, which is in the British Museum (Fawkener 5212–77).

MILESI, Palazzo, Via della Maschera d'Oro

705. TWO ALLEGORICAL FEMALE FIGURES, ONE WITH A HORN OF PLENTY, THE OTHER WITH A STAFF (5101)
208 × 192 mm. Pen and brown ink and brown wash on green paper, heightened with white.
Copy from two figures on the façade of the Palazzo Milesi. Both figures are from the third storey, that on the R. is on the extreme L., and that on the L. fourth from the L. They can be seen in the engraving of the whole façade in E. Maccari, *Graffiti e Chiaroscuri*, Rome [1876], tav. 37.

706. SCENE FROM ROMAN HISTORY (?) (5440)
400 × 264 mm. Pen and brown ink and brown wash over black chalk on blue paper, heightened with white.
Copy from the same subject on the façade of the Palazzo Milesi, for which No. 694 may be the original study.

707. *Recto:* PORTIONS OF FRIEZES WITH THE RAPE OF THE SABINES ON THE L., and, on the R., a procession of men, women and children fleeing to the R. (5484)
Verso: SATURN CASTRATING URANUS, a Roman trophy between two vases and a draped figure.
156 × 416 mm. Pen and brown ink and brown wash on blue paper, heightened with white.
Between the two scenes on the *recto* the artist has written 'uanno insieme' (these go together), and on the *verso* near the draped figure: 'questo seguita l'altra carta' (the other sheet follows this). *The Rape of the Sabines* on the *recto* and *Saturn Castrating Uranus* on the *verso* are copied from the scenes painted side by side above the first floor windows of the Palazzo Milesi, but according to the engraving by Cherubino Alberti (Bartsch XVII, p. 68, 112) the *Rape of the Sabines* continued to the R. beyond the herm of Pan. The procession of men, women and children to the R. on the *recto* is from a quite different frieze of the *Rape of the Sabine Women*, that on the façade of the Palazzo Ricci-Parracciani, still existing in the Via Giulia, which is engraved in reverse by Cherubino Alberti (Bartsch XVII, p. 109, 159). The inscription 'vanno insieme' must presumably refer to the Saturn on the *verso* and the L. hand portion of the *recto*, or possibly to another sheet. The two vases (which were engraved separately by Cherubino Alberti, Bartsch 161 and 162) and the trophy also formed part of the decoration of the Palazzo Milesi (there is also a drawing of them in the Louvre, repr. H. de Chennevières, *Les Dessins du Louvre*, Paris, 1882) as well as the draped figure.

708. A GENERAL SEATED ON A THRONE, BEFORE WHOM KNEELS A SUPPLIANT (5478)
161 × 214 mm. Pen and ink and brown wash over black chalk on blue paper, heightened with white.
Copy from the fifth scene from the L. on the frieze above the first floor windows of the Palazzo Milesi. The subject is described as the *Clemency of Scipio.*

709. A GENERAL SEATED ON A THRONE, BEFORE WHOM KNEELS A SUPPLIANT; behind him stand a young woman and an older one; on the R. a warrior with his arms tied behind his back is being led away. (5479)
166 × 283 mm. Pen and brown ink and brown wash on brown ground heightened with white.
Inscribed in ink in an old hand 'di Polidor'. Copy from the fifth scene from the L. and part of the sixth scene on the frieze above the first floor windows of the Palazzo Milesi.

710. PORTION OF A FRIEZE WITH FIGURES KNEELING TO THE L. HOLDING BOOKS; a figure standing to the R. crowns a youth with a wreath. (5442)
270 × 230 mm. Pen and brown ink and brown wash on brown paper, heightened with white; torn and damaged particularly on the R.
The whole composition is preserved in two drawings in the

Uffizi, etched in facsimile by Mulinari (Weigel 6074, 6175). One of these drawings is also reproduced in Rassegna d'Arte V (1905), p. 99. The subject, generally interpreted as Numa Pompilius giving laws to the Romans, was one of the six scenes above the first floor windows on the façade of the Palazzo Milesi.

711–715: FRIEZE WITH THE STORY OF NIOBE AND HER CHILDREN (On five sheets, 01260–01264)
Pen and brown ink and brown wash over black chalk.

711. Niobe is seated on the L. trying to protect one daughter; the six others are fleeing to the L., pursued by Diana, who stands on clouds and aims an arrow; to the R., portions of four horses and one of Niobe's sons with an arrow through his back. (01260)
262 × 615 mm.

712. On the L. are portions of four horses, two of which are mounted by sons of Niobe, each pierced with an arrow; further to the R. is Apollo, who has just discharged an arrow; separated from him by rocks surmounted by trees Apollo and Diana are seen seated side by side; to them Latona advances from the R. (01261)
262 × 736 mm.

713. The people worshipping Latona: the statue of the goddess is raised on a decorated altar; the people, men or women, kneel or stand at either side or on a platform of two steps. (01262)
262 × 760 mm.

714. On the L. stands a group of worshippers (belonging to No. 713); to the R. of them is a youth holding a horse; further to the R. Niobe, surrounded by women attendants, stands; worshippers approach from the R. and bring her offerings. (01263)
262 × 740 mm.

715. Worshippers of Niobe (continued from No. 714); they approach from the R., and include a man leading a horse on which a woman is mounted, bringing offerings, doves, a ram, vases, etc.; on the R. is a recumbent female figure with a cornucopia. (01264)
262 × 567 mm.

The five drawings reproduce the famous frieze painted in monochrome by Polidoro on the façade of the Palazzo Milesi. It is however in reverse to the fresco, and in this respect corresponds with the engraving by Pieter Saenredam from a drawing by H. Goltzius (Bartsch III, p. 231, 33). It is on a slightly larger scale than this, but it may be copied from it, though I should have supposed it rather earlier in date. Numerous copies of this frieze exist, including those described below.

716–717. FRIEZE OF THE STORY OF NIOBE AND HER CHILDREN, ON TWO SHEETS (01258, 01259)
Pen and brown ink and brown wash, heightened with white.

716. The R. hand portion of the frieze with Apollo shooting at the sons, and Diana at the daughters of Niobe. (01258)
195 × 670 mm.

717. Part of the central portion of the frieze with the people worshipping Latona on the L. and Latona before Apollo and Diana on the R. (01259)
187 × 600 mm.

Early copies, certainly of the XVI century, of parts of the frieze of Niobe on the façade of the Palazzo Milesi. These copies, unlike those previously described, are in the same direction as the fresco and are no doubt copied directly from it.

718. PART OF THE FRIEZE WITH THE STORY OF NIOBE AND HER CHILDREN (0206)
250 × 376 mm. Pen and brown ink and grey wash over black chalk on light brown paper, heightened with white (oxidised).
Copy of the portion of the Niobe frieze comprising the sons of Niobe and, to the R., Diana shooting (in the same direction as the fresco). The style of the copy recalls Pellegrino Tibaldi. On an old label attached to the bottom is the name 'Polidoro' and the figures $\frac{\text{'}5 \cdot 3\text{'}}{1 \cdot 4}$. These in the notation adopted by W. Gibson mean a valuation of 15 shillings, or alternatively £1.

719. *Recto:* PART OF THE FRIEZE WITH THE STORY OF NIOBE AND HER CHILDREN (041)
180 × 270 mm. Pen and brown ink and brown wash.
Verso: DRAPERY OF AN ANTIQUE FEMALE STATUE
Pen and brown ink (faded and damaged).
Copy, of the XVI century, of a portion of the Niobe frieze comprising the worshippers to the L. of the statue of Latona in the centre.

720. PART OF THE FRIEZE WITH THE STORY OF NIOBE AND HER CHILDREN (0403)
232 × 238 mm. Pen and brown ink and brown wash, heightened with white.
Copy, of the XVI century, of the L. hand portion, with Niobe and her attendants receiving offerings.

721. PART OF THE FRIEZE WITH THE STORY OF NIOBE AND HER CHILDREN (0404)
206 × 258 mm. Black chalk and brown wash, heightened with white; considerably damaged.
A copy, perhaps of the XVII century, of a portion towards the L. of the frieze, in which the people are bringing offerings to Niobe. It is contiguous to the portion copied in No. 720, but by a different hand and on a smaller scale.

722. PART OF THE FRIEZE WITH THE STORY OF NIOBE AND HER CHILDREN (0405)
218 × 352 mm. Pen and brown ink and brown wash, heightened with white, squared in black chalk.
A feeble copy, of the XVII century (?), of the portion of the frieze on the L. in which the people bring offerings to Niobe.

723–732. A SERIES OF TEN VASES (5443–5452)
Pen and brown ink and brown wash over black chalk, heightened with white.
Copied from the etchings by Cherubino Alberti from vases on the façade of the Palazzo Milesi (Bartsch XVII, p. 110, 161–170).

723. No. 9 in the above series. (5443)
246 × 186 mm.

724. No. 10 in same series. (5444)
246 × 184 mm.

725. No. 6 in same series. (5445)
248 × 183 mm.

726. No. 8 in same series. (5446)
248 × 186 mm.

727. No. 5 in same series. (5447)
250 × 180 mm.

728. No. 4 in same series. (5448)
233 × 184 mm.

729. No. 7 in same series. (5449)
257 × 172 mm.

730. No. 1 in same series. (5450)
267 × 170 mm.

731. No. 3 in same series. (5451)
251 × 187 mm.

732. No. 2 in same series. (5452)
255 × 184 mm.

733. *Recto:* A STUDY OF TWO VASES (5455)
222 × 188 mm. Pen and brown ink and brown wash over black chalk.

Verso: TWO MORE VASES, FOLIAGE, AND STUDIES OF A STANDING FIGURE
Pen and brown ink and brown wash and red and black chalk.

Long inscription in an old hand on *verso*, with the date 7th of November, 1592.

The two vases on the *recto* correspond with Nos. 3 and 5 in the series of etchings by Cherubino Alberti after Polidoro (Bartsch XVII, p. 110, 161–170).

Those on the *verso* are in a similar style but do not actually correspond with any of the etchings.

734. THREE VASES (5454)
175 × 245 mm. Pen and brown ink and brown wash.

Copied from Nos. 1, 2, and 3 in the series of etchings of vases by Cherubino Alberti after Polidoro (Bartsch XVII, p. 110, 161-170).

Copies after POLIDORO; originals unknown

735. THE DELUGE (0438)
259 × 390 mm. Pen and brown ink and brown wash on green paper, heightened with white.

P.M.R.P. The present drawing is an exact repetition of one in the Louvre (No. 6065) with an old attribution to 'Polidor'. The composition was engraved by Battista Franco (Bartsch XVI, p. 155, 3), who did not however name the artist after whom he was engraving. His copy is also in the Louvre (No. 4917). The style of the drawing and the types leave no doubt that the composition is in fact Polidoro's, though there seems to be no record of where it was painted, if it was in fact carried out as a fresco or a panel.

On the *verso* are the figures '280', a word 'Troppo?' and the initials (of a collector ?) 'GAF' (?).

736. SOLDIERS ARRESTING AN ELDERLY MAN AND TAKING HIM TO PRISON (5472)
292 × 385 mm. Pen and ink and brown wash on blue paper, heightened with white; the outlines indented.

The subject might be St. Peter taken to prison though, if so, the saint is represented without a halo. I can find no other copy of this frieze except that described below, No. 737, but there can be no doubt that it is after a composition by Polidoro.

737. SOLDIERS ARRESTING AN ELDERLY MAN AND TAKING HIM TO PRISON (5469)
266 × 407 mm. Pen and brown ink and brown wash on the blue paper, heightened with white.

Copy from the same subject as No. 736 on a larger scale, and cut on the R. and at the top. The style of the copy recalls that of Lattanzio Gambara.

738. ISAAC TAKING LEAVE OF HIS MOTHER (5437)
247 × 343 mm. Pen and black ink and grey wash on paper coloured pink.

There is another version of this drawing, which was formerly in the Albertina (Joseph Meder, *Handzeichnungen alter Meister aus der Albertina*, Neue Folge, Vienna, 1922, pl. 7). It is apparently the same drawing as that engraved by M. C. Prestel when in the Praun Collection (Weigel 6099). Another copy is in the British Museum (Sloane 5226–132). I do not think the Windsor drawing was copied from that in Vienna, but more probably from the façade on which the scene was no doubt painted.

739. MUCIUS SCAEVOLA IN THE PRESENCE OF LARS PORSENNA PLACING HIS R. HAND WITH THE DAGGER IN THE FLAME (5441)
330 × 207 mm. Pen and brown ink and brown wash, heightened occasionally with white, which has oxidized.

Perhaps copied from the subject painted, according to Vasari, on the side of a house on Montecavallo near Sant' Agata, together with the Horatius Cocles described above, No. 702. Vasari however describes other 'istorie' of Mucius Scaevola and Horatius 'nella Casa che comperō la Signora Gostanza sotto Corte Savella'. The copy is an indifferent one perhaps dating from the XVI century.

740. MEDEA, AFTER SLAYING HER CHILDREN, ESCAPING IN A CHARIOT DRAWN BY DRAGONS (5485)
197 × 285 mm. Pen and brown ink and brown wash over black chalk.

Coll.: N. Lanière (Lugt 2886).

Inscribed in ink in the bottom R. hand corner in an old hand (that of Lanière ?), 'Pollidoro'. The subject is adapted from that represented on various antique sarcophagi (for a copy from one of these see No. 1139 below). The style of the present drawing confirms the connection with Polidoro suggested by the old attribution, but it is obviously nothing more than a copy.

GIOVANNI ANTONIO DA PORDENONE
(About 1484–1539)

Lit.: Giuseppe Fiocco, *Giovanni Antonio Pordenone*, Udine, 1939 (quoted as Fiocco).

741. ST. AUGUSTINE SURROUNDED BY CHILD ANGELS (*Plate* 163) (5458)
246 × 194 mm. Drawn with the point of the brush on blue-green paper, heightened with white.

Lit.: Hadeln, *Hochrenaissance*, p. 37 (pl. 46); Fiocco, p. 155 (pl. 148); Tietzes, No. 1361.

The drawing shows an unmistakable resemblance in general, including the architectural background, to the fresco of

St. Augustine in the church of the Madonna di Campagna, Piacenza, painted in 1529 (Fiocco, pl. 149). The differences from the fresco are, however, so considerable that they have led the Tietzes to suggest that the drawing, which is quite elaborately finished, may have been prepared for a different representation of one of the Fathers of the Church.

742. THREE PROPHETS AND A SIBYL (*Plate* 164) (6670)
510 × 320 mm. Pen and ink and wash on faded blue paper, heightened with white, the upper part silhouetted.
A.E.P. Inscribed in pencil on the drawing 'Pordenone'. The figures correspond with those in one of the eight segments of the cupola of the church of the Madonna di Campagna at Piacenza (Fiocco, pl. 166: the segment is the central one on the L. hand side looking at the illustration). The drawing is very considerably damaged but of good quality and quite in Pordenone's style, so that I see no particular reason for condemning it as a copy. It is all the more valuable as, to judge from Fiocco's illustration, the fresco itself has suffered seriously. Pordenone was engaged on the work in S. Maria di Campagna at some time between March 11, 1531, and December 31, 1536.

743. THE ANNUNCIATION (*Figure* 142) (6658)
389 × 250 mm. Black chalk on blue-green paper, squared in black chalk, and heightened with white.

FIG. 142 Cat. No. 743

Lit.: Hadeln, *Hochrenaissance*, p. 38 (pl. 53); Fiocco, p. 155 (pl. 186); Tietzes, No. 1362.
Study for the picture over the altar in Sta. Maria degli Angeli, Murano, which was, according to Ridolfi, painted about 1537. There are considerable differences in detail between the drawing and the painting.

After PORDENONE

744. THE ADORATION OF THE MAGI (6659)
156 × 288 mm. (much cut down). Drawn with the point of the brush on blue paper, heightened with white.
Coll.: Sir P. Lely (Lugt 2092).
Lit.: Hadeln, *Hochrenaissance*, p. 37 (pl. 45); Fiocco, p. 152; Tietzes, A.1363.
Inscribed in ink on a piece of paper stuck on to the L. hand bottom corner: 'Pordenone f 1520'.
The drawing has nothing to do with the fresco of 1520 in the Duomo of Treviso, with which, no doubt, the writer of the inscription associated it. This was pointed out by Hadeln and by Fiocco, whose conclusions were accepted by the Tietzes. They reject the attribution to Pordenone: 'At the best a poor copy'. It is not as bad as that, but nevertheless probably a copy.

745. TWO EVANGELISTS (6660)
240 × 166 mm. Top corners cut. Red chalk on blue paper, heightened with white.
Lit.: Hadeln, *Hochrenaissance*, p. 38 (pl. 31); Fiocco, p. 152 (pl. 204); Tietzes, No. 29.
The drawing corresponds with the fresco in the parish church at Lestans, painted by Pordenone's pupil, Pomponio Amalteo (Fiocco, pl. 203). Fiocco, followed by the Tietzes, gives the drawing to Amalteo. This seems to me illogical. The frescoes have every appearance of having been designed by Pordenone. A drawing corresponding with them is likely to be either (1) Pordenone's original sketch, or (2) a copy from Pordenone's original drawing, conceivably by Pomponio Amalteo, or (3) a copy from the fresco by some later artist. This drawing, and the two next to be catalogued, seem undoubtedly to be copies, but I can see no particular reason why they should be by Amalteo, whose style, as shown in the Pierpont Morgan drawing attributed to him (Tietzes, No. 23) is not particularly similar. Nor is the (signed ?) drawing illustrated in de Vries Catalogue, 1929, pl. I, which conforms better to the conception of Amalteo's style I should have formed, particularly like either.

746. THE EVANGELIST ST. LUKE (6662)
273 × 183 mm. Red chalk on blue paper, heightened with white.
Lit.: Hadeln, *Hochrenaissance*, p. 38 (pl. 30); Fiocco, p. 152 (pl. 205); Tietzes, No. 31.
Inscribed in top R. corner: 'de man del Pordenon', and in lower L. 'L. S.'. Corresponds with the figure (immediately to the R. of that just discussed) in the fresco at Lestans (Fiocco, pl. 203).

747. GROUP OF ANGELS WITH MUSICAL INSTRUMENTS (6661)
265 × 185 mm. Red chalk on blue paper, heightened with white.
Lit.: Hadeln *Hochrenaissance*, p. 38 (pl. 32); Fiocco, p. 152 (pl. 206); Tietzes, No. 30.
Inscribed in top L. corner: 'de man del Pordenon'.
Corresponds with part of one of the frescoes on the vaulting at Lestans (Fiocco, pl. 203).

FIG. 143 Cat. No. 749

748. THE ADORATION OF THE MAGI (4775)
260 × 398 mm. Pen and brown ink outline over black chalk.
A.E.P. The drawing is copied from the largely destroyed fresco of the subject in the church at Travesio, a fragment of which is illustrated by Fiocco, pl. 58, and has a certain interest as reproducing the whole composition of this fresco.

Attributed to PORDENONE

749. THE CONVERSION OF ST. PAUL (*Figure* 143) (6668)
307 × 444 mm. (top corners cut, bottom R. corner torn and made up). Red chalk (rubbed and considerably injured by damp).
A.E.P. Inscribed in ink at the bottom to the L. in a hand of the XIX century: 'Tiziano'. The attribution was perhaps suggested by a supposed connection between the drawing and one of the two woodcuts of the subject after Titian (ill. Print Collector's Quarterly, XXV (1938), p. 354 and p. 476). It does in fact show a vague resemblance in composition to the latter, but the connection with Pordenone is much closer. The horseman on the R. occurs in almost identical form in the same position in a composition of the *Conversion of St. Paul* preserved (i) in a drawing in the Pierpont Morgan Library (Fiocco, pl. 180) and (2) in a picture formerly in the Vendramini Collection (T. Borenius, *The Picture Gallery of Andrea Vendramini*, London, 1923, pl. 32: the horseman only, presumably a fragment of the picture for which the drawing was the study or *modello*). The foremost horseman in the centre and the two figures behind St. Paul are also very similar to those in the Pierpont Morgan drawing. I think there is little doubt that the latter is by Pordenone. The question whether the present drawing is actually by him is more difficult. It is not in technique and style unlike studies for the Cremona *Crucifixion* (Fiocco, pl. 94–96), where indeed the horseman on the R. occurs again in a very similar form. It is possibly the work of some artist who took over Pordenonesque *motifs*, but it is better to leave it under the name of Pordenone than to relegate it to the anonymous.

750. THE SUPPER AT EMMAUS: design for a lunette. (4784)
192 × 565 mm. Pen and brown ink and brown wash on blue paper, heightened with white, squared in red chalk.
Old attribution in ink in bottom L. hand corner: 'Bordonone'. It seems to me to approach in style Pordenonesque works like the *Judgment of Daniel* in the Louvre (Tietzes, No. 24, as Pomponio Amalteo) and the predella painting of *St. Roch* in the Carrara Gallery at Bergamo (Fiocco, pl. 170). At the same time it also resembles drawings attributed to Bonifazio (e.g. Tietzes, No. 384, 378), but the whole question is very controversial, and it seems better to leave it under the old attribution. The drawing is *not* a copy as is shown by various *pentimenti*.

751. THE STONING OF ST. STEPHEN: design for an altarpiece with an arched top. (*Plate* 165) (6664)
360 × 235 mm. Pen and brown ink and brown wash on blue paper, heightened with white.
Old attribution in ink in bottom L. corner (in same hand as on No. 750): 'Del Bordonone'. The style of the composition in general is very Pordenonesque. It seems to be

by the same hand as the drawing in the Louvre already mentioned (Tietzes, No. 24, as Pomponio Amalteo).

752. GROUP OF SEVEN MUSICIAN ANGELS (6663)
253 × 170 mm. (irregular). Pen and brown ink and brown wash, heightened with white.
Inscribed top L.: 'del Pordenon'.
This is certainly of the school of Pordenone, more probably an original design than a copy from a composition of the master, close as it comes to him.

Attributed to GIUSEPPE PORTA (SALVIATI)
(About 1520–about 1575 ?)

753. AN ARMED KNIGHT (ST. GEORGE ?) ON HORSEBACK KISSES THE FOOT OF THE INFANT CHRIST, seated on His Mother's knee, as he rides past; a bearded saint with a book stands on the R. (*Plate* 169) (5052)
266 × 195 mm. Pen and brown ink and brown wash on blue paper, heightened with white.
Coll.: N. Lanière (Lugt 2886).
A.E.P. Though the pen-work seems a little fussier than is usual with Porta, that may be explained by the character of the sheet as a first sketch—there are many *pentimenti*. According to an old note on the mount there is a more finished version of the drawing at Weimar, a statement I have not been able to verify.

754. ALLEGORICAL FIGURE OF TEMPERANCE (4788)
226 × 108 mm. Pen and brown ink and brown wash on blue paper, heightened with white.
Lit.: Tietzes, No. 1396.
Attributed by the Tietzes to Giuseppe Porta. Though the handling is rather looser than is usual with that artist, this attribution seems to be right.

FRANCESCO PRIMATICCIO (1504–1570)

Lit.: L. Dimier, *Le Primatice*, Paris, 1900 (with a catalogue of the drawings, which, however, only includes one at Windsor) (quoted as Dimier (1900)); the same, *Le Primatice* Paris, 1928 (quoted as Dimier (1928)).

755. THE ENTRY OF THE WOODEN HORSE INTO TROY (5139)
385 × 540 mm. Pen and brown ink and brown wash, squared in black chalk, heightened with white.
Corresponds in reverse to the subject engraved by Giulio Bonasone (Bartsch XV, p. 134, 85) with the inscription 'BOL INVENTORE 1545'. The design is therefore assured to Primaticcio by almost contemporary evidence and must date from before 1545; its style seems to indicate his Mantuan period. The correspondence with Bonasone's engraving is not exact, the distribution of beards among the protagonists being, for one thing, different. The drawing is cut on all sides and badly faded, especially in the background figures, which have been gone over. It is therefore not easy to decide whether it is a copy (from a presumed picture, *not* from the engraving) or an original. There seems to me no reason why it should not in fact be by Primaticcio himself. It might well be by the same hand as a drawing in the Uffizi traditionally called Primaticcio (No. 1505: reproduced Olschki's *Disegni degli Uffizi*, Series II, Fasc. III, No. 25, as Niccolò dell' Abbate).

756. ILLUSTRATION EXPLAINING THE SURGICAL TREATMENT OF A DISLOCATED SHOULDER (0791)
242 × 183 mm. Pen and brown ink and brown wash.
A.E.P. The drawing is one of a series made to illustrate Vidius Vidius (Guido Guidi), *Chirurgia e Graeco in Latinum conversa* . . . Paris, 1544. It corresponds, with minor differences, to a woodcut in the last section of this work (*De Machinamentis*, by Oribasius, p. 486), and the text which appears on the *verso* corresponds with part of a section headed 'Scala preparata ad humerum restituendum in alam prolapsum', on p. 486. Dimier (1928), p. 23, refers to a manuscript in the Bibliothèque Nationale with drawings by Primaticcio for the woodcuts in Vidius Vidius' work, some of which he illustrates on plates XLIII–XLV. These drawings, to judge from the examples illustrated, are of exactly the same character and style as the Windsor sheet, which would appear to be a fragment detached from the manuscript.
The evidence for Primaticcio's authorship of the drawings, though accepted without question by Dimier, is not absolutely conclusive. It is to be found in Vidius' introduction to the work (quoted by Dimier, Bulletin des Antiquaires de France, 1910, p. 173) where he states that Johannes Santorinus and Francesco Primaticcio could witness to the pains he had taken in illustrating the work 'quorum aliquando operâ usus sum'. Santorinus was not a painter and could not have produced the drawings: therefore Primaticcio must have done so, Dimier argues. It is curious, if he did, that Vidius should not have said so more definitely. The actual style of the drawings is more like Francesco Salviati's.

757. DISCORD THROWING THE APPLE AT THE WEDDING OF PELEUS AND THETIS (*Plate* 104) (5975)
377 × 288 mm. (top corners cut). Grey chalk.
Attribution in pencil on the drawing. Though the style comes very near to that of Rosso as shown, for example, in the Uffizi drawing of the *Allegory on the Conception* (repr. Olschki, Uffizi Drawings, IV, 4 (1927), No. 17), I think the old attribution is to be accepted. There is no definite connection between its composition and that of the pendentive of the same subject in the Salle de Bal at Fontainebleau. The drawing is incomplete, the R. hand portion being in the British Museum (Fenwick Collection, Catalogue, p. 86, No. 2).

758. PUTTO RIDING ON A SEA-HORSE (*Plate* 106) (0499)
288 × 377 mm. Black chalk (the *putto* first outlined in yellow chalk).
A.E.P. The stye of this spirited small cartoon comes very near to Primaticcio's, but it is an unusual type of drawing and there is nothing exactly comparable among his sketches known to me. The horse's head occurs in an almost identical form in the engraving by Antonio Fantuzzi (Bartsch XVI, p. 339, 7) inscribed 'Bologna Inventor' and dated 1544. This, according to Dimier (1900, p. 492), reproduces one of the compositions by Primaticcio on the ceiling of the vestibule of the *Porte Dorée* at Fontainebleau. The present drawing is of course in no sense a study for this composition. The extraordinary similarity of the two horses, however, points to both being designed by the same artist possibly at about the same period.

759. TWO MEN SEATED, TURNED TO THE R., CONVERSING WITH EACH OTHER (*Plate* 105) (5973)
187 × 197 mm. Red chalk on light cream-coloured paper, heightened with white.

Inscribed in pencil in lower R. corner: 'Del Primaticcio'. The style of this characteristic, original drawing is exactly that of a series in the Louvre (Dimier (1900), p. 429 ff., Nos. 30, 32, 33, 35, 36; photographed by Braun), two of which are certainly studies for the subsidiary pictures in the embrasures of the windows of the Salle de Bal at Fontainebleau (1552–1559). I have not Alexandre Bétou's engravings from these pictures, and am unable to verify whether this is actually a study for one of them.

760. OVAL COMPOSITION: A NUDE WOMAN, WITH HER BACK TO THE SPECTATOR, RECLINES TO THE L., leaning on an urn; behind her is another woman and, to the R., a youth plying an oar. (*Figure* 144) (5500)
149 × 216 mm. Red chalk on cream-coloured paper, heightened with white, squared in red chalk.

FIG. 144 Cat. No. 760

The type of composition in an oval is nearest to that of a drawing in the Louvre (Dimier (1900), 13; photo. Braun 372), which Dimier describes as *Hylas and the Nymphs*, and tentatively connects with one of the ovals which decorated the ceiling of the thirteenth compartment of the Gallery of Ulysses at Fontainebleau. This may well be the design for one of the three remaining ovals. It is however unmistakably the same composition as that of an irregular rectangular panel in an engraving by Ducerceau (Dimier (1928), pl. XXVIII). This engraving more or less corresponds with the description of the tenth compartment of the ceiling, which represented four great rivers with, in the centre, the Hours surrounding the sun. Drawings presumed to be for three of the rivers exist, are all in irregular rectangles and different in style from the present drawing. It is, therefore, probable that Ducerceau used a composition from elsewhere in his engraving.

After PRIMATICCIO

761. OMPHALE DRESSING HERCULES AS A WOMAN (0406)
254 × 415 mm. Top corners cut. Pen and dark brown ink and brown wash over black chalk.
This is an old copy, or possibly even a tracing, of the drawing by Primaticcio in the Albertina (Wickhoff, Scuola Bolognese 19; Dimier (1900), p. 452, No. 151; photo. Braun 440). The composition is for the decoration of the vestibule of the Porte Dorée at Fontainebleau, on which the artist was at work between 1532 and 1535 (see Dimier (1928), p. 5 and pl. VIII). There is an engraving of this composition by L. D. (Bartsch XVI, p. 327, No. 55).

762. ULYSSES GIVING THANKS TO THE GODS AND OFFERING THEM SACRIFICE (5966)
194 × 267 mm. Pen and brown ink and grey wash, heightened with white.
The drawing corresponds exactly with the subject painted by Primaticcio, or on his design, in the destroyed gallery of Ulysses at Fontainebleau. It has with some justification been attributed to Tibaldi or his school, as its style shows no resemblance to that of other drawings for the series by Primaticcio. It cannot be an original design by him, spirited as it is, and it seems not impossible that it is a copy by Tibaldi (see No. 947). Though there is no record of Tibaldi having visited France, he may well have received a copy of the subject, which is No. 2 in the series of engravings by Théodore van Thulden (*Les Travaux d'Ulysse*, Paris, 1640).

763. ULYSSES AND HIS COMRADES ENTERING THE CAVE OF POLYPHEMUS (5964)
245 × 315 mm. Red chalk on reddish ground, heightened with white.
Inscribed in black chalk in lower L. corner: 'Primaticcio'. Copy of the subject in the Gallery of Ulysses at Fontainebleau, engraved by Théodore van Thulden (No. 9 in *Les Travaux d'Ulysse*, Paris, 1640). The style and technique are those of Primaticcio's original design, which is preserved at Stockholm (Dimier (1900), p. 458, No. 173), from which, rather than from the painting, this is no doubt copied.

764. ULYSSES WITH HIS FATHER LAERTES AND OTHER RELATIVES (5972)
230 × 326 mm. Red chalk, heightened with white.
Inscribed in black chalk in lower R. corner: 'Primaticcio'. Unfinished copy of the subject in the Gallery of Ulysses at Fontainebleau, engraved by Théodore van Thulden (No. 54 in *Les Travaux d'Ulysse*, Paris, 1640). Primaticcio's original finished design is, according to Dimier, at Stockholm (Dimier (1900), p. 460, No. 184). The present drawing is absolutely in Primaticcio's technique and manner, but it has certain weaknesses and the existence of the version at Stockholm (one of a series which I have not seen but which is regarded as autograph) points to its being a copy.

765. ULYSSES IN THE KINGDOM OF THE LAESTRYGONES (13054)
222 × 336 mm. Black chalk (offset).
This is an offset from a copy of one of the frescoes in the Gallery of Ulysses at Fontainebleau, engraved by Théodore van Thulden (No. 17 in *Les Travaux d'Ulysse*, Paris, 1640).

766. AN OLD MAN SEATED ON A THRONE ON THE L. BEFORE WHOM KNEELS A YOUTH, held by the hair by a fury; to the R. a draped and a nude woman conversing. (099)
197 × 422 mm. Black chalk (offset).
Lit.: Dimier (1900), p. 456, No. 166.
A study used for the figure of the old man in this composition is in the Louvre (Dimier (1900), No. 31; photo. Braun 377). According to Dimier a similar subject, painted in the third compartment of the tenth window of the Salle de Bal at Fontainebleau (between 1552 and 1556), was engraved by Alexandre Bétou. The present drawing is an offset from a copy, certainly not from an original drawing by Primaticcio.

School of PRIMATICCIO

767. MERCURY FLYING DOWN FROM OLYMPUS TO A WOMAN (5971)
305 × 232 mm. Red chalk on reddish paper, heightened with white.

The subject is not clear to me. Mercury seems to be delivering a message to the woman, who is seated under a tree on the L.; to the R. is a goat-herd looking up. In the sky are Jupiter with the thunderbolt, a goddess and another god. According to a note by Bodmer formerly on the mount, it is a copy from Primaticcio; it seems to me rather to be of his school, perhaps the composition of a French imitator, like Lerambert. The technique is exactly that of Primaticcio's composition studies for the series of Ulysses.

CAMILLO PROCACCINI (About 1551(?)–1629)

768. THE TRANSFIGURATION (*Plate* 150) (01220)
620 × 325 mm. Oil (grey and purple) on paper.

Inscribed in ink in the 'deceptive' hand in lower R. corner: 'Procacino'. Though the drawing corresponds only in general arrangement with the etching of the subject by Camillo (Bartsch XVIII, p. 20, 4) its style is so similar that the attribution to him may be accepted without question. It is possibly the *bozzetto* for the picture of the *Transfiguration* in the church of S. Fedele, Milan, with which the etching is said by Malvasia (*Felsina Pittrice*, Bologna, 1678, Parte Seconda, p. 293) to correspond.

769. ST. FRANCIS RENOUNCES HIS FATHER AND RECEIVES FROM THE BISHOP A CLOAK TO COVER HIM (?) (6439)
187 × 176 mm. Pen and ink and brown wash over black chalk on a brown ground, heightened with white, squared in black chalk.

Inscribed in ink in an old hand on one of the steps on which St. Francis kneels: 'Camilo Procaccini', an attribution which is confirmed by the style of the drawing. It looks like a design for one of a series of the life of St. Francis, but I find no record of Camillo having painted such a series. The interpretation of the subject is, however, not quite certain.

770. THE ADORATION OF THE SHEPHERDS (*Figure* 145) (3745)
420 × 298 mm. Black chalk, squared in the same medium.

Inscribed in ink in an old hand (the same as that on No. 769). 'Camilo Procaccini'.

771. SUSANNAH AND THE WICKED ELDERS (0203)
255 × 177 mm. Black chalk on blue paper, with some heightening in white.

Inscribed in pencil on the drawing 'del procaccino'. The style points to Camillo rather than to Giulio Cesare.

772. THE EVANGELIST ST. MATTHEW: design for a pendentive. (5970)
271 × 282 mm. (cut irregularly). Black and red chalk with some white, squared in red chalk.

Old attribution in ink on the drawing: 'camillo Proc.'. Though the figure corresponds with one in the 'peducci' of the cupola of the Madonna de' Monti, Rome, which, according to Baglione, were the work of Cristofano Casolani (Venturi, X 3, Fig. 459), the style is so exactly that of Camillo Procaccini that it seems wiser to retain the old attribution, even if the connection with the fresco is not easy to explain. I can see no traces of any Sienese elements, which should mark a drawing by Cristofani Casolani, apparently the son of Alessandro Casolani.

FIG. 145 Cat. No. 770

773. JUPITER AND ANTIOPE: Antiope is asleep on a bed with Cupid on the pillow; Jupiter in the form of a satyr approaches from the R. and uncovers Antiope. (0204)
224 × 342 mm. Black chalk (much damaged by damp on the R., towards the top).

At some time, perhaps anciently, attributed to Procaccini and also to the school of Giulio Romano. The attribution to Procaccini, by which Camillo is obviously intended, whatever its source, seems to me a most probable one.

774. THREE GROTESQUE HEADS, two in profile looking down to the L. and one behind full face. (5991)
316 × 217 mm. Red chalk.

Attribution 'Procaccini' in pencil on the drawing, by which Camillo is probably intended. There are similar drawings of grotesque heads in the Venice Academy (Photo. Braun 180) and at Chatsworth (No. 398) with the same name. The *genre* seems a direct descendant of Leonardo's caricatures and to have flourished unintermittently from his time in Milan.

775. SIX HEADS, the central one being that of a young negro. (5169)
176 × 250 mm. Red and black chalk, the outlines pricked. A.E.P. The heads somewhat resemble those on the sheet in the Venice Academy, already referred to under No. 774.

FIG. 146 Cat. No. 781

Attributed to CAMILLO PROCACCINI

776. MOSES HOLDING THE TABLETS OF THE LAW (0328)

155 × 67 mm. Black chalk, squared in red chalk.

George III 'Inventory A', p. 51, Raffaello d'Urbino e Scuola 39: 'A Good drawing though not by Raphael'.

Lit.: J. D. Passavant, *Raphael*, 1860, p. 492c; Ruland, p. 78, No. 26.

Photo.: Thurston Thompson 1857.

P.M.R.P. On a Richardson style mount with an XVIII century attribution to Raphael. Characterised by Passavant as the work of a pupil, it seems, however, to be that of an archaizer of the end of the XVI century, and may be attributed to Camillo Procaccini. Ruland's statement that the figure corresponds with the Moses in a niche on the R. of Cherubino Alberti's engraving after Raphael's Madonna 'La Perla' is inaccurate.

777. THE REST ON THE FLIGHT INTO EGYPT (0126)

250 × 398 mm. Pen and brown ink and blue wash, the outlines indented; damaged.

A.E.P. Apparently the design for an etching or an engraving, which I cannot find. I think, however, the style indicates Camillo Procaccini as the draughtsman.

778. AN ELDERLY MAN ADMONISHING A YOUTH SEATED AT HIS FEET (*Plate* 149) (5963)

378 × 317 mm. Red chalk (a strip, about 45 mm. wide, added on the R. is probably original though it has certainly been restored with the brush to a certain extent).

P.M.R.P. The drawing was engraved in reverse as Pellegrino Tibaldi by F. Bartolozzi, 'Londini', with the inscription 'Juvenis auscultans Seni de divinis admonenti My Son attend unto my Wisdom, and bow thine ear to my Understanding. Proverbs Ch. V'. The attribution to Tibaldi is out of the question: the drawing belongs to a different and later phase of development. It can be attributed with some confidence to Camillo Procaccini. A weaker but apparently original variant (in reverse), attributed to Camillo Procaccini, was sold at Christie's on January 30, 1948, lot 28.

779. PHARAOH'S HOST SUBMERGED IN THE RED SEA; Moses and the people of Israel are seen on the far bank. (01215)

352 × 523 mm. Rapid sketch in red chalk (damaged by damp and pieces torn from L. hand top corner and R. side).

P.M.R.P. There is another design for the same composition in the collection of Mr. E. Schapiro (pen and brown ink and wash over black chalk, heightened with white and pink, 455 × 610 mm.). Both drawings, though differing materially in detail, show the same general disposition and are clearly alternative designs by the same artist. The types suggest that this artist was no other than Camillo Procaccini.

After CAMILLO PROCACCINI

780. A NUDE MAN STEPPING FORWARD holding a rough staff in front of him with both hands. (5962)

363 × 210 mm. Red chalk.

A.E.P. The traditional attribution was apparently to Tibaldi. It is in fact the copy of a drawing in the Ecole des Beaux-Arts, Paris (No. 12070), with an old attribution, entirely convincing, to Camillo Procaccini.

A copy after Correggio, ascribed to Camillo Procaccini is catalogued under No. 252.

BIAGIO PUPINI (DALLE LAME) (Working from 1511–d. after 1575)

781. THE BETRAYAL (*Figure* 146) (0315)

194 × 290 mm. Drawn with the point of the brush and washed with brown on cream-coloured ground, heightened with white.

Inscribed in pencil on the drawing: 'Di Biaggio Bolognese'. It is similar in style to a number of others with old attributions to Pupini, notably one in the British Museum (Fenwick Collection, Catalogue, pl. XXIV, as Polidoro da Caravaggio). There is, as my attribution of this last drawing to Polidoro shows, not a little confusion between the work of the two artists. They come at times very close indeed to one another, and it is to be presumed that Biagio was imitating Polidoro. His lively assemblages of small figures, often in front of elaborate architectural backgrounds, are very similar to Polidoro's. Characteristics which mark most of the drawings attributed to Pupini are a cream-coloured or yellow or grey ground, a liberal heightening in rather chalky white, and a general carelessness and lack of precision in the drawing.

782. THE ADORATION OF THE MAGI (*Plate* 98) (0314)

275 × 212 mm. Pen and brown ink and brown wash on blue-green paper, heightened with white.

Inscribed in the bottom L. corner in the 'deceptive' hand: '[Pa]rmmegiano', and in pencil: 'Biagio Bolognese'. There is a close resemblance in style to a large drawing at Chatsworth of the *Adoration of the Kings* (No. 44: wrongly attributed to Peruzzi).

783. *Recto:* GROUP OF FIGURES, SEATED AND STANDING, for some composition like the Preaching of St. John the Baptist. (044)

214 × 220 mm. Brush and Indian ink over black chalk on blue-green paper, heightened with white.

Verso: AN ESCUTCHEON SUPPORTED BY A PUTTO

Black chalk and wash.

A.E.P. Rightly given to the Bolognese school. It is, however, clearly by the same hand as the drawing just described, Biagio Pupini's.

FIG. 147 Cat. No. 785 *r.*

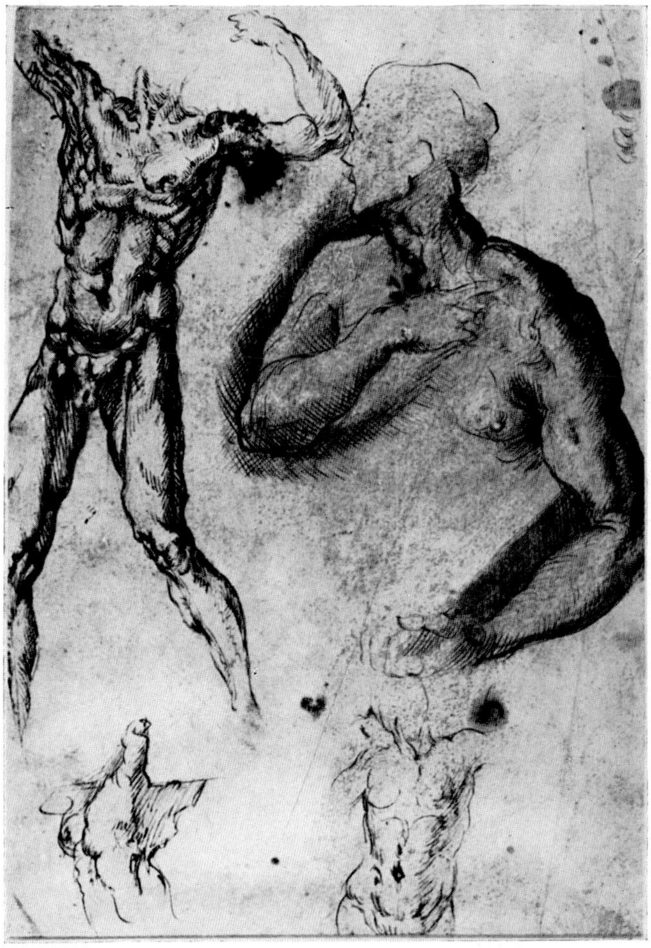

FIG. 148 Cat. No. 785 *v.*

784. FRAGMENT OF AN ANTIQUE TRIUMPH: figures in front are leading sacrificial bulls; behind is a camel with a lion on its back, and an elephant. (5487)

256 × 214 mm. Brush drawing in light brown, washed with brown, on a cream-coloured ground, heightened with white.

Clearly by the same hand as the drawing last catalogued.

785. *Recto:* A BATTLE WITH AMAZONS: on the L. is Hercules and below him a river-god. (*Figure* 147) (5435)

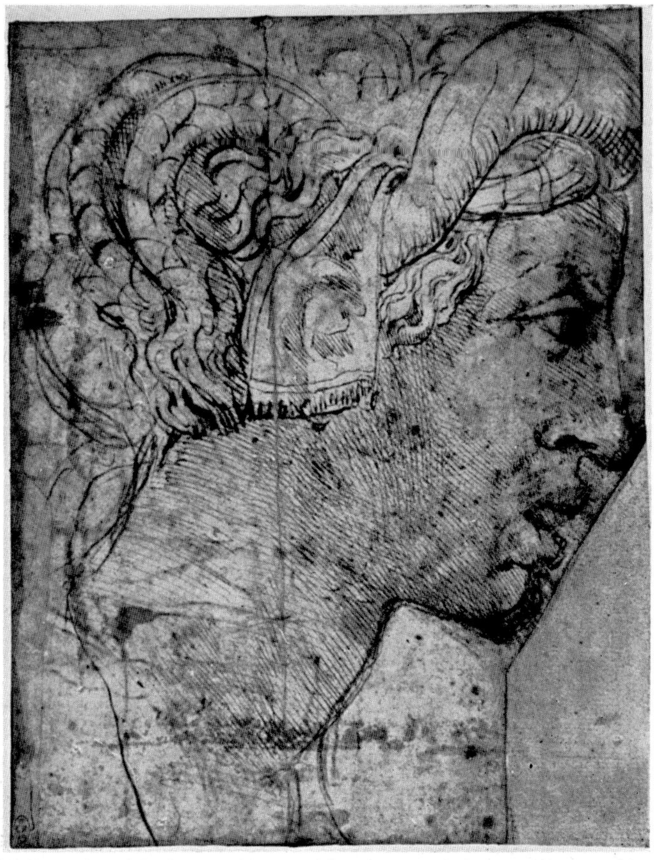

FIG. 149 Cat. No. 786 *r.*

202 × 290 mm. Pen and brown ink and brown and pink wash on a pink ground, heightened with white.

Verso: COPY FROM A DRAWING BY MICHELANGELO, NUDE MAN AND TORSO (*Figure* 148)

Pen and ink and some wash.

A.E.P. Attributed to Polidoro da Caravaggio, for whom it is too weak. The subject on the *recto*, if not from the antique, perhaps a gem, is imitated from it. The man's head and shoulders on the *verso* are copied from the drawing for the *putto* near the Libyan Sibyl at Oxford (Frey 3). That it is from the drawing is shown by the inclusion on the sheet of the study of a hand as in the Oxford drawing. The originals of the sketch on the L. of a nude headless man, with his L. arm bent, and of the torso lower down on the R. (if they are copies), are not known to me. The style of these drawings on the *verso* recall Beccafumi's (see the *Studies of Arms*, No. 134), but the evidence is hardly strong enough to separate the *recto* from the *verso* and attribute the latter to Beccafumi; the former is definitely by Pupini.

The following two drawings, which are catalogued under Copies from Raphael, are also probably by Biagio Pupini:

No. 819. Six figures to the R. of the centre in the School of Athens.

No. 827. Christ handing the Keys to Peter, after the tapestry.

What may also be a copy by Biagio Pupini after Perino del Vaga is catalogued, as No. 994, under the latter artist.

FIG. 150 Cat. No. 787 *r.*

FIG. 151 Cat. No. 787 *v.*

RAFFAELLO DA MONTELUPO

(1504 or 1505–1566 or 1567)

786. *Recto:* IMAGINARY HEAD OF A WOMAN IN A TURBAN-LIKE HEADDRESS IN PROFILE TO THE R. (*Figure* 149) (0417)

Verso: YOUNG WOMAN SEATED, AND BUST OF A BEARDED MAN TURNED THREE-QUARTERS TO THE L., WEARING A HELMET, HIS R. ARM RAISED

268 × 206 mm. Irregular shape. Pen and ink, corrected in places with black chalk; the outlines of the bearded man indented.

Inscribed in a later hand along the top and bottom edges of the *verso:* 'micael angnillo' and 'angnilo bona-rota'. The drawing on the *recto* is a free version of the head of 'Prudentia', a drawing by Michelangelo only surviving in copies, dating from about 1525–30 (see B.B. 1637). It would appear to be of the period when Montelupo was first working for Michelangelo, 1533–34. The drawings on the *verso* are the opposite way up. The woman (at the top to the L.) is from the lunette of Rehoboam and Abijah in the Sixtine chapel; the man (to the R. at the bottom) may perhaps represent Vulcan.

787. *Recto:* (1) A BACCHANAL: Bacchus sits on a barrel under a tree, on which a flask is hung; he holds a goblet in his L. hand; to the L. are a dancing satyr, a *putto* and a goat; to the R., a Bacchante with a *putto.* (2) a *Putto* with a goat sitting in front of a cave, into which a lion disappears (the lion is drawn twice). (3) head of a youth in profile to the R. (*Figure* 150) (0505)

Verso: (4) THE FALL OF PHAETHON (without Jupiter); in the background to the R. the Heliades are represented a second time, turned into trees. (5) an altar or wall-tomb. (*Figure* 151)

340 × 238 mm. Pen and ink, partly over sketches in black chalk. W.M., Robinson 11 (see Michelangelo Bibliography).

Coll.: Sir P. Lely (Lugt 2092); J. Richardson, Snr. (Lugt 2184); W. Mayor (Lugt 2799).

Lit.: Drawings . . . belonging to the late Mr. Mayor, London, 1874, p. 10, No. 44 (as Giulio Romano).

Inscribed in the artist's hand at the bottom of the *recto*, parallel with the R. margin: 'pacis. Vltima/fecit raffaello'. Sketch (1) on the *recto* is at the top of the page, with (2) underneath and merging into it; (3) is to the R. at the bottom. The latter occurs in almost identical form on a drawing by Montelupo at Oxford (B.B. 1701 *recto*). (4) on the *verso*, which occupies the lower two-thirds of the sheet, presupposes an acquaintance with Michelangelo's drawing at Windsor (No. 430); (5) (to the R. of (4) holding the sheet lengthways) is of especial interest in view of our scanty knowledge of Montelupo's work as an architect. Vasari says of him: 'negli ornamenti d'architettura seguito assai la maniera di Michelagnolo' (IV, p. 546). This applies also to this construction, in which the base and main structure are divided vertically into three, crowned by an entablature; in the centre of this is a rectangular panel, surmounted by a volute broken in the centre by a pyramid; supporting this panel on R. and L. are volutes with human figures; candelabra in the corners. For the form of the whole headpiece compare especially a design of Michelangelo's in the Archivio Buonarroti (XIII, f. 160: published by Tolnay, Münchner Jahrbuch, N.F. V. (1928), pp. 393 ff.). This I believe dates from June, 1524, and is for the papal tombs planned for the rooms adjoining the Sagrestia Vecchia (detail design for this, B.B. 1709 at Oxford). This same design was, as Tolnay has shown, also known to Montelupo's friend, Simone Mosca. Montorsoli's High Altar in the Chiesa dei Servi at Bologna and Leone Leoni's Marignano tomb in the Duomo at Milan (Venturi XI, Fig. 128; Münchner Jahrbuch, 1928, p. 396) give the impression of being more elaborate variants of (5). Now Mosca and Montorsoli, as well as Montelupo, worked for a time with Michelangelo, and Leone's work, according to his own admission as well as Vasari's statement, was based on a design of Michelangelo's—No. 787 apparently dates after 1534. A design for a tomb by Montelupo is mentioned by Annibale Caro in a letter of February 16, 1538, to the artist (Bottari-Ticozzi, III, p. 199), but we know nothing more about it.

RAPHAEL (Raffaello Santi) (1483–1520)

References are given in abbreviated form as follows:

Pass. = J. D. Passavant, *Raphael d'Urbin*, 2 vols. Paris, 1860.

Robinson = J. C. Robinson, *A Critical Account of the Drawings by Michel Angelo and Raffaello in the University Galleries, Oxford*. Oxford, 1870.

Ruland = [C. Ruland], *The Works of Raphael Santi da Urbino as represented in The Raphael Collection . . . at Windsor Castle*. Privately printed, 1876.

Crowe and Cavalcaselle = J. A. Crowe and G. B. Cavalcaselle, *Raphael, His Life and Works*. London, 1882.

Fischel (1898) = Oskar Fischel, *Raphaels Zeichnungen. Versuch einer Kritik*. Strassburg, 1898. (With full references to the earlier literature.)

Fischel = Oskar Fischel, *Raphaels Zeichnungen*. Berlin, 1913–1941, Parts I–VIII. Facsimiles of all Raphael's drawings.

K. der K. = Georg Gronau, *Raffael: Des Meisters Gemälde*. Fünfte Auflage. [Klassiker der Kunst], Berlin and Leipzig, 1923.

Thieme-Becker = Oskar Fischel in Thieme-Becker, *Künstler-Lexicon*, XXIX (1935).

I have arranged the drawings by Raphael and his school as follows:

A. Original drawings.
B. School of Raphael.
C. Copies of existing paintings and frescoes, arranged in the order adopted in the Klassiker der Kunst Raphael.
D. Copies of existing drawings.

I have abstained from adding to the confusion existing in regard to the later works by making definite attributions to Raphael's pupils. My own view is that a greater share in the design of these works than has hitherto been conceded should be given to Raphael himself, and that this applies in particular to the Tapestries, the Farnesina and the *Loggie*.

A. ORIGINAL DRAWINGS

788. STUDY OF TWO MALE HEADS (*Plate* 46) (4370)

238 × 186 mm. Grey chalk.

Lit.: A. E. Popham, O.M.D., XII (1937–38), p. 45 (pl. 50).

A.E.P. This study, for the heads of St. Paul and the apostle next to him in the Vatican *Coronation of the Virgin* (K. der K. 17), is of exactly the same style and character as two other detail studies for the same panel in the British Museum and in the Musée Wicar at Lille (Fischel, Nos. 23 and 24). Though it lacks the incisiveness of the British Museum drawing, one has only to put the reproductions of the three drawings side by side to realize the identity of hand. The sheet had lain unnoticed until quite recently with the series of drawings by Maratta. I would refer the reader to my article in Old Master Drawings for a more detailed discussion of the study.

789. LEDA AND THE SWAN (*Plate* 50) (12759)

308 × 192 mm. Pen and ink over a sketch with the stylus. W.M., a three-peaked mountain.

George III 'Inventory A', p. 51, Raffaello d'Urbino e Scuola, 37.

Lit.: Waagen II, p. 446; Fischel (1898), 508; Fischel, Part II, 79.

Engraved in facsimile by F. C. Lewis (1809) in Chamberlaine, pl. XLVI.

Photo.: Thurston Thompson, 1857.

On the *verso* is an inscription in a hand of the XVI century: 'peze 16' (= 16 pieces).

The drawing corresponds with a composition of *Leda and the Swan* by Leonardo da Vinci, known in various painted versions by pupils or imitators and in drawings of the master himself (e.g. the studies for Leda's head and coiffure at Windsor, No. 12516). Fischel suggests that Raphael had before him a drawing of this type, but comprising the whole figure, a drawing which no longer exists, and not a picture. This seems likely from the character of the pen-work. Indeed, though Leonardo was almost certainly working on the *Leda* in Florence at the time the *Battle of Anghiari* was in progress, i.e. in 1503–05, it is unlikely that he painted it (if he ever did) until after his return to Milan, when he seems to have resumed work on it. Raphael's copy must certainly date from his Florentine period.

790. THE VIRGIN AND CHILD WITH ST. ELIZABETH AND THE INFANT ST. JOHN (*Plate* 47) (12738)

234 × 180 mm. Pen and brown ink.

George III 'Inventory A', p. 49, Raffaello d'Urbino e Scuola 10.

Coll.: Bonfiglioli; Sagredo; Consul Smith.

Lit.: Fischel (1898) 73; Fischel, Part III, 130.

Engraved in facsimile by F. C. Lewis (1809) in Chamberlaine, pl. XLIX.

Photo.: Thurston Thompson, 1857.

The connection of this drawing with the *Madonna Canigiani* of about 1507 at Munich (K. der K. 47) is demonstrated by Fischel in a series of drawings (or copies of drawings) by Raphael, which he reproduces. The peculiar attitude of the infant St. John clearly connects the Windsor drawing with one in the Louvre (copy: Fischel 131), in which the Virgin has assumed substantially the same pose as in the picture. In another old copy at Chantilly (Fischel 132), in which the figures are represented nude, the composition is much as it became in the picture, and the St. Joseph makes his appearance leaning on his staff, though disconnected and in a different attitude.

Fischel argues that the drawing, originally by Raphael, whose touch is clearly recognizable in the landscape, has been gone over by a later hand, responsible also for retouching in this style sheets at Oxford (Fischel 102), and perhaps also the ruined sheet, likewise for the Canigiani *Holy Family*, in the British Museum (Fischel 133A).

FIG. 152 Cat. No. 791 *r.*

FIG. 153 Cat. No. 791 *v.*

791. *Recto:* HERCULES AND THE HYDRA (*Figure* 152)
Verso: HERCULES AND THE NEMEAN LION (*Figure* 153) (12758)
390 × 272 mm. Pen and ink over sketches with the stylus.
Lit.: Fischel, Part IV, 190.
The drawings on *recto* and *verso* of this sheet belong to a series of the *Labours of Hercules*. Another of the series, *Hercules and a Centaur*, is in the British Museum (Fischel 189). These drawings, on a scale unusually large, show a certain emptiness which has raised doubts about their authenticity. They are nevertheless so much in Raphael's manner that such doubts can be dismissed. They show, as Fischel has remarked, some affinity to youthful works of Bandinelli's, and must date from Raphael's Florentine period. The drawing of *Hercules and the Nemean Lion* on the *verso*, which is not reproduced by Fischel, corresponds fairly closely with that at Oxford (Fischel 191) of the same subject drawn on a much smaller scale. The expression of the face and the position of the arms are, however, slightly different, nor does the cloak appear in the Windsor drawing, and the R. leg is cut off by the edge of the paper.

792. STUDY FOR THE FIGURE OF POETRY (*Frontispiece*) (12734)
360 × 227 mm. Grey chalk over a sketch with the stylus, squared in black chalk.
W.M., a three-peaked mountain.
George III 'Inventory A', p. 49, Raffaello d'Urbino e Scuola 7. 'This is from Kensington.'
Lit.: Crowe and Cavalcaselle, II, pp. 22, 25; Fischel (1898) 163; Fischel, Part V, 228; Popham 133 (pl. CXIV).
Engraved in facsimile by F. C. Lewis (1809) in Chamberlaine, pl. XLIII.
Photo.: Thurston Thompson, 1857.
Study for the figure representing Poetry on the ceiling of the *Stanza della Segnatura* (K. der K. 56B). There are certain differences from the fresco as carried out, chief among which is the fact that the figure is unclothed down to the waist, but the squaring seems to imply that it was in fact enlarged and used for the cartoon. Crowe and Cavalcaselle make the suggestion that the head, which differs considerably from the head in the fresco, was used for that of Eve in the *Temptation* in another compartment of the same ceiling. There is in fact a very close resemblance.

793. *Recto:* THE MASSACRE OF THE INNOCENTS (*Plate* 55) (12737)
248 × 411 mm. Red chalk over a tracing in pencil and a sketch with the stylus.
Verso: DESIGN FOR A SALVER, WITH MARINE DEITIES (*Figure* 154)
Pen and ink. W.M., a mermaid in a circle.
Coll.: Bonfiglioli; Sagredo; Consul Smith.
George III 'Inventory A', p. 51, Raffaello d'Urbino e Scuola 29.
Lit.: Fischel (1898) 379; Fischel, Part V, 234, 235; Popham 134 (*recto*, pl. CXVII).
Photo.: Thurston Thompson, 1857.
Study for the composition of the *Massacre of the Innocents* engraved by Marcantonio (Bartsch 18, 20). The outlines of the main figures were first pricked through from the drawing in the British Museum (Fischel 233). These were then gone over with lead-point and finally finished in red chalk. Some of them, the woman whose child the executioner on the L. is seizing by the leg, part of the woman in the centre running towards the spectator, and the lower

part of the woman kneeling in the foreground to the R., remain in outline only. A few of these figures, particularly that of the woman towards the L., are studied on a complementary sheet, also in red chalk, at Vienna (Fischel 236). Subsidiary background figures, not to be found in the London drawing, have been added by Raphael on this sheet. The purpose of the composition is unknown. It is unlikely that a design so elaborately studied was originally intended merely for the engraver. There is, however, no record existing which suggests that any fresco of the *Massacre of the Innocents* was projected. It is connected with the *Judgment of Solomon* painted on the ceiling of the *Stanza della Segnatura*, as is shown by another sheet at Vienna (Fischel 231, 232) in which figures from both compositions appear.

The design on the *verso* is obviously for the border of a salver, and it is known that the goldsmith Cesarino of Perugia in fact made two bronze salvers to the order of Agostino Chigi in 1510 from Raphael's designs.

As Fischel has pointed out the fight of the sea-centaurs is a sort of translation into another element of the motives of the *Massacre of the Innocents*. One episode on the *verso*, that farthest on the R., repeats one in the British Museum drawing of the *Massacre*, which was discarded in the Windsor drawing and in the engraving of this subject.

It is tempting to connect this drawing with one seen by Richardson in 1719 in the Bonfiglioli Palace at Bologna (Richardson, *An Account*..., London, 1722, p. 30: 'Slaughter of the Innocents, first lightly sketch'd out in Bl. Ch. and then finish'd. Raffaelle'). According to the Rev. B. B. Woodward (Fine Arts Quarterly Review, I (1863, p. 164), the provenance of the Windsor drawing from the Bonfiglioli collection is a certain fact.

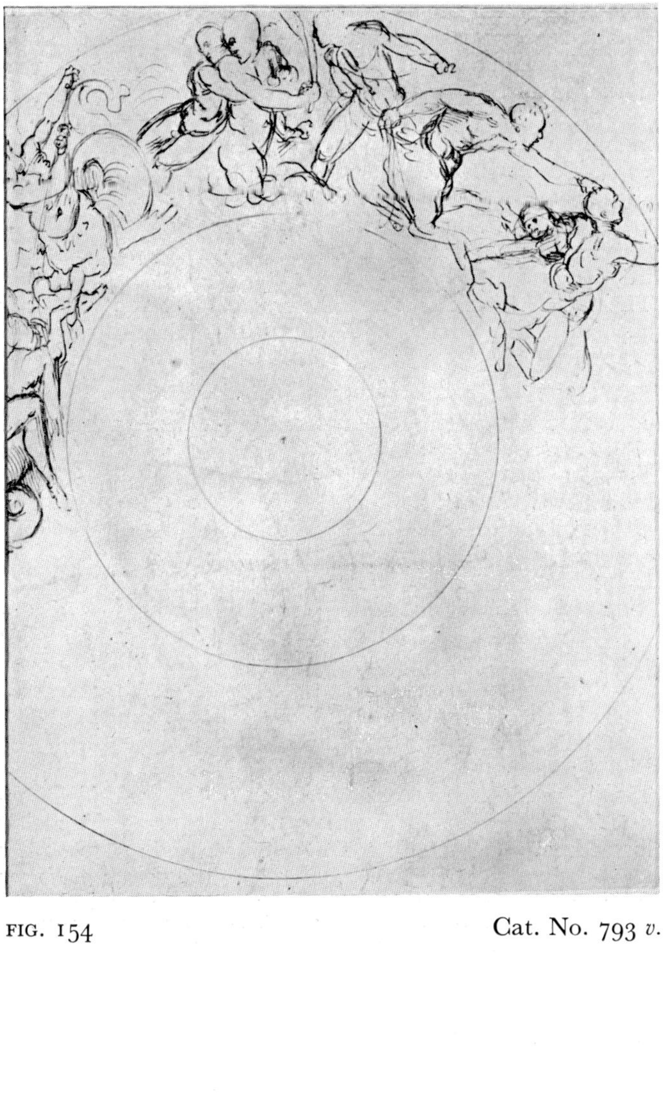

FIG. 154 Cat. No. 793 *v.*

794. EARLY DESIGN FOR THE L. HAND HALF OF THE 'DISPUTÀ' (*Plate* 54) (12732)

280 × 285 mm. Brush drawing in light brown, heightened with white, over a sketch with the stylus.

George III 'Inventory A', p. 49, Raffaello d'Urbino e Scuola 5.

Lit.: Pass. II, 429; Ruland, p. 180, No. 69; Robinson, p. 187; Crowe and Cavalcaselle, II, p. 29; Fischel (1898), 123; Fischel, Part V, 258.

Photo.: Thurston Thompson, 1857.

As recognized from the time of Ruland and Robinson, this drawing, together with another divided into two sheets between Oxford and Chantilly (Fischel 259, 260) and a third next to be described, represents the earliest stage of the design known to us. It is a composition sketch made with the purpose of blocking out the grouping of the figures and their atmospheric relation, rather than one concerned with the gestures or the expression of individuals, elaborated in the more finished drawings already referred to at Oxford and Chantilly.

The general arrangement varies considerably from that finally adopted. The relative positions of God the Father, the Saviour and the Virgin are the same, but the saints are differently disposed. St. Lawrence sits immediately on the Virgin's R. hand on the same level as another saint beside him. St. Peter and St. Paul (they can be identified by reference to the Oxford drawing, Fischel 258) are immediately below the Saviour and two Evangelists are seated further out to the L. on the same level. But the most striking difference lies in the portico which flanks the composition on the L., and which later disappeared altogether. Underneath this portico hovers a Leonardesque woman (she may be compared with the figure by Leonardo in this collection, No. 12581) pointing upwards to the heavenly vision. She is a Beatrice who introduces the spectator to these mysteries. In later designs she disappears, finally to emerge again in the form of a graceful youth with his feet planted on the earth on the extreme L. of the fresco.

795. STUDY FOR THE LOWER HALF OF THE 'DISPUTÀ' (*Plate* 56) (12733)

204 × 410 mm. Grey chalk. W.M., an eagle in a circle.

Lit.: Fischel (1898) 134; Fischel, Part VI, 261.

The sketch represents an early stage in the design of the lower half of the *Disputà*, substantially as in the sketch already described but even nearer to, and on the same scale as, the elaborate drawing of the whole of the lower half at Chantilly (Fischel 260). The groups are much closer together than in the fresco, and the altar separating them has not yet appeared. The sketch seems to have been made after the Chantilly one with the idea of recording some minor changes in the positions and actions of the figures, particularly of those on the R.

796. *Recto:* HEADS OF HOMER, DANTE AND OF THE POET NEXT TO SAPPHO IN THE 'PARNASSUS' (*Plate* 48)
Verso: STUDY FOR DANTE'S GARMENTS (*Plate* 49) (12760)

265 × 182 mm. Pen and brown ink on yellowish paper.

George III 'Inventory A', p. 51, Raffaello d'Urbino e Scuola 30.

Lit.: B. B. Woodward, Fine Arts Quarterly Review, I (1863), p. 164; Fischel (1898), 114, 115; Fischel, Part V, 246, 247.

Photo.: Thurston Thompson, 1857.

The heads correspond fairly closely with those in the fresco, except that the head of the poet next to Sappho in the drawing shows considerably more individuality than in the final version. The head of Homer, as has been remarked, is based on that of the Laocoon, a fact which is more clearly apparent in the drawing than in the fresco. The study of Dante's costume on the *verso* shows his hands holding the book, which are hardly visible in the fresco. There is an old copy of this drawing, with Lanière's mark on it, in the Albertina (S.R. 292: ill. Fischel, text to Part V, Fig. 223). It combines the head on the *recto* with the body on the *verso*.

797. *Recto:* THE DOCTRINE OF THE TWO SWORDS (Luke, xxii. 38). (*Plate* 52) (3720)
262 × 363 mm. Red chalk.
Verso: THE JUDGMENT OF ZALEUCUS (*Plate* 53)
Pen and brown ink over black chalk.
A.E.P. The composition on the *verso* corresponds with one of the *grisailles* painted in the embrasure of the window under the three allegorical figures in the *Stanza della Segnatura* (K. der K. 80B), a *grisaille* which Gronau and Fischel (in Thieme-Becker) both accept as from Raphael's own hand. The correspondence with the rather damaged fresco is almost exact except that the son of Zaleucus standing on the L. is not included (this part of the drawing has been cut away). In spite of this exact correspondence I feel certain that the drawing is not a copy from the fresco, but is Raphael's original drawing for it. The handling is masterly and entirely in Raphael's manner. Details like the R. hand of the executioner who protests against Zaleucus' order (which is not visible, at any rate in the reproduction of the fresco) and the L. hand of the soldier (the one leaning on his lance) with its reinforced outline seem to me quite convincingly original. In general style the drawing comes closest to such a study as that at Frankfort (Fischel 256) for *Gregory IX handing over the Decretals*, also in the *Stanza della Segnatura*, and known to have been painted in 1511.
The drawing in red chalk on the *recto* also corresponds with a subject painted in *grisaille* in the same window embrasure as the *Zaleucus* (K. der K. 80A). This is not mentioned by Fischel as an original, though Gronau seems to accept it. In the small reproduction the figure of Christ and the apostle on His R. look as if they might have been repainted, while the apostle on His L. appears exactly similar in style to the *Zaleucus*.
The drawing, though Raphaelesque enough, is distinctly weaker than the pen and ink sketch (that is why I have dealt first with the *verso* of the sheet). I have indeed felt some hesitation about it, but it is almost impossible to explain it except as an original drawing by the master. Nor are its weaknesses more conspicuous than those in the certainly authentic sheet in the British Museum with studies of angels for the *Disputà* (Fischel 297).
This really important example of Raphael, dating from the period of his first great undertaking in Rome, the *Stanza della Segnatura*, had unaccountably been mounted in the XVIII century in an album mainly containing Bolognese landscapes. It had remained unnoticed when Raphael was being intensively studied at Windsor at the instance of the Prince Consort, and had eluded the researches of Fischel, who missed very little indeed.

798. TWO NUDE FIGURES CROUCHING ON THE GROUND, PROTECTING THEIR EYES WITH A SHIELD (*Plate* 58) (12736)
266 × 223 mm. Black chalk.
George III 'Inventory A', p. 51, Raffaello d'Urbino e Scuola 32.

799. *Recto:* NUDE FIGURE WITH AN AXE FLEEING, BLINDED, TO THE R. (*Plate* 57) (12735)
322 × 256 mm. Black chalk. W.M., a cross-bow in a circle.
Verso: CATTLE LYING DOWN AND ONE DRINKING
Pen and ink. (*Plate* 51)
George III 'Inventory A', p. 51, Raffaello d'Urbino e Scuola 33.
Lit.: (for Nos. 798, 799) Pass., II, p. 492, Nos. 436, 437; B. B. Woodward, Fine Arts Quarterly Review, I (1863), p. 164; Robinson, p. 276; Ruland, p. 40, XXI, Nos. 8, 9; Crowe and Cavalcaselle, II, p. 142 note; Fischel (1898), 399, 179; Fischel, Prussian Jahrbuch, XLVI (1925), pp. 191 ff.; Fischel, Part VIII, 392, 393.
Photo.: Thurston Thompson, 1857; Braun 156, 157.
These two drawings were first recognized by Robinson (loc. cit.) as studies for a composition of the *Resurrection*, for which numerous other studies survive. The whole composition is most completely preserved in the drawing in the Bonnat Collection at Bayonne (ill. Prussian Jahrbuch, loc. cit., p. 193) and the lower half and separate figures in that at Oxford (ill. Prussian Jahrbuch, pp. 195, 196). Robinson's thesis was elaborated by Fischel in his article on the composition already alluded to, and he identified still other drawings for it. The crouching figures protecting their eyes with a shield are perhaps recognizable in the Bonnat sketch on the L. The figure of the blinded man with the battleaxe (on the R. in the Bonnat sketch) was used by Raphael for one of the guards in the *Freeing of St. Peter from Prison* in the *Stanza d'Eliodoro* (reversed) painted between 1511 and 1514, so that the project of the *Resurrection* must presumably have been earlier. Other similar black chalk studies from the life for soldiers in this composition are at Chatsworth (ill. Prussian Jahrbuch, p. 200), at Oxford (ibidem, p. 196), and in the British Museum (Vasari Society, 2nd Series, Part XVI, No. 6). All these figures are recognizable from their action in shielding their eyes or flying from the light emanating from the angel seated on the empty tomb.
Though the composition was never carried out as a painting, and its inception by Raphael is not noted in any contemporary record, there are other traces of it in engravings and pictures by later artists apart from the drawings referred to. Robinson believed the *Resurrection* to have been begun at the end of Raphael's life, and to have formed as it were a first edition of the *Transfiguration* commissioned in 1517 by Cardinal Giulio de' Medici, but as already pointed out, it must have preceded the fresco of the *Freeing of St. Peter* in the *Stanza d' Eliodoro*.
The sketch from nature on the *verso* of No. 799, certainly authentic, can hardly be paralleled in Raphael's work as a draughtsman.

800. THE VIRGIN AND CHILD WITH ST. ELIZABETH (*Plate* 59) (12742)
210 × 145 mm. Metal-point on a buff prepared surface, heightened with white.
George III 'Inventory A', p. 49, Raffaello d'Urbino e Scuola 9.
Coll.: Bonfiglioli; Sagredo; Consul Smith.
Lit.: Pass. II, 426; Ruland, p. 81, XLI, No. 4; Crowe and Cavalcaselle, II, p. 171 note; Fischel (1898) 330; Bollettino d'Arte XXXI (1937), p. 497 (ill.); Fischel, Burlington Mag., LXXIV (1939), p. 182; Critica D'Arte, III (1938), *Notizie e Letture*, p. xxxii; Fischel, Part VIII, 373.
Photo.: Thurston Thompson, 1857; Braun 172.
This beautiful sheet is a study for the *Madonna dell' Impannata* in the Pitti (K. der K. 110). According to Fischel it formed part of a sketch-book on buff prepared surface, other leaves of which he identifies. These are the sketch of *Roman ruins* next to be described, a study of horsemen from the Arch of Constantine at Munich, a study for the *Attila* at

Frankfort, *The Virgin Reading* at Chatsworth (repr. Vasari Society, 2nd Series, VI, No. 7), and perhaps the *Virgin embracing the Child* at Oxford (Robinson 79).

It will be observed that the present drawing only includes the Virgin and Child, St. Elizabeth, and (lightly sketched) the saint behind the last-named, the figure of St. John the Baptist not being indicated. A recent X-ray examination of the painting, the results of which were published by Piero Sanpaolesi in the Bollettino d'Arte, showed that the picture as originally painted contained on the R. a St. Joseph in profile with the head of St. John the Baptist behind him to the L., and that the *visible* painting of the Virgin, the Child, St. Elizabeth and the female saint was superimposed on another, of which the outlines were almost everywhere different, though only slightly different. Perhaps, apart from the St. Joseph, the most easily identifiable divergence as shown in Sanpaolesi's diagram is in the head-dress of St. Elizabeth. In this respect the Windsor drawing follows the lines of this earlier painting and differs from the visible one. The history of the picture as disclosed by the X-ray is not easy to make out. In its present state it has almost unanimously been regarded as the work of pupils. Fischel (in Thieme-Becker), who dates the picture from the period of the *Sibyls* in the Pace, about 1514, regards it as the earliest example of their intervention. It would appear that the first version, visible to the X-rays, was painted from the present sketch, even though the St. Joseph is not indicated (it is not of course possible to say whether this was from Raphael's own hand or from that of a pupil). But that the picture, as visible to the naked eye, was painted not so long afterwards appears likely from the existence of another drawing at Berlin. This is known to me only from the Grote reproduction made about 1883 (Part VI, No. 158), and I can find no reference to it elsewhere. It has, however, every appearance of being an original drawing by Raphael himself of about the same time as the Windsor sketch (though its size, about 211 × 205 mm., seems to make it impossible that it should have formed part of the same buff sketch-book), and contains studies for the Infant Christ (lightly sketched in at Windsor) and the St. John the Baptist (absent at Windsor). It seems in fact complementary to the Windsor sheet. This would indicate that Raphael himself must have had the idea of remodelling the composition very soon after it was painted, and a recent writer (C. L. Ragghianti) in Critica d'Arte holds the view that the whole of the picture as it stands is in fact the work of Raphael himself. He does not, however, quite incomprehensibly, accept the Windsor drawing as an original sketch by Raphael, and the Berlin one is obviously not known to him.

801. LANDSCAPE WITH CLASSICAL RUINS (*Plate* 60) (0117)

210 × 141 mm. Metal-point on buff prepared surface, heightened with white; much rubbed.

Lit.: Vasari Society, 2nd Series, XII (1931), No. 6; Fischel, Burlington Magazine, LXXIV (1939), p. 182.

As was first discovered by Sir Owen Morshead, this drawing more or less corresponds with part of the background in Marcantonio's engraving known as 'Il Morbetto' (Bartsch XIV, p. 314, 417). There can be no doubt that, unusual as the subject is, the drawing is in fact by Raphael himself. Fischel (loc. cit.) believed it to have formed part of the same buff sketch-book as the study for the *Madonna dell' Impannata* just discussed. Sir Kenneth Clark in his note to the Vasari Society reproduction suggests that the locality represented may be the forum of Trajan. There is no other drawing connected with 'Il Morbetto' which has much claim to be regarded as Raphael's.

802. CHRIST GIVING THE KEYS TO ST. PETER (*Plate* 62) (12751)

257 × 375 mm. Red chalk (offset).

George III 'Inventory A', p. 50, Raffaello d'Urbino e Scuola 26 ('an old copy').

Lit.: Pass., II, 425; B. B. Woodward, Fine Arts Quarterly Review, I (1863), p. 165; Ruland, p. 245, No. 12; Crowe and Cavalcaselle, II, p. 289; Vasari Society, 2nd Series, Part V (1924), No. 7; Fischel, Text, Part I, p. 21 (ill. p. 20).

Photo.: Thurston Thompson, 1857; Braun 166.

Perhaps the drawing seen by the younger Richardson in the Palazzo Bonfiglioli at Bologna in 1721 (Richardson, *An Account* . . ., London, 1722, p. 31: 'Feed my Sheep, an Excellent Design of *Raffaelle*; Sketch Red Ch. manner of the Baptism my Father has.').

The drawing is an offset, made no doubt by Raphael himself, from his original study from the model for the tapestry cartoon of the *Delivery of the Keys to Peter* (K. der K. 136). Only a fragment of the original drawing, the figure corresponding to that of Christ, is preserved (in the Louvre; repr. Fischel, loc. cit., p. 20). Raphael no doubt made the offset to see the effect of his composition in the direction in which it would finally appear, it being necessary to prepare the cartoon in the reverse direction for weaving.

803. THE BLINDING OF ELYMAS (*Plate* 63) (12750)

270 × 355 mm. Metal-point on grey prepared surface, heightened with white, occasionally touched up with pen and ink.

George III 'Inventory A', p. 49, Raffaello d'Urbino e Scuola 1. ('This drawing was bought at Rome.')

Lit.: Ruland, p. 250, VII, No. 13; Crowe and Cavalcaselle, II, p. 320 note; Fischel (1898), 253.

Photo.: Thurston Thompson (1857); Braun 167.

Corresponds with the tapestry cartoon of the subject (K. der K. 145). Although Crowe and Cavalcaselle regarded this drawing as a copy, its character clearly marks it as a working drawing for the cartoon. The only question is whether it is by Raphael himself or by a pupil. Fischel considered it a school drawing and the immediate model for the engraving by Agostino Veneziano (Bartsch XIV, p. 43, 48) of 1516, for which I can see no particular reason. It is primarily a perspective drawing—the whole sheet is covered with a network of fine lines, following the perspective, for it is not squared for enlargement, as at first sight might appear. It is in fact almost a counterpart to Leonardo's famous perspective study for the *Adoration of the Kings* in the Uffizi.

It would seem unlikely that Raphael himself at this stage of his career would have had time or inclination to work out the perspective of a composition with this extreme elaboration and precision, and this preliminary work may well have been entrusted to a competent pupil. The drawing of the figures is also carried out with extreme delicacy and in a style and technique which seem to me characteristic of Raphael himself. It is exactly paralleled in drawings like the study for the *Madonna dell' Impannata*, discussed above, and in the study at Chatsworth for the figure of St. Paul in the *Sacrifice at Lystra* (repr. S. A. Strong, *Chatsworth Drawings* No. 7). There are also *pentimenti* visible in parts, e.g. in the legs of the foremost of the two men carrying fasces and standing on the steps of the throne.

804. THE THREE GRACES (*Plate* 61) (12754)

203 × 260 mm. Red chalk. W.M., an anchor in a circle.

George III 'Inventory A', p. 51, Raffaello d'Urbino e Scuola 28.

FIG. 155 Cat. No. 806

Lit.: B. B. Woodward, Fine Arts Quarterly Review, I (1863), p. 165; Fischel (1898), 266; Venturi, *Raphael* (1920), 196; Popham 142 (pl. CXXII).
Photo.: Thurston Thompson, 1857; Braun 169.
Study for the group in the fresco of the *Marriage of Cupid and Psyche* in the Farnesina painted about 1516–17. The drawing, an offset of which is at Chatsworth and another at Berlin (according to the Rev. B. B. Woodward, loc. cit), is attributed by Fischel to Giulio Romano. It is not quite so free and masterly as *Christ giving the Keys to St. Peter* catalogued above, with which it must be almost exactly contemporary, and it was not first drawn with the stylus, as was usual with Raphael.

805. THE LAST SUPPER (*Plate* 64) (12745)
307 × 467 mm. Pen and brown ink, a good deal rubbed. W.M., an anchor in a circle.
George III 'Inventory A', p. 51, Raffaello d'Urbino e Scuola 41.
Lit.: Pass., II, 425; Ruland, p. 37, XII, No. 6; Crowe and Cavalcaselle, II, p. 529.
Photo.: Thurston Thompson, 1857.

The drawing corresponds almost exactly with the engraving by Marcantonio (Bartsch XIV, p. 33, 26) and is in the same direction but on a slightly larger scale. There are insignificant differences in the arrangement of the food and cutlery on the table and, on the R., there is an additional strip about 20 mm. wide, with a large amphora. This strip is drawn in rather a different tone of ink and seems to be an addition, but apparently by the same hand as the rest of the drawing. The older writers, Passavant, Ruland and Crowe and Cavalcaselle, accepted the drawing without question as Raphael's original from which Marcantonio made his engraving. I do not know that the drawing has been discussed since that time; it has apparently been disregarded as a copy. At first sight this does appear to be the case, but I do not think this view is necessarily right. In spite of its almost exact correspondence with the print, the individual details, hands, feet, faces, seem to me definitely better, and the drawing, in spite of its engraver-like formality, is extremely Raphaelesque. A passage like the three apostles behind the table on the R. is almost if not quite convincing. If it is not by Raphael we must postulate a pupil who was able to imitate his hand with extraordinary precision.

B. SCHOOL OF RAPHAEL

806. THE EXPULSION FROM PARADISE (*Figure* 155) (12729)

243 × 278 mm. Black chalk.

George III 'Inventory A', p. 49, Raffaello d'Urbino e Scuola 4. 'From the same Collection with No. 1' (i.e. No. 803).

Lit.: Pass., II, 418; Ruland, p. 214, VII; Crowe and Cavalcaselle, II, p. 408; Fischel (1898), p. 91.

Photo.: Thurston Thompson, 1857; Braun 163.

Engraved in facsimile by C. M. Metz (Weigel 6344).

The drawing corresponds with the subject painted in the first arcade of the *Loggie*. It was originally washed with brown and heightened with white, as appears from Thurston Thompson's photograph taken in 1857. It must have been drastically cleaned at some time between that date and 1879, about which year Braun first photographed it. Both the shading in brown and the whites have now completely disappeared. In its original state it closely resembled similar drawings of the *Loggie* subjects in the British Museum, in the Albertina and elsewhere. The best of these drawings, among which the present example must be counted, are either (1) originals by Raphael, who is credited by contemporary sources and by the respectable authority of Vasari with the *design* as opposed to the *execution* of the series; or (2) the work of one only of his principal assistants, who must thus in opposition to the evidence available be credited with the design of the whole series; or (3) a uniform series of copies made in Raphael's school from the cartoons. The last explanation seems to me out of the question. Some of these drawings, including the present example and the *Joseph's Dream* in the British Museum, with their *pentimenti*, their variations from the frescoes, and their squaring, have every appearance of being the original designs. The second alternative is more probable, but, of the assistants whom Vasari names, Giulio Romano seems excluded by the style of the drawings, as does Giovanni da Udine. This leaves Giovanni Francesco Penni and, if the frescoes in the *Sala di Costantino* generally given to him are indeed his, his powers as a designer would seem to be quite unequal to the really brilliant conception of the *Loggie* series. We are often asked to believe that Raphael (and other *capiscola*) were in the habit of providing their assistants with the slightest sketches (of which no convincing examples have ever been produced), and that these assistants could translate and expand these sketches into finished works indistinguishable from those of the master himself. This process has been credited to Giulio Romano and/or Penni in the case of the *Loggie*, the Tapestries and the Farnesina. It seems to me, on general principles, extremely doubtful whether such a practice has ever been usual or is indeed possible, but I think we should have to assume that this did happen if Penni was the author of the present drawing and the others of the same character. The whole problem is very much complicated by the existence of very numerous and excellent copies. Without a very thorough examination of all the *Loggie* drawings from this point of view a solution of the question may not be possible.

807. THE DISTRIBUTION OF THE LANDS BY LOT (*Figure* 156) (12728)

203 × 297 mm. Pen and brown ink, squared in black chalk.

George III 'Inventory A', p. 50, Raffaello d'Urbino e Scuola 17.

Lit.: Pass., II, 420; Ruland, p. 223, XL; Crowe and Cavalcaselle, II, p. 427; Fischel (1898), 232; L'Arte, XXIV (1921), ill. p. 54.

Photo.: Thurston Thompson, 1857; Braun 164.

FIG. 156 Cat. No. 807

Corresponds with the subject in the *Loggie* (K. der K. 194B). Apparently accepted by Passavant as an original by Raphael, this drawing was given by Crowe and Cavalcaselle to Giulio Romano. Fischel regarded it as the work of an artist near to Raphael who drew the composition in the Louvre of the Pope being carried in a litter (Reiset, No. 326). This, with its companion at Stockholm (Stockholm Catalogue, No. 316 as Giulio), has been claimed as the work of Giulio Romano, but I am not convinced that it is either by Giulio or by the same hand as the Windsor drawing. There are other versions of No. 807 in the Ambrosiana at Milan (photo. Braun 148) and in the Louvre. Both these are in the usual technique of the *Loggie* drawings, wash heightened with white, and both are fairly obvious copies. The mannerisms of drawing come very close indeed to Raphael himself, and I suspect it is a copy of his original design for the subject. The drawing is much too sloppy to be actually by him. It is certainly by the same hand as the *Baptism of Our Lord* in the British Museum, of which a copy is discussed below (No. 860).

808. THE MIRACULOUS DRAUGHT OF FISHES (*Figure* 157) (12749)

203 × 340 mm. Pen and brown ink and brown wash over black chalk, heightened with white (with a line in red chalk in the distance on the L.).

George III 'Inventory A', p. 49, Raffaello d'Urbino e Scuola 2. 'This drawing was found in an Old Bureau at

FIG. 157 Cat. No. 808

Kensington which contained part of the Collection of King Charles ye first where also was preserved the Volume of Leonardo da Vinci.'

Lit.: Pass., II, p. 243; Ruland, p. 243, No. 8; Fischel (1898), p. 238.

Photo.: Thurston Thompson, 1857; Braun 165.

Inscribed on the *verso* in a contemporary hand: 'siculo' (?).

This drawing corresponds almost exactly with the cartoon for the tapestry (K. der K. 142), but the birds in the foreground and the fishes in the boat, said by Vasari to have been painted by Giovanni da Udine, are omitted. In this respect it resembles the chiaroscuro woodcut by Ugo da Carpi (Bartsch XII, p. 37, No. 13), for which, as Fischel has suggested, it probably served as the cartoon, though there are some minor differences in the background. It is almost certainly by the same hand as a drawing in the British Museum (1860–6–16–84) of the *Death and Coronation of the Virgin*, and may perhaps be the work of Perino del Vaga. It cannot be the work of Raphael himself, excellent as it is, but it is very probably the copy from his original sketch for the composition.

There is what seems to be a copy from this particular drawing at Oxford (Robinson 117).

809. THE MARRIAGE OF ALEXANDER AND ROXANA (*Figure* 158) (12756)

255 × 362 mm. Pen and brown ink and brown wash on blue (discoloured) paper, heightened with white oil colour, the outlines pricked. Damaged by damp; a number of worm-holes.

George III 'Inventory A', p. 50, Raffaello d'Urbino e Scuola 25.

Lit.: Pass., II, p. 493 m.; Ruland, p. 285, No. 9; Crowe and Cavalcaselle, p. 547 note; Richard Förster, Prussian Jahrbuch XV (1894), p. 195 (ill.); Fischel (1898), 294.

Photo.: Thurston Thompson, 1857.

This drawing, the other existing versions of it and the subject in general, are discussed at length by Förster in the article cited above. The subject follows the description given by Lucian of the picture in Ἡρόδοτος ἢ Ἀετίων.

According to Vasari (in the life of Marcantonio, Vol. V, p. 415) Agostino Veneziano engraved this subject. There is little doubt, however, that he referred to the unsigned print (Bartsch XV, p. 95, 62), which is apparently by Caraglio.

Lodovico Dolce in his *Dialogo della Pittura*, 1557, gives an elaborate description of a drawing by Raphael, which belonged to him, a description which corresponds exactly with the Windsor drawing. There are, however, other drawings, existing or known to have existed, which have been claimed as Dolce's drawing:

(1) A drawing in the Louvre (photo. Braun 277).
(2) A drawing formerly in the Lawrence collection (Lawrence Gallery, Ninth Exhibition, 1836, No. 63), which has disappeared.

(Förster includes a drawing formerly belonging to E. Payne Knight, which was engraved in facsimile by C. M. Metz (Weigel 7057), but this I feel sure is an adaptation by Taddeo Zuccaro and can be left out of account.)

Förster argues that Dolce's drawing cannot be identical with (1) because here there is a Cupid with Alexander's sword flying over the heads of Hephaestion and Alexander, and this Cupid is not described by Dolce. He also excludes (2) on the ground that it is described as identical with the Paris drawing and therefore must also have the Cupid with the sword. The reasons for excluding these drawings do not seem to me entirely convincing. Elaborate as Dolce's description is, he might well have omitted the not very important Cupid with the sword. Förster, however,

FIG. 158 Cat. No. 809

concludes that the elimination of these two versions must leave the Windsor drawing as necessarily that described by Dolce and an original drawing by Raphael.

Even if it were the sheet described by Dolce, the Windsor drawing need not necessarily be an original by Raphael. Connoisseurs, as early even as 1557, were not infallible. The condition of the Windsor drawing is so bad that it is difficult to form an opinion on its authenticity. Against it being by Raphael himself is the fact that it is drawn on *carta azzura*, a material which Raphael and his immediate school rarely employed. The whites, which are in oil, are clearly a later addition. It is *not* the drawing actually used by Caraglio for his engraving. It is larger in size.

There are three further versions of the composition also attributed to Raphael, which differ from the Windsor and allied drawings in that the figures are represented unclothed.

(1) The red chalk drawing in the Albertina (Photo. Braun 171; Vienna Catalogue, III, No. 118).
(2) The rapid pen and ink sketch in the Teyler Museum at Haarlem (ill. Förster, loc. cit., p. 197).
(3) A pen and ink drawing of the L. hand side of the composition in the Uffizi (Alinari's Uffizi Reproductions, II, 37).

No. (1) is much the finest of the drawings so far discussed and, though it is too tentative and delicate to be by Raphael himself, it must I think be the copy of a composition by him. It might well be by the same hand as the *Venus and Cupid* described under No. 810. Though No. (2) seems to be claimed by Förster as Raphael's original sketch from which the Vienna and other versions derive, I cannot believe this to be the case. It is rather a copy by Perino del Vaga whose style seems to me recognizable in it. No. 3 has been generally and, I think, rightly recognized as a copy by Sodoma.

It is certain that Sodoma knew the composition and used it for his fresco of the subject in the Farnesina, which he apparently painted before 1512.

The composition was also painted on the ceiling in a room of the so-called Villa of Raphael, together with Michelangelo's *Archers shooting at a Herm*, but these frescoes, now in the Borghese Gallery, are obviously of a later period.

810. VENUS AND CUPID (*Figure* 159) (12757)

209 × 170 mm. Red chalk over a sketch with the stylus.

George III 'Inventory A', p. 51, Raffaello d'Urbino e Scuola 31.

Lit.: Pass., II, No. 434; Ruland, p. 277, III, No. 5; Fischel (1898), 288; Crowe and Cavalcaselle, II, p. 335 note.

Photo.: Thurston Thompson, 1857; Braun 170.
The drawing corresponds with the subject painted by Raphael's pupils from his designs in Cardinal Bibiena's bathroom. The work was completed on June 20, 1516, and still exists in a very damaged condition (see H. Dollmayr, Archivio Storico III (1890), p. 272, and Silvia de Vito Battaglia, l'Arte XXIX (1926), p. 203 ff.). The *Venus and Cupid* was engraved in the same direction by Agostino Veneziano (Bartsch XIV, p. 218, 286) with the date 1516. There is a version of this drawing in the Albertina (Catalogue III, No. 82: attributed to Giulio Romano) which is rightly characterized by Crowe and Cavalcaselle (loc. cit.) as a copy from the Windsor sheet. Neither of the two is the engraver's drawing used by Agostino Veneziano: both are considerably larger.
The Windsor drawing seems to belong to a series of copies from Raphael compositions, of which characteristic examples known to me are the drawings of the series of Apostles engraved by Marcantonio at Chatsworth. These copies are extremely delicate, almost dainty, in touch, very near to Raphael himself in style, but without his decisiveness.

811. *Recto:* THE PROPHET JONAH (*Figure* 160) (0804)
305 × 200 mm. Pen and brown ink, heightened with white, over black chalk.
Verso: SLIGHT SKETCHES OF FEMALE FIGURES
Pen and ink and black chalk.
Lit.: Pass., II, p. 494 s.
Photo.: Thurston Thompson, 1857.
The drawing is a version with very considerable variations of the statue by Lorenzetti in Sta. Maria del Popolo, Rome (ill. K. der K. 153), said to have been designed by Raphael. The drapery is on the R. instead of on the L. leg as in the statue; there is drapery round the R. arm and

FIG. 159 Cat. No. 810

FIG. 160 Cat. No. 811 *r.*

the position of the head and legs is different. I do not know Lorenzetti as a draughtsman, but this does not look like a sculptor's drawing. On the *verso* are some slight but Raphaelesque sketches in black chalk. One of them appears to be of the Psyche in the engraving of *Psyche adored by the People* (Bartsch XV, p. 213, 40), but in reverse.
The drawing is clearly by the same hand as the *Tarquin and Lucretia* (No. 812) discussed below, and probably by the same draughtsman as the *Loggie* copy (No. 807).

812. TARQUIN AND LUCRETIA (*Figure* 161) (0506)
251 × 168 mm. Pen and brown ink on light brown ground over black chalk, heightened with white.
Lit.: Pass., II, p. 494 f.; Ruland, p. 163, I, 3.
Photo.: Thurston Thompson, 1857.
Inscribed on *verso:* 'Polidoro' and '30' (?).
The drawing corresponds, in the same direction, with the engraving by Agostino Veneziano (Bartsch XIV, p. 169, 208, dated 1524, later retouched by Enea Vico, Bartsch XV, p. 287, 15), or rather the L. hand portion of this engraving. It is certainly not a copy from the print. It seems to be by the same hand as the drawing just described, one at Stockholm of the *Birth of the Virgin* ascribed to Tamagni (Siren, No. 353, ill.), and probably by the same hand as the *Loggie* drawing discussed above (No. 807). These drawings may be copies after Raphael or alternatively inventions by an artist steeped in his manner.

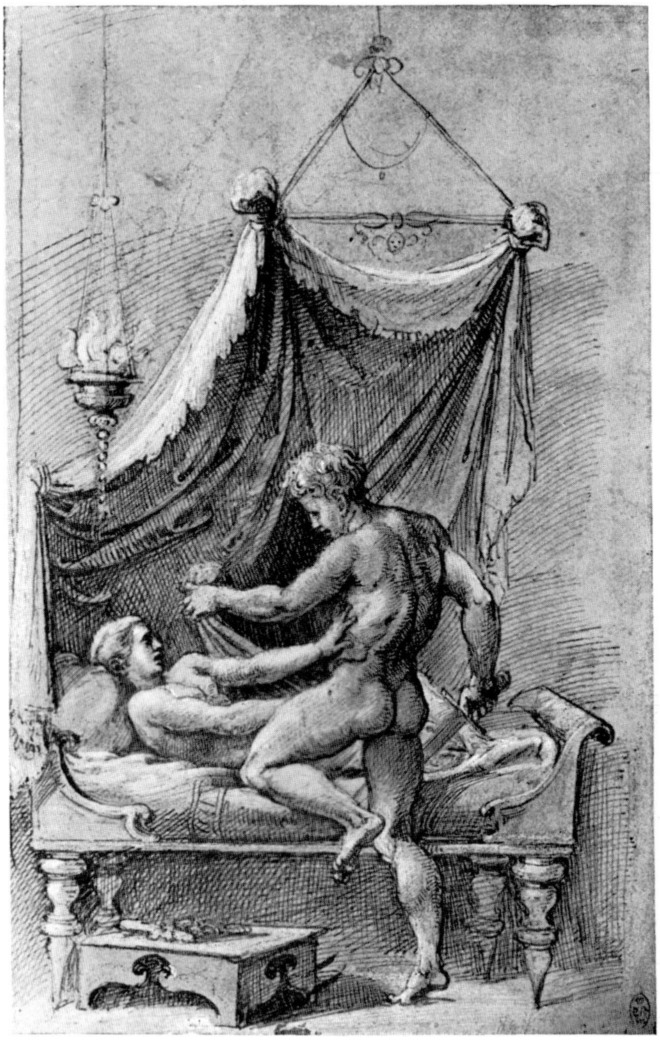

FIG. 161 Cat. No. 812

813. VENUS, VULCAN AND CUPID (0303)
288 × 195 mm. Pen and brown ink, heightened with white, the outlines indented.
George III, 'Inventory A', p. 51, Raffaello d'Urbino e Scuola 42, 'either by Julio Romano, or some of Raphael's Scholars'.
Lit.: Pass., II, p. 493i; Ruland, p. 133, XXXI, No. 5.
Photo.: Thurston Thompson, 1857.
This drawing, which is much damaged and has been cut, particularly on the L., corresponds exactly in reverse with the engraving by Agostino Veneziano (Bartsch XIV, p. 261, 349) but is considerably smaller in scale. This is signed with Agostino's initials, dated 1530, and inscribed: 'RAPH. VRB. DVM/VIVERET INVEN'. In spite of this inscription the design is generally credited to Giulio Romano, and a small cartoon in the Louvre (Catalogue Reiset No. 259), which corresponds with a picture in the same gallery, is accepted as his. The present drawing is in the style of an engraving and shows signs of having been transferred, but no copy or repetition of Agostino Veneziano's engraving is recorded by Bartsch.

814. MOSES CLOSES THE PASSAGE OF THE RED SEA, SO THAT PHARAOH'S HOST IS ENGULFED (*Figure* 162) (5432)
190 × 382 mm. Finished drawing in pen and brown ink, with some wash. Much damaged and restored.

FIG. 162 Cat. No. 814

The present drawing, as well as a corresponding one in the Uffizi (of which there is an old facsimile by S. Mulinari, Weigel 6044), was attributed to Polidoro da Caravaggio. It is too much damaged and restored for any judgment on its authorship to be made. The type of horse however does not conform to the peculiar hog-maned hobby horse which Polidoro usually depicts.
The subject corresponds in reverse with an engraving by Pietro Santi Bartoli, unnumbered but apparently forming part of the series of the tapestry borders and *chiaroscuri* in the *Stanze* dedicated to Nicolaus Simonellius and attributed, like them, to Raphael. According to Passavant (Raphael, Vol. II, p. 136, No. 103) this, and five other subjects also engraved by Bartoli, were painted in the embrasures of the windows in the *Stanza d'Eliodoro*. He says the originals are 'très déteriorés, en partie irréconnaissables' but 'à en juger par quelques vestiges de ces peintures, ils répresentaient les sujets suivants, que Petrus Sanctus Bartolus a publiés . . .' One of these six prints, the *Donation of Constantine* (which is in fact only half of the full width of the *Moses and the Red Sea*), does correspond with a chiaroscuro still existing in the embrasure of a window in the *Sala d'Eliodoro* (K. der K. 104B).
According to Fritz Baumgart in an article in the Münchner Jahrbuch (VIII (1931), p. 64 ff.), which I find generally unconvincing, the six unplaced prints by Pietro Santi Bartoli are to be divided between the *Stanza d'Eliodoro* and the *Stanza della Segnatura*. His contention is that the two apocalyptic scenes in the former (K. der K. 103) were painted over chiaroscuri corresponding with the prints, though he does not explain the completely different format. The problem would appear impossible of solution without further study on the spot. It is probable, however, that the composition of *Moses and the Red Sea* was painted somewhere in the *Stanze* and presumably formed part of the original scheme of decoration (that is before the alterations in the time of Clement VII and Perino's chiaroscuros on the *basamenti* of the *Stanza della Segnatura*).
Of another of the six unplaced subjects engraved by Bartoli, the *Joseph before Pharaoh*, there are drawings at Stockholm (Schönbrunner–Meder No. 1168) and at Oxford (Robinson 111). The former seems to be the better and is ascribed to Perino del Vaga.

815. HOPE (0415)
262 × 175 mm. Pen and brown ink and brown wash, the outlines indented.
George III 'Inventory A', p. 50, Raffaello d'Urbino e Scuola 11. 'Emblem of Hope. From Kensington.'
Lit.: Pass., II, p. 493p; Ruland, p. 144, B.4.
Engraved in facsimile in Chamberlaine's 'Imitations', pl. LII.

Photo.: Thurston Thompson, 1857.
According to Passavant this is a copy of a drawing ascribed by him to G. F. Penni in the collection of Professor Jansen at Copenhagen which (still according to Passavant) was the original study for the painting then in the collection of H. Hope. It looks as if it formed the pendant to a drawing in the Pierpont Morgan Library (repr. publication, Vol. IV, No. 12) of the Cumaean Sibyl which is engraved by Agostino Veneziano (Bartsch XIV, p. 109, 123).

816. THE VIRGIN MOURNING OVER THE BODY OF CHRIST WHICH LIES ON A BIER IN FRONT OF HER (12747)
238 × 218 mm. Pen and brown ink and brown wash.
George III 'Inventory A', p. 51, Raffaello d'Urbino e Scuola 35.
Lit.: Pass., II, p. 493h; Ruland, p. 39, XVIII, No. 2.
Photo.: Thurston Thompson, 1857; Braun 154.
The drawing corresponds in the same direction with the engraving by Giulio Bonasone (Bartsch XV, p. 126, 60) except for the absence of the rocky background and of the pillow on which the head of Christ rests. This engraving is inscribed: 'RAFAEL VRBINO IN VENTOR I. BONASONO · F'. In spite of this early testimony, and in spite of the fact that the engraving is no doubt based on the present drawing either directly or through an intermediate sheet, it cannot be the work of Raphael himself. Its style shows a considerable resemblance to that of the drawings for the *Loggie*. It is slightly less fluid, more angular in its contours than these. The figure of the Virgin is extremely near to that in the engraving of the same subject by Marcantonio (Bartsch XIV, p. 40, 34), and may have been evolved from the drawing by Raphael on which this engraving was based. The drawing in the Louvre (photo. Braun 251) is no more than a copy of the Marcantonio engraving.

C. COPIES OF EXISTING PAINTINGS AND FRESCOES

817. ST. JOHN THE BAPTIST PREACHING (12748)
280 × 542 mm. Brown wash, heightened with gold.
Lit.: Ruland, p. 58, No. 6.
The drawing is a careful copy perhaps, as suggested on the mount, by Jacopo Ligozzi, of the painting belonging to Lord Lansdowne at Bowood, which formed part of the predella of the *Ansidei Madonna* now in the National Gallery. According to Ruland (1876) the drawing was presented to the Royal Library by W. Stirling, Esq. It did not, therefore, form part of George III's collection.

818. VIRGIN AND CHILD WITH THE INFANT ST. JOHN (4326)
226 × 178 mm. Black chalk.
Copy (from the Maratta volume of copies, but apparently not by him) of Raphael's *Esterhazy Madonna* (K. der K. 46A).

819. SIX DRAPED FIGURES, STANDING TURNED TO THE L. (0322)
210 × 126 mm. Drawn with the point of the brush on blue paper, heightened with white.
Lit.: Pass., II, p. 493k3.
Photo.: Thurston Thompson, 1857.
Inscribed in the lower L. corner in ink: 'Rafael'. Copy, possibly by Biagio Pupini, of the group of philosophers just to the R. of the centre in the *School of Athens* (K. der K. 69). Another version of this particular drawing, attributed for no apparent reason to Timoteo Viti, is at Munich (Munich Reproductions, XII, 116).

820. A DRAPED MAN LEANING ON A PARAPET (0241)
207 × 117 mm. Pen and brown ink and brown wash, heightened with white (oxidised). Wormed and damaged by damp.
Lit.: Pass., II, p. 493k4.
Photo.: Thurston Thompson, 1857.
Inscribed in ink in an old hand: 'Rafaele'. Copy from the figure of the philosopher watching the young man writing towards the R. in the *School of Athens* (K. der K. 69).

821. APOLLO (0825)
181 × 84 mm. Pen and brown ink.
Lit.: Ruland, p. 192, No. 118.
Copy, probably of the XVII century, from the figure of Apollo decorating the niche on the L. in the *School of Athens* (K. der K. 69).

822. HEAD OF THE FOREMOST ANGEL IN THE EXPULSION OF HELIODORUS FROM THE TEMPLE (K. der K. 90) (12752)
277 × 230 mm. Black chalk, much rubbed.
George III 'Inventory A', p. 50, Raffaello d'Urbino e Scuola 12 (?).
Lit.: Ruland, p. 201, No. 38; Fischel (1898), 171.
Photo.: Thurston Thompson, 1857; Braun 162.
It is difficult to form an opinion of this very damaged drawing. It might be a copy of the time of Sacchi or Maratta. What is alleged to be the fragment of the cartoon for the *Expulsion of the Heliodorus from the Temple* with the heads of the two angels is in the Louvre (photo. Braun 261, 262). Fischel doubts the authenticity of the present drawing and says it has anyhow nothing to do with the *Heliodorus*.

823. GROUP OF THE STANDING WOMAN AND THE SEATED WOMAN AND CHILDREN ON THE L. OF THE MASS OF BOLSENA (0170)
353 × 204 mm. Black chalk on blue paper.
Late copy, perhaps of the time of Maratta, from the fresco in the *Stanza d' Eliodoro* (K. der K. 93).

824. THE TWO HORSEMEN GALLOPING TO THE L. IN THE MEETING OF LEO I WITH ATTILA (0319)
202 × 304 mm. (cut irregularly on the L.). Pen and brown ink.
Lit.: Pass., II, p. 493 n.; Ruland, p. 202, No. 12; Crowe and Cavalcaselle, II, p. 142 note; A. Venturi, L'Arte XXIV (1921), p. 53 (ill.).
Photo.: Thurston Thompson, 1857.
Copy, as recognized already by Passavant, from the fresco in the *Stanza d'Eliodoro* (K. der K. 101). Ruland ascribes the copy to Perino del Vaga, but it seems to me rather the work of a later mannerist. Adolfo Venturi (loc. cit.) published it as an original by Raphael.

825. TWO ARMED HORSEMEN AND OTHER SOLDIERS ON FOOT IN THE MEETING OF LEO I WITH ATTILA (01237)
297 × 455 mm. Pen and brown ink and brown wash on blue paper, heightened with white. Numerous worm-holes, especially round the edges.
Copy from the fresco in the *Stanza d'Eliodoro* (K. der K. 101). The style suggests the time of the Zuccari. According to a note on the mount the drawing was bought at Florence by R[ichard] H[olmes] in 1875.

826. THE TIBURTINE SIBYL (5961)
340 × 225 mm. Black and red chalk.
Copy of the Tiburtine Sibyl in the fresco of the four sibyls in Sta. Maria della Pace, Rome (K. der K. 113). The copy seems to have been credited to Tibaldi, which is possible.

827. CHRIST HANDING THE KEYS TO ST. PETER (0317)
164 × 285 mm. Pen and brown ink and brown wash, heavily heightened with white, on brown ground.
Lit.: Pass. II, 425 (copy); Ruland, p. 245, No. 20.
Photo. Thurston Thompson, 1857.
Inscribed in ink at centre of lower edge: 'Rafael o Giul^{o} Rom^{o}'. Copy of the tapestry cartoon of the subject (K. der K. 136). Ruland's suggestion that the copy is the work of Biagio Pupini seems probable, and had occurred to me independently.

828. *Recto:* CHRIST BEARING THE CROSS (0795)
Verso: ST. MARK AND ST. LUKE, SEATED ON CLOUDS
246 × 175 mm. Pen and brown ink and grey wash, squared in black chalk.
Inscribed in ink at lower L. corner: 'fran^{cus} Pachecus pinxit'.
This drawing by Francesco Pacheco is copied from an engraving by Agostino Veneziano (Bartsch XIV, p. 34, 28) after Raphael's *Spasimo di Sicilia* of 1517 in the Prado, Madrid (K. der K. 154). The two evangelists on the *verso* are also copied from Agostino Veneziano's engravings (Bartsch XIV, p. 83, 92 and 94) after Giulio Romano.

829. *Recto:* JUPITER, WITH HIS R. FOOT ON THE GLOBE AND THE EAGLE BETWEEN HIS LEGS; Neptune is seen behind to the L. and the draped leg of a third deity, Juno, to the R. (*Figure* 163) (0490)

FIG. 163 Cat. No. 829 *r.*

395 × 280 mm. Pen and brown ink and brown wash over black chalk, heightened with white and squared in black chalk.
Verso: STUDIES OF LEGS in the position of those of Jupiter on the *recto*, but undraped, and of an arm.
Black chalk.
Lit.: B. B. Woodward, *Specimens of the Drawings of Ten Masters*, London, 1870, p. 46 (ill.).
Inscribed on the *verso* with the name 'Julio Romano' and the prices according to William Gibson's system (6.3. = 15/– and 1.4. = 20/–). The figures correspond with those of Jupiter and Neptune in Raphael's Farnesina fresco of *Psyche received into Olympus* (K. der K. 163), except that the positions of Jupiter's head and arms, of Neptune's R. arm and the head of the eagle, have been altered. The drapery over the legs of Jupiter also corresponds fairly closely with that in Agostino Veneziano's engraving of *St. Mark* (Bartsch XIV, p. 83, 94) after Giulio Romano. It looks as if the author of this drawing, who can hardly be Giulio Romano, had at his disposal a drawing or drawings by Raphael also used by Giulio Romano.

830. CUPID AND THE THREE GRACES (12755)
240 × 218 mm. Pen and brown ink and brown wash, faded and injured by damp.
George III 'Inventory A', p. 50, Raffaello d'Urbino e Scuola 14 (?).
Lit.: Pass., II, 432; Ruland, p. 281, No. 7; Fischel (1898), 268.
Photo.: Thurston Thompson, 1857; Braun 168.
Inscribed on *verso* in ink in an old hand: 'Rafaele d'Vrbino'. Copy from the fresco in the pendentive in the Farnesina (K. der K. 158, right).

831. FLYING PUTTO WITH A TRIDENT (2036)
202 × 162 mm. Black chalk.
From the Carracci series.
Copy, probably of the XVII century, from one of the winged *putti* above the arches in the Farnesina. It is the one between the pendentive of *Psyche carried to Heaven* and *Psyche bringing the box to Venus.*

832. *Recto:* HEAD OF A WOMAN LOOKING DOWN, THREE-QUARTERS TO L. (0341)
Verso: STUDY OF DRAPERY
160 × 152 mm. Red chalk, with some added touches in dark red.
Apparently a copy, with the eyes altered, of Raphael's *Virgin with the Rose* in the Prado (K. der K. 170). I cannot connect the drapery study with anything, but the style is early and Raphaelesque.

833. VIRGIN AND CHILD WITH ST. ELIZABETH AND INFANT ST. JOHN (12740)
268 × 222 mm. Red chalk, over a sketch with the stylus. Damaged by damp and torn irregularly at both sides.
George III 'Inventory A', p. 51, Raffaello d'Urbino e Scuola 27.
Lit.: Pass., II, p. 493 f.; Ruland, p. 80, XXXIX; Crowe and Cavalcaselle, Vol. II, p. 463; Fischel (1898), 327; Fischel, Part VIII, 379A.
Photo.: Thurston Thompson, 1857; Braun 175.
This drawing is a copy from the painting *The Small Holy Family* in the Louvre (K. der K. 171). It is engraved by Caraglio (Bartsch XV, p. 69, 5), but this is larger than, and differs in many details from, the drawing. It is a careful and sensitive drawing in the style of many after the Farnesina frescoes at Chatsworth and elsewhere.

COPIES FROM THE LOGGIE

834. FOUR COPIES ON THE SAME SHEET FROM SUBJECTS PAINTED IN THE LOGGIE (0164)
166 × 188 mm. Pen and light brown ink and wash.
The subjects are: (1) Isaac blessing Jacob (K. der K. 184A); (2) Isaac and Esau (K. der K. 184B); (3) The Flight of Jacob (K. der K. 186B); (4) Jacob seeking Rachel in marriage (K. der K. 186A). The copyist is an artist of the end of the XVI century, perhaps Andrea Boscoli. On the *verso* is a sketch in pen and ink and wash of an old man holding the R. hand of a youth, and two sketches in black chalk of boats. The figures are copied from Masaccio's fresco of the *Tribute Money* in the Carmine at Florence.

835–844. SERIES OF TEN COPIES FROM THE SUBJECTS IN THE LOGGIE
Each measuring approximately 185×285 mm. Black chalk. From the Maratta series.

835. ADAM AND EVE LABOURING (K. der K. 178B) (4282)

836. ABRAHAM AND MELCHISEDEK (K. der K. 181A) (4283)

837. ABRAHAM AND THE ANGELS (K. der K. 182A) (4284)

838. GOD'S PROMISE TO ABRAHAM (K. der K. 181B) (4285)

839. ISAAC BLESSING JACOB (K. der K. 184A) (4289)

840. ISAAC AND ESAU (K. der K. 184B) (4290)

841. JACOB'S FLIGHT (K. der K. 186B) (4291)

842. THE PASSAGE THROUGH THE JORDAN (K. der K. 193A) (4293)

843. SAUL ANOINTED BY SAMUEL (K. der K. 195A) (4294)

844. DAVID AND GOLIATH (K. der K. 195B) (4295)
These ten drawings from the volume of Maratta copies, though not apparently by him, are certainly not earlier than the XVII century.

845. GOD APPEARING TO ISAAC (4286)
155 × 128 mm. Drawn with the point of the brush in brown over black chalk on blue paper, heightened with white.
A copy, probably of the XVII century, of the fresco in the *Loggie* (K. der K. 183A). The drawing, like the series just described and Nos. 846 and 847, comes from the volume of Maratta drawings, to which it seems to bear no resemblance in style. The late W. H. Carpenter suggested on the mount an attribution to Nicolas Poussin, for which, in my opinion, there is no warrant.

846. GOD APPEARING TO ISAAC (4287)
196 × 235 mm. Drawn with the point of the brush and washed in brown, on blue paper, heightened with white over black chalk; unfinished.
A copy, probably of the XVII century, of the fresco in the *Loggie* (K. der K. 183A). The drawing, with the following one, comes from the volume of drawings by Maratta, but they do not bear any resemblance to his style.

847. ISAAC AND REBECCA SPIED ON BY ABIMELECH (4288)
202 × 234 mm. Drawn with the point of the brush and washed in brown on blue paper, heightened with white.
Copy, *en suite* with No. 846, of the fresco in the *Loggie* (K. der K. 183B).

848. PHARAOH'S HOST SUBMERGED IN THE RED SEA (*Figure* 164) (0332)
230 × 374 mm. Pen and ink and brown wash on brown ground, heightened with white.
George III 'Inventory A', p. 50, Raffaello d'Urbino e Scuola 18.
Lit.: Crowe and Cavalcaselle, II, p. 517, note.
Photo.: Thurston Thompson, 1857.
Corresponds with the fresco in the *Loggie* (K. der K. 190A).

FIG. 164 Cat. No. 848

There are other drawings, similar in style, which belong to an artist independent of the Raphael school, possibly a Bolognese: (1) A similar copy from the subject of *David and Goliath* in the *Loggie* (Venice, Academy: photo. Braun 69); (2) The Coronation of Julius II (Venice, Academy: photo. Braun 26, published by Oskar Fischel, Illustrazione Vaticana, VII (1936), p. 513). What appears to be a good drawing of Pharaoh's Host in the normal style and technique for the *Loggie* is that in the Louvre (Reiset, 310; photo. Braun 275).

849. MOSES BEARING THE NEW TABLES OF THE LAW (0414)
201 × 270 mm. Pen and brown ink and brown wash on light brown paper, heightened with white.
Corresponds with the subject in the *Loggie* (K. der K. 192B). On the *verso* is an old inscription in ink: 'parmegiano: No. 4'. Though the style of the copy shows some resemblance to that of Parmigianino, it is too coarse and careless in handling for him. It is nearer to Schiavone.

850. THE MIRACULOUS DRAUGHT OF FISHES (0330)
146 × 312 mm. Corners cut. Pen and brown ink and brown wash on light red ground, heightened with white.
George III 'Inventory A', p. 49, Raffaello d'Urbino e Scuola 3. 'A Copy of the above [i.e. No. 808] once held for an Original. This of ye same Collection [Charles I]'.
Coll.: N. Lanière (Lugt 2886).
Lit.: Pass., II, 423 (copy); Ruland, p. 244, No. 13.
Photo.: Thurston Thompson, 1857.
Inscribed in ink in an old hand in bottom L. corner: 'Raphaello di Urbino'. A copy either from the drawing described above (No. 808), or from the chiaroscuro woodcut

by Ugo da Carpi. The figure steering the second boat on the extreme R. has been cut off.

851. *Recto:* THE BUILDING OF THE TEMPLE BY SOLOMON
Verso: THE UPPER PART OF A RICHLY DECORATED AMPHORA (0318)
250 × 244 mm. Pen and light brown ink. W.M., a ladder within a circle.
Corresponds with part of the subject in the *Loggie* (K. der K. 198B). The copyist may perhaps be Girolamo da Carpi (see another copy from the *Loggie* certainly by him in the Albertina: Catalogue I, 137, as Franco).

852. THE BAPTISM OF OUR LORD (0329)
245 × 393 mm. Black chalk.
George III 'Inventory A', p. 50, Raffaello d'Urbino e Scuola 15.
Lit.: Pass., II, p. 422; Crowe and Cavalcaselle, II, p. 527.
Photo.: Thurston Thompson, 1857.
Corresponds with the subject painted in the *Loggie* (K. der K. 200A). It is independent of the drawing described below (No. 860), and corresponds in all essentials with the fresco.

853. THE VIRGIN AND CHILD AND ST. JOSEPH (01357)
403 × 338 mm. Some tears along the edges and in the centre. Finished drawing in red chalk.
Careful, early copy of some version of the *Madonna of Loreto* (K. der K. 209 R.).

854. A SIBYL SEATED READING FROM A BOOK AND A CHILD HOLDING A TORCH (3479)
289 × 194 mm. Pen and brown ink and brown wash on brown paper, heightened with white.
Copy of the chiaroscuro woodcut by Ugo da Carpi after Raphael (or reputed to be after Raphael), Bartsch XII, p. 89, 6. The style is near to that of Parmigianino.

D. COPIES OF EXISTING DRAWINGS

855. THE FAINTING VIRGIN SUPPORTED BY THREE ATTENDANTS (12746)
272 × 193 mm. Pen and brown ink.
Lit.: Pass., II, p. 492 d; Ruland, p. 21, III, No. 11; Fischel (1898), 93; Fischel, Pt. IV, under 179.
Photo.: Thurston Thompson, 1857; Braun 155.
Inscribed on the *verso* in ink in an old hand: 'Gironimo (?) Cartolan (?)', an inscription which I am unable to explain.
This drawing is the copy of a lost original study by Raphael for the Borghese *Entombment*, in many ways more faithful than the British Museum version (Fischel, No. 179).

856. THE FIGURES OF THE LOWER L. HAND SIDE OF THE 'DISPUTÀ', STUDIED AS NUDES (0412)
230 × 335 mm. Pen and brown ink and brown wash.
George III 'Inventory A', p. 49, Raffaello d'Urbino e Scuola 6.
Lit.: Pass., II, p. 493 i; L'Arte XXIV (1921) p. 53 (ill.).
Photo.: Thurston Thompson, 1857.
Copy of the drawing in the Staedel Institut at Frankfort (Fischel, No. 269). It is in a different technique, torn and damaged by damp. Venturi in l'Arte (loc. cit.) seems to regard it as an original.

857. THE VIRGIN AND CHILD SEATED ON THE GROUND WITH THE INFANT ST. JOHN (12741)
145 × 110 mm. Red chalk.
Feeble copy of a fragmentary drawing in pen and ink on the *verso* of a sheet at Oxford (Fischel, 129), of which there is also a copy in the Louvre (ill. Fischel, Text III, Fig. 134) and two in the British Museum (1900–8–24–115 and Malcolm, 1895–9–15–623).

858. A SEATED PROPHET HOLDING A SCROLL WITH BOTH HANDS, TWO PUTTI SUPPORTING A TABLET ON THE R. (0334)
222 × 250 mm. Pen and brown ink and brown wash on discoloured paper. W.M., an anchor in a circle surmounted by a star.
Copy of the L. hand portion of a drawing which was in the collection of the late Sir John Leslie, Bt., and was reproduced in Sotheby's Sale Catalogue, 1936, December 9, lot 47, and lithographed in the Lawrence Gallery, No. 24 (the latter also reproduced in the Burlington Magazine XX (1911–12) p. 298). There seems, however, to be some doubt about the authenticity of the Leslie drawing.

859. VIRGIN AND CHILD (12739)
323 × 225 mm. Red chalk (damaged by damp, crumpling and tears).
George III 'Inventory A', p. 51, Raffaello d'Urbino e Scuola 40 (?).
Lit.: Pass., II, p. 493 e.
Photo.: Thurston Thompson, 1857; Braun 174.
This drawing is an exact copy of one in the Uffizi (No. 535F) also in red chalk. This last is a study, generally since the time of Morelli given to Giulio Romano, but in my opinion by Raphael himself, for the *Madonna of Francis I* in the Louvre painted about 1518 (K. der K. 165).

860. THE BAPTISM OF OUR LORD (12731)
179 × 382 mm. Pen and brown ink over black chalk.
George III 'Inventory A', p. 50, Raffaello d'Urbino e Scuola 19.
Lit.: Pass., II, p. 184 and p. 489, No. 422; Crowe and Cavalcaselle, II, p. 527.
Photo.: Thurston Thompson, 1857.
Corresponds with the subject painted in the *Loggie* (K. der K. 200A), but more exactly with a drawing in the British Museum (1865–6–8–150). It repeats this down to the irregular cutting along the bottom and is an old facsimile of it. Crowe and Cavalcaselle (loc. cit.) wrongly assume that the Windsor drawing was in the collection of the King of Holland. It is the British Museum drawing which was in that collection. This latter drawing is clearly by the hand that drew the *Distribution of the Lands by Lot* (No. 807 above).

861. FRIEZE OF THREE DANCING FIGURES; a man blowing a trumpet, a woman with cymbals, a faun playing the pipes. (0331)
170 × 342 mm. Red chalk.
Lit.: Pass., II, p. 493 o; Ruland, p. 347 XIV, No. 6.
Photo.: Thurston Thompson, 1857.
This is a later copy, perhaps of the time of the Zuccari, of the drawing at Vienna (Catalogue III, No. 84, attributed to Giulio Romano). The subject was engraved in 1516 by Agostino Veneziano (Bartsch XIV, p. 203, 250, R. half), with the positions of the faun and the trumpeter transposed. Passavant (loc. cit.) believed the Windsor drawing to be identical with a framed drawing seen by Richardson in the Bonfiglioli Collection at Bologna (*An Account* . . ., 1722, p. 33).

GIOVANNI BATTISTA RICCI (DA NOVARA) (1545–1620)

862. CHRIST ABOUT TO BEAR THE CROSS (*Figure* 165) (0228)

FIG. 165 Cat. No. 862

229 × 168 mm. Pen and brown ink and brown wash over black chalk.
P.M.R.P. Inscribed in the 'deceptive' hand in the bottom L. corner: 'Bernardo Campi'. A curved line drawn over the subject and cutting off the corners shows that it was intended to fill an oval space. The attribution of this drawing and of Nos. 863, 864 and 865 is based on the unmistakable identity of style with that of a large drawing of the *Massacre of the Innocents* in the British Museum (Sloane 5214–249), which is signed on the *verso* I.B.R. and dated October 16, 1590. Ricci seems indeed to have been in the habit of signing and dating his drawings on the back, but it has not been possible to ascertain whether the Windsor drawings are so inscribed.

863. CHRIST ABOUT TO BE NAILED TO THE CROSS: He is seen on the R. between two soldiers, while another soldier drills a hole in the Cross as it lies on the ground; other soldiers mounted and on foot are behind. (0230)
240 × 173 mm. Pen and brown ink and brown wash over black chalk.
P.M.R.P. Inscribed in the 'deceptive' hand in the bottom L. hand corner: 'Bernardo Campi'. Two intersecting circles drawn with the compass over the composition indicate that it was intended for an oval.
En suite with No. 862.

864. CHRIST TAKEN DOWN FROM THE CROSS: His body, with the arms raised above the head, is being carried by three men; in the background are groups of people. (0229)
176 × 170 mm. Pen and brown ink and brown wash.
P.M.R.P. Inscribed in the 'deceptive' hand in the bottom L. hand corner: 'Bernardo Campi'. The style is exactly that of Nos. 862 and 863, though it is not of the same format.

865. ST. BERNARDINO OF SIENA RESTORING TO LIFE A CHILD WHO HAD BEEN TOSSED BY A BULL (5987)
244 × 113 mm. Pen and brown ink and brown wash.
P.M.R.P. The old attribution was apparently to Passignano. The style is unmistakably that of the drawings previously described.

866. THE VIRGIN AND CHILD WITH ST. VINCENT, on whose shoulder she places her hand, and a bearded monk, on whose head the infant Christ places His hand. (0233)
226 × 178 mm. Pen and brown ink and brown wash, partly squared in black chalk.
A.E.P. Attribution in the 'deceptive' hand to 'Giulio Campi', with whose style it shows no connection. It is almost certainly by G. B. Ricci, and is in fact dated on the *verso* in that artist's characteristic way, 1608, with the day of the month, though not signed with his initials.

867. THE ADORATION OF THE MAGI (5058)
306 × 230 mm. Pen and brown ink and brown wash on blue paper, heightened with white. The second king, standing on the Virgin's L. hand, and the head of the camel on the R., are corrections on pieces of paper stuck on.
A.E.P. The attribution to Ricci is based on the resemblance to the drawings already described and to the *Massacre of the Innocents* in the British Museum, to which reference has already been made under No. 862. The painting of the *Adoration of the Magi* in S. Marcello al Corso (Venturi, IX 5, Fig. 533) shows also a similar composition.

868. HISTORICAL SUBJECT: A CARDINAL ENTHRONED IN THE CENTRE; to the R. and L. in front, benches with boys seated on them; from pulpits on the R. and L. two men in civilian costume address the audience. (6022)
225 × 255 mm. (cut into on both sides and damaged on the L.). Pen and light brown ink and brown wash, squared in black chalk.
A.E.P. The attribution is based on the style.

Attributed to GIOVANNI BATTISTA RICCI

869. A POPE AND A CARDINAL IN CONVERSATION IN A LIBRARY (*Figure* 166) (6023)
219 × 158 mm. Pen and brown ink and brown wash, squared in red chalk.
A.E.P. The features of the pope are those of Paul V Borghese (1605–1621). The drawing corresponds with one of five scenes painted on the wall of a room adjoining the Sixtine Library (Camera di Sta. Francesca Romana), described by Taja, *Descrizione del Palazzo Apostolico Vaticano*. Rome, 1750, p. 460, with the inscription: 'Paulus P.P.V. magnam librorum copiam typis descriptorum bibliothecae Vaticanae adiicit: Scipionem Cardinalem Burghesium ex sorore nepotem, Sedis Apostolicae Bibliothecarium creat'. It is just discernible in a photograph which I owe to the kindness of Mr. E. K. Waterhouse. The room is dated 1610 on the vaulting. There is no record in Baglione or in Taja of who decorated it, but according to Monsignore Stanislao le Grelle (*Musei e Gallerie Pontifice. V. Gallerie di Pittura*, Rome, 1925, p. 14) G. B. Ricci was responsible for the decoration of the Sale Paoline of the Biblioteca under the direction of Monsignore Baldassare Ansidei, Prefetto della

FIG. 166 Cat. No. 869

Biblioteca. This statement may or may not be based on documentary evidence, but the style of the drawing, though by no means conclusively in favour of Ricci's authorship, is at any rate not dissimilar.

Dr. Jacob Hess, to whom I am indebted for a reference to the Guide cited above, suggests that the fresco is by the same hand as the oil painting of Sixtus V approving the design of the new library submitted to him by Domenico Fontana, which is documented as the work of Pietro Facchetti about 1590 (ill. J. A. F. Orbaan, *Sixtine Rome*, London, 1911, frontispiece), a suggestion which has much to recommend it.

There is a drawing in the Albertina (Albertina Catalogue III, 364) for an adjoining fresco representing the Emperor Zeno honouring the library of Constantinople. Though this is traditionally attributed to Cesare Nebbia, the style, even in the small reproduction, is recognizable as G. B. Ricci's. I am informed by Prof. van Regteren Altena that he has in his collection a drawing for another of the series, and that there is a fourth at Copenhagen.

870. STUDY OF THE HEAD OF AN ECCLESIASTIC IN PROFILE TO THE L. and study of the head of a bearded old man looking up, both repeated on a smaller scale on the R.; below groups of women and children. (5157)

280 × 181 mm. Black chalk and pen and brown ink on yellow-tinted paper.

A.E.P. The style, particularly as shown in the pen and ink head on the R. and in the groups of women and children, seems to be that of the drawings already described.

871. GROUP OF WOMEN WITH CHILDREN SEATED ON THE GROUND (0391)

214 × 178 mm. Pen and light brown ink and pale wash.

A.E.P. Attribution in the 'deceptive' hand to 'Baccio Bandinelli'. The attribution to Ricci is based on the similarity to the drawings previously described. The drawing may well be, as suggested on the mount, part of a composition of the *Miracle of the Loaves and Fishes*. Compare Gatti's fresco of the subject in the Refectory of S. Pietro al Po, Cremona (Venturi, IX 6, Fig. 495). The style comes confusingly near to that of Aurelio Luini, to whom I had previously attributed it.

Attributed to GIROLAMO ROMANINO
(1484/89–1566 ?)

872. TWO WOMEN SEATED IN CONVERSATION (*Figure* 167) (4793)

239 × 200 mm. Drawn with the point of the brush in brown, with some wash.

Lit.: K. Clark, O.M.D. V (1930–36), p. 64 (pl. 47); G. Gronau, Thieme-Becker XXV (1931), p. 141.

Clark published the drawing as Moretto: 'the attribution to Moretto can hardly be questioned,' he writes. Nevertheless, while admitting the general similarity to Moretto, I venture to agree with Wilde, who has suggested Romanino as more probably the draughtsman. The type of face, sharply lighted and accentuating the plumpness of the cheek, is to be found constantly in Romanino (typical examples are in the frescoes of the castle of Buonconsiglio at Trent, ill. in Bollettino d'Arte IX (1929–30), pp. 323 and 329).

873. A PARTY OF MUSICIANS IN A BOAT (*Plate* 167) (0338)

236 × 333 mm. (oval). Black chalk and grey wash.

FIG. 167 Cat. No. 872

Romanino has been written in pencil on the mount. The type of *genre* scene is of course characteristic of that painter (see especially the decorations in the castle of Buonconsiglio already referred to), and it is either by Romanino himself or by some artist near to him. Certain peculiarities suggest Marcello Fogolino, who worked with Romanino at Trent, but these do not seem sufficiently marked to warrant an attribution to him.

Attributed to CRISTOFORO RONCALLI (IL POMERANCIO) (1552–1626)

874. 'ECCE HOMO' (0200)
214 × 195 mm. Black chalk.
Inscribed on the drawing in pencil: 'del Pomarancio', by which certainly Roncalli and not Circignano is intended.

ROSSO FIORENTINO (GIOVANNI BATTISTA ROSSO) (1495–1540)

875. STUDY OF THREE FIGURES FOR A MASSACRE OF THE INNOCENTS (*Plate* 36) (0311)
290 × 205 mm. Red chalk.
Inscribed 'Del Rosso Fiorentino' in pencil on the drawing. This attribution seems well-founded and the style points to Rosso's Florentine period before 1523. It perhaps most closely resembles the manner of a drawing in the Uffizi, No. 477F (Venturi, IX 5, Fig. 125).

876. MUCIUS SCAEVOLA PLACING HIS HAND IN THE FLAMES (0460)
100 × 128 mm. (top L. corner cut). Red chalk.
F.A. Inscribed in ink in an old hand in top R. hand corner: 'micaelangelo bonarot . . .' The attribution to Rosso can be justified by comparison with the drawing of fighting men in the Uffizi (No. 476F: B.B. 2400; K. Kusenberg, *Le Rosso*, Paris, 1931, No. 8).

877. HALF-LENGTH OF A YOUNG WOMAN IN THE COSTUME OF THE EARLY XVI CENTURY (0370)
157 × 96 mm. (partly silhouetted on the L.). Red chalk.
F.A. The old attribution was apparently to Andrea del Sarto. It is difficult to feel quite certain about a fragment of this character, but it seems to show Rosso's touch at about the period of the drawing in the Uffizi of *Old men lamenting over a Skeleton* (No. 6499), which was engraved by Agostino Veneziano in 1518.

Attributed to ROSSO FIORENTINO

878. BATTLE BETWEEN THE CENTAURS AND THE LAPITHS; HERCULES WITH HIS CLUB IS SEEN ON THE R. (0336)
245 × 401 mm. Black chalk (injured by damp in the L. hand bottom corner).
Inscribed in ink on the drawing: 'Del Rosso'. In style and types it comes very near indeed to Rosso, but it is obviously too childishly feeble for him. Perhaps it can be explained as the copy from a design by him. There is no resemblance between it and the subject painted by Rosso in the Galerie François I at Fontainebleau.

After ROSSO FIORENTINO

879. THREE WOMEN LAMENTING AND PART OF A WOMAN ON HER KNEES (0369)
173 × 103 mm. Red and black chalk.
Copy from the group of women on the L. in the *Descent from the Cross*, signed by Rosso and dated 1521, now in the Pinacoteca at Volterra (K. Kusenberg, *Le Rosso*, Paris, 1931, pl. VIII). The copy looks as if it were from the hand of Federico Zuccaro.

880. THE LOVES OF SATURN AND PHILYRA (0494)
182 × 139 mm. Pen and light brown ink.
Attributed to Giulio Romano. The drawing is in fact a careful copy from the engraving by Jacopo Caraglio after the design of Rosso in the series of the *Loves of the Gods*, Bartsch XV, p. 76, 23. Most of the series are after Perino del Vaga, but this is one of the two designed, according to Vasari, by Rosso.

VENTURA SALIMBENI (About 1567–1613)

881. DESIGN FOR A LUNETTE: A MIRACLE OF ST. MICHAEL (*Plate* 45) (6027)
160 × 324 mm. Pen and brown ink and brown wash.
A.E.P. The style is obviously Salimbeni's.

882. THE BEHEADING OF ST. CATHERINE; above in the sky the Virgin holding the Child, Who presents a flowering branch to a saint. (6033)
314 × 181 mm. Pen and brown ink and brown wash over black chalk, squared in black chalk.
A.E.P. The style is certainly Salimbeni's in a phase in which it can clearly be distinguished from Vanni's.

883. DESIGN FOR A LUNETTE WITH JUSTICE SEATED BEFORE A CURTAIN holding the scales in her R., and the sword in her L., hand. (5035)
136 × 272 mm. Pen and brown ink and brown wash, the outline indented.
A.E.P. The indentation of the outlines and the fact that Justice holds the sword in her L. hand suggests that the design may have been intended for engraving. Its style points to Ventura Salimbeni as the probable author.

Attributed to ENEA SALMEGGIA (TALPINO) (1546/50–1626)

884. THE VIRGIN, HOLDING THE DEAD BODY OF CHRIST ON HER KNEES, adored by a kneeling bishop with his mitre and crozier before him on the ground, and by another saint. (5102)
315 × 204 mm. (cut into on all sides). Point of the brush and wash over black chalk on blue paper, heightened with white, squared in black and red chalk.
P.M.R.P. An inscription (in the 'deceptive' hand?) in the bottom R. hand corner is partly cut away, but seems to read 'Annibale Carracci'. It shows a curiously close resemblance, as far as technique goes, to the drawings of Girolamo da Treviso, but the style of composition points to a later period. I think it can be most satisfactorily explained as being the work of the very archaistic Salmeggia.

FRANCESCO SALVIATI (1510–1563)

885. THE VIRGIN AND CHILD AND FIVE SAINTS (*Plate* 33) (051)
366 × 247 mm. Pen and brown ink and brown wash.
Inscribed on the *verso* in a hand of the XVI (?) century: 'S francescho salviato'. Its arrangement indeed resembles that of the altarpiece painted by Giorgio Vasari in his youth for the Compagnia di San Rocco of Arezzo which is now in the church of S. Sebastiano in that town (photo.

R. Soprintendenza, Florence, No. 225), but the style is rather that of Salviati, and the old attribution may be trusted.

886. A HORSEMAN WITH A SPEAR RIDING TO THE L.: upright oval. (5137)
248 × 188 mm. Pen and brown ink and brown wash on green paper, heightened with white.
A.E.P. Study for the oval to the R. of the fresco of *Camillus adding his Sword to the Tribute-money* in the Sala dell' Udienza in the Palazzo Vecchio, Florence. Salviati was at work in the Palazzo Vecchio between 1547 and 1548. The same oval appears in the fresco of the *Decapitation of St. John* in the Oratory of S. Giovanni Decollato, Rome. This fresco is attributed to Pirro Ligorio, but, as has been remarked, must be based on designs by Salviati. It is dated 1553.

887. A BEARDED MAN SEATED ON A ROCK, WITH THE BODY OF A DEAD YOUTH LYING BEFORE HIM (*Plate* 35) (6024)
257 × 391 mm. (top corners cut). Black chalk and brown wash.
F.A. I cannot suggest the subject of which this impressive group must have formed a part or for what it was intended, but the attribution to Salviati is convincing.

888. THE KING OF THE LOMBARDS, LUITPRAND, SUBMITTING TO POPE GREGORY II (?) (*Figure* 168) (5081)
224 × 170 mm. Pen and light brown ink and light brown wash.

FIG. 168 Cat. No. 888

FIG. 169 Cat. No. 889

889. A POPE HANDING THE GONFALONE OF THE CHURCH TO A DOGE (?) (*Figure* 169) (5060)
222 × 170 mm. Pen and light brown ink and light brown wash.

890. A SCENE IN THE HISTORY OF THE PAPACY: a pope celebrating Mass, while below kneels a naked hermit holding a scroll. (6321)
222 × 170 mm. Pen and light brown ink and light brown wash.
A.E.P. No. 888–890, which are *en suite*, illustrate important events in the history of the Papacy, which it is difficult exactly to identify. Closely connected with them, though different in format, is the drawing next to be described. No. 891, and a drawing at Chatsworth (No. 243) also illustrating some event in papal history.
The style of these composition sketches is that of Francesco Salviati. They are clearly by the same hand as a rather more elaborate drawing of the same character in the British Museum (Pp. 2–183), which is a preliminary design for the fresco of the *Triumph of Camillus* in the Palazzo Vecchio at Florence.
It is tempting to connect the four drawings at Windsor and the single drawing at Chatsworth with the decoration of the Sala Regia in the Vatican, where similar subjects appear. Vasari relates how Salviati and Daniele da Volterra were rival candidates for this commission on the accession of Pius V in 1559.

891. A KNEELING EMPEROR PRESENTS THE POPE WITH THE ORB OF WORLDLY POWER; a king and kneeling captives (?) to the R. (5062)

224 × 248 mm. Pen and brown ink and brown wash.

A.E.P. By the same hand as the three drawings previously described (Nos. 888, 889 and 890).

892. THE HOLY FAMILY: the Virgin kneels in profile to the R. and holds out a book in her L. hand; the Infant Christ is on her knee, the infant St. John in front to the L., and St. Joseph behind on the same side. (0219)

265 × 203 mm. Pen and brown ink and brown wash over black chalk.

A.E.P. The attribution to Salviati is based on the unmistakable resemblance in style to Nos. 888–891.

893. DESIGN FOR A SALVER WITH NEPTUNE IN THE CENTRE (*Figure* 170) (6002)

312 × 237 mm. Pen and light brown ink and brown wash on light brown paper, heightened with white. W.M., crossed arrows.

A.E.P. The very peculiar mannerisms, in the drawing of the heads in particular, are the same as in Nos. 888–891, and point clearly to Salviati as the draughtsman.

894. DESIGN FOR A DISH OR SALVER, with Neptune standing on four fighting sea-horses. (0282)

162 × 184 mm. (composition cut into at the bottom and sides). Pen and brown ink and brown wash.

Attribution in ink on the *verso* in an old hand (William Gibson's ?) to 'Francesco Salviati', an attribution which is borne out by the style of this rather mannered design.

FIG. 170 Cat. No. 893

FIG. 171 Cat. No. 895

895. NARCISSUS AND THE NYMPHS (*Figure* 171) (0335)

245 × 174 mm. Black chalk, squared in red chalk, the outlines pricked.

A.E.P. Attribution in pencil on the drawing to 'G: Romano'. The violently mannerist style points to the circle of Salviati and Vasari. Incongruously enough the composition recalls that of the latter's *Allegory of the Conception* (Venturi, IX 6, Fig. 179), but the drawing seems to be rather Salviati's than Vasari's. The figures with their exaggerated *contraposto* may be compared especially with those in Salviati's designs for tapestry, dating from about 1548.

896. DESIGN FOR A CANDELABRUM OR PILASTER DECORATION (12066)

1360 × 440 mm. at the bottom, diminishing to 290 mm. at the top. Pen and brown ink and brown wash. Drawn on four pieces of paper stuck together.

A.E.P. The style of the drawing unquestionably connects it with such designs as Nos. 891, 894, etc., in spite of the difference in scale. The R. and L. hand halves of the design are different and intended as alternatives. The secular character of the decoration—the flight of Aeneas from Troy is represented on a central escutcheon-shaped panel—excludes the possibility of its being the design for a church candelabrum.

897. DESIGN FOR THE TITLE-PAGE OF ANTONIO LABACCO'S 'LIBRO . . . APPARTENENTE A L'ARCHITETTURA,' 1558 (*Figure* 172) (19243)

356 × 237 mm. Pen and brown ink and brown wash.

FIG. 172 Cat. No. 897

Coll.: Cassiano del Pozzo, Albani.
P.M.R.P. There is no documentary evidence for Salviati's having furnished the design for this engraving, but the style leaves little doubt that the drawing is in fact from his hand. That Labacco and Salviati were acquainted is clear from the statement of Vasari (VII, p. 14) that Salviati obtained a commission on the recommendation of Labacco.
The drawing corresponds exactly in the same direction with the engraved title-page, except for the absence of the lettering in the cartouche (LIBRO D'ANTONIO LABACCO APPARTENENTE A L'ARCHITETTURA NEL QUAL SI FIGVRANO ALCVNE NOTABILI ANTIQUITA DI ROMA).

898. A CARYATID (6739)
164 × 104 mm. Red chalk.
Inscribed in black chalk in an old hand on the *verso* (visible through the backing): 'Fr^{co} Salviati'. From an antique statue engraved by Jan de Bisschop (Episcopius) in *Signorum veterum Icones* (1669 ?), pl. 100, as after F. Salviati. I had concluded before noting the old attribution that this was a late drawing by Parmigianino, but there are passages (e.g. the shading on the L. shoulder) which are not in his style, and I think the old attribution is to be accepted.

899. A CAVALRY ENGAGEMENT: design for the R. hand half of a lunette. (01241)
405 × 325 mm. Pen and brown ink and brown wash on green paper heightened with white. The horseman on the L. is on a separate piece of paper stuck on.
A.E.P. Attributed to Taddeo Zuccaro, whether anciently or not I cannot say. The style seems to me nearer to that of Salviati. It does not, however, show any of his most pronounced mannerisms. The fallen horseman on the R. has *fleur-de-lys* on his trappings, and it is possible that the subject may represent the battle of Pavia in 1525. There is an obvious relationship between the two principal figures here and those in a battle scene in the Sala dell' Udienza, Palazzo Vecchio, Florence (photo. Brogi 17319).

900. SCENE BEFORE A CLASSICAL ALTAR (*Figure* 173) (5468)
330 × 525 mm. Pen and brown ink and brown wash on blue paper, heightened with white, the outlines pricked.
A.E.P. Inscribed in ink in an old hand in the bottom R. hand corner: 'p polidoro caravagio'. The drawing is, however, obviously the work of a fully developed mannerist of about 1550, and if not by Francesco Salviati is certainly by some artist very close to him.

901. THE MARRIAGE OF THE VIRGIN (5037)
224 × 168 mm. Pen and brown ink and some wash.
A.E.P. Attributed to Parmigianino. The attitudes and gestures of the three figures correspond closely with those in Rosso's altarpiece in S. Lorenzo, Florence (Venturi, IX 5, Fig. 119), but the spirit and feeling of the drawing are as different from Rosso's as could be imagined. It certainly has nothing to do with Parmigianino, though he did imitate Rosso's altarpiece, but rather shows the peculiarities of Salviati's style, if not necessarily an original drawing by him.

902. DESIGN FOR A COMMEMORATIVE ROUNDEL WITH FIGURES OF JUSTICE AND FAITH (?) LAMENTING (5974)
138 × 166 mm. Pen and brown ink and brown wash on blue paper, heightened with white.
A.E.P. Attributed by Bodmer to the school of Tibaldi, on grounds which are not apparent to me. I should rather have thought it Florentine and probably by Francesco Salviati.

903. PORTRAIT HEAD OF A LADY, TURNED THREE-QUARTERS TO THE L. (5151)
310 × 194 mm. Black chalk touched with red chalk.
Attribution to 'F. Salviati' in pencil in L. hand bottom corner. This seems a reasonable, indeed a probable, attribution. It may be compared with the painting of a young woman in the Samuel H. Kress collection (No. 171). A

FIG. 173 Cat. No. 900

FIG. 174 Cat. No. 906

drawing of a lady's head in profile, formerly in the collection of A. G. B. Russell and now in that of Frits Lugt, might well be by the same hand and represent the same person.

904. ALLEGORICAL FIGURE OF PRUDENCE, DOUBLE-FACED, HOLDING A SERPENT ABOVE HER HEAD (5045)
487 × 264 mm. Pen and brown ink, point of the brush, and brown wash on cream-coloured ground, heightened with white.
Coll.: N. Lanière (Lugt 2886 ?).
A.E.P. The figure shows a close resemblance to an allegorical group flanking one of the subjects of *Camillus* in the Palazzo Vecchio, Florence (Venturi, IX 6, Fig. 85), that above the oval for which No. 886 is a study. The technique and handling are not exactly those usual with Salviati, and it may perhaps be a copy.

905. THE HUNTING OF THE CALYDONIAN BOAR (5098)
287 × 354 mm. (once a flat oval, which has been cut into on both sides, a little at the top and a good deal at the bottom). Pen and brown ink and water colour; considerably damaged.
It seems to me probable that the composition is Salviati's, to whom the drawing was attributed, though it is probably a copy.

ORAZIO SAMACCHINI (1532–1577)

906. A BATTLE WITH THE CAPTURE OF A CASTLE IN THE DISTANCE (*Figure* 174) (5117)
397 × 251 mm. Pen and brown ink and brown wash on light brown ground, heightened with white; squared in black chalk.
A.E.P. Attributed to Federico Zuccaro, whose style is very different. The arms on the horse trappings of the very prominent commander are those of Vitelli, and they reappear on standards in the background together with the motto (IN PERPETUO) of the family. The drawing is clearly the design for a painting glorifying the exploits of the house of Vitelli, and is likely to have been made for the decoration of one of their palaces at Città di Castello. According to Malvasia (Vol. I, p. 216), Prospero Fontana decorated the Salone of their palace there in a few weeks. Giacomo Mancini (*Istruzione storico-pittorica per visitare . . . Città di Castello*, Perugia, 1832, p. 155 ff.) gives a detailed description of the scenes represented, which were explained by Latin inscriptions. I can find no scene described corresponding to the subject of the present drawing, nor to that of a second drawing in the Library of Christ Church, Oxford (E. 24), of the same format and with the Vitelli arms, which clearly belongs to the cycle.
But Malvasia (Vol. I, p. 208) in his life of Samacchini alludes to that artist's having also worked in the Palace of the Vitelli at Città di Castello in competition with Vasari. The style of the Windsor drawing accords perfectly with that of one in the Uffizi (No. 1481F: photo. Gernsheim 2767) which is unquestionably the study for the painting by Samacchini in the Gallery at Bologna (Venturi, IX 6, Fig. 426). I think there can be little doubt that Samacchini is the author of the present drawing. Fontana's paintings were in the Vitelli palace 'a Sant' Egidio': Samacchini's may have been for their other palace at Città di Castello.

907. A PROPHET SEATED WITH A PUTTO (5077)
180 × 109 mm. Pen and brown ink and brown wash on green paper, heightened with white.

908. A SIBYL SEATED WITH A PUTTO (5078)
182 × 115 mm. Same technique.
A.E.P. Studies for the pendentives of Jeremiah and the Samian sibyl in the vaulting of the north transept of the cathedral of Parma. They can be distinguished in the L. hand bottom corner of the small reproduction given by Laudedeo Testi (*La Cattedrale di Parma*, Bergamo, 1934, p. 109), though there are differences in detail, especially in the case of the sibyl. According to Testi the decoration of this vaulting, originally given to Parmigianino in 1522, and then to Rondani, was eventually, on April 5, 1555, allocated to Girolamo Mazzola-Bedoli. It appears that Bedoli had begun the work on December 21, 1557, but that he did not continue it and that finally the commission was given on August 3, 1570, to Orazio Samacchini. The decoration of the vault in its present form seems to be substantially his and these two drawings are his preliminary designs.

909. THE VIRGIN AND CHILD WITH ST. ANTHONY ABBOT AND ST. CATHERINE OF ALEXANDRIA (5508)
210 × 170 mm. Pen and brown ink and brown wash over black chalk.
A.E.P. A drawing in the Pinacoteca at Bologna (Inv. 23–1607) exactly corresponding with this but on a larger scale, has an old attribution to Lorenzo Sabbatini, and there is another more elaborate version in the Ecole des Beaux-

Arts, Paris (No. 24290), attributed to Pellegrino Tibaldi. It is clearly not by the last-named, and it seems to me questionable whether it is by Sabbatini, in view of the closer similarity in style and handling to the drawings by Samacchini just described. It is true that Sabbatini and Samacchini were both Bolognese, were friends and died in the same year, so that it is not easy to distinguish between their work, but nevertheless it seems to me that this drawing is by the same hand as those previously described, that of Samacchini.

FIG. 175 Cat. No. 910

910. THE APPARITION OF THE ARCHANGEL MICHAEL TO ST. GREGORY as he goes in procession, carrying the miraculous image of the Virgin, to pray for intercession against the plague. (*Figure* 175) (6021)
375 × 270 mm. Pen and brown ink and brown wash over black chalk.
A.E.P. Obviously by the same hand as the drawing last described and presumably by Orazio Samacchini. It is possible that this drawing, like No. 1081, may have something to do with the picture for the Madonna del Baraccano at Bologna. It is likely to date from the pontificate of Gregory XIII (1572–1585). A very weak version of this drawing ascribed to G. B. Naldini is in the Uffizi (No. 7295F).

After ANDREA DEL SARTO (1486–1531)

911. *Recto:* LEAF OF A SKETCH-BOOK: a young man in converse with two old men and a group of women and (across the sheet) half-length figures on a smaller scale.

Verso: SLIGHT SKETCHES AND STUDIES FOR ABRAHAM SACRIFICING ISAAC (0373)
205 × 272 mm. (edges covered by mount). Black chalk. W.M., a cross-bow in a circle (cut: see J. C. Robinson, *The Drawings of Michel Angelo and Raffaello in the University Galleries*, Oxford, 1870, p. 370, 14).
Inscribed in ink in an old hand on the *recto* at the bottom: 'Andreo del Sarto'. The main sketch on the *recto* is, as recognized by Antal, a copy from the group on the extreme R. in Andrea del Sarto's *History of Joseph* in the Pitti Gallery, Florence (No. 88), while the subsidiary sketch is from another portion of the same picture. No doubt the *verso* also consists of copies but I do not know of what. The sheet is apparently by the same hand as one in the British Museum (1861–12–14–236) with copies from Michelangelo's fresco of the *Conversion of St. Paul* as well as of frescoes by Taddeo Zuccaro in S. Marcello al Corso (dating therefore from after 1564). It must, however, be stated that the Windsor and British Museum sheets can hardly have formed part of the same sketch-book as the paper is different. Antal suggested that the British Museum sheet was by Stradanus, which seems possible, though I cannot feel certain that this is necessarily so, and that the Windsor sheet was the work of Naldini. There is a third sheet certainly by the same hand as the British Museum sheet of copies, with sketches from Daniele da Volterra's frescoes in Sta. Trinità de' Monti (ill. Budapest Jahrbuch IV (1924–26), p. 118).

912. THE RESUSCITATION OF A DEAD CHILD AT THE BIER OF ST. DOMINICK (0362)
235 × 289 mm. Pen and brown ink and brown wash over black chalk.
The drawing reproduces exactly the lower part of the fresco by Andrea del Sarto in the forecourt of the Annunziata, Florence (Venturi, IX 1, Fig. 396). It is almost certainly, as remarked by Antal, the work of Bernardino Poccetti.

913. SIX SAINTS: STS. AUGUSTINE, LAWRENCE, PETER MARTYR AND FRANCIS STANDING, ST. SEBASTIAN AND ST. MARY MAGDALENE KNEELING (0374)
352 × 280 mm. Carefully finished in red and black chalk.
Copy (of the XVII century?) of the picture in the Pitti Gallery, Florence (Venturi, IX 1, Fig. 437).

914. THE VIRGIN SEATED ON CLOUDS, WITH CHILD ANGELS ON EITHER SIDE AND BELOW (0361)
315 × 447 mm. Elaborately finished in black chalk.
Copy (by an engraver of the XVIII century?) from the upper part of the *Assumption of the Virgin* in the Pitti Gallery, Florence (the later version of the subject: Venturi, IX 1, Fig. 458).

915. THE BAPTISM OF OUR LORD (01361)
316 × 384 mm. Finished drawing in brown wash, partly heightened with white (which has oxidised).
Careful copy (of the XVI century?) from Andrea del Sarto's fresco in the Scalzo, Florence (Venturi, IX 1, Fig. 410). According to a note on the back of the mount the drawing was bought in Florence in 1876 by R(ichard) H(olmes).

After LEONARDO DA SARZANA (working 1551 to 1589)

916. POPE PIUS V (1556-1572) SEATED, TURNED THREE-QUARTERS TO THE L. (0244)
331 × 177 mm. Black chalk, rather rubbed.
Copied from the statue of the Pope in the Cappella Sistina in Sta. Maria Maggiore, Rome (Venturi, X 3, Fig. 480).

FIG. 176 Cat. No. 917

ANDREA SCHIAVONE (MELDOLLA) (1522–1563)

917. ST. MARK APPEARING MIRACULOUSLY IN THE CHURCH OF S. MARCO, VENICE, to explain where his bones, which had been lost sight of, were buried. (*Figure* 176) (6677)
325 × 264 mm. Drawn with the point of the brush and washed in blue on white paper; stained and injured by damp.
Lit.: D. von Hadeln, Prussian Jahrbuch, XLVI (1925), p. 138 f. (ill. p. 137); the same, *Spätrenaissance*, p. 24, pl. 15; Tietzes, No. 1469.
Attribution to Schiavone in ink at the bottom. Ingeniously identified by Haldeln as the sketch for a picture which Schiavone was commissioned to paint in the Scuola di S. Marco in 1562, but which he was probably prevented by his death (on December 1, 1563) from completing. That it was begun is apparent from a fragment in the Vienna Gallery (ill. by Hadeln, Prussian Jahrbuch, loc. cit., p. 138), which corresponds with the figure of a woman pointing out the apparition of St. Mark to her child in the foreground of the Windsor drawing. I am informed by Dr. Johannes Wilde that, on the background of the Vienna fragment being cleaned, he found portions of the robes of the senator who stands behind the woman to the L. in the drawing, thus proving beyond question the correctness of Hadeln's identification.

918. THE MYSTIC MARRIAGE OF ST. CATHERINE (*Figure* 177) (0536)
197 × 137 mm. Red chalk, heightened with white, the outlines indented.
Photo.: Braun 135.
A.E.P. Inscribed on the *verso* in an old hand: 'franciscus parmensis' (?). It is in fact the study for the etching of the subject described in Smith's catalogue of Schiavone in Bryan's Dictionary (edition of 1889) under No. 92. It corresponds exactly with this in reverse.

919. THREE FEMALE FIGURES IN FRONT OF AN ALTAR (0352)
245 × 160 mm. Brush drawing in brown on green paper, heightened with white.
The attribution to Schiavone was suggested on the mount by the late W. H. Carpenter, Keeper of Prints and Drawings in the British Museum. Though there is a certain formality about the drawing unusual for Schiavone, it nevertheless seems to me to be by him.

920. APOLLO FLAYING MARSYAS: fragment of a composition. (5088)
178 × 111 mm. Drawn with the point of the brush and washed with brown over black chalk, heightened with white.
A.E.P. The old attribution was, apparently, to Parmigianino, and the figures are indeed Parmigianinesque, but coarser and more Venetian. The composition may be based on, or adapted from, one by Parmigianino, but I think the drawing is by Schiavone. It looks as if the figure on the R. holding the bow was Apollo, and that he was employing a subordinate to do the flaying, a version of the story otherwise unknown.

FIG. 177 Cat. No. 918

921. A WOMAN FLEEING THROUGH A WOOD TO THE R., TURNS BACK TO A CHILD ON THE L. (6700)

285 × 198 mm. Drawn with the point of the brush on blue-green paper, heightened with white.

A.E.P. Attribution to 'P. Veronese' in ink on the drawing in an XVIII century hand. The woman's figure occurs in a very similar form in the background of a painting by Schiavont of the story of Psyche in the Venice Academy (Venturi, IX 4, Fig. 509). I am not sure that the present drawing is original, but it certainly has some relation to Schiavone. Nor can I offer any suggestion as to the subject of this obviously fragmentary drawing.

922. FRIEZE WITH MEN AND WOMEN BRINGING OFFERINGS TO AN IDOL ON AN ALTAR (5465)

129 × 322 mm. Rapid sketch in pen and brown ink.

A.E.P. Absurdly attributed to Maturino, apparently merely on the ground of its being a frieze. The style of drawing is unmistakably North Italian and comes nearest to Schiavone's.

SEBASTIANO DEL PIOMBO (About 1485–1547)

923. *Recto:* STUDIES FOR A HOLY FAMILY WITH THE INFANT ST. JOHN AND A DONOR (*Plate* 80) (4813)

267 × 219 mm. Black chalk, heightened with white.

Verso: THE INFANT CHRIST (*Figure* 178)

Black chalk on a grey-blue prepared surface.

Coll.: N. Lanière (Lugt 2886).

Lit.: K. Clark, O.M.D. V (1930–31), p. 63 (*recto*, pl. 42); B.B. 2505A; L. Dussler, *Sebastiano del Piombo*, Bâle, 1942, No. 177 (*recto*, Fig. 96).

Recto: A (in the centre): the infant Christ sitting by the sphere of the world, to the R. the half-length figure of St. Joseph, at His feet the profile of a bearded donor. B (below to the L.): variant on a smaller scale of the Infant Christ with the sphere and, behind, the half-length figure of the infant St. John. C (above to the R. in the space near the principal study): the Virgin, three-quarter length to the R., standing, the upper part of her body turned slightly to the L., her head turned sharply and inclined in the same direction, her R. arm raised across her body.

Verso: D: variant of the Infant Christ in B, but on a much larger scale.

C was not apparently drawn until the artist had altered the original form of his composition; the upper part of the figure repeats in reverse the motive of the Infant Christ in A, B and D. The gesture of the Virgin is that of a woman holding a veil over her child. A version of such a figure is to be found in Sebastiano's *Madonna del Velo* at Naples (No. 149; not before 1529). The studies were perhaps made for an earlier version of this picture. Clark dates them about 1513–14, Dussler about 1514–16, but the idiom in which they are expressed points rather to a period *after* the studies for the Borgherini chapel. For the profile of the donor compare the *St. James* at Chatsworth (Popham, No. 238).

Sebastiano later used the studies made for the Child (A, B, D) for the figure of a boy embracing a dog in his mural painting of the *Visitation*, once in Sta Maria della Pace, which he began in the 1530's (see the copy of this composition in the Borghese Gallery, R. Pallucchini, *Sebastian Ventziano*, Milan, 1944, pl. 83).

924. GOD THE FATHER, HIS ARMS EXTENDED, FLOATING IN THE AIR (*Plate* 79) (4815)

301 × 237 mm. Black chalk, heightened (or corrected?) with white.

FIG. 178 Cat. No. 923 *v.*

Lit.: K. Clark, O.M.D. V (1930–31), p. 63 (pl. 43); B.B. 2505B; L. Dussler, *Sebastiano del Piombo*, Bâle, 1942, No. 178 (Fig. 97).

Inscribed below on the R. in ink: 'Sebastiano del Piombo'. Probably a study for one of the eight subjects of the Creation and the Fall, which Sebastiano was commissioned to paint inside the dome of the Chigi chapel in Sta. Maria del Popolo, and which were in the end completed by Francesco Salviati in 1554 (Vasari, V, pp. 571 f.; VII, pp. 32 f.: the paintings are nowhere, as far as I am aware, published). Another study in the Louvre for the same series (publ. by O. Fischel in O.M.D. XIV (1939–40), pp. 26 and 30 f., pl. 27) is apparently earlier in date. No. 924 is strongly influenced by Michelangelo's drawings of about 1532–33. Dussler dates the drawing about 1514–16.

After SEBASTIANO DEL PIOMBO

925. ST. FRANCIS (4810)

420 × 213 mm. Pen and brown ink and brown wash on greenish paper, heightened with white.

(George III 'Inventory A', p. 85, Scuola Veneziana, 30–34, attributes five pages of drawings to Sebastiano without specifying them.)

Inscribed underneath in the centre in ink in a hand of the XVI century: 'fra Bast. del piombo'. From the wall-painting in the Borgherini chapel in S. Pietro in Montorio, Rome. The cartoon was apparently made in 1516–17, but the painting was not carried out until later (1520?). It corresponds almost exactly with the drawing. Preparatory studies from the model for the head and R. hand of the saint are on a sheet in the Uffizi (No. 1787: ill. O.M.D. XIV (1939–40), pl. 22). The perfect preservation of No. 925 suggests that it was not a working drawing; possibly it was made by the artist from the finished cartoon for Borgherini. Its value to us is the greater in view of the present wretched state of the painting.

ERCOLE SETTI (working 1568 to 1589)

926. THE MARRIAGE FEAST AT CANA (*Plate* 112) (01222)
246 × 482 mm. Pen and brown ink and brown wash, squared in black and red chalk, the squares numbered along all four margins.
F.A. The drawing is an elaborate small cartoon for the painting of the subject in S. Pietro, Modena (Venturi, IX 6, Fig. 373), with which it exactly corresponds. The picture was formerly in the Refectory of the Benedictines of S. Pietro, and is said to date from 1589.

GIROLAMO SICIOLANTE DA SERMONETA (1521–about 1580)

927. THE VIRGIN AND CHILD (*Plate* 82) (5960)
226 × 152 mm. Drawn with the point of the brush in brown on blue paper, over black chalk, heightened with white.
P.M.R.P. Study for the group of the Virgin and Child in the important altarpiece by Siciolante, now in the church of the Assunta at Calcinate in the province of Bergamo, which was painted in 1570 on the commission of 'Georgius Moratus Armenus' for the church of S. Bartolommeo at Ancona (Venturi, IX 5, Fig. 330).

928. THE DEAD BODY OF CHRIST, with separate studies of His neck, His shoulder and His loin-cloth. (*Figure* 179) (0455)
252 × 365 mm. Black chalk.
P.M.R.P. The drawing has on the *verso* an old inscription: 'M. Angelo', and the price mark of William Gibson, '1. 4.' (= 20/–). It is the study for the figure of Christ in the painting of the *Lamentation over the Body of Christ* in the Gallery at Posen (Venturi, IX 5, Fig. 309), a copy of which is described below.

After GIROLAMO SICIOLANTE DA SERMONETA

929. THE DEAD CHRIST SUPPORTED BY ST. MARY MAGDALENE, WITH THE SWOONING VIRGIN, ST. JOHN AND OTHER FIGURES (0456)
319 × 220 mm. Drawn with the brush on blue paper, heightened with white. Much wormed, rubbed and faded.
Corresponds with the picture in the gallery at Posen, painted for SS. Apostoli, Rome, apparently an early work and supposed to be based on a drawing by Siciolante's master, Perino del Vaga (Venturi, IX 5, Fig. 309). It is not easy to decide whether this very damaged drawing is a *modello* for the picture or a copy from it, perhaps more probably the latter.

Attributed to GIROLAMO SICIOLANTE DA SERMONETA

930. THE VIRGIN AND CHILD WITH THE INFANT ST. JOHN AND ST. JOSEPH (1959)
122 × 110 mm. Pen and ink and wash over red chalk on pink-tinted ground.

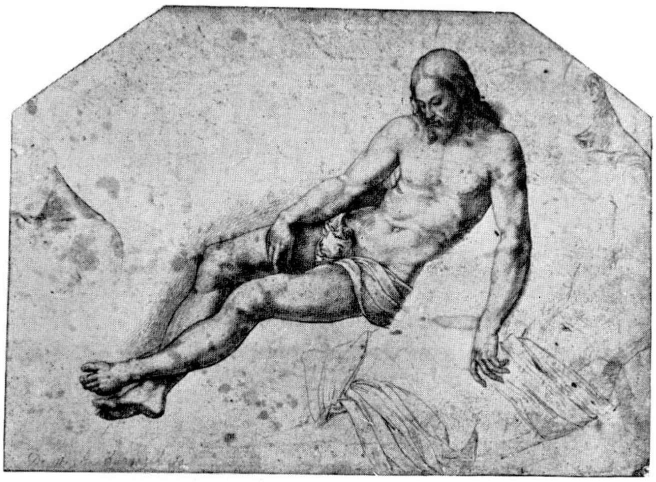

FIG. 179 Cat. No. 928

A.E.P. From the Carracci series. The attribution, which rests on the general resemblance in the types and composition to those of Siciolante, is a tentative one.

GIOVANNI ANTONIO SOGLIANI (1492–1544)

931. STUDY OF A STANDING APOSTLE (ST. THADDEUS?) (0385)
255 × 145 mm. Black chalk, heightened with white, squared in red chalk.
Not described by Berenson or Gabelentz. I do not know to whom the convincing attribution is due. It must be a late drawing and is possibly connected with the apostles painted by Sogliani in the Duomo at Pisa.

Attributed to ANDREA SOLARIO (working 1493–1515 or later)

932. THE LAMENTATION OVER THE BODY OF CHRIST: oblong composition of eight figures besides that of Our Lord. (*Plate* 138) (12819)
237 × 393 mm. Brown wash and point of the brush and some pen and ink over black chalk on faded green paper.
Inscribed in ink on the *verso* in a hand of the XVI or XVII century: 'Bernardino Lovino'. Subsequently attributed to Gaudenzio Ferrari and by W. Suida to Solario. The types and composition are quite in his manner and may be compared with those in the *Pietà* formerly in the collection of Lord Kinnaird (ill. Rassegna d'Arte, XIII (1913), opp. p. 105), and the sketch, perhaps for this picture, in the British Museum (Malcolm, 1895–9–15–771).

ANTONIO TEMPESTA (1555–1630)

933. HUNTING SCENE: three Oriental horsemen, one armed with a spear, a second with bow and arrows, and a third with a sword, are about to despatch a lion; further back on the L. another group of horsemen are attacking a second lion, which is already mauling one of their company. (0191)
222 × 364 mm. Pen and brown ink and wash over black chalk on a light brown ground, heightened with white.
En suite with No. 934. Neither of these characteristic drawings is, as far as I am aware, engraved.

FIG. 180 Cat. No. 938

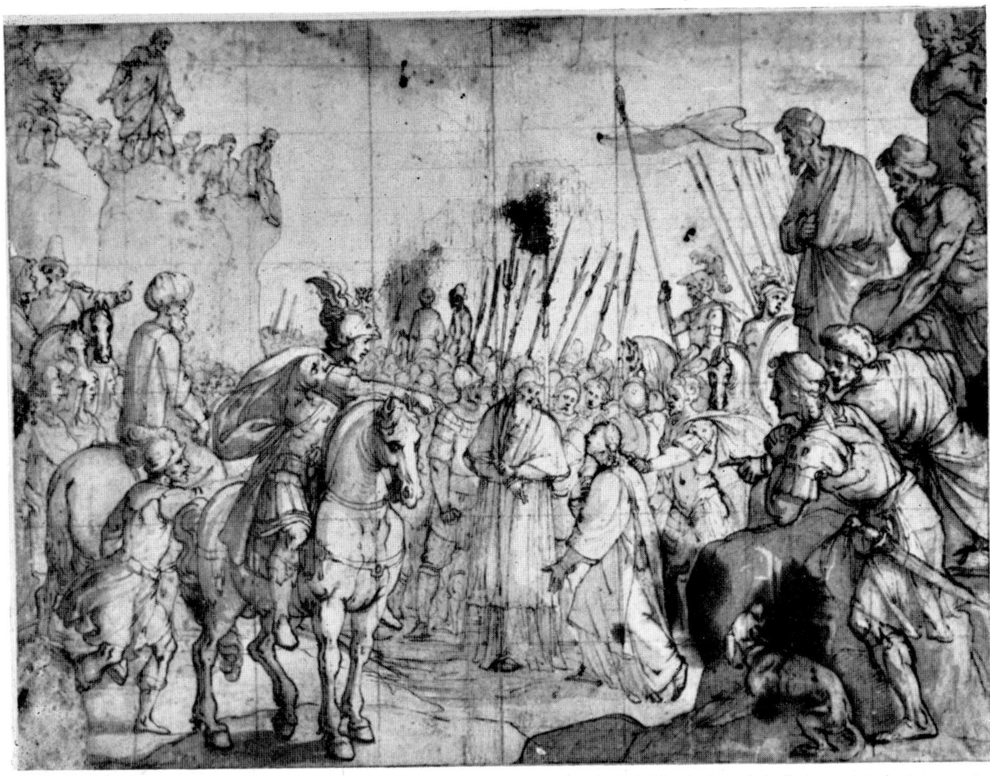

FIG. 181 Cat. No. 939

934. HUNTING SCENE: two mounted huntsmen on either side of a tree, and three hounds are attacking a wild boar; a third huntsman holds back another hound; in the background a stag and another boar are being chased. (0192)
224 × 373 mm. Pen and brown ink and wash over black chalk on a light brown ground, heightened with white.
En suite with No. 933.

935. A BOAR HUNT: on the R. two huntsmen on horseback, emerging from among trees, are about to kill a boar, which is also being attacked by hounds; in the background a stag is being chased. (6846)
408 × 652 mm. Pen and dark brown ink.
A very characteristic drawing.

936. BATTLE SCENE (6341)
160 × 226 mm. Pen and brown ink and wash over black chalk.
Numbered 24.

937. BATTLE SCENE (6342)
160 × 225 mm. Pen and brown ink and wash over black chalk.
Numbered 29. Neither of these characteristic drawings is, as far as I am aware, engraved.

938. SCENE FROM CLASSICAL LEGEND OR HISTORY: three mounted warriors mourning the death of another, over whose body as it lies on a carriage one of them, with a crown encircling his helmet, draws a shroud. (*Figure* 180) (0193)
197 × 276 mm. Pen and ink and wash on green paper, heightened with white (darkened in parts by oil stains).
Attribution to 'Tempesta' in pencil in L. hand bottom corner.

939. UNIDENTIFIED HISTORICAL SCENE: in the L. foreground are two horsemen, one bearded and wearing a turban, the other a soldier in helmet and cloak: the latter points to a suppliant deacon, who appeals to a cardinal, whose hands are bound; soldiers surround this pair, and in the R. foreground and L. background various figures seated or standing on rocks survey the scene. (*Figure* 181) (5120)
268 × 372 mm. Pen and brown ink and brown wash, with splodges of colour, squared in black chalk.
A.E.P. The attribution to Tempesta of this drawing is made purely on grounds of style. It is not precisely in the manner of such unmistakable drawings as Nos. 935, 936, and 937, but I think there is little doubt that it is by him. The differences may be accounted for by a difference in date (I have not the material for a chronology of Tempesta's work), and partly to the fact that this drawing is not, as is generally the case, for an engraving, but apparently for a painting.

After ANTONIO TEMPESTA

940. A CAVALRY ENGAGEMENT (0449)
225 × 342 mm. Pen and light brown ink and wash over red chalk.
The two drawings Nos. 940 and 941, very different in style, reproduce the same composition. No. 940 gives the impression of being of the XVII century, while No. 941 looks much earlier. The type of battle-piece beginning with Giulio Romano, and such compositions as the 'Battle with the Cutlas' (Bartsch XIV, p. 172, 212), was revived by Antonio Tempesta at the end of the century. In spite of the archaic appearance of No. 941 it must be nearer the latter period. They are apparently copies perhaps by a German or, at any rate, a provincial artist, after Antonio Tempesta.

941. A CAVALRY ENGAGEMENT (01250)
360 × 518 mm. (cut into on all sides). Pen and brown ink and grey wash on blue prepared surface, heightened with white.
A repetition on a larger scale and in quite a different technique of the composition represented by No. 940.

942. SERIES OF DRAWINGS OF ROMAN CATHOLIC RELIGIOUS RITES AND CEREMONIES (7709–7750)
Pen and brown ink and wash over black chalk. The drawings measure on an average 127 × 190 mm., and are pasted on to sheets of about 165 × 250 mm. These sheets are numbered from 1 to 42, with the exception of No. 7731, which has no such number. The drawings are mounted in a leather-bound album (A.36) with the royal crown stamped in gold on the sides.
It is probable that Tempesta etched this series (possibly in *Pontificale Romanum . . . nunc . . . auctum figuris ab A. Tempesta delineatis*, 1661, fol.), but I have not been able to verify this. Bernard Picart copied a number of the subjects for Moubach's *Cérémonies et Coutoumes Réligieuses*, Amsterdam, 1723, Vols. I and II. This work also appeared in Dutch in 1727, and this is the only edition available to me. I have, however, copied Miss Heaton Smith's references to the French edition, which are written in pencil on the mounts of the Windsor drawings.

7709. Enthroned bishop receiving offerings from a kneeling king; other ecclesiastics behind. Numbered 14. Not in Picart.
7710. Ordination of a bishop: the celebrant laying the gospels on the shoulders of the future bishop. Numbered 25. Picart, II, p. 134.
7711. A queen on horseback riding under a canopy held by courtiers. Numbered 2.
Not apparently one of the religious series and not in Picart.
7712. Consecration of a church: blessing the bell. Numbered 30. Picart, I, p. 126, pl. iv.
7713. Profession of nuns: the bishop giving the ring to the newly-made nuns. Numbered 40. Picart, II, p. 146, pl. i.
7714. Consecration of a church: the bishop sprinkling the pavement with holy water. Numbered 15. Picart, I, p. 120, pl. iii.
7715. A bishop approaching the altar under a canopy, preceded by other ecclesiastics carrying lighted torches. Numbered 33. Not in Picart.
7716. Ordination of a bishop: anointing the hands of the elect. Numbered 35. Picart, II, p. 134, pl. v.
7717. Consecration of a church: the celebrant making the sign of the cross on the front of the altar which is to be consecrated. Numbered 27. Picart, I, p. 134.
7718. Probably another in the series of the consecration of a church: a bishop approaches the altar on which candelabra are being placed. Numbered 38. Not in Picart.
7719. Ordination of a bishop: presenting the bishop elect with the Gospels. Numbered 39. Picart, II, p. 136, pl. ii.
7720. Consecration of a church: the bishop making the sign of the cross with the chrism on the front of the altar which is to be consecrated. Numbered 16. Picart, I, p. 134. Apparently the subject is identical with that of No. 7717.
7721. Ordination of a bishop: the bishop-designate taking the oath. Numbered 23. Picart, II, p. 1132, pl. ii.
7722. Ordination of a bishop: the celebrant laying the Gospels on the shoulders of the bishop-designate. Numbered 12. Picart, II, p. 134.
7723. Ordination of priests (?). Numbered 17. Not in Picart.
7724. The coronation of a king. Numbered 21. Not in Picart.

7725. Ordination of a bishop: the celebrant giving the gospels to the bishop-elect. Numbered 22. Picart, II, p. 136, pl. ii.
7726. Ordination of a bishop: the bishop-elect receives the pastoral staff. Numbered 42. Picart, II, p. 136, pl. v.
7727. A bishop seated at a table, before which stands a man, his hat in his hand; other ecclesiastics, two holding torches, and a third the crucifix, stand behind. Numbered 10. Not in Picart.
7728. Profession of nuns: the consecration (?). Numbered 18. Picart, p. 144, pl. iv.
7729. Consecration of a church: the celebrant making the sign of the cross with the censer over the altar which is to be consecrated. Numbered 29. Picart, I, p. 135.
7730. Consecration of a church: the bishop lighting the five wax crosses upon the altar which is to be consecrated. Numbered 8. Picart, I, p. 136.
7731. Ordination of a bishop: the bishop-designate taking the oath (?). Not numbered. Picart, II, p. 132, pl. ii (see also No. 7721).
7732. Consecration of a church: the bishop inscribing the alphabet on the altar (?). Numbered 36. Not in Picart.
7733. Consecration of a church: censing the altar (?). Numbered 13. Not in Picart.
7734. The coronation of a queen. Numbered 32. Not in Picart.
7735. Consecration of a church: the bishop making the five crosses upon the altar which is to be consecrated. Numbered 1. Picart, I, pp. 132, 133.
7736. Consecration of a church: the bishop sprinkling the five crosses upon the altar with holy water. Numbered 7. Picart, II, p. 125, pl. iii, and pp. 126, 127.
7737. Ordination of a sacristan: presentation of the key of the church. Numbered 3. Inscribed in lower R. corner: 'Anton Tempest fecit'. Picart, II, p. 125, pl. iii, and pp. 126, 127.
7738. Ordination of a priest: the laying on of hands. Numbered 24. Picart, II, p. 128, pl. iv.
7739. A bishop blessing the sword of a king who kneels before him. Numbered 21. Not in Picart.
7740. A bishop and a priest conversing before the altar; other priests on the L. and in the background on the R. Numbered 20. Not in Picart.
7741. Consecration of a church: the bishop lighting the five wax crosses on the altar. Numbered 26. Picart, I, pp. 134, 136.
7742. Consecration of a church: blessing the altar vessels (?). Numbered 19. Not in Picart.
7743. Profession of nuns: blessing the habits of the nuns-elect. Numbered 5. Picart, II, p. 144, pl. v.
7744. Profession of nuns: receiving the veil. Numbered 34. Picart, II, p. 144, pl. vi.
7745. Consecration of a church: the bishop sprinkling holy water on the altar. Numbered 6. Picart, I, pp. 129, 130, and 133.
7746. Consecration of a church: the bishop consecrating the vessels of the altar. Numbered 37. Not in Picart.
7747. Ordination of a bishop: the bishop-designate prostrating himself before the altar. Numbered 9. Picart, II, p. 132, pl. iii.
7748. Consecration of a church: censing the altar (?). Numbered 41. Not in Picart.
7749. Consecration of a church: the bishop sealing up the relics within the altar. Numbered 31. Picart, I, p. 130, pl. vi.
7750. Consecration of a church: the bishop making the sign of the cross in the centre of the new altar. Numbered 4. Not in Picart.

PELLEGRINO TIBALDI (1527–1596)

943. A MAN, SEEN FROM BEHIND, MOUNTING A STAIRCASE, AND HANDING A BASKET OF FRUIT TO ANOTHER MAN (*Figure* 182) (5488)
310 × 142 mm. Pen and ink and brown wash over black chalk on blue paper, heightened with white.
Identified by the late Oskar Fischel as the study for the *trompe l'oeuil* decorating a feigned doorway at the end of the Sala della Giustizia in the Castle of St. Angelo. The style of the drawing points to Tibaldi rather than to any of the other assistants of Perino del Vaga engaged on the decoration of the castle. Tibaldi was in Rome from 1549 to 1553 and is said by Baglione (*Le Vite de' Pittori* . . ., Rome, 1642, p. 62) to have painted the figure of St. Michael at one end of the Sala della Giustizia. Vasari merely says that he worked in the castle.

FIG. 182 Cat. No. 943

944. DESIGN FOR AN UPRIGHT PANEL WITH A SCENE IN WHICH A WARRIOR BINDS UP THE HEAD OF A WOUNDED MAN (*Figure* 183) (5439)
261 × 158 mm. Pen and light brown ink and wash.
F.A. The composition closely resembles those of the upright monochrome panels decorating the side walls of the Sala della Giustizia in the Castle of St. Angelo, which illustrate the story of Alexander. Near as the style of the drawing is to Perino del Vaga's, who was presumably in charge of the decoration of this room, it appears to be rather that of Tibaldi, who according to Vasari and Baglione worked in

FIG. 183 Cat. No. 944

the castle (though this must have been after Perino's death). It does not seem to be by Marco Pino da Siena, the assistant to Perino specifically mentioned by Vasari, and whom the records name as having painted at least some of the scenes in the life of Alexander.

945. DESIGN FOR THE DECORATION OF A FRIEZE, with a panel in which *putti* are supporting a wreath with a triple mountain resting on it. (*Plate* 111) (10908)
178 × 402 mm. Pen and light brown ink and wash, heightened with white.
A.E.P. Detached in 1944 from an album lettered 'Architectural Ornaments' (A III 5). It is clearly by the same hand as a drawing published by H. Bodmer in Rivista d'Arte XIX (1937), p. 19. This drawing, in the Louvre, has the arms of Cardinal Poggi and is presumably the design for the decoration of a fireplace in the Palazzo Poggi (now Università) at Bologna. I think there is little doubt that the triple mountain on the wreath is also part of the Poggi coat-of-arms and that the Windsor drawing is likewise for the decoration of the palace at Bologna. There is indeed a close resemblance between the panel of playing *putti* here and those in the Palazzo Poggi attributed to Niccolò dell' Abbate (Venturi, IX 6, Figs. 352–354). There is a copy of the panel with the playing *putti* in this frieze in the Fenwick Collection wrongly attributed to Lelio Orsi (Catalogue, p. 70, No. 5).

946. DESIGN FOR THE DECORATION OF A FRIEZE OR DADO: in the centre two nude figures flanking a tablet with the initials .D.PGIO surrounded by a spider's web. (10902)
119 × 409 mm. Pen and brown ink and brown wash, over black chalk.
A.E.P. Detached in 1944 from an album lettered 'Architectural Ornaments' (A III 5). The drawing is clearly by the same hand as that previously described and is probably connected with the decoration of the same palace. D.PGIO may well be an abbreviation of the name D(ominus (?)) .POGGIO, though it occurs in a different form as IO.P. in the existing decorations of the Palazzo Poggi.

947. A MIRACLE OF ST. MARK (?) (*Plate* 109) (5965)
423 × 286 mm. Arched top. Pen and brown ink and brown wash over red chalk, heightened with white.
Lit.: H. Bodmer, Thieme-Becker, Vol. XXXIII (1939).
As first observed by Bodmer, this is a preliminary sketch for the fresco of the subject in the Cappella Poggi in S. Giacomo Maggiore at Bologna (Venturi, IX 6, Fig. 310). The main features of the composition are as in the finished painting, but there are numerous divergences in detail. The drawing is important as an authentic example of Tibaldi's method of sketching out his ideas.

948. THE VISITATION (*Figure* 184) (0538)
228 × 170 mm. Pen and light brown ink and wash, squared; much damaged by damp.
A.E.P. Inscribed in the 'deceptive' hand: 'Parmiggiano',

FIG. 184 Cat. No. 948

and again on a label attached to the back of the mount. The drawing corresponds almost exactly with part of the painting in the Galleria Nazionale at Urbino (ill. Bollettino d'Arte I (1931–32), p. 421) except that it has obviously been considerably cut on the R. and L., and that the composition has been somewhat compressed laterally. The architecture and the figures in the distance are also different. The style of drawing is very close to that of Tibaldi himself, and it is most probably an original by him.

949. THE ANGEL OF THE LORD STRIKING THE WORSHIPPERS IN A HEATHEN TEMPLE (*Plate* 110) (5958)
396 × 279 mm. Pen and brown ink and brown wash, heightened with white, on cream-coloured paper.
The attribution to Tibaldi is Bodmer's, made, I suppose, on the basis of a resemblance to No. 947. No picture of the subject is known, but the style is evidently the same and it is clearly by Tibaldi. The subject may be the Angel of the Lord smiting the first-born of Egypt (Exodus xii. 29).

After PELLEGRINO TIBALDI

950. POLYPHEMUS, BLINDED, ABOUT TO HURL A ROCK (5968)
363 × 251 mm. Red chalk.
Unfinished copy from part of the ceiling decoration of the Stanza d'Ulisse in the Palazzo Poggi, Bologna (Venturi, IX 6, Fig. 300).

951. ULYSSES PUTTING OUT THE EYE OF POLYPHEMUS (5967)
264 × 399 mm. Red chalk.
Copy from part of the ceiling decoration of the Stanza d'Ulisse in the Palazzo Poggi, Bologna (Venturi, IX 6, Fig. 304).

Copies after Primaticcio and Raphael, attributed to Tibaldi, are catalogued under Nos. 762 and 826 above.

JACOPO (ROBUSTI) TINTORETTO (1518–1594)

952. STUDY OF A MAN SEEN FROM THE BACK, STRETCHING UP TO THE R. (*Plate* 172) (4823)
368 × 188 mm. Black chalk or charcoal on blue paper, heightened with white.
Lit.: K. Clark, O.M.D. V (1930–31), p. 64 (pl. 44); Tietzes, No. 1759.
Study for the man placing a ladder against the Cross in the centre of the *Crucifixion* in the Venice Academy (No. 231), dated by Hadeln about 1560. The sheet is in an admirable state of preservation, quite unusual for Tintoretto drawings.

School of JACOPO (ROBUSTI) TINTORETTO

953. STUDY OF TWO MEN SEEN FROM BEHIND LEANING FORWARDS TOWARDS THE R. (*Plate* 170) (4797)
274 × 192 mm. Black chalk or charcoal on blue paper, heightened with white, squared in black chalk.
Lit.: K. Clark, O.M.D. V (1930–31), p. 64 (pl. 45); Tietzes, No. 1245.
Clark gives the drawing to Jacopo and suggests that it may have been the study for a lost composition of the *Last Supper*, as the standing figure is very similar to that of one of the apostles in the S. Trovaso painting. It seems too weak and scratchy in style for Jacopo, and is rather of his school. The Tietzes attribute it to Palma Giovane, and connect it with a drawing by that artist (their No. 1127), which I have not seen.

954. STUDY OF A WOMAN KNEELING TO THE L. (4796)
215 × 136 mm. Black chalk or charcoal strengthened with pen and faint brown ink on faded blue paper, heightened with white.
Lit.: K. Clark, O.M.D. V (1930–31), p. 64 (pl. 46); Tietzes, No. 1244.
Attributed by Clark with reservations to Jacopo. He called attention to a resemblance between this figure and that of Mary Magdalene in the *Entombment* by Palma Giovane in the Cook Collection (ill. Catalogue, No. 186). This is not very close, and I am not convinced that the drawing is necessarily by Palma, as claimed by the Tietzes. It is safer to leave it as school of Tintoretto.

955. STUDY OF A TURBANED MAN IN PROFILE TO THE R., HOLDING A CENSER (4825)
245 × 144 mm. Black chalk.
Inscribed in pencil on the drawing: 'tintoretto'. It is certainly not by Jacopo, but apparently, as Wilde has suggested, by Domenico. It appears to be the study for a king in an *Epiphany*.

956. TWO MEN DRESSED IN ORIENTAL COSTUME SERVING WINE (4824)
215 × 169 mm. Pen and brown ink and brown wash over black chalk.
Attribution 'Tintoretto' in pencil on the drawing. It is clearly not from the hand of Jacopo, but in the wider sense belongs to his school. It may be as late as 1600.

957. STUDY OF A YOUTH IN CONTEMPORARY COSTUME STEPPING FORWARD WITH A GESTURE OF SURPRISE (3613)
266 × 158 mm. Black chalk on blue paper, squared in red chalk.
Old attribution to 'Tintoretto' in ink on the *verso*, visible through the backing. The drawing is certainly not by Jacopo himself, but belongs, broadly speaking, to his school.

After JACOPO (ROBUSTI) TINTORETTO

958. PART OF A COMPOSITION OF THE LAST SUPPER (6679)
213 × 286 mm. Pen and brown ink and brown wash.
Copy of part of Tintoretto's *Last Supper* in the church of S. Polo, Venice.

Attributed to MARIETTA TINTORETTO (About 1556–1590)

959. STUDY FROM A BUST OF VITELLIUS, TURNED NEARLY IN PROFILE TO THE R. (0837)
402 × 294 mm. Charcoal or black chalk on faded blue paper, heightened with white.
The attribution to Marietta is due to Wilde. It seems to be by the same hand as the drawing in the Rasini Collection (Tietzes, No. 1762), inscribed 'Questa testa si e di man di madona Marieta'.

960. STUDY FROM A BUST OF VITELLIUS TURNED THREE-QUARTERS TO THE L., SEEN FROM ABOVE (6702)
320 × 240 mm. Black chalk or charcoal on faded blue paper.
Inscribed on the mount in an XVIII century hand: 'Di P. Veronese'. The attribution to Marietta, also due to Wilde, is based on the resemblance to the drawing just described.

FIG. 185 Cat. No. 965

TITIAN (TIZIANO VECELLIO) (1485/88–1576)

961. STUDY FOR AN 'ECCE HOMO' (*Plate* 166) (4794)
145 × 95 mm. Black chalk on blue paper, heightened with white chalk (rather rubbed).

Lit.: Hadeln, *Zeichnungen des Tizian*, Berlin, 1924, p. 54 (pl. 30); L. Fröhlich-Bum, Vienna Jahrbuch, N.F. II (1928), p. 190; Tietzes, No. 2015.

Inscribed in ink in an old formed hand in the top R. corner: 'Titiano'. Though not definitely connected with any existing work by Titian, the style seems to justify the old attribution. It was accepted by Hadeln and rather doubtfully by the Tietzes.

After TITIAN

962. THE VIRGIN SEATED ON THE GROUND SUCKLING THE INFANT CHRIST (4795)
113 × 144 mm. Pen and ink and wash on blue paper, heightened with white.

Copied either from the woodcut after Titian (attributed to Niccolò Boldrini) or from the engraving by Giulio Bonasone taken from the latter (Bartsch XV, p. 129, 67).

963. FOUR SAINTS: ST. CATHERINE, ST. PETER AND TWO DOMINICANS (6669)
205 × 203 mm. Pen and brown ink and brown wash.

Copy of the XVII or XVIII century of parts of the lower half of the *Madonna and Six Saints* in the Vatican Gallery.

SANTI DI TITO (1536–1603)

964. A MIRACLE OF OUR LORD: HE RESTORES A PARALYTIC TO HEALTH (049)
299 × 218 mm. Pen and brown ink and brown wash, heightened with white.

Inscribed in an old hand on the foot of the bed on which the paralytic lies: 'Santi titi'. The composition in general is very near to that of such a painting by Santi di Tito as the *Marriage Feast at Cana* (Venturi, IX 7, Fig. 316), and the style of drawing also seems to me to be his (compare the drawing of the *Circumcision* in the Uffizi ill. by G. Arnolds, *Santi di Tito*, Arezzo, 1934, pl. XXXIII).

Attributed to ANTONIO VICENTINO called TOGNONE

965. DESIGN FOR A TONDO WITH APOLLO FLAYING MARSYAS (*Figure* 185) (6678)
200 × 194 mm. Fine pen outlines on blue paper, washed with brown and heightened with white.

Coll.: Five pointed star ★

Lit.: B.M. Add. Ms. 20,101, fol. 28, No. 1, 'Tognon di Vincenza'.

Inscribed at the bottom to the L. in ink in a hand which appears to me to date from the XVIII century: 'Tonion di Vincenza', by whom the little-known pupil of Zelotti mentioned by Ridolfi (ed. Hadeln, II, p. 227) is clearly intended. The style of the design is very near to that of the roundels on the ceiling of the Libreria Marciana by Zelotti himself, Franco and the other Venetian mannerists of the 1550's. In the absence, however, of any work published as Tognone's, this attribution must remain no more than a hypothetical one.

FIG. 186 Cat. No. 966

GIOVANNI BATTISTA TROTTI (MALOSSO)

(1555–1619)

966. THE ASCENSION OF OUR LORD (*Figure* 186) (5071)
361 × 220 mm. Pen and brown ink and grey wash.
Inscribed bottom R. in an old hand in ink: 'malosso', an attribution which is amply borne out by the very characteristic manner of this drawing.

967. CHRIST CARRYING THE CROSS (5128)
305 × 227 mm. Pen and brown ink and brown wash, squared twice, once in red, and once in black, chalk.
Inscribed bottom R. in the 'deceptive' hand: 'Malosso'. For once the attribution made by this collector or dealer is amply confirmed by the style of the drawing.

968. THE ASSUMPTION OF THE VIRGIN (*Plate* 141) (5046)
488 × 347 mm. Pen and brown ink and brown wash, with some touches of white, squared in black chalk.
A.E.P. This is a characteristic, indeed an unmistakable, drawing by Trotti.

969. THE ASSUMPTION OF THE VIRGIN (4986)
475 × 285 mm. Arched top. Pen and brown ink and brown wash on blue paper, heightened with white, squared in black chalk.
Coll.: N. Lanière (Lugt 2885).
A.E.P. Traditionally ascribed to Paolo Farinati, whose technique is, in a way, somewhat similar. The general style is, however, absolutely different and, I think, characteristic of Trotti. It is the design for a different altarpiece to No. 968, and differs somewhat in style, but types like those of the two apostles above on the R. seem unmistakably Trotti's. A drawing at Berlin (Paccetti Coll.), bearing an absurd attribution to Carpioni, is a preliminary sketch for the lower half of the composition.

970. DESIGN FOR A TONDO WITH THREE WINGED GENII ON CLOUDS (01223)
Circular, diam. 355 mm. Pen and brown ink, shaded with the point of the brush in grey and heightened with white. The head of the genius on the R. is a correction on a separate piece of paper inserted.
A.E.P. Inscribed bottom centre in the 'deceptive' hand: 'Lelio di Novilara'. The allegory is not exactly clear. The genius in the centre at the top holds up a mirror, in which his face is reflected; he has a palm branch and a torch by his side. The genius on the L. holds a fruit and is seated above a bow and a yoke. The third genius is blindfolded, holds a mask before his face and has a quiver, a bow and a bird beside him.

After GIOVANNI BATTISTA TROTTI

971. THE ENTOMBMENT (5999)
350 × 210 mm. Black chalk.
F.A. The drawing has the character of a copy after a painting which might well be by G. B. Trotti.

PERINO (BUONACCORSI) DEL VAGA

(1500/01–1547)

972. CHRIST RISING FROM THE TOMB (*Figure* 187) (01360)
383 × 465 mm. Elaborately finished with the brush and light brown on cream-coloured paper, heightened with white; injured by worm-holes and much cut into on both sides and at the bottom.
Lit.: Ruland, p. 257, VI, 4.
Engraved in reverse as Raphael by Cherubino Alberti

FIG. 187 Cat. No. 972

(Bartsch XVII, p. 58, 24) before the drawing had been mutilated at the sides and at the bottom. According to Ruland the drawing was regarded as a first sketch for the tapestry 'della scuola nuova', a connection which he denies. There is, however, a certain resemblance in the tomb situated in a wooded rock and in the figures arriving from a distance. The figure of Christ is very similar to that of the Saviour in the *Ascension* in the same series of tapestries. There is little connection between the composition and the *Resurrection* by Raphael, studies for which in this collection (Nos. 798, 799) have already been discussed, except perhaps with the angel seated on the tomb in the composition sketch in the Ashmolean (ill. Fischel, Prussian Jahrbuch XLVI (1925) p. 195).
This drawing is very uneven and extraordinarily weak in its composition, though the individual figures show some power of dramatic characterisation. The types of the faces and the style seem to indicate Perino del Vaga in his first Roman period after the death of Raphael, 1520–1527. It may be compared in general with the two frescoes from the Palazzo Baldassini now in the Uffizi (publ. by Giovanni Poggi, Bollettino d'Arte III (1909), p. 270 f.).

973. THE SACRIFICE OF ISAAC (12730)
121 × 410 mm. Pen and brown ink and brown wash on light brown paper, heightened with white.
George III 'Inventory A', p. 50, Raffaello d'Urbino e Scuola 16.
Lit.: J. D. Passavant, *Raphael d'Urbin*, Paris, 1860, Vol. II, p. 185 and p. 489, No. 419.
Photo.: Thurston Thompson, 1857.
Corresponds with the subject painted in imitation of bronze under the window of the fourth arcade of the *Loggie*, executed (according to Vasari, V, p. 594) by Perino del Vaga. A note on the mount records a similar drawing in the Teyler Museum at Haarlem. Passavant regarded the Windsor drawing as the original for the fresco.

974. ST. MARK AND ST. JOHN THE EVANGELIST WITH WINGED PUTTI SUPPORTING A CANDELABRUM (*Figure* 188) (01218)
317 × 503 mm. Red chalk, squared with the stylus.
Coll.: Six pointed star *
Lit.: A. E. Popham, Burlington Mag., LXXVI (1945), p. 65 (ill.).

As observed by the late Oskar Fischel, the drawing is the study for the fresco painted in the Cappella del Crocefisso in S. Marcello al Corso, Rome. This is illustrated in an article on the chapel by G. Fiocco in Bollettino d'Arte VII (1913), p. 91. Under a contract of February 6, 1525, Perino del Vaga was to have completed the painting of the whole chapel by March 20, 1526. It remained unfinished at the time of the sack of Rome in 1527, and was resumed by Perino on his return from Genoa and Pisa in the year 1539. Even then he did not complete the whole scheme. The Evangelists Mark and John were finished by him except for the latter's head and R. arm, which Daniele da Volterra was left to paint, together with the remaining two Evangelists.
At what stage in these long drawn-out operations was the present drawing made? It corresponds very closely with the fresco and seems to be the working drawing for it. Fiocco assumes, I think with reason, that the Evangelists Mark and John (together with the Creation of Eve in the centre of the vaulting) were painted by Perino in the first period, 1525–1527, and the style of this drawing conforms best with the earlier date.

975. JUNO VISITING AEOLUS AND NEPTUNE CALMING THE TEMPEST (*Plate* 71) (5497)
Circular, diameter 223 mm. Fine pen and brown ink on cream-coloured ground, washed with grey and heightened with white.
F.A. Inscribed on a scroll: 'Quos ego'. Neptune and his horses owe something to Marcantonio's engraving of the subject (Bartsch XIV, p. 264, 352), but are nearer to Perino del Vaga's modification of this painted in the Palazzo Doria at Genoa (Vasari, V, p. 614), which has perished but the composition of which is preserved in a drawing in the Louvre and in the engraving by Giulio Bonasone (Bartsch XV, p. 140, 104). The figure of Neptune, in fact, corresponds almost exactly. The proportions of the figures, Juno's especially, are characteristic of Perino's late style.

976. SOLON GIVING LAWS TO THE ATHENIANS (*Plate* 72) (5436)
180 × 218 mm. Pen and brown ink and grey wash on blue paper, heightened with white.
A.E.P. Attributed to Maturino, the drawing is in fact a study for the *grisaille* of the subject under Raphael's fresco of *Jurisprudence* in the Sala della Segnatura in the Vatican. It will be found engraved in outline on pl. 8 of *Le Pitture delle Stanze Vaticane . . . incise a contorno . . . con le basamenti inediti*, Rome, 1838. The space under the frescoes in the Stanza della Segnatura was originally filled by wooden panelling, the work of Giovanni da Verona. Paul III (1534–1549) wished to remove a fireplace from the Stanza d'Eliodoro to that of the Segnatura. This involved making away with the panelling and redecorating the lower portion of the Stanza della Segnatura, a task which was entrusted to Perino del Vaga. It does not seem to me probable that Perino returned to Rome from Pisa before 1539, so that the *basamenti* cannot have been begun before that date. Vasari, who relates all this (V, p. 623), further says that Perino only supplied the designs and cartoons and retouched the work when it had been carried out by pupils.

977. THE RAPE OF THE SABINE WOMEN: FRIEZE (5466)
119 × 190 mm. Pen and brown ink and brown wash over black chalk.
A.E.P. Inscribed in pencil on the drawing: 'Del maturino'. There is no reliable evidence, so far as I know, for identifying any drawing as the work of this Florentine collaborator of

FIG. 188 Cat. No. 974

Polidoro da Caravaggio and old attributions to him seem to have been quite arbitrary. The present drawing in fact seems to be by the same hand as No. 976, also ascribed to Maturino, that is, Perino del Vaga's.

978. ST. PAUL RECOVERING HIS SIGHT AT THE HANDS OF ANANIAS (*Figure* 189) (5460)

235 × 153 mm. Brush drawing in brown on discoloured, brownish paper, heightened with white, the outlines finely pricked.

One of the designs for the eight subjects of the story of St. Peter and St. Paul made by Perino del Vaga for a pluvial for Paul III (referred to by Vasari, V, p. 631 f). Vasari, it is

FIG. 189 Cat. No. 978

true, speaks of them as drawn only from the history of St. Peter, but at least one of them quite certainly had reference to St. Paul. Six of the subjects (in addition to the Windsor drawing) are known in engravings or in drawings. Of these, four are plain ovals with nearly flat sides, while two are of more complicated shape, contained in what Bartsch calls a 'cadre bombé'.

These are:—

(1) *St. Peter and St. John healing a lame man at the gate of the temple* ('cadre bombé'). Engraving by G. Bonasone (Bartsch XV, p. 130, 73). Drawing in the Uffizi (photo. Braun 175).

(2) *St. Peter walking on the waters* ('cadre bombé'). Engraving by G. Reverdy (Bartsch XV, p. 469, 6).

(3) *St. Paul preaching at Athens* (?) (oval). Engraving by G. Bonasone (Bartsch XV, p. 130, 72). Drawing in the Uffizi (facsimile by S. Mulinari, Weigel 5895). Drawing at Chatsworth (No. 158).

(4) *St. Paul banishing the devil in the form of a dragon* (according to Bartsch); oval. Engraving by G. Bonasone (Bartsch XV, p. 130, 71). Drawing in British Museum (copy ? 1848–11–25–11).

(5) *The Sacrifice at Lystra* (oval). Drawing in the Uffizi (photo. Braun 178).

(6) *St. Paul let down by night from the walls of Damascus* (oval). Anon. chiaroscuro woodcut (Bartsch XII, p. 75, 21). Drawing at Chatsworth (No. 164).

The eighth design can hardly be, as Voss suggests (*Malerei der Spätrenaissance*, Berlin, 1920, p. 71, note 1), the oval of *St. John the Evangelist* in the Uffizi (photo. Braun 472). If the subject of the present drawing is that indicated, one would expect the *Conversion of St. Paul* to form its counterpart. The Windsor drawing has every appearance of having been used as the actual cartoon by the embroiderer and has suffered accordingly. The fine pricking of the outlines seems to be characteristic of such drawings.

979. SKETCH FOR THE DECORATION OF A WALL (*Plate* 73) (10761)

305 × 353 mm. (on two pieces of paper joined 90 mm. from R. side). Pen and brown ink and grey wash on light brown ground, heightened with white. The figure marked 'Cōcordia' squared in black chalk.

Study for the decoration of the R. hand portion of the upper part of one of the end walls (that with St. Michael in the centre) of the Sala della Giustizia in the castle of St. Angelo, Rome. The fresco, as completed, corresponds almost exactly with the drawing, except for the lack of spontaneity in the former due to the work being carried out by assistants, as recorded by Vasari. The blank space in the roundel above 'Chastity' and 'Concord' was filled with a chiaroscuro medallion, representing apparently St. Paul preaching. I cannot explain the significance of the word 'conversi 5' written by the artist in this space. The drawing for the figures in the 'porto finto' underneath this decoration, apparently by Pellegrino Tibaldi, is also in the collection (No. 943).

980. DESIGN FOR THE DECORATION OF A CEILING (6828)

410 × 555 mm. Pen and brown ink and grey wash over black chalk.

A.E.P. In one corner is the coat of arms of Pope Paul III (1534–1549). The drawing appears to include one-quarter of the whole scheme. In general arrangement it corresponds with the decoration of the vaulting of the Biblioteca in the Castle of St. Angelo (photos., Anderson 3382, 24721, 24722, 22978) and must be regarded as the preliminary design for this. According to Thieme-Becker (Vol. XXIII, p. 490) the decoration of the ceiling of the Biblioteca was the work of Luzio Romano, painter and 'stuccatore' about 1543. Vasari (V, p. 629) writes: 'fu poi il resto delle stanze dato parte a Luzio Romano; ed in ultimo le sale ed altre camere importanti fece Perino, parte di sua mano, e parte fu fatto da altri con suoi cartoni'. Obviously the Biblioteca was a 'camera importante', and may be supposed to have been designed by Perino himself. The present drawing, though much looser in handling and more summary than the design for part of the wall of the Sala della Giustizia (No. 979) described above, can also I

FIG. 190 Cat. No. 981 r.

think be given to him with some confidence on grounds of style.

Another drawing in the collection (No. 10847: in album of Architectural Ornaments, A.18) is very probably also a design for the decoration of one of the rooms in the Castle of St. Angelo, and the same may apply to other drawings in this album.

981. *Recto:* HEADS OF SIX HORSES BITING EACH OTHER (*Figure* 190)
264 × 427 mm. Pen and brown ink over red chalk, the outlines indented.

Verso: MERCURY, ANOTHER GOD, AND VENUS FLOATING IN A SHELL (0498)
Pen and ink and wash.

Old attribution 'Perino' on *verso* and price in the manner of William Gibson: '6.2.' (= 15/–). A drawing in the British Museum (Fawkener 5211–72) corresponds exactly with the present drawing as to the two pairs of heads to L. and R.; for the central pair the back of a charioteer has been substituted. It must in fact have been traced from the Windsor sheet, the back of which is blackened for transfer. It is tempting to connect the drawings with the chiaroscuro panels of fighting sea-monsters and horses on the *basamenti* of the Sala della Giustizia of the Castle of St. Angelo, the decoration of which was designed by Perino del Vaga in the forties, though some at least of the work seems to have been carried out by Tibaldi. The horses' heads are not like those of Tibaldi, to whom I had at first thought of attributing the drawings; the old attribution is to Perino, and the sketch on the *verso* of the Windsor sheet is much nearer in style to him than to Tibaldi.

982. A MARINE MONSTER WITH THE HEAD OF A BULL (0502)
243 × 347 mm. Pen and brown ink over a sketch in black chalk.

Inscribed at the top in ink in an old hand: 'di pirino del vago'. On a label attached to the *verso* is another name (inscribed in the same hand ?), which has been scratched out so as to be illegible. Though I know of no drawing by Perino del Vaga quite in this style, it does not seem out of character for him. The monster's tail is practically the repetition of that of one of two confronted sea-centaurs in a drawing in the British Museum (Fenwick Collection, Catalogue, p. 60, No. 5, as Giulio Romano; copy in the Uffizi attributed to Beccafumi), which I now believe also to be by Perino del Vaga.

983. DESIGN FOR A SALT-CELLAR (10747)
215 × 345 mm. (top L. hand corner cut). Pen and brown ink and brown wash.

The attribution to Perino del Vaga and a reference to a similar design in the Uffizi (photo., Braun 167) was written on the mount in a hand of the XIX century. The latter drawing seems to be the design for a casket rather than for a salt-cellar, but it has on its side a rectangular panel with a scroll among foliage very similar to the oval in the Windsor drawing. Both drawings are probably very late works by Perino himself, rather than by artists of his school. Vasari rather contemptuously records (V, p. 630) how Perino, at the end of his life, undertook all sorts of work of this character.

After PERINO DEL VAGA

984. *Recto:* ALLEGORICAL FIGURE REPRESENTING SPECULATIVE PHILOSOPHY (0413)
265 × 170 mm. Pen and brown ink and brown wash on green ground, heightened with white.

Verso: SLIGHT SKETCHES OF A SEATED SHEPHERD (MERCURY (?)), of a hunched kneeling figure and of a figure flying downwards (cut into).
Pen and ink.

A.E.P. The *recto* is a copy from the *grisaille* of the subject painted from the cartoon of Perino del Vaga under the

School of Athens in the Stanza della Segnatura in the Vatican, about 1539 (see No. 976 above). The style of the drawing precludes it being by Perino himself.

985. ST. MARK SEATED COMPOSING THE GOSPEL (for a lunette). (3489)
166 × 245 mm. Pen and brown ink and brown wash over black chalk, heightened with white.
Engraved by G. Bonasone (Bartsch XV, p. 131, 75) with the inscription 'PIRINO DEL VAGA . I.V.'. The present drawing, though in Perino's style and technique hardly seems good enough for the master himself. It is presumably the copy from the drawing by him from which Bonasone made his engraving.

986. ST. MARK SEATED COMPOSING THE GOSPEL (5070)
230 × 300 mm. Pen and brown ink.
Copy from the engraving by Giulio Bonasone referred to above. The winged lion and the sarcophagus, in front of which the saint is seated, are omitted in this feeble copy.

987. A ROMAN NAVAL ENGAGEMENT (5471)
Circular, diameter 342 mm. (cut into at the top; on the L. at the bottom is part of the design for the border, adding about 25 mm. to the diameter). Pen and brown ink and brown wash.
Attribution in pencil on the drawing to Polidoro to whose work it shows only a vague resemblance. It seems to be the copy of a drawing *en suite* with one of a naval engagement before a city in the Uffizi (Santarelli, No. 358; photo., Braun 168), rightly there attributed to Perino del Vaga (a copy of this in the British Museum, Malcolm 1895–9–15–652). Both are certainly designs for majolica and the Windsor drawing is in fact reproduced on a wine-cooler in the Wallace Collection dated 1574 (see William King, Apollo, December, 1945, p. 300).

988. HEADS OF THREE HORSES FIGHTING (0497)
258 × 407 mm. Black and red chalk.
Though none of the heads is actually copied from any in No. 981, their relative positions and their action are so similar that there can be no doubt of the connection. The style of this elaborately finished drawing is that of the end of the century and suggests some draughtsman like Procaccini or the Cavaliere d'Arpino.

989. THE CIRCUMCISION: lozenge in decorated border. (0288)
174 × 164 mm. Pen and brown ink and brown wash on blue paper, heightened with white, the outlines pricked.
Attribution in pencil at the bottom. The decoration and the type of pricking suggest that this was the design for the embroidery of a vestment. The style and composition are characteristic of Perino, but the actual drawing is certainly not his. It is presumably a copy rather than an original composition in his manner.

COPIES OF THE OBLONG SUBJECTS BY PERINO DEL VAGA UNDER THE WINDOWS OF THE *LOGGIE*

990. THE INSTITUTION OF THE RAINBOW (0410)
117 × 268 mm. Pen and brown ink and brown wash on blue paper, heightened with white.
Corresponds with the subject painted in bronze in the third arcade of the *Loggie* under the window. According to Passavant (*Raphael d'Urbin*, Paris, 1860, Vol. II, p. 185) the original drawing for this passed from the Lawrence collection through that of the King of Holland to the Staedel Institut at Frankfort. Inscribed on the mount: 'Bought at Florence by R. H. [Sir Richard Holmes] 1875'.

991. THE SACRIFICE OF ISAAC (0491)
125 × 180 mm. Pen and brown ink and brown wash on blue paper, heightened with white.
George III 'Inventory A', p. 50, Raffaello d'Urbino e Scuola 20.
Lit.: J. D. Passavant, *Raphael d'Urbin*, Paris, 1860, Vol. II, p. 186.
Photo.: Thurston Thompson, 1857.
Copy from the central portion of the subject painted in bronze under the window of the fourth arcade of the *Loggie*. It is apparently by the same hand as Nos. 992 and 993.

992. JACOB WRESTLING WITH THE ANGEL (0492)
125 × 235 mm. Pen and brown ink and brown wash on blue paper, heightened with white.
George III 'Inventory A', p. 50, Raffaello d'Urbino e Scuola 23.
Lit.: J. D. Passavant, op. cit., Vol. II, p. 492a.
Photo.: Thurston Thompson, 1857.
Corresponds with the subject painted in bronze under the window of the sixth arcade of the *Loggie*. Another, better, version is at Oxford (Robinson, No. 108) ascribed to Penni. The present drawing is apparently by the same hand as Nos. 991 and 993.

993. JOSEPH AND HIS BRETHREN (0493)
123 × 235 mm. Pen and ink and brown wash on blue paper, heightened with white.
George III 'Inventory A', p. 50, Raffaello d'Urbino e Scuola 22.
Lit.: J. D. Passavant, op. cit., Vol. II, p. 492b.
Photo.: Thurston Thompson, 1857.
Corresponds with the subject painted in bronze under the window of the seventh arcade of the *Loggie*. It is apparently by the same hand as Nos. 991 and 992. There is an engraving of 1540 with the donkeys omitted and some other slight modifications (Bartsch XV, p. 11, 6).
According to Passavant (loc. cit.) the present drawing is the copy of one formerly in Sir Thomas Lawrence's collection, to which I can find no other reference.

994. DAVID'S CHARGE TO BATHSHEBA (0309)
234 × 425 mm. Drawn with the brush and washed on blue paper, heightened with white.
Corresponds with the subject painted in bronze under the window of the eleventh arcade of the *Loggie*. The style of the copy suggests the hand of Biagio Pupini. What is apparently the original drawing is at Oxford (attributed by Robinson, No. 109, to G. F. Penni).

Attributed to FRANCESCO VANNI (1563–1610)

995. THE FUNERAL PROCESSION OF A SAINT (*Plate* 43) (3499)
239 × 378 mm. (bottom R. corner torn). Oil sketch in brown on paper.
A.E.P. The composition, allowing for the difference in format, is extraordinarily like that of Vanni's *Burial of St. Catherine* in the Budapest Print Room (see O.M.D. VII (1932–33), pl. 3, and Budapest Jahrbuch VI (1931), p.163). In fact the half-length figure of a soldier with a halberd exactly in the centre of the foreground occurs in both compositions. It is extremely difficult in many cases to distinguish between the drawings of Vanni and his half-brother Salimbeni, and the present one might be an example of the latter's using motives from the work of the former, but I think on the whole it is more likely to be by Vanni.

996. CHRIST REMOVING THE WORLDLY HEART FROM THE BOSOM OF ST. CATHERINE OF SIENA and replacing it with a heavenly heart; a female saint kneels on the L. (3617)
318 × 230 mm. Black chalk on faded blue paper.
A.E.P. The Christ and St. Catherine correspond exactly with the figures in Pieter de Jode's engraving after Vanni in the series of eleven scenes from the life of St. Catherine, 1597. The kneeling saint on the L. does not occur. Vanni's original drawing for the whole engraving, of which this scene forms only a part, is in the Albertina (Catalogue, III, No. 422). The present drawing is larger than the engraving and quite in Vanni's style. It is perhaps a repetition from his own hand.

997. SLEEPING BOY, LYING FULL-LENGTH, WITH HIS HEAD RESTING ON HIS R. ARM (5242)
180 × 268 mm. Red chalk on blue paper, heightened with white.
Coll.: N. Lanière (Lugt 2886).
A.E.P. Inscribed in ink in the bottom R. hand corner in a hand of the XVII (?) century: 'Barocci'. The style, however, points to either Vanni or Salimbeni, more probably to the former.

998. FEMALE FIGURE SEATED, LOOKING UPWARDS, HER HANDS JOINED IN PRAYER (5236)
203 × 160 mm. (top corner cut). Red chalk on blue paper, heightened with white.
A.E.P. Attributed to Barocci, which seems to me impossible. Like the drawing last described, it is most probably by Vanni.

GIORGIO VASARI (1511–1574)

999. REBECCA AND ELIEZER (6005)
247 × 185 mm. Pen and brown ink and brown wash, squared in black chalk.
Coll.: N. Lanière (Lugt 2886).
Lit.: F. Antal, O.M.D. XIV (1939–40), pp. 47–49 (pl. 45).
The composition is obviously based on the lost painting by Rosso of this subject spoken of by Vasari and known from the drawing in the Uffizi (loc. cit., pl. 44). Whether this drawing is an adaptation of Rosso's design by Salviati (as Antal supposes) or the former's original design, as seems to me more probable, is immaterial to the present question. In his *Ricordanze* for 1559 Vasari speaks of five paintings made for Luca Manelli for export to France, one of which represented 'quando Rachel da bere al pozzo a Jacob' (*Il Libro delle Ricordanze di Giorgio Vasari*, a cura di A. del Vita, Arezzo, 1927, p. 82).

1000. THE ASSUMPTION OF THE VIRGIN IN THE PRESENCE OF FOUR SAINTS (*Figure* 191) (6323)
337 × 254 mm. Pen and light brown ink and wash.
P.M.R.P. The attribution to Vasari rests on grounds of style. It seems to me quite certain, but I can find no entry which might have reference to it in Vasari's *Ricordanze*.

1001. PROFILE HEAD OF POPE URBAN IV. (042)
197 × 127 mm. Black chalk.
Coll.: P. Crozat (?) (Lugt 474).
A.E.P. Inscribed in a contemporary hand, no doubt that of the artist, '1261 VRBANO IIII in · S · L° in perugia'. According to Vasari (I, p. 306), Giovanni Pisano was the sculptor of the marble monument to Urban IV in the cathedral church of S. Lorenzo, Perugia, erected after the pontiff's death in that city in 1264. He adds that the Perugians later destroyed the monument, and that only

FIG. 191 Cat. No. 1000

fragments in various parts of the church survived in his day. Presumably the head was one of these fragments, and the present drawing derives from it or from some drawing made, or supposed to have been made, from it. The head does not seem to be in existence now. Vasari was in Perugia in April, 1566, and may have made the sketch then.
The drawing was attributed to Clovio, but it so closely resembles the series of heads of artists by Vasari in the Uffizi (for the woodcuts in the 1568 edition of the *Vite*) that it may be confidently attributed to him. There is too little writing for a judgment from this to be conclusive, but the hand is certainly like Vasari's.
At the beginning of the third volume of the 1568 edition of the 'Lives', Vasari prints a 'Tavola de' Ritratti del Museo dell' illustrissimo e eccellentiss. S. Cosimo Duca di Fiorenza, & Siena'. A section at the end of this list, following portraits of popes, is headed 'Questi non sono messi ancora in Guardaroba ma si dipingano ora che s'e trovato i ritratti di tutti & con fatica'. Among these is Urban IV. If the present drawing is connected with this scheme of portraits of popes for the Guardaroba, as seems probable, it would follow that his portrait had not been obtained in 1568, and that the sketch must be of later date, but perhaps that is pressing the evidence too far.

Attributed to GIORGIO VASARI

1002. ALLEGORICAL FIGURE OF PRUDENCE (5095)
220 × 194 mm. Pen and ink and grey wash on greyish ground, heightened with white, the outlines pricked. Part of a W.M. with crossed arrows visible at the top.
P.M.R.P. The old attribution was to Francesco Salviati, but the type of head and general arrangement of the figure

resemble those of the Muses in Vasari's house in Arezzo (Venturi, IX 6, Fig. 176). Technically the sheet shows some resemblance to Allori's drawings, and I had thought of him as the possible draughtsman, but I think it is nearer to Vasari.

1003. PROFILE OF A BALD, BEARDED APOSTLE TO THE L. (5402)
232 × 191 mm. Black chalk on faded blue paper.
P.M.R.P. The type of head and the style of this small cartoon point fairly definitely to Vasari.

1004. THE VIRGIN AND TWO SHEPHERDS ADORING THE NEWLY-BORN CHILD (5038)
192 × 154 mm. Pen and light brown ink and wash.
A.E.P. Attributed to Parmigianino, from whom the composition may perhaps be derived, as it shows some relation, though not a very close one, to a drawing in the British Museum (Pp. 2–176), which is a copy by Vorsterman from Parmigianino. The style of the drawing seems to me to be Vasari's.

Copy from GIORGIO VASARI

1005. THE VIRGIN AND CHILD WITH ST. JOSEPH (5509)
221 × 160 mm. Fine pen and ink over black chalk.
Old attribution to 'Giorgio Vasari' on the mount. The drawing is a copy of one engraved by C. M. Metz, when in the collection of R. Udney (not catalogued by Weigel), and attributed by him to Primaticcio. The style is obviously that of Vasari. There is another old copy, presumably from the Udney drawing, in the British Museum (Sloane 5226–17).

Attributed to PAOLO (CALIARI) VERONESE (1528–1588)

1006. STUDY OF A BEARDED PROPHET WEARING A TURBAN, two studies of his head in different positions and studies of a leg, etc. (*Plate* 175) (6697)
410 × 254 mm. Black chalk and some wash on blue paper.
Inscribed in pen and ink in an old hand (of the XVI or XVII century (?)): 'Paulo Calliari · $\overline{\text{VE}}$' (= Veronese ?). The drawing, in spite of its clumsiness, has a certain majesty and power and may perhaps be a youthful work by Veronese. The style and the proportions of the figure should be compared, for instance, with those in the paintings of the history of Esther and Ahasuerus in S. Sebastiano, Venice. There is something in the proportions and drawings of the figure which suggests to me Pietro Marescalchi of Feltre (1503 (?)—1584), but in the absence of any other drawings attributable to that artist it would be rash to assume it was his work. The figure, to judge from the sketch of a niche at the bottom to the R., was intended to fill such a space. It might possibly be for one of the philosophers in niches in the Biblioteca Marciana, Venice (some illustrated by Hadeln in the Prussian Jahrbuch XXXII (1911), p. 27 f.), painted by various artists, including Veronese.

Copies from known works by PAOLO VERONESE (arranged in the order of the inventory numbers)

1007. ST. JEROME IN PENITENCE (3640)
396 × 293 mm. Red chalk.
Copy of the painting in S. Andrea della Zirada, Venice (ill. Veronese Exhibition Catalogue, Venice, 1939, No. 77).

1008. THE BAPTISM OF OUR LORD (4787)
228 × 162 mm. Pen and brown ink.
Careful and intelligent copy by an artist of the XVII or XVIII century of the picture now in the Pitti Gallery (No. 186).

1009. THE POOL OF BETHESDA (6682)
213 × 441 mm. Pen and brown ink and grey wash.
Copy of a painting engraved as Paolo Veronese in 1765 by Pietro Monaco, when in the possession of the Grassi family at S. Samuele, Venice.

1010. CHRIST IN THE HOUSE OF SIMON THE PHARISEE (6688)
350 × 476 mm. Brown wash over black chalk on blue paper, heightened with white.
Copy of the R. hand portion of the painting in the Brera at Milan (Venturi, IX 4, Fig. 785, as Benedetto Caliari).

1011. CHRIST IN THE HOUSE OF SIMON THE PHARISEE (6690)
287 × 409 mm. Black chalk on faded blue paper, heightened with white.
Copy of the L. hand portion of the painting in the Brera, Milan (Venturi, IX 4, Fig. 785, as Benedetto Caliari).

1012. THE RAPE OF EUROPA (6691)
259 × 360 mm. Pen and brown ink and brown wash on blue paper, heightened with white.
Copy or pastiche from one of the versions of Veronese's painting of the subject. It is nearest to that now in the Palazzo Ducale, Venice (Venturi, IX 4, Fig. 648). It is the work of an XVIII century Venetian.

1013. THE DEATH OF PROCRIS (6692)
233 × 177 mm. Pen and brown ink and brown wash, heightened with white.
Copy of the picture of the school of Paolo Veronese, now in the Strasbourg Gallery (ill. Gazette des Beaux-Arts, XVIII (1928), p. 49).

1014. ESTHER CROWNED BY AHASUERUS (6693)
286 × 232 mm. Pen and brown ink and brown wash over black chalk on blue paper, heightened with white.
Coll.: N. Lanière (Lugt 2886).
Copy from the painting in S. Sebastiano, Venice (Venturi, IX 4, Fig. 552). By the same hand as No. 1015.

1015. ESTHER BROUGHT BEFORE AHASUERUS (6694)
364 × 264 mm. Pen and brown ink and brown wash over black chalk on blue paper, heightened with white.
Coll.: N. Lanière (Lugt 2886).
Copy from the painting in S. Sebastiano, Venice (Venturi, IX 4, Fig. 550). By the same hand as No. 1014.

1016. THE ADORATION OF THE MAGI (6777)
207 × 254 mm. Pen and brown ink and brown wash over black and red chalk.
Inscribed in pencil at bottom: 'Antonio Gherardi'.
As pointed out to me by Blunt, the composition is the same as that of drawings at Düsseldorf (I. Budde, *Beschreibender Katalog der Handzeichnungen in Düsseldorf*, Düsseldorf, 1930, No. 104, pl. 18, wrongly attributed to Andrea Sacchi) and in the Albertina (Catalogue II, No. 105) attributed to Veronese. Studies certainly by Paolo himself, perhaps for

FIG. 192 Cat. No. 1021

this composition, are in the Teyler Museum at Haarlem (Hadeln, *Spätrenaissance*, 52). These are said by Hadeln to be for the National Gallery picture of 1573 of the same subject (No. 268). It is possible that the original of the present drawing may have been a discarded study for this.

1017. ESTHER CROWNED BY AHASUERUS (0186)
295 × 277 mm. Pen and brown ink and brown wash over red chalk.

A second copy from the painting in S. Sebastiano, Venice (Venturi, IX 4, Fig. 552).

1018. CHRIST IN THE HOUSE OF SIMON THE PHARISEE (01226)
610 × 1650 mm. (on four sheets of paper stuck together, folded). Pen and brown ink and grey wash.

Copy of the painting by Veronese in the Brera, Milan (Venturi, IX 4, Fig. 785, as Benedetto Caliari). Inscribed in ink on the *verso:* 'P. Veronese in refectorio di S. Sebastian a venetia,' 'N° 212 5– teeckeningen' and, in a different hand: '. . . gauffredie (?) kennig', presumably the name of the owner. The copy is apparently Venetian of the XVIII century. Two other copies of the R. and L. hand portions are catalogued above, Nos. 1010 and 1011.

1019. CHRIST IN THE HOUSE OF SIMON THE PHARISEE (01366)
350 × 525 mm. Brown wash on faded blue paper, heightened with white.

Careful copy of the large painting in the Turin Gallery (Venturi, IX 4, Fig. 669).

1020. CHRIST IN THE HOUSE OF SIMON THE PHARISEE (01371)
372 × 436 mm. Pen and brown ink and brown wash on blue paper, heightened with white.

Copy of the R. hand portion of the same picture at Turin.

WORKSHOP OF PAOLO VERONESE AND PRESUMED COPIES OF UNIDENTIFIED WORKS ATTRIBUTABLE TO HIM OR TO HIS WORKSHOP. (Arranged in the order of the inventory numbers.)

1021. ALLEGORICAL COMPOSITION: a female is introduced by another to the throne of a potentate, behind whom stand Minerva and Mercury, holding a wreath; in the distance on the R. a woman is chasing another through the streets of a city. (*Figure* 192) (3813)
240 × 322 mm. Pen and brown ink and brown wash.

There is apparently an old attribution to 'P. Veronese' on the *verso*, just visible from the front under the wand of Mercury. It appears to be a good original composition sketch of the school of Paolo Veronese.

1022. THE BIRTH OF THE VIRGIN (4785)
264 × 240 mm. Pen and brown ink and brown wash over black chalk.

Attributed by Bodmer to Domenico Brusasorci, the reason for which I fail to appreciate. It seems better to leave this quite interesting composition sketch with the school of Paolo Veronese, to which, broadly, it certainly belongs. It seems to be by the same hand as a drawing in the British Museum (1890–4–15–172) catalogued by the Tietzes (No. 2170) under the school of Paolo Veronese, and as No. 1035 below.

1023. VENICE ENTHRONED ACCOMPANIED BY SS. JAMES AND JUSTINA; a man on the L. presents the keys of a city on a salver, and there are two Turkish prisoners below: circle. (*Figure* 193) (4789)
220 × 222 mm. Pen and brown ink and brown wash over black chalk.

Lit.: Tietzes, No. 2211 (pl. CLXIV 3).

Inscribed in the 'deceptive' hand: 'Carletto'. As noticed by

FIG. 193 Cat. No. 1023

the Tietzes, there is a more finished version of the composition with slight modifications at Düsseldorf (I. Budde, *Beschreibender Katalog der Handzeichnungen in Düsseldorf*, Düsseldorf, 1930, No. 947), there attributed to Rottenhammer. According to the same authorities another version, showing that it was the design for part of a ceiling, was in the Graupe sale, Berlin, 1929, April 17, Lot 198 (pl. V in Sale Cat.). The Tietzes conclude that the design was connected with the battle of Lepanto and that the attribution to Carletto should be accepted. The similarity in style to other drawings identified with more or less probability as Carletto Caliari's does not seem to justify giving the present drawing to him merely on the evidence of this nearly always irresponsible annotator.

1024. DESIGN FOR THE DECORATION OF A WALL: the space is divided vertically into three, the central section being the largest, and laterally into two. In the lower, smaller, section there are trophies of arms on the L. and R. and three allegorical female figures in the centre; the vertical division of the upper part into three is continued by columns, which form part of the composition itself; on the L. is a Roman commander on an elevated throne, in the centre a group of soldiers and, on the R., other figures, one of whom clings to the dividing column. (4790)

480 × 395 mm. Pen and brown ink and grey wash.

The composition clearly derives from Veronese or from one of his immediate followers, but the drawing is almost certainly a copy.

1025. THE VIRGIN AND CHILD ON CLOUDS WITH TWO MUSICIAN ANGELS, ADORED BY ST. JOHN THE BAPTIST AND ST. JEROME (4792)

377 × 215 mm. Pen and ink and wash on faded blue paper, heightened with white.

The types and composition point to this being either a copy from a work of Veronese's school or an original design by one of his pupils.

1026. HEAD OF A BALD, BEARDED MAN, TURNED THREE-QUARTERS TO THE R. (5403)

268 × 184 mm. Red and black chalk on faded blue paper.

The type of this head is reminiscent of one of Paolo Veronese's kings in compositions of the *Adoration of the Magi*, but I do not find that it occurs.

1027. HEAD OF A MONK IN PROFILE TO THE L. (5409)

222 × 175 mm. Black and red chalk on blue paper, heightened with white.

The drawing may be by Carletto Caliari, as its style resembles that of the portrait of Paolo Paruta in the British Museum (Fenwick Collection, Catalogue, pl. XXVI), which has an old attribution to Carletto. I do not see that the Tietzes (No. 210) are justified in transferring this portrait to Leandro Bassano.

1028. THE VIRGIN STANDING IN FRONT OF A BUILDING HOLDING THE CHILD; on the L. St. Joseph is bringing a stool; on the R. are two women and another man; in the background is St. John the Baptist with a lamb. (6689)

251 × 210 mm. Pen and brown ink and brown wash over black chalk.

Lit.: Tietzes, No. 2212 (pl. CLXVII 1).

Inscribed in an XVIII century hand on the mount: 'P. Veronese'. Subsequently attributed to Zelotti. The Tietzes regard this very feeble drawing as a work by Carletto Caliari because of similarity in style to their No. 2204 in the Victoria and Albert Museum. It does resemble this, but the Tietzes' ascription of No. 2204 to Carletto seems extremely speculative.

1029. THE VIRGIN AND CHILD IN THE CLOUDS ADORED BY ST. FRANCIS AND ST. GEORGE KNEELING BELOW (6695)

299 × 217 mm. Pen and brown ink and brown wash on cream-coloured ground, heightened with white.

Inscribed in pencil on the drawing 'P. Veronese'. It appears to be a copy of some composition by Veronese or his school.

1030. VENICE ENTHRONED, WITH TWO DOGES KNEELING ON THE L. AND THREE ON THE R. (6696)

206 × 287 mm. Pen and light brown ink over black chalk, with splodges of white oil (or tempera) colour.

Lit.: Tietzes, No. 2189 (pl. CLXII 4).

Inscribed in ink in an old hand: 'Paolo Veronese'. Catalogued by the Tietzes under the heading of 'Heirs of Paolo Veronese'. They suggest that it might have reference 'to the Morosini family which up to the end of the XVI century was the only one to have produced four doges (one of the five has not donned his doge's cap)'. It is in any case a spirited original sketch close to Veronese.

1031. A COMMANDER, WHO HAS A CROSS ON HIS CUIRASS, IS CARRIED UPWARDS BY TWO ANGELS; above him are two allegorical female figures and higher still the Virgin and Child with musician angels; below are two bearded saints (?), a woman with two children and, on the R., the head of a horse. (6698)

473 × 317 mm. Black chalk outline and brown wash.

Attributed in ink in an old hand to 'P. Veronese'. The drawing is certainly a copy, probably a tracing. The original was near to Paolo Veronese in style and may have been by him, but I can find no reference to such a painting.

1032. HEAD OF A BALD SENATOR TURNED IN PROFILE TO THE R. (6703)

210 × 164 mm. Red chalk.

Attributed to Paolo Veronese. It hardly seems possible, however, that he should have drawn in red chalk in this manner, though the type of head is similar and it is conceivably a copy after him. There is a very similar head in the background on the R. in the tondo 'L'Onore' on the ceiling of the Libreria Marciana in Venice. A suggestion by Byam Shaw that it is a copy by Watteau is worthy of consideration.

1033. THE PRESENTATION IN THE TEMPLE (6704)

232 × 145 mm. Black chalk and wash on blue paper, heightened with white.

Lit.: Tietzes, No. 2190.

This feeble little drawing is catalogued by the Tietzes under 'Heirs of Paolo Veronese' on the strength of a resemblance they find in it to the chiaroscuros for S. Andrea di Torcello, exhibited at the Veronese exhibition in 1939 and illustrated in the Catalogue, pp. 138–141.

1034. INCIDENT IN THE LIVES OF THE APOSTLES (?): two apostles followed by a woman carrying a fish approach over the brow of a hill from the distance; in the foreground is a group of men, women and children, mostly seated. (6710)

307 × 210 mm. Pen and brown ink and brown wash over black chalk.

Old attribution on mount: 'Del Zelotti'. The drawing hardly seems, however, to be of the XVI century. Though there is an obvious connection with Tintoretto's painting of the *Miracle of the Loaves and Fishes* in S. Rocco, the general style seems rather to point to its being copied from a similar composition of Paolo Veronese. I can see no connection in the style of the drawing or in the composition with authentic works by Zelotti.

1035. THE ADORATION OF THE SHEPHERDS (6711)

215 × 265 mm. (damaged in L. hand bottom corner). Pen and brown ink and brown wash over black chalk.

The composition is obviously in the manner of Paolo Veronese. The drawing seems to be by the same hand as No. 1022.

A drawing of the school of Veronese is attached to one by Giulio Romano and catalogued under No. 378.

ANDREA VICENTINO (About 1542–about 1617)

1036. THE DOGE JACOPO TIEPOLO PRESENTING TO THE DOMINICANS OF SS. GIOVANNI E PAOLO THE TERRITORY FOR THEIR CHURCH AND CONVENT (6712)

153 × 365 mm. Pen and brown ink and brown wash.

Lit.: Tietzes, No. 2241 (pl. CXL 2).

Identified by the Tietzes as the *modello* (rather a composition sketch) for the painting in the Sacristy of SS. Giovanni e Paolo, Venice, signed and dated 1606.

1037. ST. JOHN THE EVANGELIST, ST. MARY MAGDALENE AND A BEARDED SAINT INTRODUCING A DONOR, WATCH THE CORONATION OF THE VIRGIN ABOVE: design for an altarpiece with an arched top. (6685)

252 × 125 mm. Pen and brown ink and brown wash over black chalk.

A.E.P. Inscribed in an old hand in ink along the bottom of the drawing: 'di Giacomo Tintoretto (?)' (nearly entirely cut away). The drawing is certainly Venetian and seems in fact to show the peculiarities of Andrea Vicentino. Its style may be compared with that of the drawing by him in the Fogg Museum (Tietzes 2216 and pl. CXXXIX 2), which is the study for the painting in the Ducal Palace, as well as with that of the drawing previously described.

PIERINO DA VINCI (1531–1554)

1038. AN OLD, BEARDED MAN WALKING TO THE L. BETWEEN TWO WOMEN, ONE OF WHOM IS POINTING FORWARD; OTHER WOMEN FOLLOW (0168)

181 × 257 mm. Pen and brown ink.

A.E.P. Inscribed at the bottom in ink: 'Rosso Fiorentino', with whom it has nothing to do. The style is that of Pierino da Vinci, to whom I would attribute it. Compare the drawing at Chatsworth for the relief of *Cosimo I expelling the Vices from Pisa*, published by U. Middeldorf in O.M.D. XIII (1938–39), pl. 9.

After PIERINO DA VINCI

1039. COUNT UGOLINO DELLA GHERARDESCA WITH HIS SONS IN THE TORRE DELLA FAME AT PISA (0648)

402 × 275 mm. (torn in places round the edges). Black chalk.

George III 'Inventory A', p. 43, Michelangelo, I, 15.

Copy from the relief of which numerous versions exist. According to a pencil note on the drawing this is from an example in terra cotta belonging to Marchese Guadagni behind the Annunziata at Florence. Perhaps this is the example now in the Bargello (Venturi, X 2, Fig. 294).

Attributed to TIMOTEO VITI (1467–1523)

1040. HEAD OF A MAN, WEARING A CAP, TURNED THREE-QUARTERS TO THE R. (*Figure* 194) (061)

235 × 223 mm. Grey chalk on yellowish paper, heightened with white.

FIG. 194 Cat. No. 1040

Lit.: B. Berenson, *Lorenzo Lotto*, London, 1901, p. 93 (ill.); Tietzes, No. A.2250.
Photo.: Braun 138.
Inscribed on *verso:* 'P. Perugino'. The attribution to Timoteo Viti, written in pencil on the mount, seems to me a probable one from the style and technique of the drawing, which are those of Timoteo or Raphael about 1500–05. It is hardly conceivable as a Venetian drawing, and Berenson's attribution to Alvise Vivarini does not seem to me possible. The Tietzes share my view as to the non-Venetian character of the drawing.

FEDERICO ZUCCARO (1542/43–1609)

(Drawings arranged in the order of the inventory numbers.)

1041. THE TRINITY (5111)
256 × 224 mm. Pen and brown ink and brown wash over black chalk on light brown ground, heightened with white.
P.M.R.P. The attribution of this drawing to Federico Zuccaro is an obvious one. There is, however, some connection with the group above the *Stoning of St. Stephen* in the Cappella Paolina, which is attributed to Lorenzo Sabbatini. The Trinity in that fresco is seen frontally, but the relative positions and actions of the persons are so similar that they might be the same seen from a different angle.

1042. A MIRACULOUS PAINTING OF THE VIRGIN AND CHILD IN AN OAK TREE APPEARS TO A KNEELING CARDINAL (5112)
446 × 318 mm. Black chalk and brown wash on green paper, heightened with white.
A.E.P. Such a picture, which a certain Battista Clavaro of Viterbo had had painted and hung on an oak in his vineyard, was venerated in the church of S. Maria della Quercia, Rome. I cannot, however, find that there was much activity in this church before the time of Benedict XIII in the XVIII century. The drawing may well have reference to some other church or chapel dedicated to the same miraculous picture. The artist has drawn a halo over the head of the cardinal, but only faintly in black chalk. The drawing seems to date from about 1600 and to be the work of Federico Zuccaro.

1043. *Recto:* HEAD OF A BOY TURNED THREE-QUARTERS TO THE L., LOOKING UP (5179)
Verso: HEAD OF THE SAME BOY TURNED THREE-QUARTERS TO THE R.
133 × 100 mm. Black and red chalk; the drawing on the *verso* is an offset.
Inscribed on the *verso* in ink in an old hand: 'F. Zuccari'. The drawing belongs to a series of portraits, of which others, from the collections of Lely and Sloane, are in the British Museum. On the *verso* of one of these (Sloane 5237–11) is an offset from the drawing on the *recto*. The series may date from Federico's Florentine period (1575–1579) as one of them is the portrait of Vincenzo Borghini.

1044. *Recto:* TWO STUDIES OF THE HEAD OF AN ELDERLY MAN: on the L. full face looking down, on the R. in profile to the R., looking up. (5215)
193 × 264 mm. Red and black chalk.
Verso: DRAWING OF MICHELANGELO'S 'DAWN' IN THE MEDICI CHAPEL
Black chalk.
The profile resembles many heads in works by Federico. It comes very close to the head of the kneeling king in the *Adoration of the Magi* in S. Francesco della Vigna, Venice (engraved in reverse by Philippe Thomassin), though it would be rash to regard it as definitely a study for that picture. I think in any case that the suggested attribution to Federico Zuccaro is correct. The study from Michelangelo's statue on the *verso* is also quite in Zuccaro's manner and suggests a date about 1575–1579, the period of his longest stay in Florence.

1045. HEAD OF A GIRL LOOKING STRAIGHT TO THE FRONT (5383)
159 × 121 mm. Red and black chalk.
Attribution to 'Zuccaro' in pencil on the mount in a XIX century hand. It seems to me, though not certain, extremely probable from the style.

1046. THE DESCENT OF THE HOLY SPIRIT ON THE VIRGIN AND THE APOSTLES (*Figure* 195) (6015)

FIG. 195 Cat. No. 1046

355 × 260 mm. Pen and ink and grey wash on blue paper, heightened with white, squared in black chalk.
Inscribed in ink in the bottom R. hand corner in an old hand: 'Federigo Zuccaro'. Study for the painting of the subject on the altar of the basilica of S. Lorenzo in the Escorial (ill. F. Julián Zarco Cuevas, *Pintores Italianos en San Lorenzo el real de el Escorial*, Madrid, 1932, opp. p. 200), one of a series painted between 1585 and 1588. There are considerable differences in detail between this drawing and the painting, but I think there can be no doubt of the connection or that it is Zuccaro's original design.

1047. ALLEGORICAL FIGURES INSCRIBED 'TIMOR DOMINI' AND 'FIDES', designed to fill the angles of an arch; the figure of 'Fides' with a spaniel is repeated in the centre of the sheet. (*Figure* 196) (6017)

FIG. 196 Cat. No. 1047

221 × 401 mm. Pen and brown ink and brown wash over black chalk on faded blue paper, heightened with white, partly squared in black chalk.
Inscribed in an old hand in ink in the bottom R. hand corner: 'Zucari'. Studies for the decoration of the Cappella Paolina in the Vatican on which Federico was working in 1579–80. The figures are painted above the arch over the altar, and can be seen in Anderson's photograph. They are, however, practically repetitions of the two figures of Adam and Eve in the angles above the arch in Sadeler's engraving of the *Annunciation* (1571), painted in 1566 for the Jesuit church of the Santissima Annunziata. According to Werner Körte (Mitt. des kunsthistorischen Instituts in Florenz, III (1919–1932), p. 526 note) these two figures must have been drawn expressly for the engraver, as there was no place for them above the lunette where the *Annunciation* was actually painted.

1048. DEMONS IN VARIOUS GROTESQUE ATTITUDES (6416)
257 × 464 mm. Pen and brown ink and brown wash over black chalk.
A.E.P. These figures recall those painted by Federico Zuccaro in the cupola of the Duomo at Florence, on which he was working from 1574 to 1579, but do not in fact occur there. They are either discarded studies for this scheme of decoration or, more probably, for some other. The style leaves little doubt that the drawing is the work of one of the Zuccari.

1049. SIBYL WITH A CHILD: for the angle above an arch. (*Plate* 86) (0123)
200 × 150 mm. Pen and ink and wash on chocolate-coloured ground, heightened with white.
Old inscription, 'Fed Sucharo,' in pen and ink on the drawing. It is the study for one of the two sibyls represented above the *Adoration of the Magi* in J. Matham's engraving (Bartsch III, p. 190, 232). This, according to Van Mander (*Het Schilder-Boeck*, Haarlem, 1604, Fol. 186), is from the altarpiece in S. Eligio degli Orefici, Rome, which no longer survives. Federico, according to Werner Körte (Mitt. des kunsthistorischen Instituts in Florence, III (1919–1932), p. 73) was paid for this work in 1569. There are considerable differences between the figures in the engraving and in the drawing, but there can be no doubt of the connection between the two works or that the latter is an original drawing by Federico.

1050. ST. FRANCIS OF ASSISI RECEIVING THE STIGMATA IN A MOUNTAIN GORGE (0158)
460 × 315 mm. Pen and ink and wash on a cream-coloured ground, heightened with white.
A.E.P. Inscribed in pencil on the drawing: 'del Mutiano', a natural attribution for a landscape drawing of this character. Nevertheless, neither the landscape nor the figures show much connection with Mutiano. It seems to me probably a very late drawing by Federico Zuccaro.

1051. A MAN SEATED AT THE HARPSICHORD, WITH ANOTHER MAN STANDING ON THE R. (0220)
135 × 189 mm. Black chalk.
Attribution in 'deceptive' hand to 'Giorgione'. There can be little doubt that it is by Federico Zuccaro. Its style may be compared with that of the drawing of the interior of the Medici chapel in S. Lorenzo, Florence (Louvre: photo. Braun 307).

Copies from FEDERICO ZUCCARO
(Arranged in the order of the inventory numbers.)

1052. ALLEGORICAL FIGURE OF FAITH, HOLDING A CROSS IN HER L. HAND (5108)
176 × 90 mm. Brown wash on reddish ground, heightened with white.
A.E.P. Corresponds with a figure on the vaulting of the chapel of Francesco Maria II of Urbino in the church of the Santa Casa at Loreto (ill. in Jahrbücher des Museums der bildenden Künste in Budapest, VI (1929–30), p. 161). There is another drawing of the same figure at Budapest (ill. loc. cit., p. 160) from which this is presumably a copy.

1053. BEARDED APOSTLE WITH HIS R. ARM RAISED A BOOK IN THE OTHER; he is talking to a Roman commander; other figures in the foreground and further back. (5125)
238 × 232 mm. Pen and brown ink and brown wash on faded blue paper, heightened with white, squared in black chalk.
An early XIX century (?) hand has written 'Query Tad. Zuccaro' on the old mount. The composition is certainly Zuccaresque, but I think it is rather by Federico, and more likely a copy from, than an original by, him. There are numerous echoes of his figures—the apostle is like the Christ in one of the drawings for the *Raising of Lazarus* in S. Francesco della Vigna, Venice; the foreground figure on the R. occurs in an almost identical form in a composition of Christ preaching, which is engraved, and there are numerous other points of resemblance, notably to the two paintings of the *Miracles of Christ* at Orvieto. The composition has obviously been cut into at the sides and even more at the top; it may once have been twice as high.

1054. A WIDOW KNEELING, TURNED IN PROFILE TO THE R.; further back the Saviour blessing and spectators. (5134)
190 × 192 mm. Red chalk with some red wash.
The figures correspond with a group in the drawing by Federico Zuccaro in the Albertina (Catalogue, III, No. 256) of the *Raising of the Widow's Son at Naim*, a study for the painting of 1570 at Orvieto, or from the anonymous engraving made from this drawing. The drawing and engraving differ considerably from the painting and from the engraving of this by Jacob Matham.

1055. MATTHIAS AND BARNABAS PRAYING TO GOD TO CHOOSE WHICH OF THEM SHALL TAKE THE PLACE OF JUDAS AS AN APOSTLE (Acts i. 23) (5197)
258 × 422 mm. Pen and brown ink and wash over black chalk.

FIG. 197 Cat. No. 1057

Attributed to Taddeo Zuccaro, but the style is rather that of Federico. There is another version of the drawing in the Uffizi (aquatint by Scacciati, Weigel 8686). Yet another version was in a dealer's hands in London in 1938. I am unable to decide which of these versions is the original. A drawing of the same subject, with very considerable differences but obviously original, is in the Victoria and Albert Museum (Dyce 195).

1056. GOD THE FATHER IN A CLOUD SURROUNDED BY CHERUBS; He points towards the sun; below deer are grazing in a mountainous landscape. (5976)

230 × 278 mm. Pen and brown ink and brown wash over black chalk on blue paper, heightened with white.

Lit.: H. Bodmer in Thieme-Becker XXIX (1935), p. 371 (as Orazio Samacchini).

A.E.P. The drawing corresponds with the *tondo* in the centre of the vault of the chapel at Caprarola, the frescoes in which are almost certainly by Federico and not by Taddeo. There exists, however, another drawing (formerly at Wilton House: repr. Wilton House Drawings, Part I, No. 9) with which the present sheet corresponds even more closely and from which it appears to be copied. The Wilton House drawing is discussed by Licia Collobi in Critica d'Arte, III (1938), p. 70 ff. The Windsor drawing is exactly in the style of Federico, and without the knowledge of the other drawing might well have been accepted as an original.

A series of copies after Correggio (Nos. 253–257), as well as a copy after Rosso (No. 879), also seem to be by Federico Zuccaro.

Follower of FEDERICO ZUCCARO

1057. THE VIRGIN ENTHRONED WITH, ON HER LAP, THE CHILD, WHO PRESENTS TO A KNEELING WARRIOR-SAINT A PALM; with him is a dog, and behind, St. Francis of Assisi; on the R. stands St. Joseph. (*Figure* 197) (5099)

333 × 247 mm. Finished drawing in pen and ink and green wash on a buff-coloured ground, heightened with white.

Lit.: H. Bodmer, Thieme-Becker XXIX (1935), p. 283 (as Lorenzo Sabbatini).

I have not been able to identify the warrior-saint, the most important personage from the point of view of discovering the place for which the altarpiece may have been designed.

1058. LUNETTE WITH FOUR WOMEN WATCHING THE DEPARTURE OF A SHIP (*Figure* 198) (6032)

232 × 366 mm. Finished drawing in pen and ink and brown wash on blue paper, heightened with white, squared in black chalk.

1059. LUNETTE WITH FOUR WOMEN WATCHING THE DEPARTURE OF A SHIP (6031)

216 × 353 mm. (lunette cut out). Pen and brown ink and brown wash on blue paper, heightened with white.

Exact copy of No. 1058.

1060. A SIBYL RECLINING ON CLOUDS, ACCOMPANIED BY TWO WINGED PUTTI (*Figure* 199) (5969)

228 × 270 mm. (a strip added at the top and both bottom corners made up). Finished drawing in pen and brown ink and brown wash on a buff ground, heightened with white.

Lit.: H. Bodmer, Thieme-Becker, XXIX (1935), p. 283 (as Lorenzo Sabbatini).

Attributed to 'Pellegrino Tibaldi' in pencil on the drawing.

1061. THE EVANGELIST ST. MATTHEW (5126)

222 × 214 mm. (cut on the R. and the top corners made up). Finished drawing in pen and brown ink and brown wash on a buff ground, heightened with white.

1062. THE ENTOMBMENT: composition of numerous figures seen by artificial light. (0293)

265 × 328 mm. (cut into on all sides). Finished drawing in pen and brown ink and brown wash on a pink ground.

Old attribution to Garofalo.

FIG. 198 Cat. No. 1058

FIG. 199 Cat. No. 1060

1063. THE PRESENTATION OF THE VIRGIN IN THE TEMPLE (*Figure* 200) (5047)

261 × 215 mm. Pen and brown ink over black chalk, not entirely completed.

There seems to me little doubt that the six drawings, Nos. 1057–1063 (the copy, No. 1059, need not be taken into account) are by the same hand, or that the artist responsible for them was closely dependent on Federico Zuccaro. The very close resemblance between No. 1057, for example, and the series of drawings for the Cupola of the Duomo at Florence by Federico and his assistants (in the British Museum and in the Albertina at Vienna) suggests that the draughtsman of the present series was a Florentine trained under Federico during the period of his activity there between 1574 and 1579. Indeed, the resemblance in the case of some of the Windsor drawings is so striking, that it might even be argued that they were by Federico himself. On the other hand, the practice of repeating drawings was very prevalent in the workshop of Federico Zuccaro, and it seems in many cases almost impossible to distinguish copy from original (the repetition of No. 1058 in the present series, for example, without the original with which to compare it would have been very difficult to identify as a copy), so that it would be rather hazardous to give them to Federico. There are also certain facial types which do not seem to be characteristic of him and which are very marked in the Windsor drawings (the women's faces in Nos. 1057, 1058 and 1063, for example). The delicacy, precision and a certain finished hardness in the technique are reminiscent of the work of the Veronese, Jacopo Ligozzi, who first came to Florence in 1575, but again the types mentioned above are different from any which occur in drawings by him known to me.

Five out of the six drawings at Windsor are very elaborately finished and must be regarded as *modelli*, or possibly drawings made for record as a sort of *Liber Veritatis*. The way in which the artist worked is shown in No. 1063, which remained unfinished. Over a slight sketch in black chalk he drew in pen and ink with great precision, somewhat in the style of an engraver, the whole design. He then apparently washed in the coloured ground over this and finally heightened it with white.

1064. THE MARTYRDOM OF ST. LAWRENCE: elaborate composition of many figures. (0380)

370 × 267 mm. Finished drawing in pen and ink and brown wash on a pink ground, heightened with white.

Inscribed in pencil on the drawing: 'di Giorgio Vasari'. The composition shows relation to various other representations of the subject, especially to that attributed to Taddeo Zuccaro (rather by Federico?) in the Chiesa dei Cappucini at Fermo (ill. *Inventario degli Oggetti d'Arte d'Italia*, VIII, Provincie di Ancona . . ., 1936, p. 264).

1065. THE MASSACRE OF THE INNOCENTS (0291)

290 × 214 mm. Finished drawing in pen and ink and brown wash on a pink ground, heightened with white.

The drawing bears a fanciful attribution 'Del Bene Figlio da Garofalo', in pencil. Antal suggested it was by Tempesta and connected it with the latter's painting of the subject in S. Stefano Rotondo, Rome, but it seems to me to be by the same hand as the drawing previously described, and to show a close dependence on Federico Zuccaro. The technique and peculiarities of handling are very similar, and it may even be by the same hand. It must, however, be admitted that it is clumsier in handling and may represent the work of another copyist or follower of Zuccaro.

FIG. 200 Cat. No. 1063

TADDEO ZUCCARO (1529–1566)

1066. OCCASION SEIZING FORTUNE BY THE FORELOCK (*Plate* 85) (5990)

360 × 240 mm. (corners cut). Pen and brown ink and brown wash over black chalk, squared in pen and ink.

A.E.P. Design for the central oval, executed in stucco, of the vaulting of a room in the Villa di Papa Giulio, Rome (photo., Anderson 4065). Vasari (VII, p. 81) says that in 1551 he called Taddeo in to help in the decoration of the

FIG. 201 Cat. No. 1068

rooms 'della vigna, che fu del cardinale Poggio, fuori della porta del Popolo in sul monte', and goes on 'e nel quadro del mezzo gli fece dipignere una Occasione, che avendo presa la Fortuna mostra di volerle tagliare il crine con le forbice; impresa di quel papa: nel che Taddeo si porto molto bene'.

1067. THE BLINDING OF ELYMAS (*Plate* 84) (6016)
392 × 530 mm. Pen and ink over black chalk on blue paper, heightened with white.
Coll.: N. Lanière (Lugt 2885).
Inscribed at the bottom in the centre: 'Taddeo [only the tops of the long letters are visible] Zuccaro'. The drawing seems to be a first idea for the subject painted in the Frangipani chapel in S. Marcello al Corso, Rome (Venturi, IX 5, Fig. 514), where Taddeo, according to Vasari, was at work in the summer of 1564. It shows very great differences from the fresco, for which No. 1068 is the definitive small cartoon. Indeed there are elements in the composition which connect it more closely with the companion painting of the *Healing of a Cripple* (Venturi, IX 5, Fig. 515), but I think in view of Taddeo's methods of work (as shown, for example, in the drawing for the Sala Regia fresco, No. 1070, discussed below), we can be fairly certain that this sketch *is* connected with the frescoes in S. Marcello and is not the design for some other unrecorded painting of the same subject.

1068. THE BLINDING OF ELYMAS (*Figure* 201) (01240)
395 × 546 mm. Red chalk, squared in black chalk. A large red stain in the top R. hand corner.
A.E.P. Elaborate, but not entirely finished, small cartoon for the fresco in S. Marcello al Corso, Rome (Venturi, IX 5, Fig. 514), for which apparently the drawing just discussed was a first idea. The subject has been cut into on all sides. The figure seated on the ground in the centre with his back to a column is in outline only.

1069. *Recto:* STUDY FOR THE DRAPERY OF A STANDING MAN HOLDING A BOOK (*Plate* 87) (6011)
373 × 222 mm. Drawn with the point of the brush in red. W.M., a diamond containing a star within a circle.

Verso: STUDY OF SIMILAR DRAPERY FOR THE SAME FIGURE AND SMALL COMPOSITION STUDY
Black chalk (the small composition sketch in pen and ink). Inscribed in red ink in bottom R. hand corner: 'zuccaro'. The drawing appears to be the study for the drapery of St. Paul in the fresco of the *Healing of the Cripple* in S. Marcello al Corso, Rome (Venturi, IX 5, Fig. 515). The position of the figure is exactly the same and the light falls from the same side, but the drapery was very considerably altered. I think such a detail as the end of the drapery falling over the edge of a step in both drawing and fresco is significant for the connection between the two. I do not know for what the composition sketch on the *verso* of a man kneeling before the throne of a potentate can be. It does not seem to be for any of the other subjects of the life of St. Paul in the Frangipani Chapel, but these are not reproduced.

1070. CHARLEMAGNE CONFIRMING THE UNION OF RAVENNA AND OTHER TERRITORIES OF THE CHURCH IN A.D. 774 (*Figure* 202) (6849)

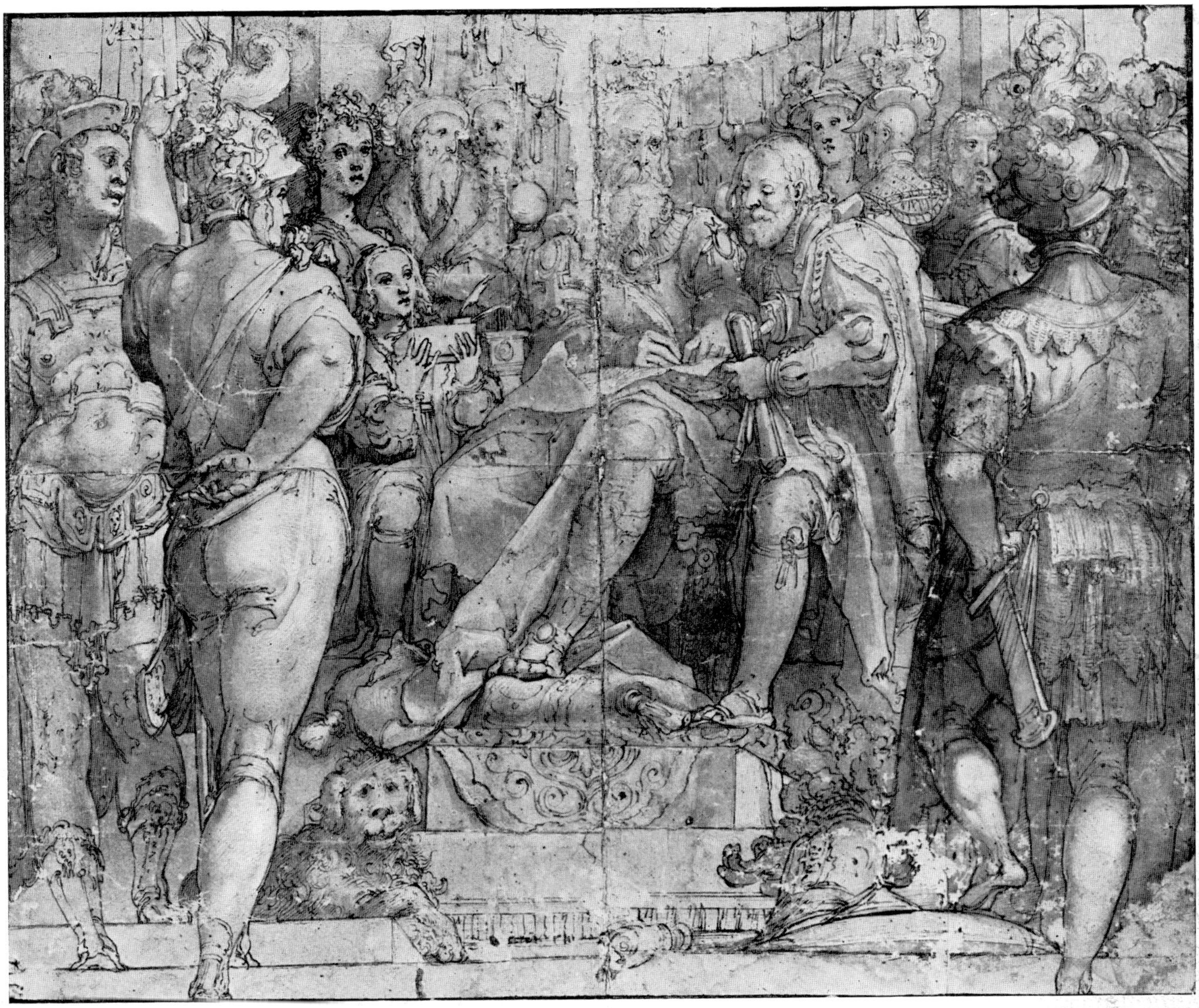

FIG. 202 Cat. No. 1070

397 × 500 mm. Finished drawing in pen and ink and wash on a cream-coloured ground, heightened with white. There is a bad fold vertically down the centre, and rubbing on either side of this. W.M., a paschal lamb in a circle.

The subject was painted by Taddeo Zuccaro as a *sopra-porte* in the Sala Regia in the Vatican (Venturi, IX 5, Fig. 513) between 1561 and 1566. The present elaborately finished drawing differs very considerably from the fresco, but corresponds in all essentials with a rougher sketch in the British Museum, Fenwick Collection (ill. O.M.D., VII (1932–33), pl. 49). It is apparently the finished *modello* based on the Fenwick drawing. There is yet another drawing, again almost entirely different except for the figure of Charlemagne, at Berlin (Voss, *Spätrenaissance*, Fig. 171). The figure on the L. in the present drawing, which is quite different from that in the fresco, was taken over by Federico Zuccaro and used in his fresco in S. Lucia del Gonfalone (drawing for this illustrated by Voss, *Spätrenaissance*, Fig. 177).

1071. GROUP OF SHEPHERDS ADVANCING FROM THE R. TO ADORE THE NEWBORN CHILD (*Plate* 89) (6019)

500 × 418 mm. Pen and brown ink and brown wash on yellow ground, the outlined indented.

Old attribution to 'Zuccaro' on the mount. The drawing is rather by Taddeo than by Federico. It is certainly by the same hand as two drawings on the same scale at Chatsworth, Nos. 193 and 194, both attributed to Taddeo. The first of these is for the attendants of the Magi approaching from the L. with horses and camels; the second is a complete composition of the *Adoration of the Shepherds* (another version in the Uffizi, No. 11040), which does not, however, correspond in any part with the Windsor drawing. I do not know whether one or more of these drawings could be connected with the *Nativity* which, Vasari records (VII, p. 85), Taddeo painted in Sta. Maria dell' Orto, Rome, or alternatively with the designs 'de' fatti di nostra Donna' which he made for the chapel in the Duomo of Urbino and which were never painted. Vasari says that in 1568 these designs were in the possession of Federico. The composition of the Chatsworth *Adoration of the Shepherds* was imitated by G. B. Ricci in his painting in S. Marcello al Corso (Venturi, IX 5, Fig. 534).

Attributed to TADDEO ZUCCARO

1072. THE DEATH OF THE VIRGIN (5042)

356 × 187 mm. Black chalk and brown wash on blue paper, heightened with white.

A.E.P. The composition of this drawing seems to me thoroughly in the manner of Taddeo Zuccaro, but I am not convinced that it is from his hand.

1073. HEAD OF A BEARDED MAN WEARING A GORGET (*Plate* 88) (5418)
427 × 283 mm. (corners cut and a bit at top R. made up). Black, red and white chalk on brown, discoloured, paper.
P.M.R.P. The features are not unlike those of a portrait of a man with a brace of dogs in the Pitti Gallery (photo., Brogi 6025), supposed, but obviously wrongly, to be Francesco Maria II della Rovere and to be by Taddeo Zuccaro. They are even more strikingly like those of Taddeo Zuccaro himself as shown in the portrait drawing by Federico Zuccaro in the Louvre (Voss, *Spätrenaissance*, Fig. 166), and this fine drawing may well be a self-portrait by Taddeo.

1074. HISTORICAL SCENE: a soldier in the centre with another running up to him; two other figures to the R.; behind, groups of people and three camels to the L.: design for an oblong oval. (5066)
216 × 316 mm. Pen and brown ink and brown wash over red chalk.
Antal saw a connection between the style of this drawing and that of one in the Albertina (Cat. III, No. 249), which is a study for the fresco by Taddeo Zuccaro in the Castello Orsini at Bracciano. It represents the wife of Darius before Alexander, and it is possible that the subject of the present drawing is also from the story of Alexander. Though it does not seem to be by the same hand, it might perhaps be a copy from Taddeo Zuccaro.

1075. THE SURRENDER OF A CITY TO A MARSHAL: a procession of horsemen advance from the gate towards a canopy held by four men and surrounded by musicians; the commander on horseback with a mounted retinue goes forward towards the canopy. (5119)
312 × 235 mm. Pen and brown ink and brown wash, squared in black chalk.
Attributed in pencil on the mount to 'Zuccaro'. The style is near to that of Taddeo's drawings for Caprarola. A drawing apparently *en suite* with this representing a battle is in the Uffizi (Santarelli 812) as Taddeo Zuccaro.

After TADDEO ZUCCARO

1076. CARDINAL ALESSANDRO FARNESE, THE LEGATE APPOINTED BY THE POPE FOR WAGING WAR AGAINST THE LUTHERANS, MEETING THE EMPEROR CHARLES V AND FERDINAND KING OF THE ROMANS AT WORMS IN 1544 (5988)
246 × 319 mm. Pen and light brown ink and wash.
The drawing corresponds with the subject painted in the Sala dei Fasti Farnesi in the Palace at Caprarola (Venturi, IX 5, Fig. 511) except that there is no attempt at portraiture in the heads, and for a few other minor differences. It is either an original drawing by Taddeo or, more probably in my opinion, a copy from such a drawing. The repetitions of the Caprarola subjects are numerous, and it is difficult to distinguish between originals and copies.

1077. FRANCIS I OF FRANCE RECEIVING THE EMPEROR CHARLES V AND CARDINAL ALESSANDRO FARNESE, THE POPE'S LEGATE, AT PARIS IN 1540 (5121)
320 × 434 mm. Pen and brown ink and brown wash over black chalk
Copy of a drawing in the Albertina, Vienna (Catalogue, III, No. 265), which is presumably the original study for the subject painted in the Sala dei Fasti Farnesi in the Palace at Caprarola (photo., Anderson 22952: engraved in *Illustri Fatti Farnesiani*, Rome, 1748, pl. 17).

1078. THE BIRTH OF THE VIRGIN (6020)
307 × 187 mm. Pen and brown ink and wash on cream-coloured ground, heightened with white.
F.A. An old facsimile of a drawing at Chatsworth (No. 191, from the collections of Lely and Lankrink: attributed to Niccolò dell' Abbate). The subject is engraved in reverse by an artist of the period of Cherubino Alberti. I think the original at Chatsworth may be attributed with considerable probability to Taddeo Zuccaro. The style may be compared with that of his early painting of the subject at Capranica (Venturi, IX 5, Fig. 501). Bodmer attributed the Windsor drawing to Federico Zuccaro.

ANONYMOUS DRAWINGS

SCHOOL OF BOLOGNA

1079. VENUS AND CUPID: she stands, with her back turned and looks towards the R.; Cupid stands on the L. and holds on to her; at his feet are two masks. (5459)
243 × 126 mm. Brush drawing in brown on a cream-coloured ground, heightened with white.
I associate this technique and coloured ground with Bologna and Raphaelesque painters like Giacomo Francia, Innocenzo da Imola and Girolamo da Treviso. The present drawing is feeble and perhaps more mannerist in style than the work of these artists, but is probably Bolognese.

1080. A WOMAN SEEN FROM BEHIND (*Plate* 108) (5130)
207 × 135 mm. Pen and ink and brown wash over red chalk on blue paper, heightened with white, squared in black chalk. The drawing is on three separate pieces of paper joined with extreme precision.
Inscribed in the L. hand bottom corner in the 'deceptive' hand: 'Paolo' (?), presumably intended for Paolo Veronese. Though the lighting had at first suggested to me some Venetian mannerist like Giuseppe Porta, the clumsy forms rather recall Bologna, and one is reminded of figures in Passarotti's paintings (e.g. Venturi, IX 6, Figs. 449, 450). But the actual technique is very much more delicate than is usual with the Bolognese, especially with Passarotti.

1081. THE APPARITION OF THE ARCHANGEL TO ST. GREGORY AND HIS PROCESSION as they carry the miraculous image of the Virgin to pray for intervention against the plague. In the background is the Castle of St. Angelo. (5993)
390 × 270 mm. (arched top). Drawn with the brush on dark blue prepared surface, heightened with white and outlined in places with ink.
Inscribed in ink at lower edge: '56'. The drawing may have some connection with the altarpiece of the subject in the Madonna del Baraccano, Bologna (Venturi, IX 6, Fig. 465), though the correspondence is general and no single figure is the same. According to Malvasia (ed. 1841, p. 250) the picture in question was supposed to have been painted by Cesare Aretusi from a drawing furnished him by Prospero Fontana in place of one, ordered of Federico Zuccaro, which did not give satisfaction. This theory is accepted by Venturi

but not by Corrado Ricci (Rassegna d'Arte VII (1907), p. 102) or by Werner Körte (*Der Palazzo Zuccari in Rom.*, Leipzig, 1935, p. 75). It is in fact known that Federico Zuccaro was commissioned by Paolo Ghiselli in 1580 to paint this subject for the church in Bologna, and both Ricci and Körte believe that the picture in the church is Zuccaro's. Ricci further published a drawing from the Santarelli collection in the Uffizi for the picture, which seems to be by Federico. The present drawing is certainly not his and almost certainly Bolognese. It is likely to be the *modello* by some other artist, but hardly by Prospero Fontana, to judge from the style. This seems nearer to Ercole Procaccini's, but in the absence of any authenticated drawings by that artist it is better to leave it anonymous.

1082. A YOUNG WOMAN STANDS ON A PEDESTAL BEFORE THE THRONE OF AN ORIENTAL POTENTATE AND HIS QUEEN: flat oval. (5959)
242 × 287 mm. Pen and brown ink and brown wash over black chalk, squared in black chalk.
Inscribed in the 'deceptive' hand: 'Nosadella allievo di Pelegrino Tibaldi'. If the attribution of No. 526 to Nosadella, which is discussed above, is correct this drawing can hardly be his. The manner of composition in an oval is reminiscent of the scenes painted in the *Studiolo* of Francesco I in the Palazzo Vecchio at Florence, but the style appears to be Bolognese, of the end of the century, approaching that of Camillo Procaccini.

1083. DESIGN FOR PART OF A FRIEZE: A NUDE MAN SEPARATING PART OF A PICTURE OF PARNASSUS FROM A COAT-OF-ARMS (nearly cut off) on the L. (6006)
151 × 125 mm. Finished drawing in pen and brown ink and wash on dark brown ground, heightened with white.
This design is apparently Bolognese of the end of the century. It shows some resemblance to works by Calvart (see L. van Puyvelde, *Flemish Drawings at Windsor Castle*, London, 1942, No. 42).

1084. THE RAPE OF PROSERPINA BY PLUTO: he stands on the L. in a chariot drawn by three galloping horses and holds Proserpina with his L. arm; in the distance on the R. are some nymphs under a tree; above them on the clouds are Venus and Cupid. (01256)
383 × 510 mm. Finished drawing in pen and ink and grey wash. The sheet has been varnished.
On the *verso* is an old (contemporary?) inscription beginning: 'di man di M . . .' This has apparently been interpreted as Pellegrino Tibaldi, but the final word does not appear to me to begin with a 'T', and in any case the style is not possible for Tibaldi. It is, however, apparently Bolognese of the end of the century.

1085. HEAD OF A YOUTH IN A WIDE RUFF (5156)
233 × 178 mm. Red chalk.
The drawing appears to be Bolognese of the end of the century.

1086. THE VIRGIN APPEARING TO ST. FRANCIS OF ASSISI, who holds the Infant Christ in his arms. (3573)
235 × 182 mm. Pen and brown ink and brown wash, the outlines indented.
The same subject is represented in an etching by P. Faccini (Bartsch XVIII, p. 272, 1), and the present drawing might well also be Bolognese, about 1600.

SCHOOL OF CREMONA

1087. HEAD OF A YOUNG MAN, wearing a chaperon of the fashion of the mid XV century, looking up to the R. (*Plate* 137) (4776)
382 × 284 mm. (on two pieces of paper stuck together). Black, red and white chalk on light brown paper; fragment of a cartoon.
The suggestion by Adolfo Venturi that it is the work of Romanino hardly seems possible. The style rather recalls that of Bocaccio Bocaccino at Cremona. It must be a XVI century copy or reconstruction of an earlier portrait, perhaps intended for insertion in a commemorative painting.

SCHOOL OF FLORENCE

1088. ST. JOHN THE EVANGELIST DRINKS FROM THE POISONED CHALICE in the presence of the Emperor Domitian, while an attendant who had previously drunk from it lies dead at their feet; spectators on the R. (*Figure* 203) (0397)
141 × 183 mm. (a strip added along the bottom, which is irregularly torn). Pen and light brown ink.
On the *verso* is the fragment of an illegible inscription in a hand of the XVI (?) century, and 'Hippol. Mau: supp' in writing of the XVII or XVIII century.

FIG. 203 Cat. No. 1088

The drawing is apparently the copy of a Florentine fresco of the XIV century from a series of the life of St. John the Evangelist. This scene, together with another from the legend of the saint above it, appears in a drawing in the Louvre (B.B. 2756E) attributed by Berenson to Spinello Aretino. The present drawing is of later date and its style is near to that of Bandinelli. There is a second copy of the same composition (St. John drinking from the poisoned cup) in the Louvre (No. 2709, attributed to Beccafumi) which, I am informed by Philip Pouncey, is certainly by Bandinelli.

1089. *Recto:* STUDY OF A R. ARM AND SLEEVE (0371)
212 × 87 mm. Red chalk.
Verso: STUDY OF A L. HAND
Black chalk.

Coll.: N. Lanière (Lugt 2886).
Inscribed in ink in an old hand: 'Andrea del sarto'. The style is not his, but it seems to be Florentine of the second decade of the century. It comes very near to Franciabigio, but it is impossible to be certain about a fragment of this character.

1090. RECUMBENT RIVER-GOD (*Plate* 38) (0444)
224 × 225 mm. Black chalk.
This able drawing is clearly by a Florentine artist, not necessarily a sculptor, of the generation of Vasari and Salviati. It may be from a statue like that by Ammanati of the Tiber in the Villa di Papa Giulio, Rome (Venturi, X 2, Fig. 322).

1091. *Recto:* STUDY OF THE BONES OF A R. HAND SEEN FROM FRONT AND BACK (0437)
373 × 250 mm. Pen and ink and red chalk.
Verso: SKETCH FOR A COMPOSITION OF ABRAHAM SACRIFICING ISAAC
Pen and ink, black chalk and wash.
The drawings of bones on the *recto* are in a formal style reminiscent of Bandinelli's. The sketch on the *verso* seems to have some connection with Michelangelo's drawing of the subject in the Casa Buonarroti (Frey 292), though it is in the reverse direction. The pen work, especially, is extremely feeble, and is not necessarily by the same quite competent hand as the bones on the *recto*. The sheet is presumably Florentine.

1092. STUDIES OF A NUDE MAN SEATED TO THE R., RESTING HIS HEAD ON HIS L. HAND, AND OF A BEARDED HEAD (0751)
228 × 151 mm. Pen and grey ink.
The artist has begun various sentences at the bottom to the L. along the length of the sheet: 'Vn nostro amicho', etc., etc. On the *verso* is more writing in a different hand obliquely across the sheet. It seems to have reference to partly erased architectural details, and the words 'la chornice', 'basa e chapitello', are among those legible. The drawing, which was attributed to Michelangelo, is no doubt the work of a sculptor or an architect of about the middle of the XVI century, probably Florentine.

1093. STUDY OF A L. FOOT (0738)
85 × 135 mm. (irregular). Pen and brown ink.
Mounted with No. 1094 and attributed to Michelangelo. It is perhaps a sculptor's drawing, of the middle of the XVI century.

1094. *Recto:* SHEET OF STUDIES: the head and body of an old man seen from the front; the body seen from the side; sketch of a head; three smaller sketches of the lower parts of male bodies. (0739)
Verso: STUDY OF THE LOWER PARTS OF A MALE BODY AND OF MUSCLES; MAN'S HEAD IN A HELMET; WRITING
280 × 188 mm. Pen and brown ink.
Coll.: J. D. Lempereur (Lugt 1740).
Mounted with No. 1093 and attributed in pencil on the drawing to: 'Michel Ang'. It is apparently the work of a Florentine sculptor of some originality, dating from the middle of the XVI century.

FIG. 204 Cat. No. 1099

1095. *Recto:* SHEET OF STUDIES: a R. leg; a nude man seen from the back advancing to the R.; a grotesque profile; a L. arm and sketches of fruit and leaves. (0469)
Verso: STUDY OF AN ARM AND SHOULDER, AND AN UNFINISHED PROFILE
300 × 207 mm. (top L. corner and L. margin torn). Pen and brown ink.
Coll.: N. Lanière (Lugt 2886).
Attributed to Michelangelo ('M.A.' in ink in bottom L.). The 'mis-en-page' and even the handling of this sheet are remarkably like Raffaello da Montelupo's, but it is not the work of a left-handed draughtsman, and there is no convincing evidence that Raffaello ever drew with his R. hand. It must be the work of a Florentine sculptor of the same generation.

1096. SEPARATE STUDIES OF A L. FOOT, the same foot *écorché* and its bones. (0216)
242 × 207 mm. Finished drawing in hard black chalk.
George III 'Inventory A', p. 44, Michelangelo I, 31.
Attributed in black chalk bottom L. to 'Buona Rota'. This appears to be one of a series of finished anatomical drawings, of which another of a L. leg in the same three stages is at Chatsworth (No. 890). They are apparently by some Florentine draughtsman of the type of Bronzino or Allori.

1097. VIEW OF A PIAZZA WITH A FOUNTAIN IN THE CENTRE; beyond is a palace through which run arcades with booths in them. (0379)
132 × 169 mm. Pen and brown ink and wash over black chalk.

FIG. 205 Cat. No. 1100

The drawing recalls the small views painted in the Palazzo Vecchio, and is probably Florentine of the second half of the XVI century.

1098. ST. ANDREW AND ST. NICHOLAS (0386)
252 × 180 mm. Pen and brown ink and brown wash over black chalk, on blue paper, heightened with white.
Coll.: N. Lanière (Lugt 2886).
Inscribed in ink in bottom R. hand corner (in Lanière's hand (?)): 'Fra Bartolomeo'. The drawing, however, certainly dates from near the end of the century. It is apparently by some Florentine artist of the generation of Passignano.

1099. THE VIRGIN AND CHILD WITH MUSICIAN ANGELS AND ST. APOLLONIA (*Figure* 204) (5131)
255 × 190 mm. Pen and ink and brown wash over red chalk, squared in red chalk.
The style suggests a Florentine artist of the end of the XVI or the beginning of the XVII century.

1100. DESIGN FOR THE SEGMENT OF A CUPOLA, WITH ST. CECILIA ATTENDED BY MUSICIAN ANGELS AND PUTTI (*Figure* 205) (3639)
198 × 510 mm. Pen and brown ink and brown wash.
Old attribution 'Zuccaro' in ink at the bottom. The drawing seems to be Florentine or Tuscan of the end of the XVI or beginning of the XVII century.

1101. SCENE FROM THE LIFE OF A SAINTED ECCLESIASTIC (*Figure* 206) (5103)
220 × 368 mm. Pen and brown ink and brown wash over black chalk, heightened with white.
The subject may represent the attack made on St. Antonino, Archbishop of Florence, by a certain Ciardi, as related in some of his lives (A. Butler, *Lives of the Saints*, London, 1812–15, V, p. 155). If this is the case the drawing might be supposed to be a design for one of the lunettes with scenes from the life of the saint in the Chiostro di S. Antonino, Florence, painted by Poccetti and various other artists at

FIG. 206 Cat. No. 1101

Cat. No. 1104

FIG. 207

the end of the XVI and during the XVII century, but the subject does not occur there. The style of the drawing comes very close to that of a design attributed to Felice Ficherelli in the British Museum (Payne Knight, Pp. 4–56), but in the absence of any other drawing attributable to this Florentine artist I would hesitate to give the present design to him.

1102. A POPE PRESENTING TO, OR RECEIVING FROM, A KNEELING ECCLESIASTIC, A CRUCIFIX (5207)

235 × 523 mm. Pen and ink and brown wash on grey prepared surface, heightened with white.

The style of this drawing may be compared with that of the two by Cigoli in the Uffizi (Nos. 286F and 830F; photo., Braun 781 and 982), one of which is signed and dated 1592 and which are the *modellos* for the paintings in the Salone of the Palazzo Vecchio at Florence. Though it is not necessarily by the same hand it appears to be Florentine of the same period.

Its types also show some resemblance to those of Lodovico Carracci.

1103. A BEARDED SAINT CELEBRATING MASS WITH AN ACOLYTE KNEELING BEHIND HIM (6014)

204 × 170 mm. Pen and ink outline with some wash, the outlines indented.

The indentation of the outlines suggests that the drawing may have been used for an engraving. It is perhaps Florentine, dating from very near the end of the century.

SCHOOL OF FONTAINEBLEAU

1104. DESIGN FOR THE DECORATION OF A PANELLED CEILING (*Figure* 207) (6003, 6004)

Divided in half, each portion measuring 448 × 390 mm. Pen and brown ink with brown and pink wash, the outlines of the figures indented.

Inscribed at the bottom of No. 6003 in ink in a hand of the XVII or XVIII century: 'monsieur de bolonge St. Martin' (Primaticcio was generally called Boulogne or Bologna from the place of his birth, and was invested with the revenues of the abbey of St. Martin at Troyes in 1544). On the *verso* of each half (visible through the backing): 'Jerom'. The general scheme of the decoration is of a central rectangle containing the coat of arms of the patron. At the four angles of an imaginary square surrounding this are four circles containing allegorical female figures. Between these are two octagons with figures of Charity and of Liberality (?), and two irregularly-shaped panels with figures and trophies of arms. Beyond the imaginary central square is at each end an oval, the one on the L. containing a figure of Fortune on her wheel, the one on the R., two nymphs with amphorae. Each corner is made of four panels of different shapes, three of them containing figures (except in the R. hand bottom corner, where one is left blank).

The coat of arms may be that of the family of Birague (d'argent à la croix engrelée de gueules), whose best known member was René (1506–1583) garde des Sceaux and chancellor of France in 1573, cardinal in 1578. I cannot determine whether during his secular career René de Birague was a member of the Order of St. Michel, the collar of which surrounds the coat of arms. There were however other members of the family, notably Jerome, chevalier de l'ordre de S. Michel (father of Horace, Bishop of Lavaur, 1583–1601).

The style of the drawing points rather to Rosso than to Primaticcio, but to a follower rather than to the master himself. It is better placed under the heading of School of Fontainebleau.

FIG. 208 Cat. No. 1105

1105. DESIGN FOR THE DECORATION OF A CARVED AND PAINTED BENCH (*Figure* 208) (6852)
360 × 585 mm. Pen and brown ink and wash and water colour.

Apparently attributed to Perino del Vaga, with whose style it shows little connection. It seems to me to come nearest to French artists like Etienne Delaune or Androuet du Cerceau, but it may possibly be by an Italian or even a Flemish artist working in France. There is some resemblance to a design for the decoration of Nonesuch Palace published by O. Kurz in the Burlington Magazine (Vol. LXXXII (1943), p. 81).

1106. SCIPIO AND HANNIBAL IN PARLEY ACROSS A RIVER, WHICH SEPARATES THEIR ARMIES: design for a cuirass. (5044)
337 × 400 mm. Pen and brown ink and brown wash.

Attribution in pencil on the drawing to 'Bernard Castelli'. Inscribed in ink in an old hand at the top to the R.: 'Scipio et hannibal./Allocutio'. The composition is freely adapted in reverse from the anonymous engraving of the school of Marcantonio (Bartsch XV, p. 31, 5), or more probably from the original of this (which was apparently one of the series of designs for tapestry made by Giulio Romano for Francis I before 1534). This fact seems to suggest that the drawing may have been made in France, and it may most conveniently be placed under the heading of School of Fontainebleau.

SCHOOL OF GENOA

1107. MEN AT WORK BUILDING OR REPAIRING SHIPS (*Plate* 152) (5474)
328 × 520 mm. Pen and brown ink and brown wash over black chalk on blue paper. Damaged by damp on the L. and cut into on all four sides.

Attributed, in pencil on the mount, to Polidoro da Caravaggio. It is certainly of later date, of the second half of the century, though it shows reminiscences of the manner of Perino del Vaga. Its closest stylistic analogy is, however, with the drawings of the story of Ulysses discussed in relation to No. 209 (attributed to G. B. Castello), though it seems less accomplished than these and more naïve in its narrative style.

The classical costume of the commander suggests that the subject may be taken from the Aeneid or the Odyssey.

1108. A LADY AND A GENTLEMAN BEING AFFIANCED BY A DOGE (6656)
230 × 276 mm. Pen and brown ink and brown wash, squared in red chalk.

Inscribed in pencil on the drawing; 'del Zellotti', with whom it has nothing to do. The style of the drawing points clearly to Genoa, and the types and composition are very like those of Bernardo Castello. If, however, the drawing No. 205, described above is, as I believe, by him, it does not seem probable that this sheet is also his.

1109. FRIEZE OF A SATYR, A WOMAN AND PUTTI WITH ANIMALS (5467)
90 × 280 mm. Pen and brown ink and grey wash.

Attributed to 'Maturino', an artist whose style as a draughtsman is unknown. The style of the drawing suggests Cambiaso and the Genoese school.

1110. THE REST ON THE FLIGHT INTO EGYPT (2333)
271 × 187 mm. Pen and brown ink and brown wash.

Copy of a drawing in the Brera at Milan (F. Malaguzzi Valeri, *I Disegni della R. Pinacoteca di Brera*, Milan, 1906, pl. 55) attributed to Luca Cambiaso, and certainly either by that draughtsman or copied from him. The present drawing, which comes from the Carracci series, was identified too late for inclusion under Cambiaso, where it should properly have been placed.

1111. DESIGN FOR THE DECORATION OF A FRIEZE (6851)

236 × 650 mm. Pen and brown ink and brown wash.

Attributed in the 'deceptive' hand to 'Piola'. The style is impossible for Domenico Piola and unlikely for any other member of this Genoese family (nor is it by the same draughtsman as another drawing, No. 6850, given by the same annotator to Piola). It is, however, certainly Genoese, and its style comes very close to that of Bernardo Castello. The subjects are taken from the story of Ulysses. On the L. he is seen taunting Polyphemus; in the centre disputing for the arms of Achilles with Ajax, who is falling on his own sword; on the R. stealing the Palladium from Troy.

SCHOOL OF MILAN

1112. HEAD OF A BEARDED MAN (*Figure* 209) (088)

376 × 261 mm. Black chalk on blue paper; damaged by worm-holes.

Inscribed underneath in ink in a hand of the XVII or early XVIII century: 'Questa Testa è assai Bella et io non la posso Giudicare se non d'un Gran . . . della gran Scola Fiorentina'. It is certainly not Florentine, nor apparently by Paris Bordone as has been suggested on the mount. It must, however, be North Italian of about 1530–40, and apparently Milanese.

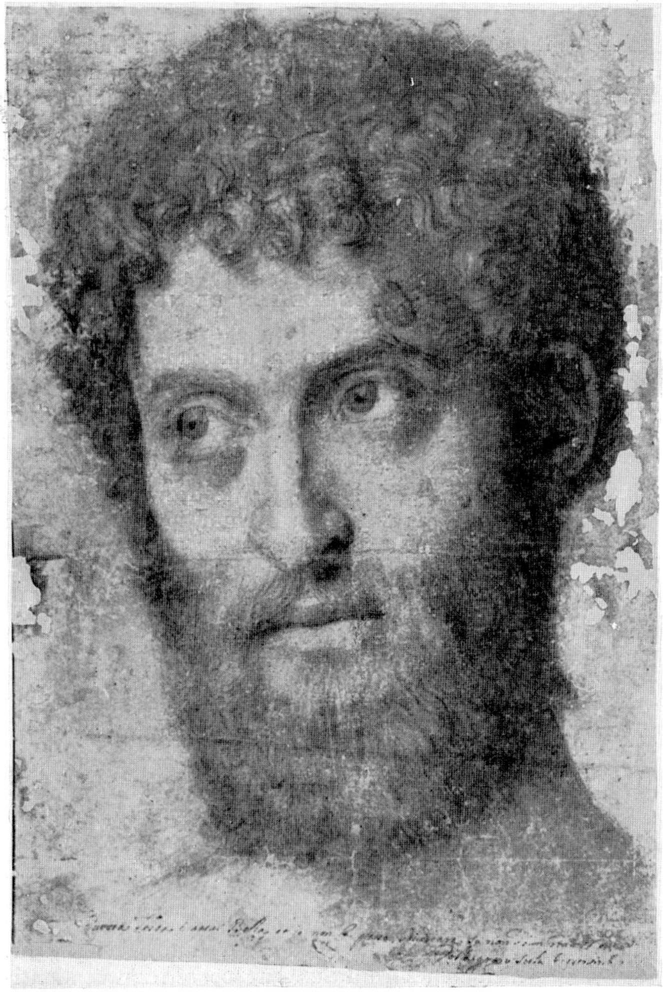

FIG. 209 Cat. No. 1112

FIG. 210 Cat. No. 1115

1113. THE VIRGIN HOLDING THE INFANT CHRIST; on the L. the head of an angel: fragment of a cartoon. (0147)

315 × 248 mm. Black chalk, damaged.

The style of this wretched drawing suggests that it is the work of some later continuator of the tradition of Gaudenzio Ferrari, the younger Giovenone, Ottaviano Cane or Granmorseo. The traditional attribution was apparently to Girolamo Mazzuola.

1114. THE ASCENSION OF OUR LORD: design for an altarpiece with an arched top and its architectural frame. (*Plate* 146) (0181)

458 × 256 mm. (the decoration of the top of the pediment of the frame, above the panel of God the Father, is on a separate piece of paper). Pen and brown ink and brown wash on blue paper, heightened with white.

Attribution of the XVIII century, 'Del Samachini', in ink on the mount. The style of the drawing is, however, quite unlike Samacchini's. It is much more Milanese, and suggests some painter of the style and generation of Ambrogio Figino or Simone Peterzano (see the latter's *Ascension* in the Certosa at Garegnano, ill. Bolletino d'Arte, XXVIII (1934), p. 112).

1115. THE ASCENSION OF OUR LORD: design for an altarpiece with an arched top. (*Figure* 210) (5059)
377 × 222 mm. Pen and brown ink and brown wash on brown paper, heightened with white.
The composition is an enlarged and more elaborate version of that in No. 1114. There are differences of detail, and the figure of Christ here has only a floating mantle, whereas in the other a garment covers Him from head to foot.

1116. THE EVANGELISTS ST. LUKE AND ST. MATTHEW (5116)
177 × 380 mm. Pen and brown ink outline washed with blue on green paper, heightened with white (the head of St. Matthew is a *pentimento* on a piece of paper stuck on).
The figures show some resemblance to those by Zelotti on the ceiling of the Library at Praglia, for which there is a drawing in the Albertina (Catalogue, II, No. 117), but the drawing is not by the same hand. It is certainly by a North Italian mannerist about 1550–60, and shows the closest resemblance in style to Giovanni Demio's work. Compare that artist's *tondos* on the ceiling of the Libreria Marciana (Venturi, IX 7, Figs. 16–18), and the frescoes on the vaulting of Sta. Maria delle Grazie, Milan (ill. Rivista d'Arte, XX (1938), p. 153 f.). There is also a close resemblance between the Evangelists in the present drawing and those by Simone Peterzano (who may have been the pupil of Demio) in the Certosa of Garegnano (ill. Bolletino d'Arte, XXVIII (1934), pp. 104, 106).

1117. THE CORONATION OF THE VIRGIN BY THE TRINITY, with angel musicians above and below. (6000)
293 × 143 mm. Pen and brown ink and brown wash over black chalk, heightened with white.
This rather mannered drawing may perhaps be Milanese, possibly by Moncalvo.

1118. HEAD OF AN OLD WOMAN (?) (5168)
187 × 202 mm. Coloured chalks on blue paper.
Attributed at some unspecified time to Barocci, no doubt on account of the technique. The type, however, is singularly unlike his. It is perhaps for the head of St. Elizabeth in a *Visitation*, and rather resembles certain drawings by Ambrogio Figino (see one in the collection of Mr. E. Schapiro, London).

FIG. 211 Cat. No. 1119

FIG. 212 Cat. No. 1121

1119. THE DEATH OF THE VIRGIN (*Figure* 211) (5049)
238 × 250 mm. Black chalk and wash on blue paper, liberally heightened with white.
An annotator has pointed out a resemblance in style to No. 1072, which I attribute to Taddeo Zuccaro. I do not think it is in fact by the same hand as the latter drawing, which is very much more mannerist in style. I have thought of some Milanese, like Cerano, as the draughtsman of the present able sketch, but I cannot be certain.

1120. THE DESCENT FROM THE CROSS (4817)
356 × 189 mm. (on two pieces of paper stuck together). Pen and brown ink and brown wash over black chalk on blue paper.
The style of this drawing is very close to that of the one last described, No. 1119, and it may be by the same hand.

1121. A CHILD BLESSED BY A BISHOP IN A CHURCH (*Figure* 212) (5124)
371 × 252 mm. Finished composition in black chalk washed with brown and heightened with white.

Inscribed at the bottom in the 'deceptive' hand: 'Lorenzo Lot . . .' The drawing seems to be North Italian to judge from the obviously realistic architecture of the church which is, I am informed by Prof. Anthony Blunt, probably Milanese.

SCHOOL OF MODENA

1122. A KNIGHT IN ARMOUR, WHOSE HORSE STANDS BEHIND ON THE R. IN THE COURTYARD OF A CASTLE, ACCOMPANIED BY A LADY; she points out to him a dragon in the basin of a fountain under a portico on the R.; in the distance on the L. a naked man, holding the dragon, is seen running away. (*Plate* 103) (6317)

322 × 350 mm. Pen and brown ink on green prepared surface, washed with green and heightened with white, the outlines pricked.

The sheet has been mutilated and a bit torn from some other part has been used to make up the lower R. corner. It was probably once oval or round, and seems to form part of a series of elaborately finished drawings of which two others are known to me. One, attributed to Perino del Vaga, is in the Uffizi (photo. Braun 166: repr. in Olschki's Uffizi Series, IV, I, Nos. 3, 4); the other in the Louvre (No. 20,746). These two drawings are in the same technique, pen and ink and wash on a brown prepared surface, heightened with white, and the outlines of the Uffizi one (perhaps also of the Louvre one) are pricked. They are of approximately the same size, 397 × 476 mm. (Uffizi), 365 × 453 mm. (Louvre), the latter being cut. The style, especially of the Uffizi drawing, is very close indeed to that of Niccolò dell' Abbate. The Louvre and Windsor drawings seem rather stiffer and might possibly be the work of a collaborator. The series would in any case date from Niccolò dell' Abbate's earliest period in Modena about 1540. These three drawings may illustrate the Orlando Furioso, which Niccolò dell' Abbate chose as the subject for paintings in the castle of Matteo Maria Boiardo at Scandiano (which no longer survive), and for others of a later date in the Palazzo Zucchini at Bologna, but I have not been able to identify them.

FIG. 214 Cat. No. 1125

FIG. 213 Cat. No. 1123

SCHOOL OF PARMA

1123. DESIGN FOR A PENDENTIVE: AN ECCLESIASTIC APPEARING TO A YOUTHFUL DEACON IN THE BOWS OF A SHIP (*Figure* 213) (0601)

210 × 158. Two shades of red chalk.

On the *verso* is a long contemporary inscription in Italian, which it is difficult to decipher in its entirety (it seems to be cut on the R.), but which obviously has reference to the marriage service and has no relevance to the drawing. This is clearly by an artist of Parma, very near in style to Correggio, to whom the drawing was attributed, and also reminiscent of Anselmi and the young Parmigianino, but I would hesitate to attribute it to either.

FIG. 215 Cat. No. 1126

1124. THE DEAD BODY OF OUR LORD SUPPORTED BY FIVE ANGELS (0600)

224 × 192 mm. Black chalk.

Coll.: A large armorial mark, stamped blind. The shield has on it a wagon, in which is an eagle, drawn by two camels (?).

Photo.: Braun 130.

Attribution in pencil on the drawing to Correggio, under whose name it was photographed by Braun. It is much nearer in style to Michelangelo Anselmi (cf. Venturi, IX 2, Figs. 572, 573), but the whole question of drawings by Anselmi is uncertain, and it is safer to place it under the school of Parma.

1125. THE TRANSFIGURATION (*Figure* 214) (01119)

805 × 527 mm. Black chalk on rough, light brown paper, heightened with white.

1126. CHRIST HEALING A CRIPPLE OR BLIND MAN (*Figure* 215) (01118)

815 × 525 mm. Black chalk on rough, light brown paper, heightened with white, the outlines indented and squared in red chalk.

Attributed on the mount of No. 1126 to Girolamo da Carpi. Philip Pouncey has pointed out to me the resemblance which these two small cartoons show in the types and general style to works by Michelangelo Anselmi, particularly to the fresco of the *Adoration of the Magi* in the Western apse of the Madonna della Steccata at Parma (ill., very inadequately, in Laudedeo Testi, *S. Maria della Steccata in Parma*, n.d., pl. XXV). They may possibly be by him. They are at any rate probably Parmese of about 1540–50.

1127. THE VIRGIN AND CHILD WITH ST. MARY MAGDALENE, ST. CLARA AND THE YOUTHFUL ST. JOHN (*Figure* 216) (5135)

300 × 216 mm. Pen and grey ink and wash on a brown ground, heightened with white.

The drawing is almost certainly Parmese of the second quarter of the XVI century, and is very near in style and composition to altarpieces by Girolamo Mazzola-Bedoli. Its style, however, is hardly compatible with that of other drawings which I believe to be Bedoli's (see No. 419, for example), and it is likely, therefore, to be the work of some contemporary Parmese painter, like Giacomo Antonio Spicciotti (see Rassegna d'Arte, XII (1912), p. 7), but there is not enough material published (or available to me) about Parmese painting to allow the attribution of this not uninteresting work to an individual.

1128. THE VIRGIN SEATED IN THE OPEN AIR WITH THE CHILD, WHO IS BEING EMBRACED BY THE INFANT ST. JOHN, ON HER LAP; on the R. is St. Lucy and on the L. St. Jerome (?) followed by a *putto* with a skull; in the foreground a winged *putto* playing with a lamb. (5496)

253 × 178 mm. Pen and grey ink and wash on a light

FIG. 216 Cat. No. 1127

brown ground, heightened with white, squared in black chalk.

The style is very near indeed to that of No. 1127, and it may in fact be by the same hand, though it gives the impression of being of a rather later date. Nevertheless the composition and sentiment are very close to that of pictures by Mazzola-Bedoli; e.g. the altar in the Parma Gallery (No. 1079: Venturi, IX 2, Fig. 593).

1129. THE VIRGIN SEATED IN THE OPEN AIR, THE CHILD ON HER LAP, St. Elizabeth to the L. and St. Joseph to the R. (0326)

210 × 185 mm. Black chalk or charcoal washed with pale yellow and heightened with white.

This drawing is apparently Parmese of about 1540–50, but not so near in style to Mazzola-Bedoli as Nos. 1127 and 1128.

1130. STUDIES OF PUTTI AMONG CLOUDS AND OF A PROFILE (5527)

105 × 132 mm. Pen and brown ink and brown wash.

Attributed to Parmigianino. It is not by him, but is probably of the school of Parma and perhaps by Anselmi.

1131. THE ENTOMBMENT (5083)

263 × 350 mm. (cut into on all sides). Pen and brown ink and brown wash over black chalk on light brown ground, heightened with white.

The composition is partly copied in reverse from the etching by Parmigianino (Bartsch XVI, p. 8, 5), perhaps through the medium of Andrea Schiavone's etching (Bartsch XVI, p. 49, 17). It would seem to be Parmese.

SCHOOL OF ROME

1132. DESIGN FOR A SCULPTURED ALTAR (*Plate* 65) (0208)

449 × 288 mm. (arched top). Finished drawing in pen and brown ink and brown wash, marked out beforehand with dividers and stylus.

On each side of the altar proper is a blank escutcheon surmounted by a cardinal's hat within a circle; in an arched niche in the centre are the Virgin and Child enthroned with two angels holding a large crown above her head and a donor kneeling on the R.; in smaller niches to the R. and L. are St. Barbara and St. Catherine of Alexandria; above each of these are two apostles in still smaller niches; the whole is surmounted by another structure with a double niche in which the angel of the Annunciation and the Virgin Mary are represented; to L. and R. of this structure are allegorical figures of Faith and Hope.

The style and general arrangement of this altar are reminiscent of Andrea Sansovino's tombs of cardinals Ascanio Sforza and Basso in S. Maria del Popolo, Rome (Venturi, XI 1, Figs. 125, 126), and the style of the drawing is not unlike that of the design for an altarpiece at Munich attributed to him (ill. ibid., Fig. 150, and by Middeldorf in Munich Jahrbuch (1933), p. 138).

There is on the other hand a resemblance, especially in the draperies, to drawings by Bambaia in the Berlin sketch book (e.g. Giorgio Nicodemi, *Agostino Busti detto il Bambaia*, Milan, 1945, Fig. 72) and in other designs for altarpieces attributed by Nicodemi to him (op. cit., Figs. 87, 90). I do not, however, think that the general architectural style of the altarpiece would justify an attribution to Bambaia, and the resemblance may be due to a natural similarity between sculptor's designs of approximately the same period. I think the connection with Sansovino is closer, and that the drawing was most probably made in Rome.

It is in any case an important architect's or sculptor's drawing of the beginning of the XVI century.

1133. HEAD OF A MIDDLE-AGED WOMAN (*Figure* 217) (066)

201 × 170 mm. (torn at the top). Red chalk, the outlines pricked.

Photo.: Braun 255.

Attributed to Sebastiano del Piombo in pencil on the mount. The drawing is an excellent one and of early date, about 1510–20, but certainly not by Sebastiano. It is apparently the cartoon used for a painting of the same size. It is difficult to place, but perhaps Roman. I have thought of Baldassare Peruzzi as possibly the author of this very able drawing.

1134. A WOMAN, CARRYING A BASKET OF FRUIT ON HER HEAD, WITH TWO PUTTI (*Plate* 68) (12959)

253 × 179 mm. Pen and light brown ink over black chalk.

An attribution to Peruzzi is written on the mount in pencil, perhaps in the hand of Sir Charles Robinson. It shows some resemblance to the series of drawings of heads by Peruzzi in the British Museum (1874–8–8–32), in the Albertina (Catalogue III, No. 126) and at Berlin (repr. *Zeichnungen alter Meister im Kupferstichkabinett . . . zu Berlin*, Berlin, 1902–1910, Vol. I, 35), but it seems too sloppy for that always rather precise and delicate draughtsman. Sodoma seems under the circumstances the natural alternative, but I cannot feel convinced that it is by him. It is presumably a drawing made between 1510 and 1520 in Rome.

FIG. 217 Cat. No. 1133

FIG. 218 Cat. No. 1135

1135. A NUDE MAN ON A HORSE GALLOPING TO THE R. (*Figure* 218) (0510)
140 × 199 mm. Pen and light brown ink.
The style of this spirited sketch lies somewhere between Peruzzi's and Cesare da Sesto's, and it is probably Roman about 1520.

1136. A WOMAN IN CLASSICAL DRAPERY STANDING IN PROFILE TO THE R., holding the ends of her sash in front of her. (0337)
143 × 86 mm. Rapid sketch in pen and brown ink. Fly-blown and discoloured.
Inscribed on a label attached to the back of the mount in a hand of the XVII century: 'Rafaele/D. Chigi Roatti (?)' followed by a 'paraphe'. The style is that of Raphael's school of about 1520. It might possibly be by Giovanni da Udine. It shows some resemblance to stucco figures on the vaulting of the *Loggie*.

1137. FRAGMENTS OF ANTIQUE SCULPTURE (0324)
120 × 177 mm. Pen and brown ink and brown wash. Separate sketch in red chalk.
There is a copy of the same fragments in the Codex Coburgensis (ill. Rassegna d'Arte, X (1910), p. 8). According to the writer of that article they were in the Palazzo della Valle. The present drawing appears to date from the early part of the XVI century.
On the *verso* are three sonnets in Italian, which have no relevance to the drawing.

1138. A FRAGMENTARY ANTIQUE RELIEF OF MARINE DEITIES (0323)
117 × 114 mm. Pen and ink and brown wash over black chalk.
Companion to No. 1137 by the same draughtsman. There are likewise three sonnets transcribed on the *verso* of this sheet.

1139. *Recto:* DEATH OF CREUSA AND FLIGHT OF MEDEA (01235)
192 × 550 mm. (folded). Pen and light brown ink and wash.
Verso: STUDY OF THE FLYING END OF A SCARF
Black chalk.
Study from the R. hand portion of an antique sarcophagus now in the Stamperia Reale, Rome (S. Reinach, *Répertoire des Reliefs, III,* Paris, 1912, p. 325). There are other closely allied antique versions of this relief, but the present drawing seems to be taken from the one mentioned. The style of the drawing resembles that of Girolamo da Carpi, but not so closely as to be conclusive.

1140. DESIGNS FOR COLUMNS WITH CONTINUOUS RELIEFS ENCIRCLING THEM, in the manner of Trajan's column. (0752)
386 × 246 mm. Pen and brown ink and some wash over black chalk.

1141. DESIGNS FOR THE SAME COLUMNS seen from the opposite side. (0753)
408 × 240 mm. Pen and brown ink and some wash over black chalk.
Parts of three columns are represented in each drawing. In the first the reliefs wind upwards to the L.; in the second, to the R. In each the whole width of the central column is seen. In has four tiers. In the first drawing the column on the L. is partially cut by the L. hand margin, so that only about four-fifths appears, while the R. hand column is seen

behind the central one and only about a quarter is represented. The arrangement of the second drawing is exactly the same only reversed.

Though the arrangement is borrowed from Trajan's column, the reliefs are not copied from it. They are original designs by an artist of the first half of the XVI century.

1142. STUDY FROM THE TORSO OF AN ANTIQUE STATUE OF A WOMAN WEARING A LION'S SKIN (0388)

272 × 110 mm. Pen and brown ink.

Copied from a statue of Atalanta similar to that in the Palazzo Vidoni, Rome (ill. S. Reinach, *Répertoire de la Statuaire Grecque et Romaine*, Paris, 1897, p. 503). The style of the drawing is near to that of Martin van Heemskerck, but it may nevertheless be Italian.

1143. *Recto:* DRAWING FROM AN ANTIQUE STATUE OF A PRISONER (0398)

Verso: THE LEGS OF A MAN IN PROFILE TO THE L.

397 × 155 mm. Finished drawing in pen and brown ink yver black chalk.

From a statue of a prisoner now in the Villa Albani, Rome (ill. S. Reinach, *Répertoire de la Statuaire Grecque et Romaine*, Paris, 1897, p. 520). The drawing appears to be of the first half of the XVI century, presumably Roman. The style of the drawing on the *verso* is distinctly Michelangelesque.

1144. A LION HUNT (4375)

148 × 263 mm. Pen and brown ink over red chalk.

From the Maratta series.

Sketch of the well-known relief engraved by Marcantonio (Bartsch XIV, p. 317, 422). It seems to be the work of a draughtsman of the XVI century.

1145. TRAJAN COMBATING THE DACIANS, relief on the Arch of Constantine. (4376)

214 × 315 mm. Fine pen outline over black chalk.

From the Maratta series.

The style of the copy recalls Battista Franco or Girolamo da Carpi, but it gives the impression of being a copy or tracing from a drawing.

1146. TRAJAN COMBATING THE DACIANS; relief on the Arch of Constantine. (4477)

246 × 410 mm. Pen and wash on green paper, heightened with white. Much wormed.

From the Maratta series.

An admirable and elaborately finished copy of the first half of the XVI century.

1147. A SECTION FROM TRAJAN'S COLUMN (0285)

250 × 390 mm. Pen and brown ink outline.

A copy probably dating from the first half of the XVI century.

1148. A BATTLE OF MOUNTED MEN; FROM THE ANTIQUE (743)

150 × 219 mm. Pen and light brown ink.

From the Domenichino series.

The style of the drawing recalls Vasari, but it was presumably drawn in Rome.

1149. A WOMAN WALKING TO THE R. HOLDING A PHRYGIAN HAT (0503)

235 × 145 mm. Pen and brown ink and brown wash.

Inscribed on the *verso* in ink in an old hand (possibly of the XVI century): 'giulio Romano' and 'S.i.'. 'Giulio Romano' is repeated on a small label stuck on below. In spite of this ancient testimony the drawing can have nothing to do with Giulio Romano. There is some relation between this figure and one by Polidoro da Caravaggio on the façade of the Palazzo Milesi, in a composition of a Roman soldier dedicating his sword, but it is in reverse. Perhaps both derive from a classical prototype which is unknown to me.

1150. *Recto:* A PROPHET WEARING A TURBAN, READING FROM A BOOK

Verso: RAPID OUTLINE COPY OF THE SEATED YOUTH WRITING IN A BOOK IN RAPHAEL'S 'SCHOOL OF ATHENS' (0507)

278 × 165 mm. Pen and light brown ink and wash.

Attribution in the 'deceptive' hand to 'Perino del Vaga', though it is obviously a drawing of the end of the XVI century.

1151. A POTENTATE, SEATED IN A PAVILION, RECEIVES A GENTLEMAN who is brought into his presence; soldiers are in attendance. (*Figure* 219) (6013)

280 × 182 mm. Pen and brown ink and brown wash, squared in red chalk.

FIG. 219 Cat. No. 1151

Attributed to Zuccaro in pencil on the mount. The drawing may well be by the same hand as No. 1076, which is probably a copy rather than an original by Taddeo. The present historical scene does not, like No. 1076, occur at Caprarola, but is very much of the same character. The seated potentate might be Philip II, but the features are not sufficiently individualized to make an identification of the persons or the event possible. It is better to leave it with the anonymous. Philip Pouncey has suggested Circignano, which seems very possible.

1152. *Recto:* DESIGN FOR AN ELABORATELY CARVED FRAME CONTAINING A PICTURE OF ST. JEROME IN PENITENCE (*Figure* 220) (0207)
400 × 250 mm. (including a strip 20 mm. deep added at the top). Pen and brown ink and brown wash.

Verso: A WOMAN IN AN ATTITUDE OF SURPRISE AND THE EXTERIOR AND INTERIOR OF A BUILDING
Black chalk and pen and ink.
The style of decoration suggests to me an artist working in Rome about 1570–80, like Jacopo Zucchi.

1153. TWO SOLDIERS CARRYING OFF A YOUNG MAN; OTHER ROMAN SOLDIERS ADVANCING TO THE R. (0344)
282 × 195 mm. Pen and ink and brown wash.
Attributed to Giulio Romano in pencil on the mount. The drawing is rather of the end of the XVI century, though I think it may well be copied from Polidoro da Caravaggio (see his two friezes of the Rape of the Sabines). One thinks in this connection of Cherubino Alberti and his engravings after Polidoro.

1154. THE VIRGIN SEATED ON THE CRESCENT MOON FLOATS UP TO HEAVEN WHERE SHE IS PRESENTED WITH A SCEPTRE BY GOD THE FATHER (5109)
156 × 142 mm. Pen and brown ink and wash and some yellow, over black chalk.
There is a hardly legible inscription in the bottom L. hand corner, which appears to be 'Rosso'. This composition recalls Federico Zuccaro. It may be a copy from him or a work of his school.

1155. A MIRACLE OF CHRIST: HE RESUSCITATES A DEAD MAN (5039)
275 × 245 mm. (the composition is cut into on both sides). Drawn with the point of the brush in brown.
Inscribed in ink on the *verso:* 'pasigna' (Domenico Passignano). I cannot, however, see any connection with that artist. It would seem to be the work of a Roman mannerist of the type of Paris Nogari.

1156. A MIRACLE PERFORMED BY A HOLY BISHOP (ST. ANTONINO?) WHO RESTORES A DEAD MAN TO LIFE (5985)
166 × 114 mm. Pen and brown ink and brown wash; a figure on the L. squared in red chalk.
An attribution to Passignano, written in pencil on the mount, is presumably old, but the style of this insignificant drawing does not seem to me to be his. It rather suggests one of the artists working for Gregory XIII in Rome.

1157. STUDIES OF THREE SEATED NUDE FIGURES SEEN FORESHORTENED FROM BELOW; in the largest study the figure has his foot on a sphere. (0457)

FIG. 220 Cat. No. 1152 *r.*

Irregular 217 × 200 mm. (stuck on to a rectangular sheet). Slight sketches in pen and brown ink.
The style of the drawing suggests Cherubino Alberti and the Sala Clementina in the Vatican.

1158. ST. PETER HEALING THE CRIPPLE AT THE GATE OF THE TEMPLE (?): design for a triangular space. (5504)
184 × 255 mm. Red chalk.
Attribution in ink on the drawing to 'Santi di Titi', with whose style it has nothing in common. The types suggest a connection with the Cavaliere d'Arpino.

1159. CHRIST DISPUTING WITH THE DOCTORS (5048)
194 × 147 mm. Red chalk.
The drawing appears to be by the same hand as No. 1158 and therefore probably also Roman.

1160. DESIGN FOR THE DECORATION OF A CEILING: in the central compartment God the Father surrounded by cherubim and musician angels; in four square compartments at the corners, angels with tubas; in six flat ovals surrounding the central compartment: (1) (at the bottom) the Creation of Eve; (2) the Creation of Light; (3) (on the L.) the Creation of Animals; (4) (on the R.) the Creation

FIG. 221 Cat. No. 1160

of the Earth (along the top, the other way up) the Creation of the Sun and Stars; (6) the Creation of the Sea, of Fishes and Birds. (*Figure* 221) (01195)
378 × 583 mm. Pen and brown ink and two shades of brown wash, one shade representing the gilt of the framework.
Coll.: Ja. Matravers (inscribed in ink on the drawing and twice again on the *verso*).
The curious types and soft spineless forms suggest the Cavaliere d'Arpino, like the drawings Nos. 1158 and 1159 described above.

1161. A NUDE MAN RUSHING FORWARD IN TERROR, HIS HANDS CLASPED TO HIS HEAD (5216)
249 × 130 mm. Red chalk.
Attribution in the 'deceptive' hand to 'Cristofalo Utous', a name of which I can make nothing. The figure is apparently for a soldier in a *Resurrection* or a *Conversion of St. Paul*. Its style suggests either Camillo Procaccini or perhaps rather the Cavaliere d'Arpino.

1162. A CARDINAL SEATED ON A THRONE IN CONFERENCE WITH SOME MONKS SEATED BEFORE HIM (5498)
220 × 167 mm. Black chalk, washed with brown.
The scene, in its general arrangement, is somewhat like the relief by Cristoforo and Francesco Stati on the tomb of Paul V in Sta. Maria Maggiore (Venturi, X 3, Fig. 564). It may well be one of the scenes painted in that part of the Vatican Library which he had decorated, but I do not find any scene described in Taja which would correspond.

SCHOOL OF SIENA

1163. A FEMALE SAINT STANDING UNDER A COLONNADE DISPUTES WITH SOME OLD MEN; in the foreground are a cripple, another man and a woman; there is a blank space on the L. to allow for a door or a window. (5063)
328 × 234 mm. Pen and brown ink and brown wash, heightened with white, squared in red chalk.
The drawing is certainly Sienese of the beginning of the XVII century, but it does not appear to be by Vanni, Salimbeni or Casolani, and I cannot suggest a name for it. A part of the composition is reproduced in a drawing in the Masson Collection, Ecole des Beaux-Arts, Paris, with the curious attribution to Cristofano Gherardi.

1164. THE VIRGIN, ATTENDED BY TWO HOLY WOMEN, CLASPING THE FOOT OF THE BARE CROSS; in the background on the R. she looks into the empty tomb. (0160)
257 × 162 mm. Pen and brown ink and brown wash, squared in black chalk.
Attributed to Muziano. On the *verso* are three lines in Latin, difficult to decipher, but apparently liturgical in character. I can see in the style of this feeble drawing no particular connection with Muziano. It rather recalls the circle of Vanni and Salimbeni in Siena.

SCHOOL OF VENICE

1165. ST. GEORGE, BAREHEADED IN ARMOUR, STANDING ON THE DRAGON (*Figure* 222) (0696)
302 × 185 mm. Black chalk on blue paper, with some heightening in white.
Lit.: A. M. Hind, *Early Italian Engraving*, Part 1, Vol. I, London, 1938, p. 281.
The old attribution was apparently to Francia, but the drawing is quite obviously Venetic. It is nevertheless copied from a figure in a drawing of a group of warriors attributed to Pintoricchio (Fischel, *Umbrer*, No. 101, Fig. 269). The head is quite different and the dragon is an addition. It is difficult to assign this quite attractive drawing to any particular artist. It might be by some Veronese like Bonifazio or by Jacopo Bassano in his youth or even by Giulio Campi.

1166. HEAD OF A VENERABLE, BEARDED MAN LOOKING UP IN PROFILE TO THE R. (5173)
100 × 67 mm. Pen and brown ink.
Attributed in a hand of the XVIII century to Passarotti. It seems rather to be Paduan or Venetian in the manner of Domenico Campagnola.

1167. HEAD OF A HANDSOME YOUTH, WEARING A LARGE HAT; he is turned three-quarters to the R. and looks down with parted lips. (5174)
99 × 117 mm. Pen and brown ink.
Apparently Venetian of the early XVI century, near to Titian.

1168. BUST OF A LADY IN THE COIFFURE OF ABOUT 1510–20 (6666)
430 × 296 mm. Black chalk on yellowish paper.
Obviously the copy from a picture, probably Venetian. It is of the XVII century and may be by the same hand as No. 407.

1169. LANDSCAPE WITH FARM-BUILDINGS AMONG TREES, A CHURCH TOWER ON THE R. (3546)
197 × 280 mm. Pen and brown ink.

FIG. 222 Cat. No. 1165

This feeble little drawing is either a copy from, or a later imitation (possibly Bolognese) of, the Campagnola type of landscape.

1170. DESIGN FOR A DECORATED FRAME containing a representation of Christ and the woman of Samaria; below this in front is a font. (3494)
353 × 189 mm. Pen and black ink and grey wash.
This appears to be Paduan, of the school of Domenico Campagnola, though the *putti* supporting the bust on top of the frame are very Parmigianinesque.

1171. THE VIRGIN AND CHILD AND ST. JOSEPH (6748)
156 × 113 mm. Pen and brown ink and brown wash over black chalk.
Apparently Venetian about the middle of the century.

1172. THE TWELVE APOSTLES GROUPED ROUND THE EMPTY SARCOPHAGUS OF THE VIRGIN (?) (5521)
196 × 166 mm. Pen and brown ink and brown wash.
The drawing is certainly Venetian and more or less derivative from Paolo Veronese.

1173. THE LAST SUPPER (4821)
191 × 275 mm. Drawn with the brush and washed with brown over black chalk, on faded blue paper, heightened with white.
Lit.: A. Blunt, Warburg Journal, II (1938–39), p. 273, pl. 42.
Attribution in the 'deceptive' hand to 'Tintoretto'. Blunt, in the article referred to above, suggests that the draughtsman is Stradanus in view of the relation in composition to engravings after that artist, but I confess I find it impossible to reconcile the style with his. I think it more probably Venetian, though I have thought of Morazzone (see No. 514) as the possible draughtsman. I would refer the reader to Blunt's article on the subject of the 'triclinium' in art.

1174. STUDY OF AN OSTRICH (6675)
505 × 336 mm. Black chalk on blue paper, heightened with white.
If this drawing is Italian it must be Venetian by Tintoretto or his school.

1175. ST. JEROME IN THE WILDERNESS (3505)
203 × 102 mm. Pen and brown ink and brown wash on blue paper, heightened with white, squared in red chalk.
This drawing is clearly by an artist of the circle of Palma Giovane. It might perhaps be by Johann Rottenhammer.

1176. ST. PETER DELIVERED FROM PRISON (3633)
228 × 322 mm. Pen and brown ink and brown wash on oiled paper, heightened with oil colour.
From the technique the drawing would appear to be Venetian.

SCHOOL OF VERONA

1177. CHRIST AND THE WOMAN TAKEN IN ADULTERY (5027)
500 × 353 mm. (cut into considerably at the sides and bottom). Brown wash on oiled paper, heightened with white oil paint; the outlines indented.
The drawing appears to be Veronese by an artist of the type of Brusasorci.

1178. ST. ANTHONY ABBOT STANDING ABOVE IN THE CENTRE BETWEEN TWO COLONNADES; on the L., St. John the Baptist holding the lamb on a book and three musician angels; on the R., St. Dominick kneeling: design for an altarpiece with an arched top. (6699)

505 × 242 mm. Drawn with the brush in grey on blue paper, heightened with white.

Design for, or copy from, an altarpiece. It may be Veronese, near to Farinati.

1179. THE ENTOMBMENT (6701)

415 × 319 mm. Pen and brown ink and brown wash on yellow ground heightened with white, the outlines indented.

The technique and, to a certain extent, the style suggest Paolo Farinati's entourage. The indentation of the outlines points to its having in all probability served for an engraving.

NORTH ITALY

1180. THE PRESENTATION OF OUR LORD (*Figure* 223) (5085)

325 × 285 mm. Pen and brown ink and grey wash on yellowish ground, heightened with white.

Inscribed in an old hand in ink at the bottom of the drawing: 'Nerone juniore'. This should apparently indicate Matteo Neroni, a landscape painter of Siena working in Rome between 1567 and 1581, but the style hardly seems compatible with that of such a painter. Nor is there much resemblance to the works of the best-known Neroni, Bartolommeo, called Il Riccio. Perhaps it is the work of some otherwise unknown artist of the name about 1530–40. It is clearly by a very provincial North Italian. There are drawings by the same hand in the Uffizi: Santarelli 9079, the *Ascension of Our Lord*, attributed to Lelio Orsi; No. 13507, the *Mystic Marriage of St. Catherine*, attributed to Perino del Vaga; and Santarelli 801, attributed to Taddeo Zuccaro.

FIG. 223 Cat. No. 1180

FIG. 224 Cat. No. 1181

1181. THE ADORATION OF THE MAGI (*Figure* 224) (5057)

313 × 242 mm. Pen and grey ink and grey wash on a yellow ground, heightened with white.

This drawing, of about 1530–40, seems to be by the same hand as No. 1180.

1182. THE INCREDULITY OF ST. THOMAS: design for an altarpiece with an arched top. (5067)

338 × 232 mm. Pen and brown ink and grey wash on blue ground, heightened with white.

The draughtsman is perhaps the author of Nos. 1180 and 1181.

1183. THE ADORATION OF THE SHEPHERDS with, above, the Santa Casa of Loreto being carried by four angels. (*Figure* 225) (5056)

360 × 244 mm. Pen and brown ink and brown wash on a prepared ground partly pink and partly grey, heightened with white.

This peculiar and very provincial drawing appears to be by the same hand as a drawing in the Dyce Collection (No. 166) in the Victoria and Albert Museum, which belongs perhaps to the School of Fontainebleau. Its technique recalls that of the drawings described above, Nos. 1180, 1181, and 1182, but it is not necessarily by the same hand, though clearly North Italian.

1184. THE NATIVITY (*Figure* 226) (0364)

375 × 237 mm. Pen and brown ink and brown wash on cream-coloured ground, heightened with white.

Antal has made the ingenious suggestion that the drawing might be by Girolamo da Treviso, with whose compositions, as shown in the woodcuts after him by Francesco de Nantis, it has some affinity. Nevertheless, I think it is too little Raphaelesque and too odd for Girolamo da Treviso. It might be by the same hand as No. 1181.

1185. THE MARRIAGE FEAST AT CANA: elaborate composition of numerous figures in the costume of the late XVI century. (6687)

292 × 390 mm. Pen and brown ink and brown wash.

The composition is obviously the work of some provincial, probably North Italian, artist. It shows a general resemblance to Luca Longhi's painting of the subject in the Biblioteca Classense, Ravenna (Venturi, IX 5, Fig. 412), and to Ercole Setti's composition for which the drawing has been described above (No. 926), but it cannot be attributed to either of these artists.

1186. A QUEEN, WITH HER TWO CHILDREN ON BOARD A SHIP, TO WHOM IN THE AIR A YOUTHFUL SAINT APPEARS: design for a lunette. (6315)

205 × 380 mm. Pen and brown ink and brown wash, with touches of white, which has oxidised.

Attribution to Salviati in pencil on the mount. It appears to be a provincial North Italian work of the late XVI century, showing some resemblance in style to the drawing of the *Marriage Feast at Cana*, No. 1185.

FIG. 225 Cat. No. 1183

FIG. 226 Cat. No. 1184

1187. STUDY OF AN ECCLESIASTIC SEATED ON CLOUDS, BLESSING (5239)

258 × 229 mm. Black chalk on blue paper, heightened with white chalk.

Coll.: N. Lanière (Lugt 2885).

Attributed to Barocci, with whom it has nothing to do. Its style recalls Cesi's, but the drawing seems too woolly for him. It may be Bolognese of that period, probably in any case North Italian.

1188. A YOUTHFUL SAINT (?), SEATED ON CLOUDS, LOOKING UP TO THE L. AND WRITING ON A TABLET (5240)

259 × 189 mm. Black and white chalk with some additions in pen and ink, on blue paper.

Apparently by the same hand as No. 1187.

1189. AN ECCLESIASTIC HOLDING A SALVER KNEELING ON THE STEP OF AN ALTAR (?) (5243)

236 × 162 mm. Black chalk on blue paper heightened with white.

Attribution in pencil on the drawing to 'Baroccio'. It might be by some painter, like Claudio Ridolfi, influenced by Barocci, but I cannot feel sufficiently certain, though it is probably North Italian.

1190. THE ADORATION OF THE SHEPHERDS (5140)

190 × 238 mm. Pen and brown wash on discoloured blue paper, heightened with white.

Attributed to Luca Penni. The composition is Raphaelesque, though the drawing is much later and close to Morazzone (see No. 514). I suspect it may be a copy by this artist of some earlier work, but I have not sufficient evidence to substantiate this belief.

1191. THE CONVERSION OF ST. PAUL (5104)

237 × 194 mm. Brush drawing in brown on brown ground, heightened with white.

The method of drawing is similar to drawings in the Uffizi by Morazzone, *Christ led from the Garden of Olives* (photo. Braun 733) and the *Agony in the Garden* (oval; photo. Braun 795 as G. B. Moroni), but the resemblance may be fortuitous. It is probably North Italian.

1192. AN ANTIQUE NAVAL ENGAGEMENT (6848)

295 × 527 mm. Pen and ink and brown wash on discoloured blue paper, heightened with white, squared in pen and ink.

Attribution to Tintoretto in the 'deceptive' hand. The method of drawing is reminiscent of No. 514, authenticated as Morazzone's, but it may in fact be Venetian, as the old attribution suggests.

UNCERTAIN SCHOOL

1193. MAP OF THE NORTHERN HEMISPHERE IN FOUR SEGMENTS (01393)

276 × 285 mm. Pen and light brown ink.

MAP OF THE SOUTHERN HEMISPHERE IN FOUR SEGMENTS (01393 bis)

283 × 287 mm. Pen and light brown ink.

Lit.: R. H. Major, *A Mappemonde by Leonardo da Vinci*, London, 1865; Wieser, *Magalhâes-Strasse und Austral-Continent auf den Globen des Johannes Schöner*, Innsbruck, 1881, pp. 54–58; C. Kretschmer, *Die Entdeckung Americas in ihrer Bedeutung für die Geschichte des Weltbildes*, Berlin, 1892, pp. 389, 390; M. Fiorini, *Il Mappamondo di Leonardo da Vinci ed altri consimili mappe* in Rivista Geografica Italiana I (1894), p. 213 f.; E. Müntz, *Leonardo da Vinci*, Paris, 1899, II, p. 94.

The two sheets are numbered in the same manner as the Leonardo drawings: '192, 193'. They were therefore presumably in Leoni's collection, and were attributed to Leonardo da Vinci, but neither the drawing nor the handwriting is his. A comparison between the writing here and that, also written from L. to R., on the map of the country north-west of Florence (No. 12685 *recto*), for example, makes this clear. The sheet is hardly of interest as a drawing: for its cartographical importance the reader is referred to the articles cited above. The interest for older writers lay in the date of the map and whether it was the first map on which the name 'America' appeared. As the evidence for dating (the authorship of Leonardo and the *ante quem* date this provided being disproved) must depend on details of place-names, comparison with other mappemonds, etc., this point seems to have lost its importance.

The eight segments are so shaped that they could be cut out and pasted on to a globe.

1194. A WINGED PUTTO: cartoon. (1480)

600 × 373 mm. (partially silhouetted). Black chalk or charcoal, the outlines pricked.

From the Domenichino series.

The attitude of the *putto* reaching up to the R. suggests that he is holding up a shield or some device. It is very difficult, in the absence of any clue, to place a drawing of this character, but I should suppose it to be of the school of Raphael, 1520–30. It might also be by a Raphaelesque imitator of the XVII century.

1195. *Recto:* ST. CATHERINE DISPUTING WITH THE DOCTORS (?)

149 × 247 mm. Pen and brown ink.

Verso: MASK OF A FAUN IN PROFILE TO THE R. (046)

Red chalk.

On the *verso* there is also some looking-glass writing in a hand of the XVII century, which seems to consist of names and to be irrelevant. The style of the drawing points to a date before 1540. It has a slightly Flemish look and a suggestion of Lambert Lombard, but it may in fact be Italian.

1196. A GROUP OF ELDERLY WARRIORS EXPOSTULATE WITH A YOUNGER ONE WHO STANDS ON A STEP ON THE L.; BEHIND ARE TENTS (5065)

Circular, diam. 150 mm. Pen and brown ink and brown wash (rubbed).

The subject might be Agamemnon expostulating with Hector. The drawing, which seems to belong to the second half of the century, is difficult to place.

1197. A SIBYL (?) SEATED POINTING TO A TABLET WHICH SHE HOLDS (0509)

169 × 123 mm. Pen and brown ink and grey wash.

Inscribed on the *verso* in William Gibson's hand: 'J. Romano 1.2.', an attribution rejected by Loeser, who suggests the manner of Sodoma. The style of the drawing, as has been pointed out to me by Wilde, is remarkably like that of one at Vienna (Catalogue II, No. 140) with an old attribution to Lambert Sustris, but this may be no more than a coincidence.

1198. DESIGN FOR THE PORTRAIT OF A CARDINAL IN A CARTOUCHE, FLANKED BY ALLEGORICAL FIGURES (5209)

190 × 257 mm. Pen and brown ink; some oil stains.

The style of the decoration points to the period 1580–90 or later, and suggests a possible connection with Lodovico Carracci.

1199. THE VIRGIN AND CHILD BEFORE WHOM, ON THE L., KNEEL ST. FRANCIS, AND ON THE R., ST. CLARA WITH ST. CATHERINE OF SIENA STANDING BEHIND (0313)

188 × 158 mm. Pen and ink and brown wash on cream-coloured ground, heightened with white.

Attribution in pencil on the drawing to Andrea da Salerno, which, like all other attributions to that artist I have seen, is quite arbitrary. I do not know where to place this uninteresting drawing of the end of the XVI century.

INDEX OF COLLECTIONS

INDEX OF SUBJECTS

(Subjects in the Figino album, No. 326, are not indexed)

I. OLD TESTAMENT AND APOCRYPHA

II. NEW TESTAMENT

III. VIRGIN MARY

IV. SAINTS

V. RELIGIOUS SUBJECTS

VI. ANCIENT HISTORY AND LEGEND

X. ALLEGORY

XI. DAILY LIFE

XII. FIGURE STUDIES

XIII. ANATOMICAL STUDIES

XIV. HEADS

XV. PORTRAITS

XVI. ANIMALS

XVII. LANDSCAPE

XVIII. ARCHITECTURE AND ORNAMENT

XIX. COPIES FROM THE ANTIQUE

CONCORDANCE

Windsor Inventory No.	Popham Catalogue No.
040	413
041	719
042	1001
043	513
044	783
046	1195
047	345
048	329
049	964
050	692
051	885
059	27
060	34
061	1040
062	1
066	1133
069	31
070	30
087	6
088	1112
099	766
0101	248
0102	66
0104	140
0106	268
0107	57
0110	150
0111	396
0114	1204
0117	801
0123	1049
0124	192
0126	777
0133	147
0139	58
0140	686
0143	54
0144	53
0145	44
0146	49
0147	1113
0148	235
0157	207
0158	1050
0160	1164
0162	523
0163	521
0164	834
0168	1038
0170	823
0172	221
0173	222
0174	218
0181	1114
0182	541
0186	1017
0187	212
0191	933
0192	934
0193	938
0200	874
0201	240
0202	239
0203	771
0204	773
0206	718
0207	1152
0208	1132

Windsor Inventory No.	Popham Catalogue No.
0213	483
0215	446
0216	1096
0217	252
0218	406
0219	892
0220	1051
0221	188
0224	534
0225	535
0226	536
0227	195
0228	862
0229	864
0230	863
0231	184
0232	189
0233	866
0234	64
0241	820
0244	916
0280	136
0282	894
0283	364
0284	197
0285	1147
0286	697
0287	410
0288	989
0289	653
0290	134
0291	1065
0292	515
0293	1062
0294	383
0295A, 0295B	378
0297	328
0298	373
0300	355
0301	361
0302	386
0303	813
0304	353
0305	363
0306	365
0307	387
0308	350
0309	994
0311	875
0312	198
0313	1199
0314	782
0315	781
0317	827
0318	851
0319	824
0320	67
0321	228
0322	819
0323	1138
0324	1137
0325	402
0326	1129
0327	202
0328	776
0329	852
0330	850

Windsor Inventory No.	Popham Catalogue No.
0331	861
0332	848
0334	858
0335	895
0336	878
0337	1136
0338	873
0339	348
0340	438
0341	832
0342	55
0343	362
0344	1153
0345	582
0346	581
0347	655
0348	656
0349	199
0350	654
0351	190
0352	919
0353	419A
0355	657
0356	194
0361	914
0362	912
0364	1184
0368	687
0369	879
0370	877
0371	1089
0372	85
0373	911
0374	913
0375	73
0376	75
0377	420
0378	79
0379	1097
0380	1064
0381	330
0382	245
0383	690
0384	331
0385	931
0386	1098
0387	77
0388	1142
0389	80
0390	671
0391	871
0392	78
0393	82
0394	74
0395	84
0396	76
0397	1088
0398	1143
0399	83
0400	673
0401	664
0402	138
0403	720
0404	721
0405	722
0406	761
0407	681
0408	391

Windsor Inventory No.	Popham Catalogue No.
0409	462
0410	990
0411	393
0412	856
0413	984
0414	849
0415	815
0416	81
0417	786
0418	451
0419	454
0420	494
0421	503
0422	497
0423	498
0424	464
0425	452
0426	506
0427	512
0428	508
0429	509
0430	510
0431	486
0432	455
0433	461
0434	133
0435	450
0436	500
0437	1091
0438	735
0439	520
0440	518
0441	449
0442	456
0443	263
0444	1090
0445	511
0446	241
0447	143
0448	445
0449	940
0450	219
0451	496
0452	86
0453	243
0454	72
0455	928
0456	929
0457	1157
0458	495
0459	463
0460	876
0461	411
0462	242
0463	68
0464	223
0465	224
0467	444
0469	1095
0470	265
0471	458
0472	459
0473	341
0474	442
0475	443
0483	351
0484	385
0485	379

Windsor Inventory No.	Popham Catalogue No.
0486	357
0487	367
0488	368
0489	196
0490	829
0491	991
0492	992
0493	993
0494	880
0495	349
0496	380
0497	988
0498	981
0499	758
0502	982
0503	1149
0504	366
0505	787
0506	812
0507	1150
0508	354
0509	1197
0510	1135
0525	600
0526	601
0527	564
0528	565
0529	566
0530	599
0531	650
0533	598
0534	574
0535	576
0536	918
0537	575
0538	948
0539	573
0540	626
0541	592
0542	624
0543	625
0544	602
0545	604
0546	583
0547	588
0548	589
0549	590
0550	591
0551	630
0552	631
0553	632
0554	633
0555	634
0556	635
0557	636
0558	646
0559	647
0560	648
0561	649
0562	603
0563	586
0564	587
0565	595
0566	567
0567	568
0568	569
0569	637
0570	638

Windsor Inventory No.	*Popham Catalogue No.*	*Windsor Inventory No.*	*Popham Catalogue No.*	*Windsor Inventory No.*	*Popham Catalogue No.*	*Windsor Inventory No.*	*Popham Catalogue No.*	*Windsor Inventory No.*	*Popham Catalogue No.*
0571	639	0751	1092	01367	352	4348	215	4985	291
0572	640	0752	1140	01368	465	4365	227	4986	969
0573	641	0753	1141	01369A	467	4370	788	4987	292
0574	642	0791	756	01369B	468	4375	1144	4988	293
0575	643	0795	828	01370	466	4376	1145	4989	294
0576	644	0802	440	01371	1020	4477	1146	4990	295
0577	645	0803	441	01393	1193	4768	152	4991	296
0578	563	0804	811	01397	613	4769	153	4992	297
0579	577	0825	821	01398	614	4770	154	4993	298
0580	578	0835	121	01399	615	4771	155	4994	299
0581	580	0837	959	01400	617	4772	156	4995	300
0582	579	01106	374	01401	612	4773	157	4996	301
0583	584	01107	375	01402	616	4774	158	4997	302
0584	585	01108	376	01403	618	4775	748	4998	303
0585	621	01109	377	01404	619	4776	1087	4999	304
0586	622	01118	1126	01411	360	4777	412	5000	305
0587	628	01119	1125	01414	39	4778	124	5001	306
0588	627	01195	1160	206	266	4779	125	5002	307
0589	593	01196	206	743	1148	4780	126	5003	308
0590	596	01215	779	1480	1194	4781 }	127	5004	309
0591	629	01218	974	1835	570	4782 }		5005	310
0592	594	10220	768	1959	930	4783	131	5006	311
0593	623	01221	236	1960	571	4784	750	5007	312
0593B	250	01222	926	1976	665	4785	1022	5008	313
0594	246	01223	970	2032	419B	4786	50	5009	314
0595	340	01224	137	2036	831	4787	1008	5010	315
0596	249	01225	371	2160	670	4788	754	5011	316
0597	247	01226	1018	2185	597	4789	1023	5012	317
0599	337	01232	339	2194	271	4790	1024	5013	318
0600	1124	01233	369	2204	542	4791	529	5014	319
0601	1123	01234	399	2279	652	4792	1025	5015	320
0602	272	01235	1139	2309	572	4793	872	5016	321
0603	63	01236	370A	2333	1110	4794	961	5027	1177
0624	439	01237	825	2349	693B	4795	962	5029	135
0625	487	01238	370B	3384	201	4796	954	5030	384
0626	488	01239	372	3394	1206	4797	953	5031	237
0627	489	01240	1068	3479	854	4799	546	5032	208
0628	490	01241	899	3489	985	4800	547	5033	203
0629	502	01246	259	3494	1170	4801	548	5034	415
0630	507	01247	260	3499	995	4802	549	5035	883
0631	501	01249	667	3505	1175	4803	550	5037	901
0632	481	01250	941	3546	1169	4804	551	5038	1004
0633	482	01254	262	3573	1086	4805	552	5039	1155
0634	469	01256	1084	3613	957	4806	553	5040	210
0635	470	01257	213	3617	996	4807	408	5042	1072
0636	471	01258	716	3629	524	4809	403	5043	277
0637	472	01259	717	3633	1176	4810	925	5044	1106
0638	473	01260	711	3634	543	4811	335	5045	904
0639	474	01261	712	3635	544	4812	183	5046	968
0640	475	01262	713	3638	1201	4813	923	5047	1063
0641	476	01263	714	3639	1100	4814	244	5048	1159
0642	479	01264	715	3640	1007	4815	924	5049	1119
0643	478	01328A	40	3712	229	4816	276	5051	678
0644	479	01328B	41	3720	797	4817	1120	5052	753
0645	480	01328C	42	3745	770	4819	514	5054	238
0646	492	01341	605	3812	545	4821	1173	5056	1183
0647	505	01342	606	3813	1021	4823	952	5057	1181
0648	1039	01343	607	3817	142	4824	956	5058	867
0649	485	01344	608	4282	835	4825	955	5059	1115
0650	493	01345	609	4283	836	4827	278	5060	889
0696	1165	01346	610	4284	837	4836	528	5061	527
0697	327	01347	620	4285	838	4973	279	5062	891
0736	394	01348	611	4286	845	4974	280	5063	1163
0737	51	01357	853	4287	846	4975	281	5064	334
0738	1093	01358	358	4288	847	4976	282	5065	1196
0739	1094	01359	359	4289	839	4977	283	5066	1074
0740	253	01360	972	4290	840	4978	284	5067	1182
0741	254	01361	915	4291	841	4979	285	5069	336
0742	255	01362	504	4293	842	4980	286	5070	986
0743	256	01363	491	4294	843	4981	287	5071	966
0744	257	01364	499	4295	844	4982	288	5072	323
0745	685	01365	453	4320	484	4983	289	5073	395
0746	414	01366	1019	4326	818	4984	290	5074	409

Windsor Inventory No.	*Popham Catalogue No.*
5075	230
5076	62
5077	907
5078	908
5079	324
5080	382
5081	888
5082	389
5083	1131
5084	538
5085	1180
5086	677
5087	1202
5088	920
5089	274
5090	193
5091	533
5093	275
5094	682
5095	1002
5098	905
5099	1057
5100	65
5101	705
5102	884
5103	1101
5104	1191
5105	390
5108	1052
5109	1154
5110	185
5111	1041
5112	1042
5113	516
5114	209
5116	1116
5117	906
5118	186
5119	1075
5120	939
5121	1077
5122	381
5124	1121
5125	1053
5126	1061
5127	144
5128	967
5130	1080
5131	1099
5132	537
5133	200
5134	1054
5135	1127
5136	71
5137	886
5138	405
5139	755
5140	1190
5142	519
5143	60
5144	56
5145	669
5147	261
5151	903
5156	1085
5157	870
5158	264
5168	1118
5169	775
5173	1166
5174	1167
5179	1043
5189	234
5190	233
5195	688
5196	141
5197	1055
5199	187
5207	1102
5208	540
5209	1198
5210	149
5215	1044
5216	1161
5217	217
5219	214
5220	61
5222	88
5223	89
5224	90
5225	91
5226	92
5227	251
5228	93
5229	94
5230	95
5231	96
5232	97
5233	98
5234	99
5235	100
5236	998
5238	101
5239	1187
5240	1188
5241	102
5242	997
5243	1189
5317	448
5324	69
5345	1207
5357	103
5358	104
5359	105
5383	1045
5386	225
5390	129
5397	226
5402	1003
5403	1026
5404	216
5409	1027
5410	128
5418	1073
5423	258
5425	106
5432	814
5433	691
5434	693A
5435	785
5436	976
5437	738
5438	694
5639	944
5440	706
5441	739
5442	710
5443	723
5444	724
5445	725
5446	726
5447	727
5448	728
5449	729
5450	730
5451	731
5452	732
5453	356
5454	734
5455	733
5456	347
5457	346
5458	741
5459	1079
5460	978
5461	400
5462	333
5463	332
5464	401
5465	922
5466	977
5467	1109
5468	900
5469	737
5470	702
5471	987
5472	736
5473	695
5474	1107
5475	1200
5476	703
5477	53
5478	708
5479	709
5481	699
5482	700
5483	701
5484	707
5485	740
5486	698
5487	784
5488	943
5489	704
5490	1205
5491	522
5492	684
5493	132
5495	683
5496	1128
5497	975
5498	1162
5499	338
5500	760
5502	526
5504	1158
5508	909
5509	1005
5518	679
5521	1172
5524	231
5527	1130
5528	417
5583	120
5722	159
5726	160
5958	949
5959	1082
5960	927
5961	826
5862	780
5963	778
5964	763
5965	947
5966	762
5967	951
5968	950
5969	1060
5970	772
5971	767
5972	764
5973	759
5974	902
5975	757
5976	1056
5977	651
5978	148
5979	676
5980	674
5981	675
5982	680
5984	689
5985	1156
5987	865
5988	1076
5989	87
5990	1066
5991	774
5992	211
5993	1081
5999	971
6000	1117
6001	388
6002	893
6003 6004	1104
6005	999
6006	1083
6007	70
6010	416
6011	1069
6012	539
6013	1151
6014	1103
6015	1046
6016	1067
6017	1047
6018	59
6019	1071
6020	1078
6021	910
6022	868
6023	869
6024	887
6025	232
6026	1203
6027	881
6029	270
6031	1059
6032	1058
6033	882
6034	554
6035	139
6037	658
6038	663
6039	659
6040	666
6041	662
6042	672
6043	660
6044	661
6045	668
6315	1186
6317	1122
6318	45
6321	890
6322	404
6323	1000
6324	696
6325	525
6337	205
6341	936
6342	937
6368	555
6416	1048
6439	769
6656	1108
6657	151
6658	743
6659	744
6660	745
6661	747
6662	746
6663	752
6664	751
6665	407
6666	1168
6668	749
6669	963
6670	742
6671	123
6672	130
6673	122
6674	556
6675	1174
6676	204
6677	917
6678	965
6679	958
6680	517
6682	1009
6684	557
6685	1037
6686	269
6687	1185
6688	1010
6689	1028
6690	1011
6691	1012
6692	1013
6693	1014
6694	1015
6695	1029
6696	1030
6697	1006
6698	1031
6699	1178
6700	921
6701	1179
6702	960
6703	1032
6704	1033
6710	1034
6711	1035
6712	1036
6739	898
6741	418
6744	558
6748	1171
6754	220
6760	559
6777	1016
6781	560
6782	561
6809	562
6828	980
6829	344
6830	107
6844	146
6845	145
6846	935
6848	1192
6849	1070
6851	1111
6852	1105
6869–6989	326

Windsor Inventory No.	Popham Catalogue No.
7215	273
7708	267
7709–50	942
7764	161
7765	162
7766	163
7767	164
7768	165
7769	166
7770	167
7771	168
7772	169
7773	170
7774	171
7775	172
7776	173
7777	174
7778	175
7779	176
7780	177
7781	178
7782	179
7783	180
7784	181
7785	182
9063	37
10747	983
10761	979
10897	532
10899	530
10900	531
10902	946
10908	945
12066	896
12069	191
12728	807
12729	806
12730	973
12731	860
12732	794
12733	795
12734	792
12735	799
12736	798
12737	793
12738	790
12739	859
12740	833
12741	857
12742	800
12743	392
12744	22
12745	805
12746	855
12747	816
12748	817
12749	808
12750	803
12751	802
12752	822
12753	14
12754	804
12755	830
12756	809
12757	810
12758	791
12759	789
12760	796
12761	437
12762	425
12763	422
12764	434
12765	421
12766	430
12767	427
12768	428
12769	433
12770	423
12771	429
12772	435
12773	426
12774	460
12775	436
12776	432
12777	431
12778	424
12779	119
12780	118
12781	110
12782	113
12783	114
12784	115
12785	116
12786	112
12787	117
12788	111
12789	109
12790	5
12791	35
12792	23
12794	15
12795	16
12796	33
12797	24
12798	28
12799	18
12800	2
12801	21
12802	17
12803	343
12804	9
12805	29
12806	447
12807	4
12808	32
12809	342
12810	3
12811	11
12812	10
12813	36
12814	38
12815	26
12816	25
12817	8
12818	7
12819	932
12820	325
12821	12
12822	13
12823	20
12824	19
12825	108
12959	1134
12995	46
12996	47
12997	48
13035	43
13036	457
13054	765
19243	897
19263	397
19264	398